GENERAL AVIATION MARKETING AND MANAGEMENT

Third Edition

Operating, Marketing, and Managing an FBO

GENERAL AVIATION MARKETING AND MANAGEMENT

Third Edition

Operating, Marketing, and Managing an FBO

C. Daniel Prather, Ph.D., A.A.E.

KRIEGER PUBLISHING COMPANY
Malabar, Florida

Original Edition 1994, Alexander T. Wells and Bruce C. Chadbourne
Second Edition 2003, Alexander T. Wells and Bruce C. Chadbourne
Third Edition 2009, C. Daniel Prather
Based on General Aviation Marketing

Use of any and all material from previous editions has been delegated to
C. Daniel Prather from Alexander T. Wells and Bruce C. Chadbourne

Printed and Published by
KRIEGER PUBLISHING COMPANY
KRIEGER DRIVE
MALABAR, FLORIDA 32950

Library of Congress Cataloging-In-Publication Data

Prather, C. Daniel., 1971-
General aviation marketing and management : operating, marketing, and managing an FBO / Daniel Prather. — 3rd ed.
p. cm.
ISBN-13: 978-1-57524-301-6 (alk. paper)
ISBN-10: 1-57524-301-6 (alk. paper)
1. Airplanes—Marketing. 2. Aircraft industry—Management. I. Title.
HD9711.A2W45 2009
629.133'3404220688—dc22

2008053506

10 9 8 7 6 5 4 3

Contents

Preface

The third edition of this text was written during 2007 and 2008, a time of turbulence in the aviation industry. Skyrocketing fuel prices, continuing security threats, airline bankruptcies, airline merger discussions, and labor-management problems were all contemporary issues. In fact, in a two-week period in spring 2008, four airlines (ATA Airlines, Aloha Airlines, Frontier, and Skybus) filed for bankruptcy protection. At the same time, the General Aviation Industry was experiencing challenges, DayJet ceased operations, Eclipse Aviation filed for bankruptcy, Adam Aircraft declared bankruptcy, fixed base operators (FBOs) had difficulty keeping qualified flight instructors on staff, and the number of student pilot starts weakened.

Although much of the news was negative during 2007 and 2008, there was positive news as well, specifically for General Aviation (GA). General Aviation billings reached an all-time high of $21.9 billion in 2007; worldwide shipments of GA aircraft totaled 4,272, which is the strongest year since 1981; and business jet shipments also reached an all-time high of 1,138. In addition to record numbers of GA aircraft being shipped, FBOs experienced strong demand from business aviation and many enjoyed positive returns from their focus on improved customer service. With the relatively new Sport Pilot and Light Sport Aircraft Rule, FBOs geared up to provide flight instruction and services to the new breed of light sport aircraft and sport pilots.

However, at the time of this revision, the U.S. economy is slowing down and, as some analysts suggest, we may be headed for a recession. Due to this dynamic environment, it is imperative for collegiate aviation students and future FBO managers to be aware of the many challenges facing this industry and learn how to best navigate the FBO business into a successful future.

For the third edition, the text has been reviewed, revised, and updated where appropriate. Just as in the previous two editions, the text maintains its major objective: to enable a student with little or no background in general aviation (or FBO) marketing or management to proceed through the material in a step-by-step manner beginning with a historical perspective and scope of the industry, followed by the many aspects of operating, marketing, and managing an FBO.

Students should find the text easy to read and understandable. Every effort was made to provide practical information and allow the material to be easily applied; thus, the reader will find a number of useful review questions and scenarios throughout the text, allowing the reader to synthesize the information and apply it, even in classroom discussions.

Major Changes in the Third Edition

After a thorough review of the second edition, a decision was made to re-structure the text based on how this text is used in the FBO Management course at Middle Tennessee State University. In this class, the majority of students have never worked at an FBO, while some do have some FBO line service experience. To educate both groups of students and prospective FBO managers, it is necessary to discuss the basics of operating an FBO while also discussing marketing and managing an FBO. As a result, a new chapter on line service was added. New chapters on FBO Services, Customer Service, Management Functions and Organization, Risk Management, Human Resources, and Future Challenges were added as well. In addition to the review questions and key terms present at the end of each chapter in the second edition, this third edition introduces scenarios at the end of chapters 3 through 16. These scenarios are designed to present real-world situations to readers, who must then apply their knowledge of the FBO business to resolving the unique situation presented in each scenario. Instructors using this text are encouraged to develop additional scenarios as necessary to supplement those in the text. Specifically, this third edition is structured as follows:

PART ONE: INTRODUCTION

Chapter 1. General Aviation: A Historical Perspective

Chapter 1 provides a historical sketch of the general aviation industry from its early roots in the barnstorming period of the 1920s to the tremendous growth years of the 1960s and the period of retrenchment starting in the early 1980s. The factors causing the decline in aircraft sales are thoroughly explored. Major initiatives taken by government and the GA industry that revitalized the industry during the 1990s are thoroughly discussed, as are future trends of the new millennium.

Chapter 2. The Scope of General Aviation

This chapter defines general aviation and discusses the variety of uses of general aviation aircraft including the statistics that describe the various segments of the industry. Other components of the industry, including general aviation airports, pilots, FAA services to pilots, and airframe manufacturers, are also covered in detail. A discussion of the significance of pilots to aircraft manufacturing follows this section. The chapter concludes with a comprehensive listing of over 500 general aviation Web sites.

PART TWO: OPERATING AN FBO

Chapter 3. The Fixed Base Operator

Chapter 3 explains the important role and functions provided by the FBO, truly the backbone of general aviation. The size and scope of the FBO industry is covered along with current trends in the business and future outlook. The critical decisions in establishing an FBO are explored, including the proper legal structure and the advantages and disadvantages of remaining independent or joining a chain. A comprehensive customer services checklist covering all areas of an FBO's operation is included at the end of the chapter.

Chapter 4. Line Service

Those desiring to manage a fixed base operation someday must understand the basics of FBOs prior to managing them. This new chapter is designed to provide essential knowledge about line service—that most visible aspect of an FBO's operation. By learning about GA aircraft, fueling, towing, marshalling, and fire safety, the student will be well versed in line service and ready to advance to learning about other aspects of FBOs, including marketing and management.

Chapter 5. FBO Services

Also new to the text, this chapter contains some information from the second edition, but also adds information on aircraft maintenance, flight operations, sales of aircraft and parts and supplies, and other specialized commercial flight services.

Chapter 6. Customer Service

The nature of the competitive FBO industry today requires an entire chapter devoted to customer service. This chapter discusses internal and external customers, addresses methods of effective customer service, and highlights what makes a bad FBO or good FBO. Current customer service initiatives are also explained to allow students to have a sense of what proactive FBO customer service looks like.

PART THREE: MARKETING AN FBO

Chapter 7. The Role of Marketing

This chapter investigates the role of marketing in a firm and demonstrates how essential marketing is to the firm's long-term survival. The chapter begins with a definition of marketing and then discusses marketing management as a three-phase process of planning, implementing, and controlling marketing plans. Marketing activities described are determining objectives, segmenting the market, selecting target markets, and establishing unique market mixes (product, price, promotion, and place) for each market. The chapter concludes with a discussion of the major uncontrollable influences which the marketing manager must recognize and understand to aid the decision-making process.

Chapter 8. Promotion and Sales

Promotion is the communication with identified target markets with the objective of informing, persuading, or reminding them about products or the firm. This chapter discusses the components of the promotion mix which involve advertising, sales promotion activities, publicity, and personal sales. Since personal sales is the major activity in aircraft sales, the seven steps in the personal selling process are covered in detail.

Chapter 9. Marketing Research

Unquestionably, one of the most critical and yet most difficult tasks facing marketing management is that of research activities and the search for new customers. The scope of marketing research is investigated and steps to carry out research are suggested. Special emphasis is given to the collection of primary and secondary data by means of sampling techniques. The chapter concludes with a discussion of methods of collecting data and presenting the findings.

Chapter 10. Transportation Needs Assessment

The major marketing tool used by FBOs and aircraft manufacturers to help potential customers uncover the need for their own air transportation is called a travel analysis. This chapter covers some of the key characteristics of business-to-business marketing and includes all of the components in a travel analysis for a hypothetical company, Champions Stores, which is used to illustrate the process of aircraft selection and the tax and financial implications of acquiring an aircraft.

Chapter 11. Methods of Acquiring a Business Aircraft

The decision to acquire a business aircraft is certainly one on which management expends a great deal of time and effort. Chapter 11 reviews the methods of acquiring a company aircraft including company-owned and -operated aircraft, company-owned, management company operated, leasing, fractional ownership, and charter. Because of the continued importance of the used aircraft market, a whole section is devoted to buying and selling used aircraft, listing the major items to be considered in evaluating a used aircraft. The chapter concludes with a discussion comparing the various methods of acquiring a business aircraft.

PART FOUR: MANAGING AN FBO

Chapter 12. Management Functions and Organization

This chapter contains information from the second edition, but organizes it in a more effective manner. The typical management functions are discussed, including the functions of planning, organizing, directing, and controlling. The staffing (HR) function is reserved for chapter 15.

Chapter 13. Risk Management

This new chapter discusses risks. Quite simply, these are present in any industry and must be faced by every business. However, there are certain measures an FBO manager can take to mitigate potential risks and ensure a safer workplace and organization. Security is also discussed, with emphasis on new guidelines from the Transportation Security Administration for General Aviation Airports.

Chapter 14. Financial Planning and Control

This important chapter on financial planning and control remains from the second edition. Although students may have some knowledge of financial planning and budgeting, it is important to examine this in light of the needs of the FBO manager. Decision making without proper financial information will likely result in decisions made "in the dark."

Chapter 15. Human Resources

This chapter discusses the all-important Human Resources function and provides insight into a typical FBO interview process. By placing an emphasis on the human resources of an FBO, the wise FBO manager cultivates this resource to ensure a productive work environment with satisfied employees and high morale.

Chapter 16. Future Challenges

Although the second edition discussed future trends for FBOs, this new edition highlights important trends and challenges by incorporating them into this new chapter. The industry remains challenging and it is important to present these challenges to students to ponder before moving into an FBO management position.

APPENDICES

Appendix A
Three Week On-site Training Program for a New Aircraft Salesperson

Appendix B
Corporate Aircraft Sales Presentation

Appendix C
Sample FBO Lease Agreement

Appendix D
FAA Advisory Circular 150/5190-7

Appendix E
Value Analysis: Costs versus Benefits

As this third edition has been significantly restructured from the second edition, I encourage any comments and suggestions for improvement. It is my intent to create a text that is not only enjoyable and interesting, but practical and useful to collegiate aviation students and others interested in the operation, marketing, and managing of an FBO.

Acknowledgments

It was a great honor of mine to be asked by Drs. Wells and Chadbourne to write the third edition of *General Aviation Marketing and Management*. With less than two years of faculty experience under my belt, and ten years of recently concluded aviation industry experience, I was motivated to tackle this challenge and strongly encouraged by both of these fine academicians. Both current and former collegiate aviation students and faculty have greatly benefited from these two professors and the textbooks which they have authored. Specifically regarding the second edition of *General Aviation Marketing and Management*, this text greatly relieved the dearth of textbooks in the GA field. I hope to continue this with the publication of the third edition.

As noted in the second edition, this text owes its existence to many individuals. The text was created by Dr. Alexander Wells and Dr. Bruce Chadbourne, but was contributed to by many individuals, including Mr. Gary Kitely, current Executive Director of the Aviation Accreditation Board International. Just as in the second edition, this third edition was also contributed to by several experts in the field. Specifically, Mr. Joseph Hawkins, Assistant Professor of Aerospace at Middle Tennessee State University, contributed to the maintenance knowledge in this text. Also, Mr. Ryan Switalski, Aircraft Sales Assistant and Researcher at CFM Jet, and Mr. Blake Tumbleson, President of CFM Jet, both contributed to the aircraft sales knowledge in this text. Mr. John Atnip, an MTSU Aerospace student with extensive line service experience, contributed to the fueling knowledge in this text. Being able to rely on these experienced individuals greatly enhanced these sections of the text.

I would also like to thank Mr. Robert Krieger and the Krieger Publishing team for placing their trust in me with this third edition. With no previously authored textbooks under my belt, Krieger Publishing was clearly taking a risk in allowing me to write this third edition, and I am deeply indebted to them for that. Additionally, the copyediting expertise of Adria Carey Perez vastly improved this edition.

PART ONE: INTRODUCTION

Chapter 1
General Aviation: A Historical Perspective

OUTLINE

General Aviation's Roots
- The Barnstormers
- Wichita: Home of General Aviation
  - Beech Aircraft Corporation
  - Cessna Aircraft Company
  - Piper Aircraft Corporation

The Immediate Postwar Period
The 1950s—A Period of Introspection
The Soaring Sixties
The 1970s—Inflation, Regulation, and Record Sales
The 1980s—A Decade of Retrenchment
- Factors Causing the Decline in General Aviation Sales
- The Downturn in Pilot Numbers
- Industry Challenges
- Government/General Aviation Initiatives
- Manufacturer/General Aviation Initiatives

The 1990s—Revitalizationof an Industry
The New Millennium

OBJECTIVES

At the end of the chapter, you should be able to:

- Discuss some of the major developments in aviation that took place up to the outbreak of World War I.
- Describe the role of the barnstormers in the development of general aviation.
- Explain how Wichita became the home for many general aviation aircraft manufacturers.
- Describe how Beech, Cessna, and Piper got started and some of their early successes in aircraft development.
- Highlight the general feeling of the light aircraft manufacturers regarding market potential in the immediate postwar period.
- Discuss the change in market orientation which took place in the 1950s.
- Explain why it can be said that general aviation reached maturity in the 1960s.
- Discuss the factors that led to record sales of general aviation aircraft during the 1970s. List the primary factors leading to the decline in general aviation aircraft sales during the 1980s.
- Describe the challenges faced by the industry during the 1980s and early 1990s. Identify some of the initiatives taken by government, manufacturers, and the GA industry.
- Discuss some of the factors causing a revitalization of the industry during the 1990s.
- Discuss the factors present in the new millennium and their impact on General Aviation.

General Aviation Roots

It can be said that general aviation was born on December 17, 1903, when Orville Wright completed the first sustained powered flight in a heavier-than-air aircraft. However, it was not until 1908 that the U.S. Army purchased its first Wright Flyer and not until 1911 that it received five more. Consequently, most of the early Wright models were used to instruct new pilots and for pleasure flying. Others became attractions for special events such as fairs, and some were used to take paying passengers aloft.

As early as 1909, the Wright brothers encountered their first competition from the Curtiss Aeroplane and Motor Corporation as well as from several foreign models shipped to the United States to take part in flying contests and exhibitions. On June 26, 1909, the first commercial sale of an airplane took place. An improved version of the 1908 Curtiss "June-Bug" was sold to the Aeronautic Society of New York for $7,500.

Like the Wright brothers, Glenn Curtiss was a bicycle maker. By 1902 he had graduated to motorcycles, both building and racing them, and by 1908 his company had grown to over 100 employees, working round-the-clock to meet demand. Part of the demand came from budding aviators who were charged a premium for Curtiss's coveted air-cooled engines. In 1905 the famed Alexander Graham Bell, inventor of the telephone, hired Curtiss to head a group of aviation experimenters known as the Aerial Experimental Association. On July 4, 1908, Curtiss' June Bug won the

Scientific American prize of a silver trophy for the first officially observed flight in the United States exceeding one kilometer.

In August 1909 Curtiss traveled to Reims, France, to enter the first Gordon Bennett Speed Trophy race. He won the $10,000 prize money with an average speed of 47.4 miles per hour, which captured the public's imagination on both sides of the Atlantic. Aviation activity experienced a sharp increase between 1909 and 1911 partly as a result of fierce competition among newspapers for aviation news. Another reason was the public's sudden interest in flying. In October 1910 the first international air meet was held in the United States at Belmont Park, New York. Britisher Claude Graham-White won the second Gordon Bennett Speed Trophy with a speed of 60 miles per hour.

More and more people were entering the general aviation picture, and by 1911 several manufacturers were building airplanes as "professional" devices. Many amateur airplane builders were also involved with aviation projects; some were killed or injured trying to fly their home-built machines. At the close of 1911, there were 82 pilots in the United States licensed to fly in air meets and exhibitions. In addition to the licensed pilots, about 50 more individuals had flown solo. The licensing authority at that time was the Aero Club of New York.

When war broke out in Europe in 1914, the United States had as many as 12 aircraft manufacturers including some companies that were producing only three or four airplanes per year. Fewer than 200 flying machines had been commercially produced since 1903 and about one-half had gone to the U.S. Army and Navy. The Curtiss Aeroplane and Motor Company, successor to the Aerial Experimental Association, was the largest company in America producing airplanes.

During World War I, Curtiss produced about 6,000 JN-4 Jenny trainers for the army (along with the navy version of the Jenny, the N-9). The Jenny was first built in 1914 to meet U.S. Army requirements for a training aircraft. Over 95 percent of the 10,000 American pilots trained during the war years flew this aircraft. Thousands of Curtiss OX5, water-cooled 90 hp V-8 engines were built. So durable were Jennies that they stayed around for many years after the war, becoming the standard barnstorming plane during the 1920s and continuing in use by the Air Corps until 1927. These aircraft—which had cost the government in the neighborhood of $17,000 new depending upon how they were equipped—became surplus after the war and were sold for as high as $750 new, and as low as $50 used.

The Barnstormers

Many of the early barnstormers were ex-World War I pilots who could not get aviation out of their systems. Flying war surplus aircraft such as the Curtiss Jenny, they toured the country putting on aerial shows and giving rides to curious townspeople. Teams of pilots working together as a "flying circus" put on thrilling exhibitions, including wing walking and plane changes, in which a stunt man would transfer between planes in the air.

An ex-automobile racer and salesman, Ivan R. Gates, developed the biggest and best known of the circuses. The Gates Flying Circus attracted some of the best stunters and wingwalkers ever to thrill a crowd. Pilots like Clyde Pangborn and Ormer Locklear would fly inverted over a field and perform loops for an astonished audience. These two individuals were as popular as movie stars of the day. The barnstormers kept aviation alive during the early 1920s when most people looked upon the airplane as good for only two things: war and exhibitions.

By 1925 crashes and neglect had diminished the surplus warplanes and the barnstormers needed new and better performing airplanes. Federal legislation also had its effect in shaping the industry. The Kelly Air Mail Act of 1925 turned the transport of mail over to private carriers. The newly formed airlines and airmail service lured the barnstormers into more settled work. The Air Commerce Act of 1926 created the first Aeronautics Branch and provided the establishment of airports, airways, and navaids, as well as the first licensing of planes and pilots. It also made stunting difficult, if not illegal in many instances.

The gypsy pilots, as they were called, became more of an oddity and the flying circuses came to be looked upon as bad for aviation. More and more bad days curtailed their barnstorming seasons. In December 1928 the Gates Flying Circus broke up. In its career it had appeared in 2,500 towns and cities and carried more than 1.5 million passengers.

Commercial and general aviation truly began to go their separate ways around this time. The government asked the budding manufacturers to build aircraft for airmail service, and companies like Boeing, Ryan, Douglas, and Lockheed chose to develop mail and passenger planes. Others, including Wright, Laird, Bellanca, and Aeronca concentrated on smaller planes for racing and sport flying.

Another significant civil market, the corporate user, was also developing. In 1927, 34 nonaviation companies were operating business aircraft; by 1930 that number had grown to 300, and manufacturers such as Stinson, Travel Air, Waco, and Fokker were actively cultivating the market. Even private flying, largely the province of the wealthy, was being eyed as a possible market.

Wichita: Home of General Aviation

Jake Moellendick was a wealthy oilman who resided in Wichita, Kansas. He was also a gambler. The gamble of aviation appealed to him, and in 1919 he agreed to put up $15,000 to back several barnstormers who needed three new planes to replace their worn-out Curtiss Jennies. Billy Burke was sent to the 1919 Chicago Air Show to find the new aircraft. He approached an aircraft builder by the name of Matty Laird who had recently formed the E. M. Laird Company and was developing plans for a new three-place biplane. Burke realized that Laird's aircraft could easily become the country's first successful commercially sold private plane. Burke wired Jake about the new plane and suggested that instead of forming the flying circus, they get into the airplane-building business. The idea appealed to Jake with the one stipulation that the company be moved from Chicago to Wichita.

The Burke-Moellendick-Laird partnership began work, and in April 1920 the first Laird Swallow rolled out of the hangar. It was everything Billy Burke had hoped for in a barnstorming aircraft: a sturdy, well-built, and easy-to-fly craft that set the standard for all subsequent private biplanes of the 1920s. Production went from two planes a month to four, and Jake Moellendick went on a hiring spree to keep the plant meeting its orders. He assembled a group of unknowns, mostly ex-barnstormers like Buck Weaver, who later organized the Weaver Aircraft Company (subsequently shortened to "WACO"). Others included Lloyd Stearman and his brother Waverly, and Walter Beech. The company should have prospered, but Jake was impossible to work for and one by one his fine team quit. After 43 Laird Swallows had been sold, Matty Laird went back to his own company in Chicago, which built high-quality private aircraft until World War II. Jake renamed his plant the Swallow Airplane Manufacturing Company, but the next year, 1924, the Stearman brothers and Beech also left Moellendick. In partnership with another barnstormer named Clyde V. Cessna, they formed the Travel Air Manufacturing Company in Wichita. Beech, Cessna, and Stearman eventually went their separate ways, each establishing his own company. By now, Wichita had come to house the greatest concentration of aircraft-building talent in the country and to this day remains the heart of the American general aviation industry.

Beech Aircraft Corporation

In 1905 at the age of 14, Walter H. Beech made his first flight in a homemade glider in Pulaski, Tennessee. He later went on the barnstorming circuit, where he developed the experience and piloting skill that helped Travel Air Manufacturing Company to become the country's number one plane maker by 1928.

In 1929 Travel Air merged with Curtiss-Wright, and Beech went to New York as vice president of sales and chief pilot. He quit in 1930 and headed back to Wichita. In the depth of the depression in April 1932, he established the Beech Aircraft Corporation, with his wife Olive Ann as director and secretary/treasurer, and rented part of an inactive factory. With chief engineer T. A. Wells, he got the first Model 17—a luxurious, five-place, 200 mph cabin biplane called the Staggerwing—into the air on November 4, 1932. It could fly almost 1,000 miles, and in January 1933 it won the Texaco Trophy at the Miami races. The prototype was bought by the Ethyl Corporation, and the money helped the young company to keep producing. By 1934 the Model 17, already famous, had begun to sell, and by the end of 1935, a total 54 units had been sold. The company moved into a new plant to rival those of Stearman and Cessna (also in Wichita) . The Staggerwing Beech continued to sell (up to 781 in 1948) and its distinctive shape had no rival.

In 1937 the Model 18 Twin Beech was born. An eight-place monoplane, it was as fast as the Model 17; but instead of being priced at $12,000 to $24,000, it sold for $35,000 with two Jacobs engines, or $38,000 with more powerful 350 hp Wright radials.

Employment peaked during World War II when the U.S. Army and Navy needed transports and trainers for bombardiers and gunners. The Twin Beech remained in production until November 1969, a 32-year history during which 7,091 were built, almost all with neither of the original engines but with the 450 hp Pratt & Whitney Wasp Junior instead.

In 1946, Beech again hit the market exactly right with the V-tail Bonanza. It featured seating for four people (including the pilot), full flight and navigation instruments necessary for day or night VFR cross-country flights, and even a two-way radio as standard equipment. It had fully retractable tricycle landing gear and a 165 hp Continental engine. The price tag was set at $7,500 and Beech had over 500 orders from eager customers before publicity was released about performance. By 1950 the Bonanza represented 53 percent of the aviation industry's deliveries of high-performance, single-engine airplanes. It was Walter Beech's last classic. He died of a heart attack in 1950, and Mrs. Beech was elected president and chairman of the board.

The number of production models tripled, and three additional plants were established. The company supplied the popular T-34 military trainer and, in conjunction with other major firms, produced transports, fighters, and helicopters. Eventually, Beech had contracts for the Gemini, Apollo, and lunar-module projects.

Cessna Aircraft Company

Clyde V. Cessna was one of the original barnstorming pioneers. He bought a French-built Bleriot monoplane in 1911, and until the war years, Cessna improved and refined the basic design. Barnstorming was profitable and more fun than building aircraft at that time. On July 5, 1917, Cessna set a notable speed record of 125 mph on a cross-country flight from Blackwell, Oklahoma, to Wichita—an event prophetic of many more racing and competition triumphs to be scored by Cessna airplanes.

In 1924 with a total of six successful airplane designs to his credit, which he personally built and flew, Cessna joined Walter Beech and Lloyd Stearman in establishing the Travel Air Manufacturing Company at Wichita and became its president. He sold out his interest in Travel Air to Beech in 1927. Part of the trouble at Travel Air had been Cessna's lack of interest in biplanes. If anything, he was ahead of his time, for he believed the monoplane did not have to be covered with wires and struts in order to be strong and efficient.

Cessna's first independent production-model airplane, built in 1927, was the four-place, full cantilever high-wing "Comet" monoplane. His 1928 Model A, an expensive four-seater, won the New York-Los Angeles Air Derby and also flew to Siberia and back. Developments followed, but the depression almost brought business to a stop. Despite a $398 glider and a $975 powered version, the new plant closed in 1931. Not until January 1934 did the directors agree to restart the business. Cessna installed his nephew, Dwayne Wallace, as plant manager. A recent aeronautical engineering graduate from Wichita University, he went to work with no salary, but with the opportunity to design, build, test, sell, and even race new Cessnas.

Wallace's first creation was the C-34, a high-wing, four-place cabin monoplane with a 145 hp Warner Super-Scarab engine. The airplane refined the fully cantilevered wing of earlier Cessnas, but added flaps. In 1935 the C-34 won the Detroit News trophy race, part of the prestigious National Air races which put Cessna in the first rank of aircraft builders. The company's reputation as a builder of fast, efficient aircraft was assured and Cessna retired the following year. The C-34 was developed into various Airmaster models, but Wallace was looking for a light twin-engine aircraft, easy to fly and not too sophisticated to build. By 1939, the T-50 was flying; by 1940 it was in production and ready for buyers. War came and the military bought 5,401 as the AT-17 Bobcat (RCAF Crane) advanced trainer and UC-78 light transport.

After the war, Cessna built the 120/140 series followed by the 190/195 series. These airplanes were strong and simple single-engine aircraft that helped Cessna survive the postwar shakeout and launched it into the 1950s. Modern twins began with the 310, flown in January 1953, and the 318 in 1954 which led to the T-37 twin-jet trainer. The Fanjet 500 (later renamed Citation) began a family of business jets in 1968, and the low-wing Ag aircraft entered the market in 1971. The first turboprop was the highly efficient Conquest announced in 1974. Wallace retired in 1975 and was succeeded by Russ Meyer. By 1979 the Pawnee factory, where single-engine aircraft are made, had topped 120,000, and Cessna had become the number one builder of general aviation aircraft.

Piper Aircraft Corporation

William T. Piper entered aviation at a relatively older age than most of the pioneers. When he was 48 years old and a successful oilman in Bradford, Pennsylvania, Piper invested in a local company, the Taylor Brothers Aircraft Corporation, which had designed several light planes. Serving as treasurer, he ended up acquiring the company for $761 when it fell into bankruptcy in 1931. Piper reorganized the assets into Taylor Aircraft Company, giving C. Gilbert Taylor half interest in the new enterprise as an inducement to stay with the company. The new company's formula was simple: build easy-to-fly machines and price them low enough to attract buyers.

After an unsuccessful attempt to design a glider, the Taylor Aircraft Company developed the E-2 Cub, an excellent example of Piper's idea of the simple airplane. By 1934, the Taylor Cub was making money for the company; it was priced at $1,425 with a 38 hp Continental engine. Throughout many years of refining the design, Piper resisted changing the Cub's airfoil or flight characteristics, even though to do so would have increased its speed. He also resisted building fancier, more costly aircraft.

In 1936, Taylor resigned and set up his own company, which eventually went bankrupt in 1946. Piper hired a new chief engineer by the name of Walter Jamouneau and changed the name to the Piper Aircraft Corporation.

Following Piper's penchant for simple aircraft, the company did well. In recognition of Jamouneau's contribution to enhancing the E-2, subsequent models were called the J-2 and J-3. The PA-ll followed next in the Cub line and finally the PA-18 Super Cub. From its first flight in September 1930, through widespread wartime service and with various improvements and derivations thereafter, the Cub formula provided business for Piper up to the 1950s and for a total of more than 40,000 aircraft. Eighty percent of the U.S. World War II pilots received their initial training in the Cub.

Piper Aircraft Corporation boomed and then nearly busted during the difficult period that hit general aviation following World War II. The company rebounded to produce the popular Pacer and Tri-Pacer series and to introduce light twin-engine aircraft to buyers who previously had considered nothing but single-engine planes. The model line expanded, as did the Piper facilities, when a major development center was built in Vero Beach, Florida.

Active in the business well into his eighties, William T. Piper died in 1970. Walter Jamouneau retired in 1977.

The Immediate Post War Period

Even during the darkest days of World War II, the general aviation aircraft manufacturers were aware of the ordinary citizen's desire to fly and were preparing for the postwar period. In 1943, Cessna advertised in *Flying Magazine* that "Texas won't be much larger than Rhode Island when you are driving your Cessna Car-of-the-Air, the airplane that everyone can fly." Piper called for "Wings for all America." Other advertisements featured pretty girls in bathing suits, fishermen in remote trout streams, flying couples basking under the Florida sun while their nonflying friends faced winter winds up north.

Surveys, polls, questionnaires, and other marketing studies conducted for and by the industry and the government were the basis for highly optimistic predictions of a staggering potential requirement for light aircraft after the war. The Department of Commerce, which administered civil aviation at that time, informed the Congress that there would be a demand for as many as 200,000 light aircraft a year for the civilian market. With an eye on the 12 million veterans who would be taking advantage of the educational benefits under the newly legislated GI Bill, industry experts concurred that there would be at least 1.3 million private pilots within five years after the war and as many as 400,000 privately owned aircraft by 1950.

Many leading magazines in 1943 and 1944, including journals with such diverse audiences as *Business Week* and *Better Homes and Gardens*, regularly carried major articles featuring postwar airplanes for the common man and woman. Time reported that there were 5,750,000 people "conditioned to flying." These included army and navy pilots who at the time numbered 350,000; civilian pilots and students, 150,000; skilled aviation men in the war (other than pilots), 2,500,000; students taking aviation courses, 250,000; and employees during the war in aircraft factories listing 2,500,000 men and women. A *Woman's Home Companion* survey showed that 39 percentof the women interviewed were interested in flying themselves and 88 percent had no objection to anyone in their family owning a plane.

The aviation industry acted as quickly as it could to meet the anticipated avalanche of new student pilots and returning veterans who would be the first buyers of postwar civilian aircraft. Surveys indicated that prices should be about $2,000 for a two-place aircraft and $4,000 for a four-place plane. All the wartime light aircraft manufacturers wanted to be in on the market with new models within a few months.

Piper, which had delivered 5,000 Cubs to the armed services, announced that it would soon come out with a two-place, low-wing, tricycle-gear, all-metal plane to be called the Skycycle. Beech and Cessna reorganized their production lines to roll out all-metal planes. Some of the manufacturers of combat aircraft entered the market. Republic Aircraft, which had produced thousands of P-47 fighters, geared up to offer a four-place single-engine amphibian called the Seabee for sportsman pilots at an announced price of $3,995. North American Aviation, developer of the P-51 fighters and B-25 bombers, designed a bulky, four-place retractable-gear "family car of the air" called the Navion for a price of $5,000.

Despite all the design activity, the first airplanes to appear on the civilian market were the prewar models: Aeronca's Champion, Piper's Cubs, Taylor's Taylorcraft, Stinson's Voyager, and Luscombe's Silvaires. Cessna came out with the 120/140 series and Globe produced the Swift. Production increased and by the end of 1945, when the war was over, there were 37,789 aircraft of all categories (including airline equipment) in the U.S. civil aircraft fleet.

During 1946 hundreds of civilian flight training schools blossomed all over the country as recently discharged veterans took advantage of the new VA flight training legislation. It was apparent that the ordinary citizen did want to fly; the dream of a mass market was coming true. In 1946, the first full year of peace, 33,254 light aircraft were built and sold.

No one was concerned that the demand for 200,000 airplanes did not materialize in the first year; everything with wings that was made was sold. It would be better to have the market develop slowly to the 200,000 level. More important, the sales volume was 455 percent higher than it had ever been before the war.

Airline services expanded rapidly after the war and it was not long before the airlines were demanding that the government regulate small airplanes out of "their" airspace and keep them out of "their" airports. The government refused and the light aircraft manufacturers seemed to be receiving good news on all fronts. The year 1946 had been a record-setting period: Piper,7,780; Aeronca ,7,555; Cessna,3,959; Taylorcraft,3,151. The non-spinnable Ercoupe sold a surprising 2,503, and Globe and Stinson both went over the 1,000 mark.

Beech introduced the Bonanza for $7,435, and a small aerobatic biplane called the Pitts Special came on the market. Twenty manufacturers were engaged in making planes for the general aviation community. However, there were clouds on the horizon. The all-around utility of the automobile far surpassed that of the light airplane for the simple reason that there were not enough ground-support facilities where people could land which were close to resort and vacation areas. The airplanes also cost a lot more than people had been led to believe they would, particularly when compared with automobiles. The $3,995 Seabee of 1945 had been more realistically priced at $6,000 by the end of 1946. The Bonanza was up to $8,945, Navion to $4,750,the Swift to $3,750, and the

Cessna 170 to $5,475—all a long way from the $2,000 price tag advertised during the war.

As for the less expensive models, there were complaints that most were basically prewar models and not very good for cross-country transportation. They were noisy, drafty, cramped, uncomfortable, and not at all reliable for taking carefully planned vacation trips to the mountains or the beach.

The industry also experienced a high percentage of VA students dropping out of flying soon after receiving their private pilot certificate and an increasing number quitting immediately after soloing. Once airport circling had lost its charm, many ex-GIs began to take a hard look at the practicalities versus expenses, particularly when they learned how easily low ceilings or fog could ground them (if not instrument-rated).

Army and navy veterans who had been flying high-performance airplanes were simply not satisfied to poke along at 95 or 100 miles an hour, especially after a long cross-country flight against a headwind when they could see automobiles making better time on the highways below.

Another problem faced by the light aircraft manufacturers was the availability of war surplus aircraft at bargain prices. In 1946, the Reconstruction Finance Corporation sold more than 31,000 aircraft ranging from Cessna T-50 "Bamboo Bombers" to P-51s. Many ex-military C-47s and Twin Beeches, as well as bombers, went into the corporate market to be modified as executive transports.

The manufacturers began to realize that the general public might have been oversold on light plane flying, and that they could not hope to have a mass-production industry comparable to the automobile industry. In 1947, a year before Cessna introduced its 170—which would eventually be developed into the 172, the world's most successful light plane—the industry was beginning to flounder.

Manufacturing companies with delivery ramps clogged with unsold airplanes began to feel the pinch. Globe was in bankruptcy. Republic had discontinued the Seabee. North American had sold the Navion design to Ryan. Stinson was in deep financial trouble. Taylorcraft was looking for new capital. By the end of 1947, the severity of the problem was evident. Sales were down 44 percent from the previous year, to 15,617 units. Things got worse in 1948. Sales again dropped by more than 40 percent when only 7,302 airplanes were manufactured.

The public's reluctance to spend money on private flying was understandable. A cold war had developed with the Russians, culminating in the blockade of Berlin in the summer of 1948. The United States countered by mounting the Berlin Airlift, and the possibility of another major conflict was on the horizon. GI flight training was restricted to vocational pursuits and tougher regulations were enacted to restrict private flying.

The downward trend followed the deteriorating international situation resulting in an even more dismal year in 1949, when 3,545 aircraft were built. New aircraft designs appeared on the scene, only to disappear from sight forever as light aircraft manufacturers ran out of operating capital.

The 1950s—A Period of Introspection

The 1950s began a period of introspection and review by the general aviation aircraft manufacturers. Executives began to look at the future from a different angle. Mass-producing airplanes for everyone at low prices was not the answer to growth. The future lay in developing a fleet of airplanes that would provide solid, comfortable, reliable business transportation. Aircraft that could operate in instrument conditions with speed and range would be the wave of the future. A certain number of training airplanes would have to be built to get new people started, but a utility airplane that businessmen could afford was the target design for the future. Some such airplanes were already available, but the business community doubted their utility. The Twin-Bonanza and the Twin Beech were well thought of, but there was a lingering doubt in the public's mind about single-engine aircraft. One event that helped to change that attitude was a flight by William P. Odom in January 1949 from Hawaii to Oakland, California, in a Beech Bonanza. Three months later he flew the same Bonanza from Hawaii to Teterboro, New Jersey, 5,273 miles, nonstop.

Cross-country navigation was being made simpler and more efficient by the new very high-frequency omni-directional radio ranges—the VORs. Spotted around the country, the pilot merely had to follow a needle on the instrument panel. No longer did pilots have to keep sectional charts on their legs hour after hour to check their position, or to keep working with their calculators to dead reckon their way under instrument conditions.

In June 1950 the Korean War broke out and once again the public's attention was focused on the international scene. General aviation continued to limp along, although the ranks of the manufacturers were thinning. Beech, Bellanca, Cessna, Piper, and Ryan were still producing airplanes, but not all of these companies were sure that they could hang on much longer. Production in 1950 was only 3,520 units.

On the positive side, more and more omni stations were commissioned; VHF radios—static free and easy to navigate by—became factory options on more and more airplanes. In 1950 general aviation airplanes were awarded their own frequency, 122.8, called "unicom." Bill Lear developed the first light plane three-axis autopilot in 1950, which made cross-country flying easier and more relaxing. Toward the end of the year, Ryan stopped production of the Navion, but a new company, Aero Design and Engineering, was ready with its five-place Aero Commander. Mooney also unveiled its single-place, $1,000 Mooney Mite. Piper put a nosewheel on its little Pacer, renamed it the Tri-Pacer, and created a new surge of interest in light aircraft for pleasure as well as for business.

Aircraft production hit bottom in 1951 with only 2,477 units produced all year, just half the number produced in the month of August 1946. The situation began to look brighter in 1952. Max Conrad flew a Piper Tri-Pacer to Europe and back, which again demonstrated the capability and reliability of light aircraft. In 1952, 3,509 airplanes were delivered, an increase of 1,032 over the previous year. Things were beginning to move. Cessna discontinued the 195 in 1953 and produced the four-place 180, a more powerful aircraft than the 170. Piper stayed with the Tri-Pacer and the Super Cub; Beech was backlogged with orders for the Bonanza, the Twin Bonanza, and the Super-18. Total production hit 3,788 units in 1953, up 279 from the previous year. Growth was solid as the industry emerged from a period of readjustment.

In 1954 Cessna and Piper introduced their four-place light twins—the 310 and the Apache, which would start a long line of descendents. Max Conrad ferried an Apache to Europe and started the transatlantic ferry business. No longer would general aviation aircraft be crated and shipped to Europe for reassembly.

By the mid-1950s aircraft production hovered around the 4,500 per year mark and the need for IFR capability increased. Companies like ARC, Bendix, Collins, Lear, Mitchell, and Wilcox entered the avionics business. By the end of the decade, Cessna introduced the Skylane as a package airplane—one with basic avionics already installed.

The Soaring Sixties

As the 1950s turned into the 1960s, general aviation was developing an unmistakable stability and purpose. Although pleasure flying was far from extinct, it was clear that the general aviation airplane was developing into a viable means of business transportation. In 10 years, the general aviation fleet had more than doubled to 60,000 aircraft, more than half of which were equipped for instrument flying. General aviation had become a major part of the nation's transportation system, with an inventory of light aircraft that were fully capable of flying people in comfort 1,500 miles in one day to thousands of places not served by the commercial air carriers. Expansion, modernization, and increasing complexity characterized the aviation world of the 1960s. A decade that began with radial-engine transports ended with the Concorde and landing a man on the moon.

Beech brought out the Travel Air, to be followed by the Baron, the Queen Air, and the King Air. Cessna put tricycle landing gear on their 170s and 180s in developing the 172 and 182 series, which became the best selling airplanes in history. Piper terminated the TriPacer and entered the Cherokee, Comanche, and Twin Comanche in the market. Many of the old names such as Bellanca, Mooney, Navion, and North American would come back.

By 1965 the general aviation aircraft fleet had grown to 95,000 airplanes, and production totaled 11,852 new aircraft. The following year, 1966, saw a record 15,768 units produced. General aviation growth during the late 1960s paralleled growth in the economy and all segments of aviation at that time.

Three airplanes in particular that were introduced in the 1960s—the Piper Cherokee, the Beech King Air 90, and the Lear 23—proved to be bellwether designs for years to come.

The Cherokee was the first Piper model to be produced at the company's new Vero Beach, Florida, manufacturing plant. Vero Beach and the Cherokee were Piper's solutions to the high cost of building airplanes in Lock Haven, Pennsylvania. The production line was designed for speed and volume.

Piper dedicated the Vero Beach plant, rolled out the first Cherokee, and celebrated William Piper's eightieth birthday, all on January 8, 1960. The Cherokee was certified in 1961. Two versions were offered. The PA-28-150 sold for $9,795. An additional $200 bought 10 more horsepower.

The Cherokee marked Piper's break with its traditional tube-and-fabric, high-wing design approach to light singles. It became the template for all of the piston-powered models Piper would develop over the next 20 years, with the exception of the Tomahawk and Navajo.

Beech entered the 1960s with a pair of piston-powered, cabin-class executive transports in the Model 18 and the Queen Air. But the company had been studying turboprops for several years. Beech had a technical agreement with a French firm, Societe Francaise d'Entretien et du Reparation de Materiel Aeronautique, to test Turbomeca turboprop engines on a Travel Air, the new Baron, and a Beech 18.

In December 1962, Beech unveiled a mock-up of a turboprop-powered, pressurized Model 120, an all-new design. The goal was to test the marketing waters before committing to an expensive development program. At the same time, Beech was working on a new pressurized version of the Queen Air 80.

As the potential costs and time to develop a new top-of-the-line turboprop began to mount, Beech executives opted to take a less risky road and adapt turbine power to the Queen Air.

Details of the forthcoming King Air were revealed in August 1963. Two 500-shaft horsepower Pratt & Whitney turboprop engines would provide the power to cruise at 270 mph at 16,500 feet, with the cabin pressurized to an altitude of 8,000 feet. The price was projected at about $300,000. In a press release announcing rollout of the first production prototype in November 1963, Beech said it had received $11 million in orders for King Airs. The potential market was estimated to be at least 200 airplanes over the next few years.

The King Air 90 was certified in May 1964, five months after its first flight. Contrary to Beech's modest expectations, the King Air 90 proved to be the tip of a product-line iceberg. A through F model 90s would be introduced, along with larger and more powerful King Air 100s, 200s, and the 300.

Beech has dominated the turboprop market from the beginning. Other designs have a considerable performance edge, but the King Air's combination of roomy cabin, docile handling, and commanding presence have made it the passenger-carrying choice for thousands of companies, government agencies, and individuals. Over 4,000 have been built, including 500 for the U.S. Army, Air Force, Navy, and Marines. No other airplane is in service with all four branches of the military.

Just as the King Air 90 started Beech on a new product line that was to define the executive turboprop, Lear Jet Corporation's Lear 23 launched corporate aviation into the jet age.

The Learjet has its roots in a European private-venture military jet that never went into full production. The P-16 was a ground-attack warrior that a Swiss firm hoped to sell to the Swiss air force. Four were built, but two crashed during test flights. The accidents saddled the airplane with a suspect reputation, and as a consequence, the military could not be sold on it.

One person who was sold was William P. Lear. The prolific inventor, showman, marketer, and chairman of Lear, Incorporated, flew in it several times and was very impressed.

It was to be the first jet designed specifically for general aviation. The Lockheed JetStar and North American Sabreliner already were in service, but they were originally designed to ferry military VIPs and were much larger, heavier, and costlier than the airplane Lear envisioned.

Speed and style were a large part of that vision. The Model 23, with its two small but powerful military derivative General Electric CJ610 turbojet engines, would cruise at 458 knots and look every bit as fast. Today the Learjet still is regarded by many as the finest example of what a civilian jet should be: fast and easy to handle.

Learjet passengers would ride comfortably above the weather in a cocoon-like office. Bill Lear professed disdain for walk-around airplane cabins with lavatories—at least until he designed the Learstar, which eventually became the widebody Canadair Challenger.

The prototype Lear 23 was built in seven months by the new Lear Jet Corporation in Wichita. It flew for the first time on October 7, 1963. Eight months later the second prototype (the first was destroyed a few days earlier in a nonfatal off-airport landing) was flown to the Reading Air Show for a dramatic first public appearance. Certification took just 10 months, a remarkable achievement considering that the Model 23 was the first under-12,500-pound jet the FAA had been asked to certify. It went on the market for $595,000.

The Lear 23 and Lear Jet Corporation would suffer a series of unexplained accidents and a financial recession soon after deliveries began. The airplane survived; the company did not. Bill Lear, who had been forced to sell his shares in Lear, Incorporated, in order to finance development and certification of the 23 and its immediate successor, the 24, had to sell Lear Jet Corporation to avoid financial collapse.

Gates Rubber bought it in 1967 and, before the decade ended, certified the Model 25, a longer version of the 23/24. Later, the turbofan-powered Lear 35 and 55, an enlarged, stand-up cabin version, would be certified.

The 1970s—Inflation, Regulation, and Record Sales

The 1970s can be briefly summarized as the decade of the Terminal Control Area (TCA), the Airport and Airways Development Act, and fuel crises.

In 1970 the manufacturers of light aircraft established a strong and effective lobbying and public relations organization in Washington, the General Aviation Manufacturers Association (GAMA). The National Business Aircraft Association (NBAA) blossomed into a highly professional Washington-based service organization for business users. The Aircraft Owners and Pilots Association (AOPA) and other special-aircraft-use organizations developed into effective lobbying groups. The Federal Aviation Administration (FAA), under administrator Jack Shaffer, appointed a deputy administrator for general aviation.

Despite an economic recession during the first two years of the 1970s and an oil embargo in 1973, general aviation continued to grow, reaching a high point in 1978 with 17,808 units produced. Personal aviation's production heyday came at a most unusual time. While the post-World War II airplane manufacturing spree held production records for decades (the sales crash that followed in 1947 also set records), the record sales days came, surprisingly, in a decade of sky-rocketing inflation, fuel shortages, and increasingly more restrictive airspace. Despite those factors, more aircraft were sold in the 1970s than before or since.

While the number of aircraft sold was a departure, the aircraft themselves largely were not. Aircraft based on existing models—some dating back to the 1940s and 1950s—formed the bread-and-butter models of this decade of record sales.

In the meantime, the industry saw upstarts like the fast Grumman-American singles mature, and the Rockwell Commanders reached full bloom in the 1970s, even though their production numbers could not touch those of the recycled Cessnas and Pipers. Beech also worked to refine the Aero Club airplanes—the Sierra and Sundowner singles, to name two—but continuing reluctance on the part of the sales staff and buying public ultimately was cited for the closing of that line.

Mooney saw its fortunes change in the 1970s. Finally with stable financial ground under it, the company performed a thorough remake of the M-20-series airplanes. The short- and long-fuselage M-20 line, which for a time included both 180- and 200-hp power plant options, was condensed into the quick and far more refined 201.

Cessna gambled on improving its product and market image for the 1970s. Although the venerable Skyhawk was selling in unprecedented numbers, Cessna felt the competition from the newer Cherokee line and wanted to respond with something new, bold, and exciting. Their answer was the Cardinal but it was never a complete success. Sales of the popular 172 continued to grow.

Cessna tried another tack in 1978 by adding new features to a well-known airframe and, in the process, brought pressurization to the piston single. The idea was not new—Mooney tried it with the Mustang, but fewer than 30 were sold before it was terminated in 1970. Cessna introduced the pressurized 210 with weather radar, known-icing equipment, and more radios at a base price of $40,000. A total of 874 were built before the line was shut down in 1986.

While Cessna gambled that the market was there for the P210, Piper took no such risks with its new trainer. Although the Cherokee 140 had been the maker's primary trainer, it was more expensive to buy, maintain, and refuel than the Cessna 150 it competed against. Piper wanted a model to once and for all capture the trainer market from Cessna's 150. Piper queried thousands of flight instructors and fixed base operators. Respondents indicated the need for an airplane with low maintenance requirements, an engine that would tolerate 100LL fuel, good visibility, and flight characteristics that would make the student respect what a real stall could do, unlike those of the nearly stall-proof Cherokees.

Piper went to work and produced the Tomahawk, which, when it debuted in 1978, appeared to be the answer to every instructor's dream.

In nine months, Piper churned out nearly 1,000 of the PA-38s, about eight per day, according to the company. With that substantial production rate came quality problems, which severely hurt sales in its second year. Also, some feel that Piper went too far in giving the Tomahawk very noticeable stall characteristics. The 150 and 152 were much easier to handle.

Nearly 1,500 of the Piper trainers had been made by production's end in 1982. Interestingly, Beech's nearly identical Skipper suffered an equally truncated life: Only 312 were made from 1979 to 1981.

A new market segment opened up in the late 1970s that Piper turned to its advantage. With the price of fuel higher than it had been since the 1973-1974 fuel crunch, the manufacturers perceived a demand for relatively inexpensive, efficient twins—aircraft that could provide low-cost multiengine training; the light-light twin was born. Piper stepped up with the Seminole, Beech with the Duchess, and Grumman-American with the Cougar.

Of the three, the Seminole sold the best. Piper sold three quarters as many Seminoles the first year, 1979, as Beech made Duchesses in that airplane's entire five-year life span. When the bottom fell out of the light-light twin market, the Seminole fell too, and the total run of PA-44s, ending in 1982, numbered just 468 units (including 86 turbocharged models, produced in the last two years), a handful more than the quantity of Duchesses produced.

While not as noteworthy for being a technological hotbed of activity as the 1940s and 1950s, the 1970s was a decade of immense production, providing harsh lessons for the marketing departments of both Cessna and Piper—lessons learned that ultimately helped shape the kinds of airplanes kept alive (or brought back to life) during the lean times of the 1980s.

By the late 1970s, both manufacturer and user began to experience a confidence that general aviation had seldom enjoyed before. Perhaps for the first time, the general aviation community perceived that its potential problems of government controls, charges, fees, and taxes, as well as restrictive legislation, were manageable. Unfortunately, the 1980s brought on a new round of challenges for the industry.

Soaring interest rates and a depressed economy during the early 1980s had an effect on sales. Aircraft shipments dropped from 11,877 in 1980 to 9,457 in 1981 and 4,266 in 1982. By 1985 the number had reached a record low of 2,032 units.

The 1980s—A Decade of Retrenchment

The first five years of the decade had been rough for the general aviation community. The nation's air traffic controllers went on strike in August 1981 and were subsequently fired by President Reagan. As a result, the General Aviation

Reservation (GAR) system was put into effect for two years. This program put quotas on the number of IFR general aviation flights in each of the nation's ATC centers. Changes also took place in ownership of the three leading airframe manufacturers. At the turn of the decade, only Piper Aircraft was owned by a conglomerate. All that had changed by the end of 1985. Ironically, at the end of the decade, Piper was the only independently owned company of the big four.Beech and Raytheon Corporation signed a merger deal in 1980. Cessna was acquired by General Dynamics in 1985. France's Euralair—an air charter, executive jet, and cargo operator—bought Mooney in 1984. Piper's owner, Bangor Punta Company, was bought by Lear Siegler, which was bought by Forstmann Little & Company. Finally, in 1987 a businessman by the name of M. Stuart Millar purchased the company.

In the mid-1980s, the problems posed by growing costs of insuring newly manufactured airplanes against product liability claims threatened to choke off the nation's supply of new airplanes. The general aviation fleet at large was —and still is—rapidly aging. With $l-million-plus accident settlements now commonplace, each new airplane had to bear the insurance premium burden for all other airplanes. Cessna Aircraft Company's chairman, Russell W. Meyer, Jr., reported in 1985 that 20 percent to 30 percent t of the cost of a new airplane reflected the cost of escalating product liability insurance.

Other financial pressures working against aircraft ownership were also taking place at the same time. The Internal Revenue Service announced a proposal to do away with the 10 percent investment tax credit (ITC) on December 31, 1985, denying prospective owners of aircraft used in business a considerable tax incentive. In a later congressional action (the Tax Reform Act of 1986), the ITC was extended for one year, as long as aircraft purchased by the end of 1986 were put in service before July 1987.

During the 1980s the manufacturers focused their efforts on turboprops and jets. Among the variety of twin turboprops offered was the 425 Corsair, later to become the Conquest 1. The 425 is a turboprop version of the 421 Golden Eagle. For operators who preferred to stick to piston engines, Cessna offered a lower cost version of the pressurized 340A in the Model 335. About the only difference between the two was the lack of pressurization in the 335.

Cessna also offered its line of Citation business jets. The Citation III was certified in 1982 with a new airframe and supercritical swept wing and Cessna's only medium-sized jet. Cessna announced a further fuselage stretch in the Citation V. The booming small-package delivery industry in the 1980s was a benefit to Cessna and the Caravan I, the single engine turboprop it designed to replace and supplement the workhorse Otters, Beavers, and even smaller Cessna 180s and 206s of earlier decades. Certification was granted in 1984 and a stretched model was certified in 1986.

While production of the larger business aircraft had remained steady for Cessna, sales of single-engine piston aircraft and even the twin turboprops continued to decline in the first half of the decade. In 1986 Cessna announced that it was stopping production of all but the Caravan and Citation models.

Similarly, because of the product liability situation Beech stopped producing its Sundowner and Sierra light aircraft in the mid-1980s. One single-engine piston aircraft that has withstood the test of time is the F33 Bonanza. For a number of years, the Bonanza has been the best-selling single-engine aircraft, though the 1980s saw the last of new V-tail V35 Bonanzas. The twin-engine Baron also remained a steady seller.

Like Cessna, Beech felt it needed a machine for its turboprop operators to step up to. In late 1985, it acquired the Mitsubishi Diamond II business jet design from its Japanese builder. While Diamond sales did not live up to expectations for Mitsubishi, Beech turned the Beechjet 400 into a success. Early in 1988 Beech certified the 1300, a 13-seat commuter airliner version of the King Air B200. Another big hit in the airline industry has been the Beech 1900, a 19-seat commuter aircraft certified in 1983. The Super King Air 300, also a derivative of the B200, was certified in January 1984.

In 1983 Beech contracted with Rutan's Scaled Composites, Incorporated, to build an 85 percent scale model of the airplane, called Starship 1. The aviation community watched intently as Beech moved from scaled model to prototype to certification and finally in June, 1988, the first aircraft was delivered at the Paris Air Show.

The Starship not only looked different from other aircraft—with no tail, giant winglets called tipsails, a movable canard, and pusher engines—it is also built differently of different material. The airframe was mostly composite. The whole thing went together like a plastic model, and then it was baked in a high-pressure autoclave.

Mooney Aircraft also tried new things. Most notable is the Mooney PFM. The PFM stands for Porsche Flugmotor, a 217-hp derivative of the engine in the Porsche 911 automobile. The engine is housed in a stretched version of the Mooney 252 fuselage with interior appointments given the Porsche touch of class. The panel, too, with many electronic instruments, is different from those of all other Mooneys. The PFM was certified in May 1988, joining the 201, 205, and 252, also introduced in the 1980s. In 1987 Mooney joined French builder Aerospatiale to develop the TBM 700, a single-engine, pressurized turboprop. The first delivery was made in 1990.

The TBM 700 competed for customers in the same class as Piper's most innovative 1980s airplane—the Malibu. Of the general aviation manufacturers, none was the subject of more industry gossip during the 1980s than Piper Aircraft. The rumors of its demise were rampant in the 1980s when it abandoned its Lock Haven, Pennsylvania, plant, which had become synonymous with Piper, and production slowed to a trickle. But within months of his purchase of the company in 1987, Millar announced that he was putting the venerable Super Cub back into production and that he would also offer the airplane for sale in kit form. At the same time, he announced the Piper Cadet, a stripped-down training version of the Warrior. By the end of 1989, Piper was producing a full line of aircraft from the Cub to the Cheyenne 400 twin turboprop, with the Cheyenne IIIA rapidly becoming the trainer of choice for foreign airlines.

The six-seat Malibu, claiming to be the first cabin-class, pressurized single-engine aircraft, was certified in 1983 with a 310-hp turbocharged Continental engine. The marriage between engine and fuselage was a difficult one, and in 1988 the Continental was replaced with a 350-hp Lycoming engine resulting in the Malibu Mirage.

While the builders of small aircraft had to seek new niches and markets in order to survive the 1980s, others simply made the big and fast bigger and faster. An example is Gulfstream Aerospace. While it too was acquired by a conglomerate in the 1980s (Chrysler Corporation), it steadily continued to produce and sell large business jets. The Gulfstream IV, a bigger and faster version of the G-III, was certified in 1987.

Learjet, too, took the same basic fuselage it developed in the 1960s and continued refining it to produce airplanes that appealed to the 1980s buyer. The Learjet 60 was the latest larger variant, while the Learjet 31A has been called an "entry-level jet." The 31, certified in 1988, combines the usual Lear good looks and speed with good handling characteristics.

Factors Causing the Decline in General Aviation Sales

Historically, the general aviation industry has paralleled the economic cycle of the national economy. The 1980s proved to be an exception to that analysis. In the early 1980s general aviation followed the rest of the economy into recession. Interest rates were at an all-time high when the new administration took office in 1980. Everything from housing starts to durable goods sales, including autos and general aviation aircraft sales, plummeted. The economy began to recover in 1983, but general aviation did not. In fact, the number of general aviation aircraft delivered fell from a high of 17,811 in 1978 to 928 in 1994 (see Table 1-1). This was the worst record in at least a 47 year history.

A number of factors have been cited:

1. **Costs**. No doubt the high interest rates of the late 1970s and early 1980s had an effect at the beginning of the slide. Acquisition costs, including avionics equipment, rose sharply during the early to mid-1980s despite very little change in design of features in the typical single-engine aircraft. Used aircraft were available, and prospective buyers were reluctant to purchase new equipment at considerably higher prices. Total operating expenses—including fuel, maintenance, hangaring charges, insurance—all steadily increased during the 1980s, making it more expensive for the occasional flier.
2. **Airline Deregulation**. Deregulation of the U.S. com--mercial airline industry in 1978 affected general aviation. Increased service combined with better connections and lower fares by the air carriers (including regional/commuter carriers) reduced the desirability of using general aviation aircraft when planning business or pleasure trips. As a result, business aircraft proved more difficult to justify.
3. **Product Liability Claims**. Another major factor mentioned earlier is the product liability claims, which caused the light aircraft manufacturers to concentrate on their higher-priced lines of turbine equipment. During the 1980s, annual claims paid by the manufacturers increased from $24 million to over $210 million despite an improved safety record. In 1985, the annual premiums for the manufacturers totaled about $135 million, and based on unit shipments that year of 2,029, the price almost approached $70,000 per airplane. This was more than the selling price of many basic two and four place aircraft. Dropping its piston aircraft production in 1986, Cessna self-insured up to $100 million. Piper decided to operate without the benefit of product liability coverage, and Beech insured the first $50 million annual aggregate exposure with their own captive insurance company.
4. **Taxes**. Passage of the Tax Reform Act in 1986 eliminated the 10 percent investment tax credit on aircraft purchases. This was followed by a luxury tax on boats and planes, which only exacerbated the problem of declining new aircraft sales.
5. **Foreign Aircraft Manufacturers**. In 1980, there were 29 U.S. and 15 foreign manufacturers of piston aircraft. By 1994, there were 29 foreign and only nine U.S. manufacturers. In 1980, 100 percent of the single-engine pistons sold in the United States were manufactured in the United States. In 1994, less than 70 percent were manufactured in the United States. Many foreign governments have supported their fledgling aviation industries by subsidizing research, development, production, and financing. Foreign manufacturers continue to gain an ever-increasing foothold in the U.S. market. By the early 1990s, aircraft made abroad accounted for more than 50 percent delivered to U.S. customers. Even in the high-end

Table 1-1

Shipments by Type: Manufactured in U.S.

New U.S. Manufactured General Aviation Airplane Shipments by Type of Airplane (1959-2006)

Year	Grand Total	Single-Engine	Multi-Engine	Total Piston	Turboprop	Turbojet/ Turbofan	Total Turbine
1959	**7,689**	6,849	840	**7,689**	0	0	**0**
1960	**7,588**	6,569	1,019	**7,588**	0	0	**0**
1961	**6,756**	5,995	761	**6,756**	0	0	**0**
1962	**6,697**	5,690	1,007	**6,697**	0	0	**0**
1963	**7,569**	6,248	1,321	**7,569**	0	0	**0**
1964	**9,336**	7,718	1,606	**9,324**	9	3	**12**
1965	**11,852**	9,873	1,780	**11,653**	87	112	**199**
1966	**15,768**	13,250	2,192	**15,442**	165	161	**326**
1967	**13,577**	11,557	1,773	**13,330**	149	98	**247**
1968	**13,698**	11,398	1,959	**13,357**	248	93	**341**
1969	**12,457**	10,054	2,078	**12,132**	214	111	**325**
1970	**7,292**	5,942	1,159	**7,101**	135	56	**191**
1971	**7,466**	6,287	1,043	**7,330**	89	47	**136**
1972	**9,774**	7,898	1,548	**9,446**	179	149	**328**
1973	**13,646**	10,780	2,413	**13,193**	247	206	**453**
1974	**14,166**	11,562	2,135	**13,697**	250	219	**469**
1975	**14,056**	11,439	2,116	**13,555**	305	196	**501**
1976	**15,449**	12,783	2,120	**14,903**	359	187	**546**
1977	**16,907**	14,057	2,195	**16,252**	428	227	**655**
1978	**17,811**	14,398	2,634	**17,032**	548	231	**779**
1979	**17,050**	13,286	2,843	**16,129**	639	282	**921**
1980	**11,860**	8,640	2,116	**10,756**	778	326	**1,104**
1981	**9,457**	6,608	1,542	**8,150**	918	389	**1,307**
1982	**4,266**	2,871	678	**3,549**	458	259	**717**
1983	**2,691**	1,811	417	**2,228**	321	142	**463**
1984	**2,431**	1,620	371	**1,991**	271	169	**440**
1985	**2,029**	1,370	193	**1,563**	321	145	**466**
1986	**1,495**	985	138	**1,123**	250	122	**372**
1987	**1,085**	613	87	**700**	263	122	**385**
1988	**1,143**	628	67	**695**	291	157	**448**
1989	**1,535**	1,023	87	**1,110**	268	157	**425**
1990	**1,144**	608	87	**695**	281	168	**449**
1991	**1,021**	564	49	**613**	222	186	**408**
1992	**941**	552	41	**593**	177	171	**348**
1993	**964**	516	39	**555**	211	198	**409**
1994	**928**	444	55	**499**	207	222	**429**
1995	**1,077**	515	61	**576**	255	246	**501**
1996	**1,105**	607	42	**649**	223	233	**456**
1997	**1,549**	898	86	**984**	223	342	**565**
1998R	**2,200**	1,434	94	**1,528**	259	413	**672**
1999	**2,504**	1,634	114	**1,748**	239	517	**756**
2000	**2,816**	1,810	103	**1,913**	315	588	**903**
2001R	**2,634**	1,581	147	**1,728**	306	600	**906**
2002R	**2,207**	1,366	130	**1,496**	187	524	**711**
2003	**2,137**	1,519	71	**1,590**	163	384	**547**
2004	**2,355**	1,706	52	**1,758**	194	403	**597**
2005	**2,857**	2,024	71	**2,095**	240	522	**762**
2006	**3,146**	2,208	79	**2,287**	256	603	**859**

Source: GAMA

market, sales of foreign manufactured business jets were close to 40 percent of all business jets sold here in the early 1990s. Although domestic sales are now strong, sales of foreign manufactured aircraft continue to trouble U.S. manufacturers.

6. **Other Factors**. Other factors have had an effect on general aviation, especially the personal and business use of aircraft. In 1979, Congress repealed the GI Bill of Rights, which provided dollars for thousands of ex-service personnel to take flying lessons. Changes in redundant, discretionary income; increases in air space; restrictions applied to VFR aircraft; reductions in leisure time; and shift in personal preferences as to how free time is spent all had their effect on the decline in the 1980s. Interest in sports cars and boats by the traditional aircraft customer, which require less training and recurrence, seemed to have peaked during the 1980s. Finally, the Clean Air Act of 1991 threatened the availability of aviation gasoline because it required the phase-out of leaded gasoline after December 1995. Initially, it was feared that the ban would include piston aircraft, as well as automobiles. The Environmental Protection Agency (EPA) clarified that the ban on lead-fuel-burning engines would not apply to general aviation. Though this was good news, the possibility still exists that market forces could lead refiners to stop production of 100-octane low-lead aviation gasoline, or alternatively, lead to very high prices for leaded fuel. With rising fuel prices and possible governmental restrictions, research and development into alternative aviation fuels is gaining momentum.

The Downturn in Pilot Numbers

From the late 1970s through the early 1990s, student starts were in a virtual free fall, as equally dramatic as the downward slide in light plane production. In 1978, there were 137,032 new student pilot certificates issued. By 1996, this number had reached 56,653, almost a 60 percent decline. Similarly, newly rated private pilots went from 58,064 in 1978 to 24,714 in 1996 and the total number of private pilots fell from 357,479 to 247,604 during the same period.

Although this disappearance of pilots and prospective pilots at airports may seem mysterious, it really is not. The onset of the phenomenon simply coincided with the end of the chain of great economic programs and the beginning of a natural life cycle. Beginning in 1939, the United States Government provided virtually free flight training for approximately the next 40 years, until the late 1970s. The Civil Pilot Training Program, the war training service after Pearl Harbor, trained an amazing 435,165 pilots between 1939 and 1944. The World War II GI Bill and its subsequent extension, the Korean War GI Bill, continued this trend of providing free flight instruction and flight training for those who only had to claim that they were interested in using it as "career development." But the government subsidy finally ran out in the late 1970s. The effect of the civil pilot training, the GI Bill, and other training programs was enormous. They were responsible for the majority of flight training students for many years; they were responsible for general aviation's infrastructure being larger than it would have been without these programs; and they were responsible for the sale of more airplanes, particularly trainers, than ever before.

Military pilots and others who had received their training during the war and immediate postwar periods, when they were in their twenties and early thirties, were reaching their sixties in the 1980s. They were beginning to retire from flying. Fundamentally, what we were seeing in the 1980s was our general aviation community seeking its natural level, shrinking back to the size it might have been had there never been civil pilot training, war training service, and the GI Bill.

There were other elements at work. In the 1980s, by the time prospective new pilots were typically age forty-plus and were established in their careers and could meet their financial obligations, time and attitudes had changed dramatically. These were people who were in their twenties in the 1960s, the era of the cold war, the race to the moon, The Beatles, the Great Society, the Vietnam War, hippies, and the antiwar protests. For them, flying was no longer the highest aspiration a young person could have, as it had been in the 1930s; there was no patriotic memory of World War II and the dramatic air battles that were trumpeted every evening on the radio news.

Having come of age in an era when the very foundations of our political and social systems were challenged, they were far less tolerant than previous generations of the hassle factor imposed through militaristic regulation and enforcement by government agencies like the FAA. Economically, they had higher expectations for ownership of consumer goods and services. At a time when their real income, adjusted for inflation, was decreasing, so was competition for their disposable income. General aviation, which was complacently mired in the attitudes and technology of the 1940s, was simply not able to compete in the marketplace of the 1980s and beyond. By the end of the 1980s, the top sellers in the personal airplane field were no longer the decades-old designs offered by the few light plane manufacturers still in the business but, rather, sleek homebuilts that were more attuned to the times.

Industry Challenges

The long-term decline in the number of manufacturers, combined with the precipitous decline in the shipments of single engine piston aircraft and the number of pilots during the 1980s and early 1990s was a major concern for the general aviation industry. The single engine piston aircraft is the base on which general aviation had to build its future. Historically, new pilots are trained in single-engine piston aircraft and work their way up through retractable landing gear and multiengine piston and turbine aircraft. When the single-engine piston market is in decline, it signals a slowing of expansion in the general aviation fleet and, consequently, a slowing in the rate of growth of general aviation activity.

In addition to the long-term decline in the production of single-engine piston aircraft, there was an accompanying deterioration in the flight-instructor and flight-training infrastructure in this country. Over the years, the number of flight schools declined. In addition, there were fewer FBOs offering flight training and fewer formal flight training programs offered at other facilities.

The physical facilities of many of the FBOs and flight schools deteriorated. This was partially due to the economic strain experienced by a large number of FBOs. The FBO problems were further compounded by the fact that there were no new training aircraft built in the United States during this period. Only a small number of imported aircraft were available.

For the long term, there were a number of challenges faced by the general aviation industry. In order to stimulate growth in the student and private pilot populations, as well as generate demand for new single-engine piston aircraft, the industry had to make fundamental improvements in both its infrastructure and how it promoted itself.

In the post "product liability reform environment," manufacturers realized that they must develop and incorporate new production processes, new materials, and new technologies in the production of single-engine piston aircraft. Their overall aim was to improve the quality and safety of their product while at the same time reducing the perceived cost of their product to the consumer.

On the pilot side, the industry had to develop programs or incentives that would entice or attract greater numbers of individuals to want to fly. The industry had to develop incentives that would reduce the number of people who drop out of aviation due to time and cost factors. There was nothing more fundamental to increasing the number of new aircraft purchases than a growing pilot population.

However, there were proportionally fewer young people during the late 1980s and early 1990s than in the past, and most of them had less disposable income than in previous generations at a comparable point in time. This posed the greatest single threat to the future growth in the number of new pilots and successful resumption of demand for single-engine piston aircraft.

To counter this threat, the general aviation industry had to make every effort to make it easier to access general aviation flying, to improve student starts, and to add to the number of FBOs. Training costs had to be reduced, while still improving safety. The industry also needed to develop innovative and alternative training methods that would reduce the time and cost of learning to fly in order to attract and retain new pilots.

Government/General Aviation Initiatives

During the 1990s, there was a growing climate of partnership between the FAA and the general aviation community. The FAA streamlined its certification process for new entry level aircraft (Primary Category Rule), and this could also increase production of new light, affordable aircraft.

Another example of cooperation was the formation of the General Aviation Action Plan Coalition by eleven general aviation organizations to support implementation of the FAA's General Aviation Action Plan.

The General Aviation Action Plan was based on four principles associated with President Clinton's "reinventing government" program. These principles included cutting red tape, putting the customer first, empowering employees, and getting back to basics. Within this framework, the plan set forth three goals relating to general aviation safety, provision of FAA services to general aviation, general aviation product innovation and competitiveness, system access and capacity, and affordability.

The goals of the plan sought to provide for:

- Regulatory relief and reduced user costs achieved through reduced rules and processes and implementation of a general aviation parts policy that was consistent with maintaining or increasing safety.
- Improved delivery of FAA services achieved by reducing excess layers of management, decentralization of the decision-making process, and giving the general aviation customers a voice in the development of FAA programs and how services are delivered.
- The elimination of unneeded programs and processes, and investment of FAA resources in those programs that provide the greatest government productivity and responsiveness to its customers' needs.

The FAA continued its efforts to develop common aviation standards. The FAA and the European Joint Aviation Authority (JAA) established a program in 1991 with the goal of making FAA Federal Aviation Regulations (FARs) and the JAA's Joint Aviation Regulations compatible for smaller aircraft (under 12,500 pounds) seeking type certification. In February 1996, the two organizations developed a new set of "common harmonization patterns" for both U.S. and European small aircraft.

These standards apply to new types of aircraft. They are

intended to expedite certification and increase safety standards. Under these rules, U.S. manufacturers can use the same standard aircraft design to comply with U.S. regulations, as well as those in each JAA member country.

In addition, the FAA continued to expend considerable effort cooperating with aviation authorities in Russia, China, and elsewhere to develop common aviation standards. It was felt that these initiatives, combined with efforts by industry, could tap vast new markets for general aviation products in places where general aviation does not currently exist.

There was also a growing effort to unlock general aviation's transportation potential through product innovation. The FAA and the National Aeronautics and Space Administration (NASA) collaborated with the general aviation community to implement a research program aimed at fostering new technologies in general aviation. This program, the Advanced General Aviation Transport Experiments (AGATE) Consortium, provided a unique partnership between government, industry, and academia that was established to help revive the general aviation industry. The goal of AGATE was to utilize new technology to produce aircraft that are safer, easier to operate, and affordable to today's pilot. The purpose is to make learning to fly less time consuming and less costly. This goal will be accomplished through employing improved avionics and more crashworthy airframes.

NASA and the FAA also started sponsoring a General Aviation Design Competition for students at U.S. aeronautical and engineering universities in 1994. This competition allowed students to participate in the monumental rebuilding effort of this country's general aviation aircraft sector by attempting to design their own general aviation aircraft in a manner that focuses on current design challenges.

Another example of the programs involving new technology are two contracts signed in September 1996 between NASA and several industry leaders to develop technologies for new intermittent and turbine engines. Under the support of NASA's General Aviation Propulsion (GAP) program, two companies were selected to begin three-year design projects for new, smoother, quieter, and more affordable engines. The hope was for NASA, aircraft manufacturers, and supplier industries to work together and share their technical expertise, financial resources, and facilities to demonstrate new general aviation propulsion systems.

Teledyne Continental Motors (TCM) was selected to work with NASA to design a revolutionary intermittent combustion aircraft engine, the CSD-283. One of the goals specified in NASA's GAP research program was to reduce the complexity of future aircraft engines. CAD (computer-assisted design) and CAM (computer-assisted manufacturing), along with special software, have provided manufacturing processes that have never been used before on piston-powered aircraft engines. TCM's CSD 283 engine is being manufactured using a monoblock process. This means that the case, cylinder walls, and cylinder heads for one-half of the engine are all one piece. Bolt the two halves together after installing the reciprocating parts and actuating gears, and the assembly is finished

In the year 2000, Williams International began working with NASA to design an ultra-quiet, more efficient turbofan engine with low exhaust emissions, the FJX-2. The new design is expected to improve the cruise speed and range of general aviation aircraft at costs competitive with piston engines.

The Aviation Weather Information (AWIN) program was another effort started in the 1990s to put real-time weather information in the cockpit. The FAA Safer Skies Initiative was an effort to improve weather, airspace, and other critical information in graphic and text form for pilots while also reducing the number of fatal air carrier accidents.

The FAA is committed to improving navigation through satellite-based systems such as Global Positioning System (GPS) for airport precision approaches. This includes the use of Wide Area Augmentation System (WAAS) and Local Area Augmentation System (LAAS). WAAS is designed to provide corrections to GPS signals on a regional or national basis. It consists of a network of ground reference stations, master stations, and a geosynchronous communications satellite, which broadcasts corrections to the GPS signal to aircraft. WAAS can support CAT I approaches. The initial 25 WAAS stations were installed in 1998. LAAS consists of a reference station at or near an airport and a monitor station that make it possible to measure any GPS errors at that airport. LAAS can support CAT I, II, and III GPS approaches. The FAA began prototype testing of LAAS in 1998. With LAAS and WAAS, advantages are comparable to ILS and the older MLS, yet the signal does not decline as distance from the runway increases.

More recent governmental initiatives include NextGen and SATS. The Next Generation Air Transportation System (NextGen) is the FAA's plan to modernize the National Airspace System (NAS) through 2025. Through NextGen, the FAA is addressing the impact of air traffic growth by increasing NAS capacity and efficiency while simultaneously improving safety, environmental impacts, and user access to the NAS.

The Small Aircraft Transportation System (SATS) is conceived by the National Aeronautics and Space Administration (NASA) as a safe travel alternative, freeing people and products from existing transportation system delays, by creating access to more communities in less time. The SATS concept of operations uses small aircraft for business and personal transportation, for on-demand, point-to-point travel between smaller regional, reliever, general aviation and other landing facilities, including heliports. The SATS architecture contemplates near-all-weather access to any landing facilities in the U.S.

Manufacturer/General Aviation Initiatives

The general aviation industry launched a series of programs and initiatives during the early 1990s to promote growth. These included the "No Plane, No Gain" campaign sponsored jointly by GAMA and the National Business Aviation Association (NBAA); "Project Pilot," sponsored by AOPA; and the "Learn to Fly" campaign sponsored by the National Air Transportation Association (NATA).

The "No Plane, No Gain" program was directed at the business community and designed to promote the use of general aviation aircraft as an essential tool of business. The thrust of the effort was to show that companies that use GA aircraft in the performance of their day-to-day business are well managed, more efficient, and more profitable than those that do not. The program uses videos, speaker's kits, slide shows, and advocacy materials for distribution among the business community to highlight the benefits of general aviation to business and to the bottom line of the company's balance sheet.

"Project Pilot" and "Learn to Fly" were programs directed at individuals and were designed to promote the growth in the number of new student starts and general aviation flying.

AOPA's "Project Pilot" encouraged its members to identify individuals who would benefit from special encouragement and assistance in the pursuit of becoming a private pilot. The sponsoring AOPA member then served as a mentor to the student, offering support and assistance to the student during his or her training. AOPA members/mentors were provided with materials designed to help them identify students who would benefit from the program. The participating students were also introduced to the program through a special program kit that included such items as a video on the joy of flying, decals, a special issue of *Pilot* magazine, and AOPA membership information. By year-end 1999, AOPA claimed that, over the course of the program, more than 22,910 members had identified and mentored nearly 33,240 students. Today, AOPA encourages its 408,000 members to become involved as a Project Pilot mentor.

The purpose of NATA's "Learn to Fly" campaign was to increase the number of active GA pilots by increasing the number of student starts and by motivating inactive pilots to return to active flying. The program was designed to promote the benefits of learning to fly. It stimulated the interest of a targeted audience through advertising and promotional efforts. In addition, it provided interested prospects with fast and easy access to information on how to go about learning to fly. This was accomplished through the use of a toll free telephone number (1-800-I-CAN-FLY), information packets provided through direct mail response resulting from telephone inquiries, and follow-up calls by participating flight schools in the interested caller's ZIP code area.

Beyond the goal of bringing new pilots into general aviation, both "Project Pilot" and "Learn to Fly" programs were interested in rekindling the desire to fly of students who had abandoned their training by encouraging them to complete their certification, as well as to convince licensed pilots who stopped flying to return to active status.

Another program started in the mid1990s to stimulate new interest in learning to fly was the "Young Eagles" program sponsored by the Experimental Aircraft Association (EAA). This program involved taking young people ages 12 to 14 on their first flight in a small aircraft and could spark an interest in their learning to fly.

On July 3, 1996, Cessna dedicated its new 500,000-square-foot final assembly plant in Independence, Kansas. Cessna committed to resume production of selected single-engine piston aircraft models—the 172, the 182, and the 206. It would be the first new single-engine piston Cessna produced since 1986.

Another important industry program called the Piston Engine Aircraft Revitalization Committee (PEARC) completed its work in 1996. The committee included senior managers and directors from GAMA member companies, aviation organizations, academic institutions, and the FAA. The committee's goal was to find new methods of expansion and growth for the general aviation industry and to review the efforts already undertaken by the industry in order to adopt the best practices. The committee estimated that there were approximately 1.2 million individuals—900,000 men and 300,000 women—interested in flying. According to the committee's findings, 57 percent of the potential pilots were between the ages of 25 and 40. In addition, committee findings indicated that many potential pilots generally overestimate both the time and the cost of learning to fly.

"GA Team 2000" was a direct result of the work performed by PEARC. This program, started in 1996, was sponsored jointly by AOPA and GAMA, and supported by more than 100 industry organizations. The goals of GA Team 2000 were multifaceted:

- To revitalize the influx of new pilots.
- To generate flight training leads.
- To encourage improvement in flight school marketing and training infrastructure.
- To secure additional funding to expand the GA Team 2000 effort.

The program encourages people of all ages to "Stop Dreaming and Start Flying." Renamed the "Be A Pilot" program, it began issuing introductory flight certificates to interested respondents in May 1997. The certificates could be redeemed for a first flight lesson at a cost of $35.

In the four years since the program started, over 110,000 certificates have been requested. In 2000, there were more than 35,000 requests for certificates. The program has over 3,500 participating flight schools and attracts new market entrants via the Internet and cable television advertising. Although today's Intro Flight Certificates are priced at $99 (or less), the Be A Pilot Web site is interactive and the program is still doing a great job of attracting new pilots.

During the 1990s, the light aircraft manufacturers launched programs to make aircraft ownership easier. The New Piper Aircraft Company created Piper Financial Services (PFS), which offers competitive interest rates for the purchase and/or leasing of Piper aircraft. Cessna accepted refundable deposits for nontransferable position reservations for its new aircraft. The Experimental Aircraft Association entered into an agreement with TFC Textron (formerly Green Tree Aircraft) to finance kit-built planes. The general aviation industry also sought to increase the number of lending institutions that offered special low, competitive rates for aircraft financing.

The number of fractional ownership programs for general aviation aircraft continued to grow. NetJets (formerly Executive Jet) became the dominant name in fractional ownership. However, manufacturers also joined the movement. They formed their own programs or allied themselves with ongoing programs. Boeing Business Jets and Gulfstream started working relationships with NetJets. Raytheon established Raytheon Travel Air (now Flight Options). Bombardier Aerospace (Flexjet) also entered the competition, along with Dassault Falcon Jets. Fractional ownership also arrived in the rotorcraft market with the entry of the Lynton Group. These programs have greatly increased the accessibility to aircraft ownership for many who could not otherwise afford it (refer to chapter 11 for more on fractional ownership).

Finally, several industry organizations are also targeting young people through the Internet to pique their interest in the world of aviation. The NBAA sponsors "AvKids," a program designed to educate elementary school students about the benefits of business aviation to the community and career opportunities available to them in business aviation. The National Agricultural Aviation Association developed a Web page with information on careers in aerial application. GAMA offers publications, awards, and scholarships to bring education into the nation's classrooms. AOPA's "Apple Program" brings aviation into the classroom, targeting middle and high school students.

The 1990s—Revitalization of an Industry

Even with these many efforts, GA continued its downward slide into the mid1990s, reaching a low of 928 shipments in 1994 (see Table 1-1). However, there were a number of reasons for guarded optimism in the industry. Several ongoing events suggested that general aviation may experience a renaissance. There was a growing realization in the aviation community that general aviation must reinvent itself and create a new demand growth curve, much as it did in the 1950s.

The main reason for this optimism at the time was the industry perception that product liability legislation would hopefully soon be enacted by Congress. The industry felt that passage of this legislation would not only lower its insurance costs, but would enable manufacturers to begin to design and produce new technology and cheaper general aviation aircraft.

Additionally, the amateur-built aircraft market showed steady growth during the early 1990s. Almost 1,000 new amateur-built experimental aircraft received airworthiness certificates, and 2,000 kits were sold by 14 major kit manufacturers in 1992. By 1995, it was estimated that 23,000 experimental aircraft were included in the general aviation fleet. This represented an increase of roughly 20,900 over the estimated 2,100 in 1970.

The popularity of amateur-built aircraft resulted from several factors, including:

- **Affordability**: Amateur-built aircraft are substantially less expensive than new production aircraft (aircraft produced under a type and production certificate) because of the large amount of labor that the builder provides.
- **Performance**: Many amateur-built aircraft have superior speed, maneuverability, fuel economy, and/or handling characteristics compared to light production aircraft. In many cases, the performance benefits are due to features and technologies not available on used or even most new production aircraft. These benefits include (1) new technology engines, (2) low-drag, natural laminar flow wings and carefully contoured fuselage aerodynamics, and (3) very smooth surfaces held to high tolerances and crafted from advanced composite technologies.

These aircraft represented the test bed for new technologies, which eventually are introduced in the development and manufacture of the next generation of light general aviation production aircraft.

Some kit builders became production companies at the entry level. For instance, Cirrus Design began in 1984 as a kit airplane design and manufacturing company in Baraboo, Wisconsin. The company's first airplane, the VK-30, became an inspiration for developing technologically advanced production aircraft. The SR20, with composite construction and advanced aerodynamics, was awarded FAA Type Certification in 1998. It incorporated flat-panel, multi-function display technology and state-of-the-art safety innovations, including a final level of protection known as the Cirrus Airframe Parachute System (CAPS).

The used aircraft market also remained strong during the early 1990s with almost 36,000 aircraft changing hands in 1992. Additionally, prices for piston aircraft also remained strong, thus reflecting some pent-up demand for these aircraft. The success of the kits and the strength of the used aircraft market showed the creativity and resilience that still existed in the market.

The international use of general aviation aircraft increased. Based on sample flight-strip data obtained from the North Atlantic oceanic centers, weekly operations of general aviation aircraft increased from 119 in 1983 to 338 in 1991, 293 in 1992, and 396 in 1993. Some of this increase resulted from concerns of business for the safety and security of its traveling employees. However, a large part of it was the result of business adapting to meet expanding global markets and opportunities. The corporate flying market anticipated the new Gulfstream V, capable of flying 7,500 miles nonstop.

Passage of the General Aviation Revitalization Act (GARA) of 1994 ushered in a new wave of optimism in the general aviation industry. With some exceptions, GARA imposed an 18-year statute of repose, limiting product liability suits for aircraft having fewer than 20 passenger seats not engaged in scheduled passenger-carrying operations. Cessna immediately announced that it would resume production of single-engine aircraft in 1996. The New Piper Aircraft Corporation was formed, and, in 1995, general aviation aircraft shipments finally increased after a 17-year decline.

In 1997, the optimism so prevalent in the industry since the passage of GARA was evidenced by the release of new products and services; expansion of production facilities; increased student starts; increased aircraft shipments, and record-setting gains in aircraft billings. These conditions suggested continued improvement in the general aviation industry in 1998 and beyond. According to a poll of Aircraft Owners and Pilots Association (AOPA) members conducted in March 1992, only 41 percent said that they were optimistic about the future of general aviation. In response to a similar poll in January 1997, 61 percent responded optimistically, and, by April 1998, the poll of certificated pilots reported that 74.5 percent of its members thought the state of aviation was the same or better than it had been. This renewed optimism among the pilot community, aircraft manufacturers, and the industry as a whole could be directly attributed to the strong economy and the passage of GARA in 1994.

In January 1997, Cessna delivered its first new single-engine piston aircraft since 1986. In addition, Lancair International, Diamond Aircraft, and Mooney also produced new piston models. Galaxy Aerospace rolled out its new business jet in the fall of 1996. Aerospatiale and Renault announced plans to join forces to produce light aircraft piston engines for certification in 1999. Piper announced plans to manufacture the Meridian, a single-engine turboprop scheduled for its first flight in 1999 with delivery in 2000.

New manufacturing facilities opened to support expanded production. Cirrus broke ground on two facilities to support production of the SR 20. Also, Sabreliner started a large expansion program at their Missouri facility.

In 1999, Cessna announced plans and orders for new Citation models, including the CJ2, Sovereign, and Ultra Encore. Raytheon announced that it would begin deliveries of its Premier I, an entry-level jet that features a composite fuselage with metal wings, in 2000. Mooney delivered its first Eagle in 1999.

Boeing Business Jets announced its plan to build a larger version of its long-range corporate jet, the BBJ-2. Boeing Business Jets, a joint enterprise of Boeing and General Electric, entered the market in 1998 with the long-range BBJ based on a hybrid of the 737-700/800 aircraft. Twenty-eight aircraft were delivered in 1999. Airbus and Fairchild are also marketing business jets that are based on aircraft originally designed for commercial operations.

During the 1990s, fractional ownership programs offered by NetJets, Bombardier's Flexjet, Raytheon's Travel Air, Flight Options, and TAG Aviation grew at a rapid pace. From 1993 through the end of 1999, these five major fractional ownership providers increased their fleet size and shareholders at average annual rates above 65 percent. According to AvData, Inc., by the end of 1999, the fractional ownership fleet numbered 329 and shareholders totaled 1,567. Despite this record growth, it is believed, only a small percentage of this market has been developed.

Fractional ownership programs are filling the niche for corporations, celebrities, and business people that do not generate enough flying to warrant a flight department. Fractional ownership providers offer the customer a more efficient use of time by providing a faster point-to-point travel time and the ability to conduct business while flying. In addition, shareholders of fractional ownership find the minimum startup concerns and easier exiting options of great benefit.

The business aviation community was initially concerned that the success of fractional ownership programs would result in a shutdown of corporate flight departments. These concerns were unfounded. Fractional ownership providers have generally found their business base to be first-time users of corporate aircraft services, users that traditionally utilized commercial air transportation. Once introduced to the benefits of corporate flying, some users of fractional programs found it more cost effective to start their own flight departments, instead of incurring the costs of a larger share in a fractional ownership program. As a result, the fractional ownership community may be partially responsible for the increase in traditional flight departments since 1993.

The 1990s truly represented a revitalization of the industry. Total billings in 1999 soared 35.1 percent over 1998, reaching $7.9 billion, and units shipped increased from 2,200 to 2,504, or 12.6 percent. Put into perspective, general aviation sales in 1999 quadrupled those of 1991. The last year of the decade also marked the first time in GAMA's history that both billings and shipments increased for five consecutive years. It marked the first full year of deliveries of the Cessna 206H Stationair and T206H Turbo Stationair. Deliveries of the composite-construction Cirrus Design SR 20 began, and Mooney Aircraft Corporation began production of the Ovation 2, a faster and more fuel-efficient version of the firm's best-selling model, the Ovation.

The biggest jump in 1999 sales revenue, similar to 1998, was in the turbofan aircraft segment. Sales rose 23.9 percent, in large part due to strong incremental growth and fractional ownership programs. Gulfstream Aerospace, for example, racked up almost $2.4 billion of sales, with 70 deliveries. Cessna's revenues topped $1.8 billion, most of which were Citation sales. Bombardier delivered the first 34 Global Express aircraft into completion. Sales of the 4000-nm range Challenger 604 remained strong, with 40 deliveries in 1999. The Learjet division also delivered 43 Learjet 45 aircraft. At the end of Bombardier's January 31 fiscal year, its order backlog had climbed to $18.9 million.

According to AvData, the number of corporate flight departments in the United States grew by 6.6 percent in 1999, from 8,236 to 8,778. The National Air Transportation Association reported that charter activity was up by over 20 percent in 1999. The decade closed with across-the-board growth in general aviation activity, corporate flight departments, fractional programs, and charter flights.

The New Millennium

As the year 2000 approached, the future of general aviation looked bright as evidenced by the industry's actions to stimulate the development and production of new general aviation products and services. New manufacturing facilities were being built and old facilities were being expanded. Sales of general aviation aircraft were setting new records for value of aircraft shipped. Much of this record sales value was for aircraft at the higher priced end of the general aviation fleet—turbine powered aircraft—and was likely due in part to the increase in fractional ownership. More than 900 turbine aircraft were delivered in 2000 (see Table 1-1) as production capacity soared to keep up with record backlogs in manufacturers' order books. Cessna, for example, doubled the number of Excels it delivered and increased Bravo production by 50 percent. Dassault Falcon Jet deliveries reached 73, five more than in 1999, while its backlog of orders increased. Learjet 45 deliveries were up from 43 in 1999 to 71 in 2000. Even deliveries of the venerable Raytheon Hawker 800 XP increased by 22 percent.

Piston aircraft shipments grew by almost 11 percent, buoyed by an infusion of new technology from Lancair and Cirrus Design, as well as increased piston deliveries from Cessna's Independence, Kansas, plant. The year 2000 saw the first deliveries of Lancair's Columbia 300. Cirrus delivered 95 new four-seat SR 20 models. Cessna piston singles deliveries increased to 912 units.

In 2001, Cirrus Design's 310-hp SR 22, capable of flying faster than a Raytheon Bonanza A36 at less than half the price, joined the piston-engine singles market. Cessna's Turbo Skylane went back into production, this time with a fuel-injected Lycoming 540 engine.

The business jet section, though, is where major changes were occurring. The Sino Swearingen SBO-2, having made its first test flight in production configuration in 2000, made its debut as the second least-expensive entry-level fanjet. While having the smallest cabin cross section of any business jet in production, the SBO-2 offered midsize jet speed and range.

Embraer's Legacy, a derivative of its best-selling EMB-145 regional jet fitted with winglets, made its introduction in two forms—a 19-passenger corporate shuttle and a 12-passenger executive transport. The Legacy Executive, fitted with auxiliary fuel tanks, has the most cabin volume of any midsize business jet and virtually the same tanks—full range as a Dassault Falcon Jet 50EX.

Boeing Business Jets offered its BBJ2 in 2001, a $60 million version of its next generation 737-800 fitted with auxiliary fuel tanks, winglets, and upgraded engines, enabling it to fly 22 passengers from Los Angeles to London.

However, two of the most substantial enhancements to GA during the first decade of the new millennium can be characterized simply as LSAs and VLJs. Light Sport Aircraft (LSA) are a new breed of aircraft having a maximum gross weight of 1,320 pounds (1,430 for seaplanes), an unpressurized cabin, a fixed or ground adjustable propeller, a single, reciprocating engine, fixed landing gear (retractable landing gear for seaplanes), one- or two-person occupancy, maximum stall speed of 45 knots, and maximum speed in level flight with maximum continuous power of 120 knots. These aircraft were developed in response to the long-awaited Sport Pilot and Light Sport Aircraft rule, which was implemented in July 2004. GA industry organizations, such as AOPA, lobbied for this new rule for nine years, mainly to provide a means for pilots without current medicals to be able to fly again. As expected, the Sport Pilot must accrue 20 hours of flight instruction, be at least 17 years of age, have a valid state driver's license, be proficient in the English language, and be able to affirm general good health without use of substances or medications that impede judgment, cognition, or motor skills.

Very Light Jets (VLJs) are a new breed of aircraft that may also be known as Personal or Micro Jets because they are designed as small jet aircraft that hold few passengers and can fly into smaller airports which are typically closer to the passenger's intended destination. These aircraft weigh 10,000 pounds or less maximum certificated takeoff weight, are certificated for single pilot operations, have slower approach speeds than a typical jet, are capable of flight level (FL) 380-450, have a range of 1,000-1,400 miles, and contain advanced flight automation systems (such as moving map GPS and multifunction displays). Current manufacturers include Cessna, Diamond, Eclipse, Embraer, Honda, Spectrum, and Piper. These new jets are expected to change the face of business and personal aviation. They cost 1/4 the initial purchase price of a typical corporate jet and have 1/3 the operating cost. Specifically, VLJ prices range from $1-3 million, with operating costs around $1,700 per flight hour. These jets are also being adopted by fractional ownership companies and air taxi operators. For instance, DayJet was established in 2002 and was providing point-to-point on demand service utilizing Eclipse 500 VLJs before ceasing operations in September 2008. One major obstacle for VLJ operators is insurance rates, as many insurance companies are skeptical of the safety of such a new concept. However, mentor pilot programs are industry's response to this concern. With a focus on safety, the mentor pilot is a new concept that allows an experienced pilot to "coach" less experienced pilots as they transition into VLJs. Within a few years, the GA industry will certainly have a new face as VLJs begin flying into and serving small, GA airports with shorter runways.

Dollars spent on research and development are advancing avionics and computer technology; advances that are not only expected to increase aviation safety and aircraft efficiency, but are expected to make it easier to pilot an aircraft. For instance, VLJs are certified for single pilot operations due to these advances in technology and automation systems. Of course, without pilots to fly the planes, there would be no industry. To stimulate growth in the pilot population, the industry is continuing to promote flying with "learn to fly" programs. The industry is also developing programs to assist schoolteachers in bringing aviation into the classroom with the hope of encouraging students to pursue careers in the field of aviation.

Overall, these trends bode well for general aviation industry in the foreseeable future. However, unexpected events such as the tragedy on September 11, 2001 and the economic slowdown during the first two years of the new millennium vividly demonstrate that the future, as in the past, will bring new challenges to this ever-changing industry.

KEY TERMS

Wright Brothers
Glenn Curtiss
Barnstormers
Gates Flying Circus
Kelly Air Mail Act of 1925
Air Commerce Act of 1926
E.M. Laird Company
Weaver Aircraft Company
Swallow Airplane Manufacturing Company
Travel Air Manufacturing Company
Beech Aircraft Corporation
Cessna Aircraft Company
Piper Aircraft Company
VA flight training
William P. Lear
GAMA
NBAA
AOPA
FAA
General Aviation Reservation System
NextGen
SATS

REVIEW QUESTIONS

1. How did Glenn Curtiss get started in manufacturing aircraft? What military trainer did Curtiss develop that became the most popular aircraft with the barnstormers? Did the barnstormers make any contribution to the development of general aviation? How?
2. How did Wichita become the home for many of the light aircraft manufacturers? What successful aircraft was developed in 1932 that brought the Beech name into prominence? Cessna gained prominence in 1935 with the development of which aircraft? What were some other successful aircraft developed by Cessna during and immediately after World War II? Piper's Cub developed out of which aircraft?
3. Why did the manufacturers have such a feeling of optimism concerning market potential during the postwar period? What were some of the reasons why sales did not live up to expectations?
4. What was the new direction that the manufacturers took

for light aircraft starting in the early 1950s? What were some of the developments that took place during the 1950s that helped general aviation grow?

5. Why can it be said that general aviation arrived at a level of maturity during the 1960s? Describe some of the new aircraft that were developed during the 1960s. What was the first jet designed specifically for the general aviation market?
6. Describe some of the major events during the 1970s that impacted general aviation. What are some of the reasons for the decline in general aviation aircraft sales during the 1980s? Why did Cessna stop production of single--engine training aircraft? Specifically, why did the light aircraft manufacturers concentrate on turbine aircraft?
7. Discuss the reasons for the downturn in the number of pilots from the late 1970s through the early 1990s. Describe the challenges faced by the industry in light of the decline in all segments of the general aviation community. How did the government agencies, manufacturers, and the general aviation community respond to these challenges?
8. How was the general aviation industry revitalized during the 1990s? What was the purpose of the General Aviation Revitalization Act (GARA) of 1994? Describe the role that fractional ownership has played in revitalizing the industry.
9. In what manner will LSAs change the face of general aviation? How should FBOs cater to the owner/operators of these aircraft?
10. What are the advantages and disadvantages of the new Very Light Jet category of aircraft? How will these new jets help business and personal aviation compete with the commercial airline industry?

REFERENCES

Cessna Aircraft Company: An Eye to the Sky-Cessna-First Fifty Years 1991-1961. Wichita, KS: Cessna Aircraft Com_ pany, 1961.

Chant, Christopher. *Aviation An Illustrated History*. New York: Crescent Books, 1978.

Christy, Joe. *High Adventure: The First 75 Years of Civil Aviation*. Blue Ridge Summit, PA: TAB Books, Inc., 1985.

Department of Transportation, Federal Aviation Administration, FAA Aerospace Forecasts, various years, FAA, APO-llO, Washington, D.C: U.S. Government Printing Office.

Hedrick, Frank E. *Pageantry of Flight: The Story of Beech Aircraft Corporation*. Wichita, KS: Beech Aircraft Corporation, 1967.

Piper. *The New Piper Aircraft, Inc.: A History of the Legendary Company*. Vero Beach, FL: The New Piper Aircraft, Inc., 2000.

VLJs. Retrieved February 27, 2008, from Very Light Magazine. http://vljmag.com.

Notes

Chapter 2
The Scope of General Aviation

OUTLINE

OBJECTIVES

At the end of this chapter, you should be able to:

- Define "general aviation."
- Identify the FAA primary use categories.
- Describe the purpose of public use flying.
- Distinguish between executive/corporate transportation and business transportation. Discuss the importance of personal flying.
- Give several examples of general aviation aircraft used for aerial application and aerial observation.
- Describe the size and scope of general aviation airports in the United States.
- Discuss the economic role of general aviation airports.
- Identify the primary FAA services provided to pilots.
- Discuss the changing size and scope of the airframe manufacturers.
- Understand the importance e-commerce in the marketing and sales process.
- Realize the impact of GA on the Web.

What is General Aviation?

In 1848 the English historian Thomas Babington Macaulay postulated that "of all the inventions, the alphabet and the printing press excepted, those which bridge distance have done the most for civilization of our species." The role aviation has played in helping America achieve its position of world preeminence can hardly be overstated. In fact, the growth and success of our nation during its 200-year existence have always been closely related to the innovative abilities of its various forms of transportation.

Land, water, and air transportation systems historically have provided the lines of communication and distribution required to unite the nation and foster the development of its commerce. Throughout history, progress has depended upon developing a better transportation system.

Air transportation is a purely 20th-century phenomenon. It has developed with almost incredible swiftness from scarcely noted experiments on the hills of Kitty Hawk in 1903 to its role today as a vital public necessity that touches the lives of everyone.

Today, transportation as an industry, in its many public and private forms, accounts for fully 20 percent of the total gross national product of the United States. Air transportation makes a significant contribution to this total economic impact.

The term *general aviation* refers to all civil aviation activity except that of the certificated airlines and the military. Together, general aviation and the airlines make up America's balanced air transportation system, which is the safest and most efficient aviation network in the world.

Air service in America is available to almost everyone because the airlines and general aviation fulfill separate but compatible transportation roles. The general aviation fleet of some 220,000 business, commercial, and personal planes serves all of the nation's 19,000 airports, bringing the benefits and mobility of air transportation to virtually everyone, including millions of people who live outside of the metropolitan areas that the airlines serve through some 600 airports.

General aviation is air transportation on demand. It moves millions of passengers a year and tons of cargo and mail faster and farther than any earthbound mode of transportation—and with almost unlimited flexibility. Statistically, the general aviation fleet represents 96 percent of all civil aircraft registered in the United States.

- General aviation aircraft range from two-seat training aircraft to international business jets.
- General aviation is estimated to be an $18 billion industry, generating more than $64 billion annually in economic activity.
- General aviation exports nearly one-quarter of its production and leads the world in development of new technology aircraft.
- General aviation aircraft fly over 32 million hours (nearly two times the airline flight hours) and carry 166 million passengers annually.
- Approximately 70 percent of all the hours flown by general aviation aircraft are for business and commercial purposes.
- Most people learn to fly in a general aviation aircraft.

Before general aviation became a factor in the nation's transportation system, most factories and distribution centers were located in or near large metropolitan areas. Today, industrial decentralization is locating facilities away from major population centers to smaller communities—those that have a general aviation airport.

General aviation is a major reason why the map of United States industry is changing perceptibly and constantly. As a result, business flying is one of the largest categories in general aviation. General aviation aircraft are also used for instruction, to fight fires, carry medical patients, perform aerial mapping and pipeline patrol, fertilize crops, enhance law enforcement, and many other functions.

Today's general aviation airplane, because of advances in technology that provide better speed, range, fuel efficiency, and flexibility, has become an integral business tool.

The Uses of General Aviation Aircraft

The size and diversification of general aviation create difficulty when attempting to categorize it for statistical purposes. General aviation has no reporting requirements comparable to those of the certificated air carrier industry. Aircraft flown for business during the week may be used for personal transportation on weekends, as a family car is used. Instructional aircraft may be used for charter (air taxi) service or rented to customers for business or personal use. An air taxi airplane may be used for advanced flight instruction, for rental to business or personal use customers, and so on.

Even though aircraft have multiple purposes, the Federal Aviation Administration's Statistics and Forecast Branch conducts an annual survey of owners requesting the number of flight hours for the previous year by primary use category.

Based on the results of the latest GA survey, there were an estimated 217,500 active general aviation aircraft in 2000. An active aircraft is an aircraft flown at least one hour during the survey calendar year (see Table 2-1). Although the total active fleet of GA aircraft had increased each year from 1995 to 1999, the year 2000 saw a slight decrease in the number of active GA aircraft. Nonetheless, during the 1995-1999 period, the active fleet had increased 26.9 percent.

Single-engine piston aircraft continue to dominate the fleet during this period, accounting for approximately 70 percent of the total active fleet. The next largest groups are multiengine piston and experimental aircraft, which make up close to nine percent each. Turboprops, turbojets, rotorcraft, and all others represent small shares of the active fleet, accounting for roughly three percent each. The number of active experimental aircraft increased by close to 70 percent during this five-year period.

While turboprops, turbojets, and rotorcraft represented less than 10 percent of the active fleet in 2000, they accounted for approximately 23 percent of total hours flown (see Table 2-2). The number of hours flown by general aviation aircraft increased for five consecutive years, showing an increase of 32 percent for the five-year period.

Public Use

The public use category includes owned or leased aircraft for fulfilling a federal, state, or local government function. Government aircraft are an essential part of our national air transportation system. These 4,000 plus aircraft, most of which were designed for civilian use, are flown thousands

Table 2-1

GENERAL AVIATION ACTIVE AIRCRAFT BY AIRCRAFT TYPE

(In Thousands)

AIRCRAFT TYPE	2000	1999	1998	1997	1996 1/	1995 1/
Fixed Wing - Total	**183.3**	**184.7**	**175.2**	**166.8**	**163.7**	**162.3**
Piston -- Total	**170.5**	**171.9**	**163.0**	**156.1**	**153.6**	**152.8**
One Engine	149.4	150.9	144.2	140.0	137.4	137.0
Two Engine	21	20.9	18.7	15.9	16.1	15.7
Other Piston	0.1	0.1	0.1	0.1	0.1	0.0
Turboprop -- Total	**5.8**	**5.7**	**6.2**	**5.6**	**5.7**	**5.0**
Single Engine	0.7	1.0	1.0	0.7	0.7	0.7
Two Engine	5.0	4.6	5.1	4.9	4.9	4.3
Other Turboprop	0.0	0.0	0.1	0.0	0.1	0.0
Turbojet -- Total	**7.0**	**7.1**	**6.1**	**5.2**	**4.4**	**4.6**
Two Engine	6.2	6.4	5.5	4.6	4.1	4.1
Other Turbojet	0.8	0.7	0.6	0.5	0.3	0.5
Rotorcraft -- Total	**7.2**	**7.4**	**7.4**	**6.8**	**6.6**	**5.8**
Piston	2.7	2.6	2.5	2.3	2.5	1.9
Turbine	4.5	4.9	4.9	4.5	4.1	4.0
Single Engine	3.8	4.0	4.0	3.8	3.4	3.2
Multi-engine	0.7	0.8	0.8	0.8	0.6	0.7
Other -- Total	**6.7**	**6.8**	**5.6**	**4.1**	**4.2**	**4.7**
Experimental -- Total	**20.4**	**20.5**	**16.5**	**14.7**	**16.6**	**15.2**
Total All Aircraft	**217.5**	**219.4**	**204.7**	**192.4**	**191.1**	**188.1**

SOURCE: 1995 - 2000 General Aviation Activity and Avionics Surveys.
1/ Estimates have been revised to reflect changes in edit and estimation procedures, and may not be comparable to estimates prior to 1995.

of hours a year on government business, from fire fighting and pest control to operations requiring high levels of security, such as prisoner transportation. Public use aircraft also play a critical role in ensuring timely responses to disasters and emergencies, such as used by the National Transportation Safety Board (NTSB) and FAA (see Tables 2-3 and 2-4).

Many areas of our country are inaccessible to ground transportation, so people and equipment must be airlifted. With lives, property, or national security often at stake, many government missions cannot wait for the next airline departure. For security reasons, air transport of key personnel on government aircraft is often the only choice.

Government aircraft are often configured for unique jobs. Some are fitted with firefighting apparatus; others are stripped of all furnishings to accommodate heavy equipment and cargo; still others are equipped with communications equipment and modified so that cameras, radar, and other equipment can be installed.

Fifty-one percent of the public use aircraft in 1999 are powered by piston engines. An additional 39 percent are helicopters. Eight percent of the fleet are turbine-engine powered aircraft. Many of these aircraft are used for research or in-flight checking of navigational aids. Only a small number of government operated jets are configured for passenger travel.

Government missions include:

- Firefighting. The air dropping of water, chemicals, and fire retardant slurry by aircraft is a major weapon in the control of forest and brush fires, from the pine woods of New Jersey to the Florida Everglades, from the forests of the Big Sky country to the hills of Southern California.
- Law Enforcement. Several government agencies use aircraft to patrol borders; locate, chase, and apprehend crime suspects; transport prisoners; and play a major role in drug interdiction.
- Scientific Research and Development. Atmospheric research, especially severe weather prediction such as hurricanes, represents a major share of air operations in this category.

Table 2-2

TOTAL GENERAL AVIATION HOURS FLOWN BY AIRCRAFT TYPE

(In Thousands)

AIRCRAFT TYPE	2000	1999	1998	1997	1996 1/	1995 1/
Fixed Wing - Total	**26,986**	**27,444**	**24,392**	**24,111**	**23,402**	**23,196**
Piston -- Total	**22,199**	**22,895**	**20,402**	**20,743**	**20,091**	**20,251**
One Engine	18,798	19,325	16,823	18,345	17,606	17,831
Two Engine	3,372	3,551	3,567	2,380	2,474	2,416
Other Piston	28	18	11	19	11	4
Turboprop -- Total	**2,031**	**1,811**	**1,765**	**1,655**	**1,768**	**1,490**
Single Engine	278	357	289	321	328	292
Two Engine	1,727	1,450	1,459	1,326	1,419	1,181
Other Turboprop	26	4	17	9	22	17
Turbojet -- Total	**2,755**	**2,738**	**2,226**	**1,713**	**1,543**	**1,455**
Two Engine	2,338	2,435	1,995	1,557	1,385	1,352
Other Turbojet	417	303	231	155	158	102
Rotorcraft -- Total	**2,308**	**2,744**	**2,342**	**2,084**	**2,122**	**1,961**
Piston	531	556	430	344	591	337
Turbine	1,777	2,188	1,912	1,740	1,531	1,624
Single Engine	1,424	1,744	1,415	1,311	1,282	1,218
Multi-engine	353	443	497	429	249	406
Other -- Total	**374**	**318**	**295**	**192**	**227**	**261**
Experimental -- Total	**1,307**	**1,247**	**1,071**	**1,327**	**1,158**	**1,194**
Total All Aircraft	**30,975**	**31,754**	**28,100**	**27,713**	**26,909**	**26,612**

SOURCE: 1995 - 2000 General Aviation Activity and Avionics Surveys.
1/ Estimates have been revised to reflect changes in edit and estimation procedures, and may not be comparable to estimates prior to 1995.

- Flight Inspection. Flight checking hundreds of navigational aids across the country to ensure safe and accurate readings is accomplished by government aircraft.
- Surveying. Aircraft operated by the Department of the Interior agencies, such as Fish and Wildlife and Park Service, help to conduct geological surveys such as wetlands mapping and volcano monitoring. Pilots conduct regular and annual wildlife surveys for certain mammals and waterfowl, such as migratory bird surveys.
- Search and Rescue. U.S. Coast Guard and other govern-ment agencies save many lives every year through search and rescue.
- Drug Interdiction. To a great degree, the war on drugs is fought in the skies through the work of government pilots. These government pilots, flying air patrol, aircraft escort, and aerial spotting of suspect fields and plantings, help stop the flow of drugs into the U.S.
- Transport of Government Personnel. Because of security, timeliness, remote locations, and other reasons, government aircraft are often the only viable transportation choice. Safe and efficient transport of government officials is an important and legitimate use of public use aircraft.

Business Flying

Business flying includes two primary use categories. They are:

- Executive/Corporate Transportation. Any use of an aircraft by a corporation, company, or other organization for the purposes of transporting its employees and/or property not for compensation or hire, and employing professional pilots for the operation of the aircraft.
- Business Transportation. Any use of an aircraft not for compensation or hire by individuals for the purposes of transportation required by business in which they are engaged.

Table 2-3

U.S. Fleet by Type and Use

2005 General Aviation and Air Taxi Number of Aircraft by Primary Use by Aircraft Type. Includes Air Taxi Aircraft. Excludes Commuter Aircraft

	General Aviation Part 91 Use													On-Demand FAR Part 135 Use		
Aircraft Type	Total Active	Personal	Business	Corporate	Instructional	Aerial Apps	Aerial Obs	Aerial Other	Ext. Load	Other Work	Sight See	Air Med[1]	Other	Air Taxi[2]	Air Tours	Air Med
Total All Aircraft	**224,352**	**151,408**	**25,524**	**10,553**	**13,399**	**3,548**	**4,663**	**811**	**226**	**732**	**945**	**418**	**3,612**	**6,926**	**613**	**976**
% Std. Error	1.5	2.2	1.9	1.0	1.8	1.4	1.3	1.2	0.8	1.3	1.5	1.2	1.3	0.7	1.0	0.7
Piston Total	**167,608**	**121,295**	**21,371**	**2,012**	**11,384**	**2,412**	**2,773**	**440**	**5**	**408**	**333**	**185**	**2,063**	**2,651**	**167**	**109**
One-Engine	148,101	112,105	15,780	719	10,487	2,353	2,492	344	3	354	304	85	1,736	1,169	137	34
Two-Engine	19,412	9,166	5,591	1,293	887	44	281	96	2	44	21	100	319	1,465	28	75
Other Piston	95	25	0	0	11	14	0	0	0	10	8	0	7	17	3	0
Turboprop Total	**7,942**	**1,300**	**1,868**	**2,372**	**70**	**517**	**112**	**89**	**0**	**69**	**7**	**21**	**96**	**1,256**	**24**	**141**
One-Engine	2,595	557	715	222	25	482	20	19	0	23	0	2	41	444	21	23
Two-Engine	5,307	743	1,153	2,150	44	12	92	70	0	38	7	19	46	812	3	118
Other Turboprop	40	0	0	0	0	23	0	0	0	8	0	0	9	0	0	0
Turbojet Total	**9,823**	**720**	**834**	**5,508**	**25**	**0**	**0**	**4**	**0**	**5**	**0**	**15**	**604**	**2,025**	**3**	**79**
Two-Engine	9,097	649	806	5,004	25	0	0	4	0	5	0	12	575	1,939	3	75
Other Turbojet	727	71	28	505	0	0	0	0	0	0	0	3	29	87	0	4
Rotocraft Total	**8,728**	**1,368**	**529**	**522**	**1,246**	**536**	**1,704**	**258**	**218**	**46**	**121**	**197**	**144**	**912**	**281**	**647**
Piston	3,039	1,006	251	35	1,166	162	239	18	21	10	48	3	46	28	7	0
Turbine Total	5,689	362	278	487	79	374	1,465	240	197	36	73	194	98	884	274	647
One Engine	4,537	336	227	241	78	350	1,427	228	115	36	67	100	91	696	263	283
Two Engine	1,151	26	51	246	2	24	39	13	83	0	6	94	6	188	11	365
Gliders Total	**2,074**	**1,806**	**7**	**0**	**208**	**0**	**0**	**0**	**0**	**0**	**47**	**0**	**5**	**0**	**0**	**0**
Lighter-than-air Total	**4,380**	**3,652**	**11**	**0**	**36**	**0**	**0**	**0**	**0**	**156**	**386**	**0**	**3**	**0**	**136**	**0**
Experimental Total	**23,627**	**21,151**	**899**	**139**	**394**	**83**	**75**	**20**	**3**	**49**	**52**	**0**	**683**	**80**	**0**	**0**
Amateur	19,817	18,367	700	0	343	0	14	0	0	0	37	0	357	0	0	0
Exhibition	2,120	1,914	28	0	41	0	0	0	0	24	2	0	112	0	0	0
Other	1,691	871	171	139	11	83	62	20	3	25	13	0	214	80	0	0
Light-sport	**170**	**115**	**5**	**0**	**36**	**0**	**0**	**0**	**0**	**0**	**0**	**0**	**14**	**0**	**0**	**0**

1 Excludes Air Medical Services conducted under FAR Part 135.

Source: FAA

2 Excludes Air Tour and Air Medical FAR Part 135. Starting in 2004, Far Part 135 Air Taxi, Air Tours, Air Medical, and Commuter use categories were added and tabulated separately from other general use categories. Beginning in 2004, commuter activity is excluded from all estimates. 2003 and prior, commuter activity was included in the Air Taxi use category. The small number of aircraft in some of the 'other' categories (e.g., "Piston: Other", "Turbojet: Other") may result in relatively high standard errors for estimates of the number of active aircraft and hours flown. For this reason estimates reported for 'other' categories may vary greatly from year to year and should be evaluated with caution. Columns may not add to totals due to rounding procedures. In 2004, the FAA expanded the General Aviation Air Taxi Activity & Avionics Survey to include 100 percent of turbine and non-scheduled Part 135 airplanes. Similarly, 100 percent of aircraft in Alaska aircraft were also surveyed. Furthermore, the FAA Registry sample was also adjusted. This change in survey methodogy resulted in improved accuracy in the GAATAA information.

2005 General Aviation and Air Taxi Aircraft by Primary Use

Piston Engine Airplane	167,608
Turboprop Airplane	7,942
Turbojet Airplane	9,823
Rotorcraft	8,728
Gliders	2,074
Lighter-than-Air	4,380
Experimental	23,627
Light Sport Aircraft	170

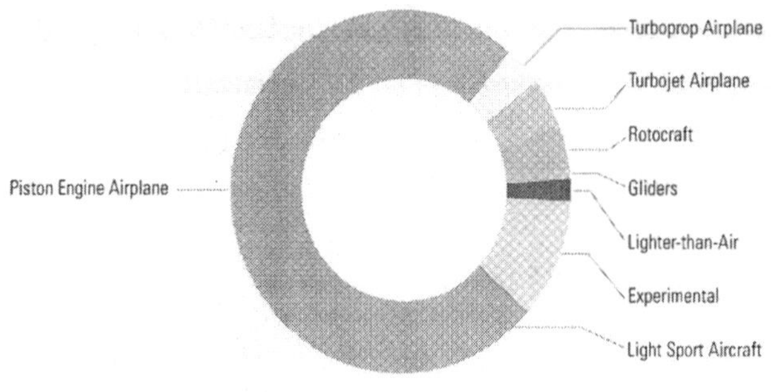

Table 2-4

U.S. Fleet Flight Hours by Type and Use

2005 General Aviation and Air Taxi Total Hours Flown (in Thousand) by Actual Use By Aircraft Type. Includes Air Taxi Aircraft. Excludes Commuter Aircraft.

	General Aviation Part 91 Use													On-Demand FAR Part 135 Use		
Aircraft Type	Total Hours	Personal	Business	Corporate	Instructional	Aerial Apps	Aerial Obs	Aerial Other	Ext. Load	Other Work	Sight See	Air Med[1]	Other	Air Taxi[2]	Air Tours	Air Med
Total All Aircraft	**26,982**	**9,266**	**3,244**	**3,072**	**3,635**	**1,031**	**1,265**	**148**	**134**	**176**	**191**	**111**	**894**	**2,857**	**352**	**605**
% Std. Error	1.0	0.9	2.0	3.5	3.4	6.3	5.8	10.5	20.3	17.3	10.0	12.5	4.0	4.3	15.4	10.8
Piston Total	**16,434**	**7,538**	**2,460**	**394**	**3,152**	**619**	**593**	**56**	**1**	**80**	**106**	**37**	**328**	**934**	**66**	**70**
One-Engine	13,739	6,794	1,842	143	2,903	612	515	42	1	60	99	24	258	381	53	12
Two-Engine	2,677	742	618	250	248	5	78	14	0	14	6	13	69	547	13	58
Other Piston	18	1	0	0	0	2	0	0	0	6	1	0	1	6	0	0
Turboprop Total	**2,106**	**198**	**298**	**597**	**24**	**241**	**30**	**18**	**0**	**30**	**5**	**7**	**54**	**529**	**11**	**65**
One-Engine	846	76	104	67	9	232	9	6	0	20	0	1	18	281	10	11
Two-Engine	1,252	122	194	530	14	1	20	12	0	8	4	5	36	249	2	54
Other Turboprop	8	0	0	0	0	7	0	0	0	1	0	0	0	0	0	0
Turbojet Total	**3,771**	**239**	**306**	**1,884**	**12**	**0**	**1**	**1**	**0**	**2**	**0**	**4**	**350**	**922**	**0**	**51**
Two-Engine	3,488	222	299	1,673	12	0	1	1	0	2	0	4	336	890	0	50
Other Turbojet	282	17	7	212	0	0	0	0	0	0	0	0	14	31	0	1
Rotocraft Total	**3,056**	**109**	**88**	**158**	**378**	**140**	**623**	**69**	**133**	**28**	**53**	**63**	**88**	**449**	**257**	**419**
Piston	617	80	30	8	342	34	63	2	3	4	24	0	8	13	4	0
Turbine Total	2,439	29	57	150	37	106	561	66	130	24	29	63	79	436	253	419
One Engine	1,863	26	33	66	30	94	541	53	84	21	28	34	61	356	246	190
Two Engine	576	3	24	84	6	12	20	13	46	3	1	29	19	80	7	229
Gliders Total	**121**	**92**	**1**	**0**	**23**	**0**	**0**	**0**	**0**	**0**	**4**	**0**	**1**	**0**	**0**	**0**
Lighter-than-air Total	**146**	**74**	**0**	**0**	**4**	**0**	**0**	**0**	**0**	**31**	**14**	**0**	**6**	**0**	**17**	**0**
Experimental Total	**1,339**	**1,010**	**89**	**40**	**40**	**32**	**18**	**4**	**0**	**6**	**9**	**0**	**67**	**23**	**0**	**0**
Amateur	987	853	66	0	29	0	2	0	0	0	2	0	34	0	0	0
Exhibition	113	97	2	0	2	0	0	0	0	2	0	0	8	0	0	0
Other	239	60	21	40	8	32	16	4	0	3	7	0	25	23	0	0
Light-sport	**9**	**5**	**0**	**0**	**2**	**0**	**0**	**0**	**0**	**0**	**0**	**0**	**1**	**0**	**0**	**0**

1 Excludes Air Medical Services conducted under FAR Part 135.

Source: FAA

2 Excludes Air Tour and Air Medical FAR Part 135. Starting in 2004, Far Part 135 Air Taxi, Air Tours, Air Medical, and Commuter use categories were added and tabulated separately from other general use categories. Beginning in 2004, commuter activity is excluded from all estimates. 2003 and prior, commuter activity was included in the Air Taxi use category. The small number of aircraft in some of the 'other' categories (e.g., "Piston: Other", "Turbojet: Other") may result in relatively high standard errors for estimates of the number of active aircraft and hours flown. For this reason estimates reported for 'other' categories may vary greatly from year to year and should be evaluated with caution. Columns may not add to totals due to rounding procedures.

2005 General Aviation and Air Taxi Aircraft Total Hours Flown by Primary Use

Piston Engine Airplane	16,434
Turboprop Airplane	2,106
Turbojet Airplane	3,771
Rotorcraft	3,056
Gliders	121
Lighter-than-Air	146
Experimental	1,339
Light Sport Aircraft	9

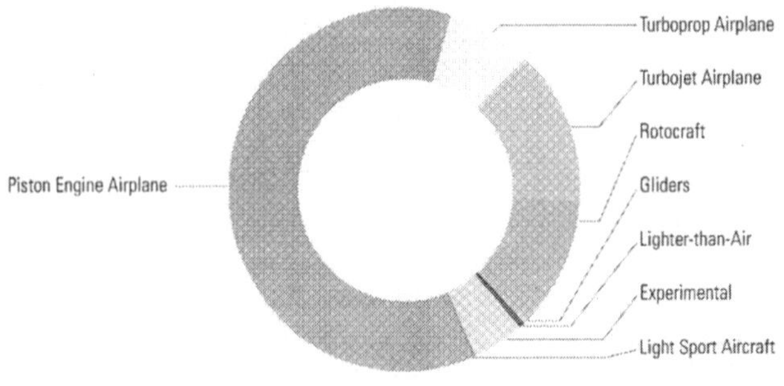

The corporate business fleet included 36,077 aircraft in 2005, which represented 16 percent of the total active, general aviation aircraft and 23 percent of the estimated total hours flown (see Tables 2-3 and 2-4).

Business aircraft complement airline services in satisfying the nation's business transportation requirements. Although airlines offer transportation to the largest cities and business centers, business aviation specializes in many areas where major airlines cannot satisfy demand. These aircraft provided quick, safe, and reliable transportation whenever and wherever business needs required them.

Business aviation operators use all types of aircraft from single- and twin-engine, piston-powered airplanes, helicopters and turboprops to the fastest jets to ensure maximum business effectiveness. Over two-thirds of the Fortune 500 companies operate business aircraft, and virtually all of these aircraft operators are members of the National Business Aviation Association (NBAA). NBAA is the principal representative of business aviation before Congress, the administration, and its regulatory agencies such as the Federal Aviation Administration. It represents over 8,000 companies that operate over 8,000 aircraft. Turbojets are the most widely used type of aircraft. Some two-thirds of NBAA members have turbojets, approximately one-third have turboprops, and about one-eighth use multi-engine piston powered aircraft. While most of these aircraft are operated domestically, an increasing number are utilized to expand markets overseas.

Numerous examples of typical traveling schedules purport to demonstrate the advantages of business aircraft over use of the commercial airlines. Because of the proliferation of airline hub and spoke systems since deregulation, flying business aircraft directly between airports has become a big advantage. The monetary-equivalent savings in terms of executives' time which would otherwise be spent in traveling to and from air carrier airports and in waiting for scheduled air carrier flights, plus hotel expenses, meals, and rental car expenses, loom large on the benefit side of such calculations. Normally unquantified are the advantages of flexibility and prestige (which may or may not bring about pecuniary benefits) and the fact that business meetings may be held in privately owned aircraft.

The same is also generally true of smaller businesses that have discovered the benefits of their own aircraft. Keeping business appointments in several cities hundreds of miles apart—on the same day—is not unusual for general aviation aircraft operators.

Today's business aircraft are quieter, more efficient, and safer than ever before. Much like the computer, business aircraft are powerful business tools that make a company more profitable by making better use of a company's most valuable assets—time and personnel.

Personal Flying

Personal flying includes any use of an aircraft for personal purposes not associated with a business or profession, and not for hire. A personal plane is like a personal car. When the owner (or renter) uses a car or plane for a business trip, it becomes a business automobile or a business aircraft. It does not change its appearance. There is no way for anyone to tell whether a car or an airplane is being used for business or pleasure just by looking at it. A multimillionaire may own a large airplane as a purely private conveyance, with no business use. However, since the majority of privately owned (as distinguished from company-owned or corporate-owned) aircraft are of the light single or light twin-engine variety, it is appropriate to discuss this important segment of the general aviation industry.

Just as automobiles and boats are used for personal transportation and recreation, personal flying is a legitimate use of the sky. Flying is an efficient and effective business tool, but it is also a pleasant recreational vehicle. Thousands of private pilots use their aircraft to visit friends and relatives, attend special events, and reach distant vacation spots.

These aircraft are also flown by doctors, lawyers, accountants, engineers, farmers, and small business owners in the course of conducting their business. Typically, such persons use their aircraft partly for business and partly for pleasure. They differ primarily from the purely business flier with respect to the type of aircraft flown. A much higher proportion of the 151,408 aircraft they fly are single-engine piston aircraft (see Table 2-3). Aircraft flown primarily for personal purposes represented two-thirds of the general aviation fleet and 34 percent of the total flying hours in 2005 (see Table 2-4).

A number of organizations represent the interests of the business and pleasure flier. By far the most important is the Aircraft Owners and Pilots Association (AOPA). This organization, headquartered in the Washington, DC, area, includes over 408,000 members, which represents over one-half of the pilots in the United States. In addition to its function of congressional liaison, the AOPA provides a variety of services for its members, many of which are designed to enhance air safety.

Instructional Flying

Instructional flying accounted for 13,399 aircraft or 6 percent of the total in 2005 (see Table 2-3). This category includes any use of an aircraft for formal instruction, either with the instructor aboard or when the student is flying solo but is carrying out maneuvers according to the instructor's specifications, excluding proficiency flying. It is dominated by instruction leading to the private pilot certificate, and close to 90 percent of the aircraft used for instruction are single-engine.

Obtaining a private pilot certificate for business or personal reasons is the primary goal for some students. Others use it as a stepping-stone to an airline or military aviation career. Most people learn to fly through a local fixed base operator (FBO). FBOs provide fuel and service, and they also rent and sell airplanes. They usually have a professional flight instructor on staff who provides ground and flight instruction. Many individuals also learn to fly through a local flying club that offers flight training. Such clubs are groups of individuals who own aircraft and rent them to members. They usually offer flight instruction and other flying-related activities to their members. Many vocational and technical schools, colleges, and universities offer aviation programs that include flight training.

Aerial Application, Aerial Observation, and Other Aerial

Aerial application includes any use of an aircraft for work that concerns the production of foods, fibers, and timber production and protection. This category primarily includes aircraft that distribute chemicals or seeds in agriculture and reforestation.

The use of aircraft in agriculture is a major factor in the production of food and fiber all over the world. Countries such as Japan, Russia, and China are committing a large amount of financial resources in developing aerial application of fertilizers to spread seeds in inaccessible locations, to control pests, and to harvest crops.

Although the public image of crop dusters is that they are flying daredevils who operate flimsy crates and pollute the environment, the fact is that the industry is a major factor in the production of cotton, vegetables, and beef (by seeding and fertilizing grazing lands) and in the eradication of pests, such as the fire ant, the screw worm, and the gypsy moth.

It is an expensive business. These specially designed Ag aircraft can cost in excess of several hundred thousand dollars each. Needless to say, the operators, many of whom have fleets of as many as 50 aircraft, are involved in big business, requiring bank loans for equipment renewal, which in turn requires insurance coverage. If the business were as hazardous as the common impression, no banker or insurance company would deal with it.

Aerial observation includes any aircraft engaged in aerial mapping/photography, surveillance, fish spotting, search and rescue, hunting, highway traffic advisory, ranching, oil and mineral exploration, and criminal pursuit.

Land-use planners, real estate developers, beach erosion engineers, businessmen seeking new industrial sites, as well as city officials and highway designers, are relying more and more on photographs taken from aircraft in their deliberations. For years now, general aviation aircraft have been used to inspect pipelines and powerlines. These inspections must be made every couple of weeks. The locations of most pipelines and powerlines are remote and hard to reach by land, but general aviation aircraft can take care of this vital need economically and efficiently, saving thousands of gallons of fuel and power outages if undetected leaks or damage to pipelines or powerlines were not discovered.

Geophysical survey pilots search for new sources of energy using general aviation aircraft. With sophisticated instruments in the aircraft, a general aviation aircraft can locate and identify oil and gas deposits, coal, diamonds, and even water below the earth's surface.

Commercial fishing fleets on both coasts have found that their operations are more productive and profitable when they can be directed to concentrations of fish schooling far from the shore. Hence light aircraft for that purpose have evolved into making a major contribution to the industry.

The Fish and Wildlife Service retains commercial operators to survey herd and flock movements and to count the size of herds, as well as to air-drop food when natural forage is unavailable. Ranchers also use general aviation aircraft to inspect fences, round up strays, and check cattle for possible injuries. Because of the versatility of these aircraft, they can land and make necessary repairs or take care of cattle that may need treatment.

Major metropolitan police departments have found that road patrols by aircraft are highly effective for keeping watch over the flow of traffic during morning and evening rush hours and as an aid in apprehension of lawbreakers. Most police air patrols are performed in aircraft leased from general aviation operators.

Another specialized service usually performed on a contract basis is flying at very low levels along public utility rights-of-way to inspect the integrity of energy lines and check for transformer failures, broken insulators, short circuits, or line breaks. Inspection by air is frequently the only economical means of performing such service.

Other aerial services include the use of aircraft for weather modification, fire fighting, and insect control. Weather modification includes efforts by ski resorts to create snow and by governmental authorities in arid regions to create rain. Additionally, air-dropping chemicals and fire retardant slurry by aircraft is a major weapon in the control of forest and brush fires.

Resort operators have found that spraying light oils and suspensions by aircraft (as distinguished from agricultural use of similar aircraft) has enhanced their business by eliminating the irritations of small flying insects. In addition to the elimination of a nuisance, aerial application of pesticides has been highly effective in controlling and, in many cases, eliminating diseases transmitted by insects, such as malaria.

These three primary use categories included 9,022 aircraft, or four percent of the total fleet in 2005 (see Table 2-3). There is no way to put a specific figure on the value of these commercial aviation operations, but we would not have the crops, the fibers, and the meat available at reasonable prices without it. The protection of natural resources, land planning, and disease and pest control are valuable, but their worth is difficult to quantify financially.

Sightseeing, Air Tours, and Air Taxi

Aircraft flown for the purpose of sightseeing and air tours totaled 1,558 in 2005, or less than one percent of the active fleet. Sightseeing includes commercial sightseeing conducted under FAR Part 91, whereas air tours are conducted under FAR Part 135 (see Table 2-3). More than one-half of the sightseeing flights are made in lighter-than-air aircraft. The majority of air tours are conducted in rotorcraft and lighter-than-air aircraft.

Air taxi or charter firms serve as on-demand passenger and all-cargo operators. This category covers all types of aircraft, including single- and multi-engine piston, turbine, and rotorcraft operating under FAR Part 135. The great advantage of the on-call air taxi or charter operator is its flexibility.

Chartering an airplane is similar to hiring a taxi for a single trip. The charter company or air taxi operator provides the aircraft, flight crew, fuel, and all other services for each trip. The charter customer pays a fee, usually based on mileage or time, plus extras such as waiting time and crew expenses. An air taxi is particularly attractive for a firm that does not frequently require an airplane or does not often need a supplement to its aircraft. Firms will also charter aircraft when they need a special-purpose aircraft, such as a helicopter.

As commercial operators, air taxi firms must conform to more stringent operating and maintenance requirements called for in the Federal Aviation Regulations (FARs). In addition, each air taxi or charter operator, regardless of the types of airplanes used, must have an air taxi certificate on file with the FAA. This certificate is issued by the FAA after proper application and local inspection. It also evidences certain minimum insurance coverage and limits. In 2005, the FAA listed 6,926 air taxi aircraft, which represented three percent of the general aviation fleet (see Table 2-3).

External Load and Medical

External load includes aircraft under FAR Part 133. The majority of aircraft under this category are rotorcraft used for external load operations, such as hoisting heavy loads and hauling logs from remote locations. If it were not for general aviation aircraft, primarily helicopters that transport heavy, expensive drilling equipment, as well as people (day and night, good weather and bad), America's dependence on foreign oil would be far greater and would surely impact negatively on the American consumer.

The medical category is also dominated by helicopters, which present more than 50 percent of the aircraft flown to carry people or donor organs for transplant. There are times when the American Red Cross needs to transport emergency supplies to disaster victims or blood of rare types or in large quantities. The entire medical emergency evacuation process was changed when state and local governments began establishing medevac units to respond to critically injured persons such as those involved in auto accidents. The survival rate in life-threatening injuries has been greatly enhanced when a person can be transported quickly to nearby hospitals. The 1,620 aircraft in these two categories represent less than one percent of the active fleet (see Table 2-3).

Other

The FAA defines other flying as any other use of an aircraft not included under the previously listed categories. Examples include aircraft for research and development, testing, air shows, air racing, parachuting, towing gliders, and aerial advertising. Aerial advertising is a highly specialized—but very lucrative—part of commercial aviation. On the basis of "cost per thousand," key words in the advertising business, a towed banner or a message written in smoke over a city will draw a larger audience for less cost than any other form of advertising. A banner towed over a sports stadium or along a hundred miles of crowded beach is seen by more eyes than a similar message carried for the same price in any other communications medium. A message sky-written over Manhattan on a clear day can be seen by 10 million people at one time.

In 2005, a total 3,612 aircraft fell into this category, which represented one percent of the total active fleet.

General aviation aircraft save time, lives, and money and provide efficient energy-saving transportation for people in all walks of life who are involved in all different kinds of activities. But the ultimate value of general aviation, which contrasts it with the air carriers, is the flexibility and utility of the aircraft and the pilots. General aviation operates when the air carriers do not, and it goes to locations not served by air carriers.

General Aviation Airports

In a broad sense, all airports are general aviation airports because they can be used by general aviation aircraft, including those used by the certificated air carriers, which are sometimes referred to as Commercial Service airports. At the end of 2006, the gross figure of aircraft landing facilities reported by the FAA was 19,983 (see Table 2-5). However, this figure is not restricted to airports, but includes other forms of landing facilities not used by conventional aircraft. It includes heliports, stolports (short takeoff and landing airports), and seaplane bases. It also includes airports located on American Samoa, Guam, Puerto Rico, the U.S. Virgin Islands, and U.S. Trust Territories in the South Pacific.

There are 5,092 publicly owned airports in the United States, ranging in size from the enormous Dallas/Ft. Worth International Airport (DFW) and Denver International Airport (DIA) layouts to the small grass fields owned by local communities. All of these may be used by light general aviation aircraft, although the larger commercial-service airports typically have more congestion and are not as GA-friendly.

An airport owned by a government body can usually be regarded as permanent and stable, particularly if federal funding has been obtained for improving the facilities. In addition, there are 14,862 private-use airports that are not open to the general public, but are restricted to the use of their owners and the invited guests of the owners on an exclusive-use basis. Such airports are comparable to private roads or private driveways.

Economic Role of General Aviation Airports

General aviation airports play an important role in the transportation network, but this fact is not well publicized. The United States has the finest scheduled air transportation system in the world. The service points, the equipment, the personnel, and the schedules are as excellent and as much in the public interest as it is humanly, mechanically, and economically possible to make them. This does not alter another fact: that unless the traveler is flying among the major metropolitan areas, many gaps in airline service still exist, including infrequent schedules requiring roundabout routes, time-consuming layovers, and frequent aircraft changes.

Since deregulation, many smaller cities have lost airline service from the major and national carriers, who simply find it uneconomical to serve these points with their jet equipment. Regional air carriers are now serving many of the smaller cities, but voids in service throughout the nation are apparent.

In scheduling, it is economically sound for the air carrier to place more flights at the most popular times in service between pairs of cities that have the highest passenger loads. This factor also leads to very sparse service during off-peak hours.

Thousands of smaller cities, towns, and villages also need air transportation service. There are close to 20,000 incorporated communities in the 48 contiguous states and an additional 15,000 unincorporated communities. Because the scheduled airlines serve less than four percent of the nation's 19,916 landing facilities with approximately 7,000 aircraft, many communities are without immediate access to the nation's commercial airline system.

The role of general aviation airports serving 220,000 aircraft, or 96 percent of the total active aircraft in the United States, in providing air access is increasing. By having air access to all the nation's airports, general aviation aircraft can bring the benefits and values of air transportation to the entire country.

Attracting Industry

Cities and towns that years ago decided not to build an airport have learned that lack of an airport jeopardizes community progress. Time and again, the lack of an airport has proved to be the chief reason that a community has been bypassed as a location for a new plant or a new industry.

Although scheduled air service is concentrated in major metropolitan areas, business and industry are moving to less populated areas. Shifts in population, lower taxes, room for expansion, less congestion, and better access to highways are some of the factors causing this trend. With geographically diverse production plants, the source of production is nearer the distribution points, but management is farther away from its responsibilities. Without flexible transportation, industry faces the dangers of absentee management both in the widely spread branches and in the home office (because of extended trips).

The general aviation airport has become vital to the growth of business and industry in a community by providing access for companies that must meet the demands of clients, cope with competition, and capitalize on expanding market areas. Communities without general aviation airports place limitations on their capacity for economic growth and generally have a difficult time attracting business and the subsequent job opportunities created.

Flexibility is the key word in business flying—flexibility to go whenever and wherever necessary. The key to flexibility is airport facilities. The shorter the time between the office and the aircraft, the greater the benefits of the business airplane. This flexibility in reaching destinations serves not only in direct point-to-point travel but also is a factor that has made business aviation one of the biggest suppliers of passengers to the airlines. Business and private airplanes feed passengers into major terminals. Charter and air taxi services let passengers step from a long-distance wide-body commercial aircraft into a single-engine or twin-engine air taxi for

Table 2-5

Airports by Geographic Area

U.S. Civil and Joint Use Airports, Heliports, Stolports, and Seaplane Bases on Record by Type of Ownership in December 31, 2006

		Total Facilities		Airports Open to the Public***				
	Total	By Ownership		Paved Airports		Unpaved Airports		Total
FAA Region and State	Facilities	Public	Private	Lighted	Unlighted	Lighted	Unlighted	Airports
Grand Total	**19,983**	**5,121**	**14,862**	**3,666**	**282**	**372**	**921**	**5,241**
United State-Total*	**19,916**	**5,092**	**14,824**	**3,649**	**279**	**372**	**920**	**5,220**
Alaskan-Total	**687**	**390**	**297**	**53**	**6**	**117**	**238**	**414**
Alaska	687	390	297	53	6	117	238	414
Central-Total	**1,564**	**495**	**1,069**	**381**	**13**	**36**	**53**	**483**
Iowa	322	134	188	96	0	12	13	121
Kansas	409	134	275	103	6	14	19	142
Missouri	539	134	405	107	4	6	14	131
Nebraska	294	93	201	75	3	4	7	89
Eastern-Total	**2,627**	**366**	**2,261**	**341**	**35**	**35**	**89**	**500**
Delaware	49	5	44	7	0	3	1	11
District of Columbia	16	6	10	2	1	0	0	3
Maryland	225	24	201	30	1	2	6	39
New Jersey	388	54	334	35	5	4	7	51
New York	583	96	487	89	15	14	39	157
Pennsylvania	806	75	731	89	10	10	28	137
Virginia	435	75	360	62	2	1	2	67
West Virginia	125	31	94	27	1	1	6	35
Great Lakes-Total	**4,263**	**903**	**3,360**	**760**	**29**	**116**	**177**	**1,082**
Illinois	842	123	719	89	2	19	5	115
Indiana	632	87	545	77	6	7	19	109
Michigan	487	136	351	129	4	27	71	231
Minnesota	513	151	362	117	1	16	23	157
North Dakota	307	92	215	68	3	11	8	90
Ohio	726	132	594	123	10	11	30	174
South Dakota	191	80	111	56	0	14	7	77
Wisconsin	565	102	463	101	3	11	14	129
New England-Total	**799**	**144**	**655**	**115**	**15**	**4**	**49**	**183**
Connecticut	152	16	136	18	1	0	5	24
Maine	162	48	114	33	6	2	28	69
Massachusetts	235	35	200	31	4	0	5	40
New Hampshire	132	17	115	16	1	2	6	25
Rhode Island	30	8	22	7	1	0	0	8
Vermont	88	20	68	10	2	0	5	17
N.W. Mountain-Total	**2,215**	**688**	**1,527**	**421**	**44**	**17**	**162**	**644**
Colorado	451	90	361	63	6	2	5	76
Idaho	266	136	130	46	7	2	65	120
Montana	273	124	149	75	10	8	32	125
Oregon	458	101	357	65	10	1	22	98
Utah	144	60	84	42	4	0	1	47
Washington	511	128	383	95	7	3	32	137
Wyoming	112	49	63	35	0	1	5	41
Southern-Total	**2,991**	**831**	**2,160**	**647**	**33**	**25**	**47**	**752**
Alabama	280	103	177	87	1	5	4	97
Florida	825	159	666	106	1	9	15	131
Georgia	466	134	332	101	4	2	2	109
Kentucky	212	72	140	52	7	0	1	60
Mississippi	245	88	157	74	3	1	3	81
North Carolina	394	91	303	84	6	6	16	112
Puerto Rico	48	19	29	10	1	0	0	11
South Carolina	197	70	127	57	3	2	5	67
Tennessee	316	90	226	74	7	0	1	82
Virgin Islands	8	5	3	2	0	0	0	2
Southwest-Total	**3,406**	**811**	**2,595**	**629**	**51**	**17**	**70**	**767**
Arkansas	325	115	210	90	5	0	4	99
Louisiana	515	110	405	71	3	1	4	79
New Mexico	170	68	102	46	6	0	7	59
Oklahoma	443	156	287	109	15	6	13	143
Texas	1,953	362	1,591	313	22	10	42	387
Western-Total	**1,412**	**483**	**929**	**312**	**54**	**5**	**35**	**406**
Arizona	299	89	210	59	11	0	8	78
California	933	317	616	210	36	2	13	261
Hawaii	48	19	29	14	1	0	0	15
Nevada	132	58	74	29	6	3	14	52
South Pacific**	**19**	**10**	**9**	**7**	**2**	**0**	**1**	**10**

Source: FAA

* Excludes Puerto Rico, Virgin Islands and South Pacific.

** American Samoa, Guam, Midway Atoll and Northern Mariana Islands.

*** Includes all airports open to the public, both publicly and privately owned.

swift completion of their trips to cities and towns hundreds of miles from airline hubs.

Time equals dollars to business people who cannot afford the luxury of a long wait between business appointments or who arrange their travel work schedules to fit the rigid timetables of public transportation. Between cities with frequent service, this is not a problem. It is easy to go from New York City to Chicago or Atlanta, but considerably more difficult to go with equal speed between Peoria, Illinois, and Rochester, Minnesota, or between Decatur, Illinois, and El Dorado, Arkansas.

The competitive nature of today's business and the value of an individual's time prohibits unproductive or uneconomical periods. A person who saves only 30 minutes a day in one year will accumulate 125 hours of productive time—more than three weeks' additional time on the job rather than in transit.

In most large metropolitan areas, business fliers can choose among several general aviation airports that are not available to the scheduled airlines. For example, Atlanta has 12 general aviation airports within a 30-mile radius of the city. One or more of these alternative airports are commonly used by the majority of business aircraft operators in the region and, in most instances, are chosen for their more convenient location to the business office. Such airports typically offer closer and more available parking, more rapid boarding, better security, and much shorter walking distances than a major airline terminal.

Stimulating Economic Growth

Airports and related aviation and nonaviation businesses located at the airport represent a major source of employment for many communities around the country. The wages and salaries paid by airport-related businesses can have a significant effect on the local economy by providing the means to purchase goods and services while generating tax revenues, as well. But local payrolls are not the only measure of an airport's economic benefit to the community. Indirectly, the employee expenditures generate successive waves of additional employment and purchases, which are more difficult to measure, but nevertheless substantial.

In addition to the local economic activity generated by the regular expenditures of resident employees, the airport also stimulates the economy through the use of local services for all cargo, food catering, aircraft maintenance, and ground transportation on and around the airport. Regular purchases of fuel, supplies, equipment, and other services from local distributors inject additional income into the local community. The airport retail shops, hotels, and restaurants further act to recycle money within the local community as dollars pass from one person to another, supporting many people and businesses. This beneficial multiplier effect operates in all cities as aviation-related dollars are channeled throughout the community.

Airports provide an additional asset to the general economy by generating billions of dollars per year in state and local taxes. These taxes increase the revenues available for projects and services to benefit the residents of each state and community. Whether the extra tax dollars improve the state highway system, beautify state parks, or help prevent a tax increase, airport-generated tax dollars work for everyone.

Cities with good airport facilities also profit from tourist and convention business. This can represent substantial revenues for hotels, restaurants, retail stores, sports clubs, nightclubs, sightseeing, rental cars, and local transportation, among others. The amount of convention business varies with the size of the city, but even smaller communities show a sizable income from this source.

Beyond the benefits that an airport brings to the community as a transportation facility and as a local industry, the airport has become a significant factor in the determination of real estate values in adjacent areas. Land located near airports almost always increases in value as the local economy begins to benefit from the presence of the airport. Land developers consistently seek land near airports, and it follows inexorably that a new airport will inspire extensive construction around it.

Pilots

At the end of 2006, the FAA reported 597,109 active pilots in the United States, including 84,866 student pilots and 219,233 private pilots (see Table 2-6). Although the numbers have varied year to year, the current number of active pilots in the U.S. has been declining since the year 2002. Indeed, the current number is down five percent and has fallen below 600,000 threshold.

It is easy to become caught up in the business and economic aspects of general aviation and the contribution it makes to the local economy and yet overlook another important aspect of general aviation's contribution—personal flying. There is a widely held attitude that commercial airlines are a business and are, therefore, important, and that personal flying is just an unimportant frivolity. However, one must keep in mind that the certificated airlines carry just about as many people for vacation travel and visiting friends and relatives as they do for business purposes. On special commercial charters, virtually all the passengers are on pleasure trips to such exciting destinations as Orlando and Las Vegas.

The flexibility of transportation offered by general aviation is not restricted to business use. By light plane, it is

Table 2-6

Pilots by Certificate and Rating

Active U.S. Pilots and Non-Pilot Certificates Held (1985-2006)

Category	2006	2005	2004	2003	2002	2001	2000	1999	1998	1997	1996
Pilot–Total	**597,109**	**609,737**	**618,633**	**625,011**	**631,762**	**612,274**	**625,581**	**635,472**	**618,298**	**616,342**	**622,261**
Student	84,866	87,213	87,910	87,296	85,991	86,731	93,064	97,359	97,736	96,101	94,947
Recreational Airplane (only)	239	276	291	310	317	316	340	343	305	284	265
Sport (only)	939	134	N/A	N/A	N/A	N/A	N/A	N/A	N/A	N/A	N/A
Airplane [1]											
- Private	219,233	228,619	235,994	241,045	245,230	243,823	251,561	258,749	247,226	247,604	254,002
- Commercial	117,610	120,614	122,592	123,990	125,920	120,502	121,858	124,261	122,053	125,300	129,187
- Airline Transport	141,935	141,992	142,160	143,504	144,708	144,702	141,596	137,642	134,612	130,858	127,486
Rotorcraft (only) [2]	10,690	9,518	8,586	7,916	7,770	7,727	7,775	7,728	6,964	6,801	6,961
Glider (only) [2]	21,597	21,369	21,100	20,950	21,826	8,473	9,387	9,390	9,402	9,394	9,413
Flight Instructor											
Certificates [4]	**91,343**	**90,555**	**89,596**	**87,816**	**86,089**	**82,875**	**80,931**	**79,694**	**79,171**	**78,102**	**78,551**
Instrument Ratings [4,5]	**309,333**	**311,828**	**313,545**	**315,413**	**317,389**	**315,276**	**311,944**	**308,951**	**300,183**	**297,409**	**297,895**
Nonpilot–Total [7]	**521,353**	**518,984**	**515,293**	**509,835**	**515,570**	**513,100**	**547,453**	**538,264**	**549,588**	**540,892**	**534,427**
Mechanic [7]	323,097	320,293	317,111	313,032	315,928	310,850	344,434	340,402	336,670	332,254	329,239
Repairmen [7]	40,329	40,030	39,231	37,248	37,114	40,085	38,208	35,989	52,909	51,643	50,768
Parachute Rigger [7]	8,252	8,150	8,011	7,883	8,063	7,927	10,477	10,447	10,459	10,336	10,269
Ground Instructor [7]	74,849	74,378	73,735	72,692	73,658	72,261	72,326	71,238	70,334	69,366	68,573
Dispatcher [7]	18,610	18,079	17,493	16,955	16,695	16,070	16,340	15,655	14,804	13,967	13,272
Flight Navigator	264	298	336	382	431	509	570	642	712	782	847
Flight Engineer	55,952	57,756	59,376	61,643	63,681	65,398	65,098	63,891	63,700	62,544	61,459

Category	1995 [8]	1994 [9]	1993	1992	1991	1990	1989	1988	1987	1986	1985
Pilot–Total	**639,184**	**654,088**	**665,069**	**682,959**	**692,095**	**702,659**	**700,010**	**694,016**	**699,653**	**709,118**	**709,540**
Student	101,279	96,254	103,583	114,597	120,203	128,663	142,544	136,913	146,016	150,273	146,652
Recreational Airplane (only)	232	241	206	187	161	87	*	*	*	*	*
Airplane [1]											
- Private	261,399	284,236	283,700	288,078	293,306	299,111	293,179	299,786	300,949	305,736	311,086
- Commercial	133,980	138,728	143,014	146,385	148,385	149,666	144,540	143,030	143,645	147,798	151,632
- Airline Transport	123,877	117,434	117,070	115,855	112,167	107,732	102,087	96,968	91,287	87,186	82,740
Rotorcraft (only) [2]	7,183	8,719	9,168	9,652	9,860	9,567	8,863	8,608	8,702	8,122	8,123
Glider (only) [2]	11,234	8,476	8,328	8,205	8,033	7,833	7,708	7,600	7,901	8,411	8,168
Lighter-than-air	N/A [3]	N/A [3]	N/A [3]	N/A [3]	N/A [3]	N/A [3]	1,089	1,111	1,153	1,133	1,139
Flight Instructor											
Certificates [4]	**77,613**	**76,171**	**75,021**	**72,148**	**69,209**	**63,775**	**61,472**	**61,798**	**60,316**	**57,355**	**58,940**
Instrument Ratings [4,5]	**298,798**	**302,300**	**305,517**	**306,169**	**303,193**	**297,073**	**282,804**	**273,804**	**266,122**	**262,388**	**258,559**
Nonpilot–Total [7]	**651,341**	**571,358**	**559,726**	**540,548**	**517,462**	**492,237**	**468,405**	**448,710**	**427,962**	**410,079**	**395,139**
Mechanic [7]	405,294	411,071	401,060	384,669	366,392	344,282	326,243	312,419	297,178	284,241	274,100
Repairmen [7]	61,233	N/A	N/A	N/A							
Parachute Rigger [7]	11,824	8,631	8,417	8,163	7,616	10,094	9,879	9,770	9,659	9,535	9,395
Ground Instructor [7]	96,165	77,789	76,050	73,276	70,086	66,882	64,503	62,582	60,861	59,443	58,214
Dispatcher [7]	15,642	13,410	12,883	12,264	11,607	11,002	10,455	10,020	9,491	9,025	8,511
Flight Navigator	916	990	1,039	1,154	1,225	1,290	1,357	1,400	1,445	1,512	1,542
Flight Engineer	60,267	59,467	60,277	61,022	60,236	58,687	55,968	52,519	49,328	46,323	43,377

Source: FAA

Note: The term airmen includes men and women certified as pilots, mechanics or other aviation technicians.

1. Includes pilots with an airplane only certificate. Also includes those with an airplane and a helicopter and/or glider certificate. Prior to 1995, these pilots were categorized as private, commercial, or airline transport, based on their airplane certificate. In 1995 and after, they are categorized based on their highest certificate. For example, if a pilots holds a private airplane certificate and a commercial helicopter certificate, prior to 1995, the pilot would be categorized as private; 1995 and after as commercial.
2. Glider and lighter-than-air pilots are not required to have a medical examination; however, the totals above represent pilots who received a medical examination within the last 25 months.
3. Lighter-than-air type ratings are no longer being issued.
4. Not included in total.
5. Special ratings shown on pilot certificates, do not indicate additional certificates.
6. Data for 1996 and 1997 are not comparable to earlier years.
7. Numbers represent all certificates on record. No medical examination required. Data for 1996 and 1997 are limited to certificates held by those under 70 years of age.
8. Beginning in 1995, includes non-pilots who were excluded in prior years because of incomplete addresses and/or a request to be excluded from any mailing list.
9. 1994 counts based on medical certificates issued 27 or less months ago. All other years based on medical certificates issued 25 or less months ago.

N/A Not available. Prior to 1995, repairmen were included in the mechanic category. Recreational certificate first issued in 1990.

possible for a citizen of the middle-Atlantic states or the Midwest to visit the warm climate of Florida for the weekend or to fly from Montgomery, Alabama, to Canadian lakes in a few hours. Air transportation for vacationing is unabashedly advertised by the air carriers. It should not be overlooked as an aspect of general aviation.

Many pilots who start off as weekend pilots upgrade into high-performance equipment and obtain higher ratings and pilot privileges and eventually become business as well as pleasure air travelers in light aircraft. Others start out to obtain their Commercial and Airline Transport certificates with the intention of making a career in aviation. Many pilots now flying for the airlines, corporate aviation, or the military got their start in general aviation. Because of the downsizing of the military during the 1990s, it is anticipated that an ever-increasing number of individuals who started their careers in general aviation will be called to fill the needs of the air carriers and corporate aviation in the future.

The decline in the number of active student pilots and student starts began in 1980 following the repeal of the GI Bill of Rights in 1979. As discussed in chapter 1, the effect of the Civil Pilot Training Program, the GI Bill, and other training programs was enormous. They were responsible for the majority of flight training students for many years. They were responsible for general aviation's infrastructure being larger than it would have been without these programs. Things began to stabilize in the late 1990s, and after reaching a low point in 1995, student starts increased for the remainder of the decade. This was the result of a concerted effort on the part of the general aviation community and government to increase the number of general aviation pilots.

FAA Service to Pilots

Today's sophisticated air navigation network has its roots in the 1920s, when pilots relied on scattered radio stations and rotating light beacons to hop from one landing field to the next. During periods of poor visibility, however, the usefulness of light beacons was severely limited. Eventually, the federal government introduced the first of many navigational aids that could serve the pilot day or night, fair weather or foul. This was the four-course radio range, a device that transmitted radio signals in four directions. The government installed a network of these facilities to guide pilots to their destinations.

As aviation grew, more than four paths were needed to handle the navigational needs of air traffic, and the original radio range was replaced by the very-high-frequency omnidirectional range (VOR), a device developed during World War II. VORs were deployed on the airways in large numbers after the war and are still the chief air navigation aids on the U.S. airways. By 2005, there were 1,111 VORs (see Table 2-7).

Today's VOR has sophisticated electronics but operates on the same principle as its predecessors. It emits signals in the pattern of a huge wheel, with the station at the center and 360 spokes radiating from the hub. Each radial represents a radio course that a pilot can use to guide an airplane accurately along a desired track.

Navigational facilities also help a pilot descend from cruising altitude to land on an airport runway, even under poor weather conditions. The Instrument Landing System (ILS) is the most widely used equipment in the world for making safe runway approaches in difficult weather. The FAA had deployed 1,490 of these systems at airports across the United States by the end of 2005 (see Table 2-7).

An ILS sends out two radio beams to approaching aircraft. One beam, the localizer, gives the pilot left-right guidance; the other, the glide slope, gives the pilot the correct angle of descent to the runway. Even when visibility from the approach end of the runway is only a few hundred feet, properly instrumented aircraft can now land with pinpoint accuracy.

The air traffic control system is crucial to civil aviation, keeping airplanes safely separated from each other and regulating their flow into and out of airport terminal areas. Under instrument flight rules, standard separation between two airplanes depends on a number of factors, including the size of the airplanes being separated and the kind of airspace they occupy. Generally, airplanes close to an airport are kept apart by at least three miles horizontally and 1,000 feet vertically. When airplanes are flying between major terminal areas, standard separation is never less than five horizontal miles and 1,000 vertical feet.

Making this system work are the personnel who staff air traffic control towers, terminal area radar facilities, air route traffic control centers, and automated flight service stations. Each type of facility performs a different task. Tower and terminal-area controllers handle airplanes that are landing and taking off, taxiing on the ground, and flying in the vicinity of the airport. There were 693 airports in the United States with control towers in 2005 (see Table 2-7). With the exception of the major hubs that serve large metropolitan areas, general aviation is the primary user of the tower-controlled airports.

The busier tower-controlled airports have an additional facility for the safe and expeditious movement of air traffic: radar. Many civil airports have Airport Surveillance Radar which is also available to general aviation pilots who operate in the areas of their coverage. In 2005 there were 226 airports

Table 2-7

Aeronautical Facilities

FAA Air Route Facilities and Services (1972-2005)

Calendar Year	VOR VORTAC	Non-Directional Beacons	Air Route Traffic Cont. Ctr.	Air Traffic Cont. Towers	Flight Service Stations	Int'l Flight Service Stations	Instrument Landing Systems	Airport Surveillance Radar
1972	991	706	27	355	324	7	403	125
1973	995	739	27	403	315	7	467	142
1974	1,000	793	26	417	320	7	490	156
1975	1,011	848	25	487	321	7	580	177
1976	1,020	920	25	488	321	7	640	175
1977	1,021	959	25	495	319	7	678	182
1978	1,020	988	25	494	319	6	698	185
1979	1,028	1,015	25	499	318	6	753	192
1980	1,037	1,055	25	502	317	6	796	192
1981	1,033	1,123	25	501	316	6	840	199
1982	1,029	1,143	25	492	316	6	884	197
1983	1,032	1,183	25	494	316	5	934	197
1984	1,035	1,211	25	497	310	5	955	197
1985	1,039	1,222	25	500	302	4	968	198
1986	1,043	1,239	25	686	293	3	977	312
1987	1,039	1,212	25	500	302	4	968	312
1988	1,043	1,239	25	686	293	3	977	311
1989	1,046	1,263	25	686	255	3	1,100	312
1990	1,045	1,271	25	686	235	3	1,120	311
1991	1,045	1,295	24	694	192	3	1,114	318
1992	1,044	1,314	24	691	179	3	1,177	312
1993	1,046	1,263	24	686	255	3	1,100	312
1994	1,045	1,271	24	686	235	3	1,120	311
1995R	1,045	1,295	24	694	192	3	1,114	318
1996R	1,044	1,314	24	691	179	3	1,177	312
1997R	1,041	1,344	24	684	135	3	1,231	310
1998R	1,039	1,348	24	683	128	3	1,238	307
1999	1,041	1,320	24	680	75	3	1,327	295
2000R	993	1,199	25	663	75	3	1,370	297
2001	1,116	1,675	24	678	76	3	1,388	292
2002	*	*	21	*	76	3	*	*
2003	*	*	21	*	76	3	*	*
2004	1,119	1,685	24	688	72	3	1,473	227
2005	1,111	1,613	24	693	80	3	1,490	226

Includes non-federal and military.
** Includes Automated Flight Service Stations.

Source: FAA

with surveillance radar, down from 300 plus in earlier years (see Table 2-7). When flying into airports with such equipment, the majority of general aviation pilots use radar assistance because it is available and in some cases required.

Another service available to all fliers is the en route air traffic control complex, which consists of 24 air route traffic control centers (ARTCCs). These centers provide radar air traffic separation service to aircraft operating on instrument flight plan within controlled airspace. No aircraft may be operated when the visibility or ceiling falls below prescribed limits unless they are operated on instrument flight plan under instrument flight rules (IFR). Air carrier category aircraft, particularly those operated by certificated air carriers, operate under instrument flight rules all the time, no matter how good the actual weather may be, as a matter of course. General aviation pilots who are instrument qualified, or instrument "rated," tend to file instrument flight plans only when it is necessary to make a flight in adverse weather.

The most widely used service previously provided by the FAA to general aviation pilots was the Flight Service Station (FSS) network of 75 facilities for collecting and disseminating weather information, filing flight plans, and providing in-flight assistance and aviation advisory services. Although these services remain available to pilots, they are now offered by Lockheed Martin. This is due mainly to a General Accounting Office (GAO) study in 2001, which revealed escalating costs to maintain the FSS program, the FAA's inability to effectively modernize the FSS computer system, and widespread inefficiencies in the FSS program. As a result, in 2005, Lockheed Martin was awarded a $1.9 billion, 10-year contract by the FAA to provide these flight services to pilots. Lockheed Martin's new flight services system is called "Flight

Services 21" (FS21) and, when complete, will provide a fully integrated nationwide network that gives all flight service specialists and pilots access to flight plan information from a single, common database. By 2005, there were 80 flight service stations in the U.S. (see Table 2-7).

Flight service stations are the sole means of general aviation's filing flight plans, which are required under actual instrument conditions and are optional in good weather. They are the sole source from which to obtain official weather information, either in person (face-to-face briefings) or by telephone, or, when airborne, by air/ground radio communications.

The FSS system is vitally important to general aviation operations, and it is used by pilots of every level, from student pilots to air transport-rated pilots of large business jets. Indeed, flight service stations are indispensable to all general aviation flight operations.

Airframe Manufacturers

The period from 1980 through the mid1990s was one of considerable restructuring, downsizing, and consolidation for the general aviation aircraft manufacturers. The large-scale manufacturing of single-engine aircraft virtually ceased. The emphasis of major U.S. manufacturers shifted almost entirely to turbine business aircraft. With the maturation of the U.S. market being hastened by a lack of growth being supplied from smaller aircraft markets, the foreign manufacturers of piston and turbine aircraft made inroads into the market. In 1992, for the first time ever, a foreign manufacturer, Aerospatiale, sold more single-engine airplanes than any U.S. manufacturer.

Between 1994 and 2006, general aviation shipments and billings more than tripled (see Table 1-1). The General Aviation Manufacturers Association (GAMA) estimated that more than 25,000 manufacturing jobs were created during that time period. GAMA also reported increases in general aviation exports and new products as a result of increases in research and development.

Significance of Pilots to Aircraft Manufacturing

The significance of pilots to the growth in airframe manufacturing cannot be overstated. Traditionally, the industry has looked at pilots in two ways. First of all, as people who would learn to fly, and in some form or fashion, then buy an airplane. They might buy a new or used aircraft, join a flying club, or rent from an FBO, but in essence, they were purchasing the aircraft, either in total, or by the hour. The manufacturers also looked at pilots as those who would fly their products for a living with the air carriers, military, corporate, utility, agricultural, air ambulance, state, local or federal government, or other operations.

The overwhelming majority of business aircraft sales are by companies that already own and operate an aircraft and are acquiring more capable, new equipment. The awareness of aviation—the influences that go into creating the potential for a company to use aircraft as a business tool—comes significantly from pilots. Over the years, manufacturers have recognized that one of the key indicators of aircraft usage or acquisition by a company is the presence of a pilot, even a noncurrent pilot, in the senior management ranks of a company. These advocates inside the company are often much more influential in the sales process than the manufacturers' sales and marketing staffs.

Industry Outlook

For a thorough discussion and statistical analysis of the industry, see FAA Aerospace Forecasts and FAA Statistical Handbook of Aviation which are published annually and may be obtained by phone: (202) 267-3355, or by writing Federal Aviation Administration, Office of Aviation Policy and Plans, Statistics and Forecast Branch (APO-llO), 800 Independence Avenue, S.W., Washington, DC 20591. The FAA Aerospace Forecasts covers a ten-year period and covers all segments of the industry. APO Web sites which include annual conference proceedings, statistical publications, and latest data are:

Forecasts/Statistical Publications: http://api.hq.faa.gov/apo_pubs.htm

APO Data System: http:///www.apo.data.faa.gov

Another excellent source for current and forecasted statistics is the *General Aviation Statistical Databook* which may be obtained by phone: (202) 393-1500, or by writing General Aviation Manufacturers Association, 1400 K Street, N.W., Suite 801, Washington, DC, 20005. It is also available on their Web site at http://www.gama.aero.

General Aviation on the Web

The aviation industry, like most industries, has been affected dramatically by the dawning of the Information Age. For example, the challenges confronting dealers of pre-owned business airplanes have become particularly acute. In the past, a handful of experts possessed an advantage simply because they had access to information that others did not. Being the first (and preferably the only) person to know where a certain aircraft type was available meant a competitive advantage, and it was to be protected at all costs. Today, with immediate access to information about pre-owned aircraft available at the click of a mouse, the monopoly on such information has been broken. The Information Age has irreversibly democratized the industry. Information flows so freely, in fact, that many buyers and sellers today work without any broker or

Table 2-8

Piston Airplane Shipments by Manufacturer (1996-2006)

Number of Units

	1996	1997	1998	1999	2000	2001	2002	2003	2004	2005	2006
Adam Aircraft	**0**	**0**	**0**	**0**	**0**	**0**	**0**	**0**	**0**	**2**	**4**
A500	-	-	-	-	-	-	-	-	-	2	4
American Champion	**53**	**46**	**74**	**91**	**96**	**56**	**53**	**63**	**94**	**89**	**60**
7EC Champ	-	-	-	-	-	-	-	-	-	-	1
7ECA Aurora	2	6	6	9	3	2	3	2	2	3	2
7GCAA Adventurer	1	2	11	19	23	8	12	9	12	12	6
7GCBC Citabria Explorer	17	11	18	31	22	21	13	12	24	26	16
8GCBC Scout	7	7	14	5	23	6	11	8	18	9	14
8KCAB Super Decathlon	26	20	25	27	25	19	14	32	38	39	21
Aviat Aircraft	**56**	**61**	**85**	**83**	**91**	**57**	**38**	**47**	**42**	**47**	**0**
A-1 Huskey	46	-	-	-	-	-	-	-	-	-	-
A-1A Huskey	-	54	58	23	4	-	-	-	-	-	-
A-1B Huskey	-	-	6	44	76	50	34	37	30	41	n/a
Huskey Pup	-	-	-	-	-	-	-	3	3	1	n/a
S-1 11B Pitts	-	1	1	-	-	-	-	-	-	-	-
S-1T Pitts	-	-	-	-	-	-	-	-	-	-	-
S-2B Pitts	10	6	3	-	-	-	-	-	-	-	-
S-2C Pitts	-	-	17	16	11	7	4	7	9	5	n/a
Bellanca	**2**	**2**	**1**	**1**	**1**	**1**	**0**	**0**	**0**	**0**	**0**
Super Viking 17-30A	2	2	1	1	1	1	-	-	-	-	-
Britten-Norman	**5**	**0**	**1**	**1**	**2**	**0**	**0**	**0**	**0**	**0**	**0**
BN-2B Islander	5	0	1	1	2	-	-	-	-	-	-
Cessna Aircraft Company	**0**	**360**	**775**	**899**	**912**	**821**	**559**	**588**	**654**	**822**	**865**
Cessna 172 Skyhawk	-	287	358	180	150	107	57	58	32	37	87
Cessna 172S Skyhawk	-	-	64	272	340	341	258	291	204	314	322
Cessna 182 Skylane	-	73	338	248	267	142	109	118	196	241	140
Cessna 182T Turbo Skylane	-	-	-	-	-	96	79	47	133	118	187
Cessna 206 Stationair	-	-	12	79	53	41	18	16	22	29	25
Cessna 206T Turbo Stationair	-	-	3	120	102	94	38	58	67	83	104
Columbia Aircraft (form. Lancair)	**0**	**0**	**0**	**0**	**5**	**27**	**24**	**51**	**78**	**114**	**185**
Columbia 300	-	-	-	-	5	27	24	19	-	-	-
Columbia 350	-	-	-	-	-	-	-	32	28	25	39
Columbia 400	-	-	-	-	-	-	-	-	50	89	146
Cirrus Design Corporation	**0**	**0**	**0**	**9**	**95**	**183**	**397**	**469**	**553**	**600**	**721**
Cirrus SR-20	-	-	-	9	95	59	105	112	91	116	150
Cirrus SR-22	-	-	-	-	-	124	292	355	459	475	565
Cirrus SR-V	-	-	-	-	-	-	-	2	3	9	6
Commander Aircraft	**15**	**14**	**13**	**13**	**20**	**11**	**7**	**0**	**0**	**0**	**0**
Commander 114AT	3	-	-	-	-	-	-	-	-	-	-
Commander 114B	7	10	8	8	-	-	-	-	-	-	-
Commander 114TC	5	4	5	5	1	-	-	-	-	-	-
Commander 115	-	-	-	-	11	5	1	-	-	-	-
Commander 115TC	-	-	-	-	8	6	6	-	-	-	-
Diamond Aircraft	**142**	**88**	**0**	**0**	**0**	**0**	**155**	**228**	**261**	**329**	**438**
DA-20	142	88	n/a	n/a	n/a	n/a	70	75	58	54	55
DA-40	-	-	-	-	-	n/a	85	153	203	207	220
DA-42	-	-	-	-	-	-	-	-	-	68	163
Embraer	**35**	**23**	**24**	**30**	**17**	**17**	**1**	**0**	**0**	**0**	**0**
EMB-201A Ipanema	12	16	22	-	-	-	-	-	-	-	-
EMB-202 Ipanema	-	-	-	12	15	1	-	-	-	-	-
EMB-720 Minuano	2	1	1	2	-	-	-	-	-	-	-
EMB-810 Seneca II	9	7	7	3	2	-	-	-	-	-	-
Gippsland Aeronautics	**0**	**0**	**0**	**0**	**0**	**0**	**0**	**19**	**20**	**22**	**20**
GA-8 Airvan	-	-	-	-	-	-	-	19	20	22	20
Liberty Aerospace	**0**	**0**	**0**	**0**	**0**	**0**	**0**	**0**	**0**	**2**	**29**
XL2	-	-	-	-	-	-	-	-	-	2	29

Table 2-9

Piston Airplane Shipments by Manufacturer (1996-2006) (continued)

Number of Units

	1996	1997	1998	1999	2000	2001	2002	2003	2004	2005	2006
Maule Air Incorporated	**63**	**54**	**63**	**68**	**57**	**54**	**46**	**31**	**25**	**27**	**38**
M-4-180A	-	-	-	-	-	-	-	-	-	1	-
M-4-180V	-	-	-	-	-	-	-	-	-	-	7
M-6-235	-	-	-	-	1	-	-	-	-	-	-
M-7-235, A, B, C	18	18	11	24	24	19	21	12	8	11	8
M-7-260, C	-	-	2	16	10	11	3	4	3	4	2
MT-7-235	4	2	6	4	5	16	12	7	1	2	9
MT-7-260	-	-	-	2	1	4	1	-	-	2	4
MX-7-160, C	3	-	-	1	-	-	-	-	-	-	-
MX-7-180, A, B, C, AC	14	9	11	3	3	1	4	6	5	3	4
MX-7-235	-	-	-	-	-	-	-	-	-	-	-
MXT-7-160	-	-	5	-	-	-	-	-	-	-	-
MXT-7-180, A, AC	24	25	28	18	13	3	5	2	8	4	4
Micco	**0**	**0**	**0**	**0**	**6**	**10**	**0**	**0**	**0**	**0**	**0**
SP-20	-	-	-	-	5	-	-	-	-	-	-
SP-26	-	-	-	-	1	10	-	-	-	-	-
Mooney	**73**	**86**	**93**	**97**	**100**	**29**	**10**	**36**	**37**	**85**	**75**
M20J MSE											-
M20J Allegro	25	19	17	-	-	-	-	-	-	-	-
M20K Encore	-	15	18	-	-	-	-	-	-	-	-
M20M TLS	-	-	-	-	-	-	-	-	-	-	-
M20M Bravo	15	18	17	25	26	8	-	5	9	20	5
M20R Ovation	33	34	41	24	-	-	-	-	-	-	-
M20R Ovation 2	-	-	-	10	55	16	8	30	28	65	63
M20S Eagle	-	-	-	38	-	-	-	-	-	-	-
M20S Eagle 2	-	-	-	-	19	5	2	1	-	-	-
M20 Acclaim	-	-	-	-	-	-	-	-	-	-	7
Piper Aircraft, Inc.	**183**	**222**	**295**	**341**	**377**	**343**	**265**	**205**	**163**	**193**	**189**
PA-28-161 Warrior III	5	10	20	20	43	32	29	31	18	37	19
PA-28-181 Archer III	45	47	90	107	102	88	38	49	19	16	29
PA-28-236 Dakota	-	-	-	-	-	-	-	-	-	-	-
PA-28R-201 Arrow IV	7	3	2	6	18	23	26	16	12	9	5
PA-32-301FT Piper 6X	-	-	-	-	-	-	-	10	24	18	10
PA-32-301XTC Piper 6XT	-	-	-	-	-	-	-	11	14	16	11
PA-32R-301 Saratoga II HP	43	38	27	28	28	22	5	9	9	8	10
PA-32-301T Saratoga II TC	-	26	45	52	70	68	45	28	31	37	37
PA-34-220T Seneca IV	18	-	-	-	-	-	-	-	-	-	-
PA-34-220T Seneca V	-	38	54	57	42	38	43	28	10	12	26
PA-44-180 Seminole	8	7	2	8	11	62	60	16	11	29	11
PA-46-350P Malibu Mirage	57	53	55	63	63	10	19	7	15	11	31
Symphony Aircraft (prev. OMF)	**0**	**0**	**0**	**0**	**0**	**0**	**0**	**19**	**1**	**10**	**5**
Symphony 160	-	-	-	-	-	-	-	19	1	10	5
Pacific Aerospace Corporation	**0**	**0**	**0**	**0**	**0**	**0**	**0**	**0**	**6**	**0**	**0**
CT/4E Airtrainer	-	-	-	-	-	-	-	-	6	-	-
Raytheon Aircraft Company	**149**	**134**	**137**	**144**	**153**	**136**	**83**	**82**	**93**	**99**	**118**
Beech-33 Bonanza F33 A/C	8	-	-	-	-	-	-	-	-	-	-
Beech-36 Bonanza A36	83	85	73	77	85	63	51	55	62	71	80
Beech-36TC Bonanza B36TC	14	14	22	20	18	26	5	-	-	-	-
Beech-58 Baron 58	44	35	42	47	50	47	27	27	31	28	38
Socata EADS	**37**	**32**	**39**	**37**	**48**	**63**	**70**	**40**	**5**	**9**	**0**
TB-9 Tampico	1	14	14	0	2	2	3	2	0	1	0
TB-10	18	4	0	2	5	8	7	7	3	4	0
TB-20	13	11	20	31	26	33	44	19	0	1	0
TB-21	2	1	2	4	8	12	14	9	2	3	0
TB-200	3	2	3	0	7	8	2	3	0	0	0
Tiger Aircraft	**0**	**0**	**0**	**0**	**0**	**0**	**14**	**18**	**19**	**15**	**3**
AG-5B Tiger	-	-	-	-	-	-	14	18	19	15	3
Total Number of Airplanes	**801**	**1,123**	**1,606**	**1,801**	**1,980**	**1,792**	**1,721**	**1,896**	**2,051**	**2,465**	**2,750**
% Change	**20%**	**40%**	**43%**	**12%**	**10%**	**-9%**	**-4%**	**10%**	**8%**	**20%**	**12%**
Total Billings for Airplanes ($M)	**191**	**238**	**377**	**440**	**512**	**541**	**483**	**545**	**692**	**805**	**857**
% Change	**13%**	**25%**	**58%**	**17%**	**16%**	**6%**	**-11%**	**13%**	**27%**	**16%**	**6%**

Table 2-10

Business Jet Shipments by Manufacturer (1996-2006)

Number of Units

	1996	1997	1998	1999	2000	2001	2002	2003	2004	2005	2006
Airbus	**0**	**0**	**0**	**0**	**0**	**5**	**2**	**0**	**0**	**9**	**10**
Airbus Corporate Jet	-	-	-	-	-	5	2	0	0	9	10
Avcraft (form. Fairchild)	**0**	**0**	**0**	**0**	**0**	**4**	**4**	**9**	**9**	**1**	**0**
Envoy 3	-	-	-	-	-	4	4	9	9	1	-
Boeing Busines Jet		**0**	**0**	**7**	**29**	**14**	**16**	**11**	**7**	**3**	**13**
Boeing Business Jet	-	-	7	29	14	11	9	4	2	3	12
Boeing Business Jet 2	-	-	-	-	-	5	2	3	1	1	1
Bombardier Business Aircraft	**67**	**78**	**100**	**173**	**207**	**179**	**101**	**70**	**129**	**188**	**213**
Learjet 31A	12	21	22	24	27	17	9	2	-	-	-
Learjet 40	-	-	-	-	-	-	-	-	17	21	26
Learjet 45	-	-	7	43	71	63	27	17	22	28	30
Learjet 60	22	24	32	32	35	29	17	12	9	18	15
Challenger 300	-	-	-	-	-	-	-	1	28	50	55
Challenger 601	6	-	-	-	-	-	-	-	-	-	-
Challenger 604	27	33	36	42	39	41	31	24	29	36	29
Global 5000	-	-	-	-	-	-	-	-	4	17	18
Global Express	-	-	3	32	35	29	17	14	20	13	22
CL 850/870/890	-	-	-	-	-	-	-	-	-	5	18
Cessna Aircraft Company	**122**	**174**	**195**	**216**	**252**	**306**	**305**	**196**	**181**	**247**	**307**
C510 Mustang	-	-	-	-	-	-	-	-	-	-	1
C525 CJ1	44	63	64	59	56	61	30	22	20	14	-
C525 CJ1+	-	-	-	-	-	-	-	-	-	4	25
C525A CJ2	-	-	-	-	8	41	86	56	27	23	1
C525A+ CJ2+	-	-	-	-	-	-	-	-	-	-	36
C525B CJ3	-	-	-	-	-	-	-	-	6	48	72
C550 Citation Bravo	-	28	34	36	54	48	41	31	25	21	18
C560 Citation Ultra	52	47	41	32	-	-	-	-	-	-	-
C560 Citation Encore	-	-	-	-	6	37	36	21	24	13	12
C560XL Citation Excel	-	-	15	39	79	85	81	48	23	-	-
C560XLS Citation XLS	-	-	-	-	-	-	-	-	32	64	73
C650 Citation VII	19	8	11	14	12	-	-	-	-	-	-
C680 Citation Sovereign	-	-	-	-	-	-	-	-	9	46	57
C750 Citation X	7	28	30	36	37	34	31	18	15	14	12
Dassault Falcon Jet	**33**	**51**	**47**	**69**	**73**	**75**	**66**	**49**	**63**	**51**	**61**
Falcon 50	1	-	-	-	-	-	-	-	-	-	-
Falcon 50EX	-	10	13	11	18	13	10	8	5	5	5
Falcon 900B	8	7	5	8	-	-	-	-	-	-	-
Falcon 900C	-	-	-	-	6	6	4	3	3	1	-
Falcon 900EX	3	16	15	16	23	21	17	6	1	-	-
Falcon 900DX	-	-	-	-	-	-	-	-	-	2	4
Falcon 900EX EASy	-	-	-	-	-	-	-	4	14	16	16
Falcon 2000	21	18	14	34	26	35	35	12	11	6	6
Falcon 2000EX	-	-	-	-	-	-	-	16	10	-	-
Falcon 2000EX EASy	-	-	-	-	-	-	-	-	19	21	30
Eclipse Aviation	**0**	**0**	**0**	**0**	**0**	**0**	**0**	**0**	**0**	**0**	**1**
Eclipse 500	-	-	-	-	-	-	-	-	-	-	1
Embraer	**0**	**0**	**0**	**0**	**0**	**0**	**8**	**13**	**13**	**20**	**27**
Legacy Executive	-	-	-	-	-	-	8	13	13	20	27
Gulfstream Aerospace	**36**	**57**	**75**	**80**	**88**	**101**	**85**	**74**	**78**	**89**	**113**
G100/150 (form. IAI Astra)	9	6	14	9	11	5	9	24	22	26	42
G200 (form. IAI Galaxy)	-	-	-	1	6	25	15				
G300/350/400/450 (f. GIV/IVSP)	24	22	32	39	37	36	29	50	56	63	71
G500/G550 (f. GV / VSP)	3	29	29	31	34	35	32				
Raytheon Aircraft Company	**58**	**78**	**91**	**100**	**118**	**98**	**94**	**100**	**115**	**141**	**140**
Premier I/A	-	-	-	-	-	18	29	29	37	30	23
Hawker 400XP	29	43	43	45	51	25	19	24	28	53	53
Hawker 800XP	26	33	48	55	67	55	46	47	50	58	8
Hawker 850XP	-	-	-	-	-	-	-	-	-	-	56
Hawker 1000	3	2	-	-	-	-	-	-	-	-	-
Total Number of Airplanes	**316**	**438**	**515**	**667**	**752**	**784**	**676**	**518**	**591**	**750**	**885**
% Change	5%	39%	18%	30%	13%	4%	-14%	-23%	14%	27%	18%
Total Billings for Airplanes ($M)	**3,881**	**6,019**	**7,216**	**10,190**	**11,661**	**12,117**	**10,427**	**8,616**	**10,229**	**13,161**	**16,555**
% Change	16%	55%	20%	41%	14%	4%	-14%	-17%	19%	29%	26%

dealer representative. Indeed, the Internet has brought about the convergence of information gathering and purchasing decisions. Customers are armed with data before they ever get in touch with the company and hence, are more empowered than ever before. Similarly, to be successful on the Web, one must give a lot to get a lot. A business must learn to grapple with large amounts of fast-changing data and use that information to help its clients. An effective Web site can then be used to bridge time and distance to create new levels of customer intimacy and a higher level of dealer/broker availability.

Those who adopted the Internet early have already taken the risks and made mistakes from which others can learn. There is now less risk than ever in applying resources to a strong Web presence. In some ways, the risks are higher for those few companies who have not implemented an Internet strategy.

Customers are struggling with the deluge of information they face in making decisions. Unfortunately, the Internet has developed a lot of useless, redundant, and even wrong information. It is the company's responsibility to help clients gain access to the right data and interpret and apply that data intelligently. This is where the true value of the Information Age lies and smart customers are willing to pay to have access to it.

Gaining an edge in the Information Age, therefore, will depend on leveraging Internet technology to create niches based on a company's particular area of expertise and service delivery. For example, each dealer and broker must stake out a unique place in the new marketplace and stream critical information out to the audience most interested in it. In so doing, the company will become a consultative resource for its clients and will realize tangible benefits through the unique networking opportunities made possible by a connected aviation community.

Included at the end of this chapter is a listing of general aviation Web sites chosen for their relevance and usefulness to the general aviation community. Space constraints do not permit listing every beneficial aviation site, but the list provides an excellent starting point. Another excellent source of aviation-related organizations is the World Aviation Directory.

Airframe Manufacturers

Airframe manufacturers face a dilemma when developing Web sites. On the one hand, the site can be tremendously useful in disseminating information to operators; but it can also generate a flood of casual queries from the general public, as well as sales leads from dubious sources.

Each manufacturer with a Web site has attacked the problem differently, choosing either to deliver some information along with password-limited access to customer service areas or simply to use the Web as a brochure-like publishing and distribution medium.

The Web has a tremendous potential for saving manufacturers money by allowing them to distribute the kind of information their customers need. Sites can provide basic product information, as well as links to sales and support personnel, including contact phone numbers and e-mail addresses. They can also be used to order parts or download technical information such as service bulletins. Customers who have clicked through online parts catalogs and updated their maintenance manuals over the Web recognize that it can be a tremendous time saver. Not only does it save the customer time, but it also allows the manufacturer to devote its resources to other areas.

The greatest potential for aviation Web utility is with customer-oriented aircraft manufacturers. Aircraft manufacturing does not stop after the product is delivered. There is a constant need for two-way communication between manufacturers and aircraft owners and operators, and the Web is the perfect way to enable that type of dialogue.

Aircraft Sales

In the world of Web classifieds, Trade-A-Plane (TAP) is the dominant source. For an annual fee (free to print subscribers), Web users can access TAP's entire content, which includes more than 5,000 aircraft and other aviation products. Access to display advertisers' material is free.

Searches can be done for aircraft by manufacturer or model, location (by state), price, model year, total time, engine time, and keywords. To finish a search request, the user selects either to browse listings or to see the complete ads. For aircraft, browsing works better because it delivers a list of all the aircraft that fall close to the search constraints, depending on a one to five order of importance that the user assigns to each search category.

Another excellent site is Aircraft Shopper Online (ASO), a Web-only directory of aircraft for sale, accessible free of charge. Using ASO's PowerSearch, visitors can look for airplanes and helicopters by manufacturer, price range, year built, and time on airframe. Links are provided to contact the seller by mail and telephone, and many listings have photos showing the exterior and interior of aircraft for sale.

Sales of pre-owned aircraft over the Web may not be threatening traditional aircraft selling, but dealers and brokers are using it extensively to help develop leads. And for the buyer, the Internet is a great place to comparison-shop for pre-owned aircraft.

Business Aviation Services

Service companies such as maintenance shops, training organizations, and FBOs face a special challenge when publishing on the Web: What content can they deliver on a Web site that will bring in new customers and serve the needs of existing customers?

Much of the information that an aviation service company publishes is brochure-like and does not need frequent updating. But without timely updating, material on a Web site does not change often enough to attract repeat visitors.

Although some aviation sites have focused on the repeat visitor problem in unique ways, such as offering discount coupons, some companies simply feel it is good enough to have a Web site with descriptions of services, photos, and no dynamic information. FBOs, in particular, may utilize other third party Web sites such as http://www.airnav.com and http://www.100LL.com to post dynamic information such as ever-changing fuel prices.

Flight Planning and Weather

There are excellent resources for professional online assistance for every facet of trip planning. Retrieval of weather information online has become the most popular use of the Web among pilots, either through commercial vendors or no-fee government and university-sponsored sites. Beyond that, flight plans can be filed, bargains on fuel can be discovered, parts can be ordered, federal regulations and safety-related information can be accessed, trips can be scheduled and hotels, rental cars, and restaurants can be located.

Charter Reservations

Because the Web can provide a high level of interaction between buyer and seller, it is fast becoming the preferred tool for an array of online charter reservations services. For example, Skyjet, which was acquired by Bombardier in 2000, allows visitors to check fares and book flights on any of over 1,300 aircraft in its charter network.

Avionics

For a glimpse into aviation's future, the avionics manufacturers provide excellent sites for emerging airspace issues from RVSM and ADS-B to Free Flight and WAAS/LAAS. Some of the best sites for taking a look into the future are those maintained by Honeywell, Rockwell Collins, and UPS Aviation Technologies. All three update their sites regularly with interesting and useful information.

Parts Suppliers

There are sites that provide huge parts databases for technicians. One of the best-known parts distributors, Aviall, provides its customers with full access to its entire inventory online. Users can search by part number and find out if the part is available, how much it costs, including discount, and whether any parts are on back order or have been shipped. Once parts are located, users can order them online.

Training

Flight training organizations are mainly using their Web sites to list course schedules and locations. CAE SimuFlite allows customers to sign up for courses over its Web site, although confirmation does not come until an account representative contacts the customer. All of CAE SimuFlite's simulators are listed, along with detailed specs for each aircraft type in which training is offered.

Publications

Because the Web is such an inexpensive communications medium, accessible by anyone with a computer and Internet connection, hundreds of electronic only (no print counterpart) publications have appeared online. In their wake, nearly all the nation's major newspapers and magazines have launched sites of their own, with the result being that a seemingly unending source of news and information is available online, 24 hours a day.

Aviation print publications have approached the Web in similar fashion, but most are still grappling with issues such as how much content to provide for free, how to serve existing readers and attract new readers online, and the extent of resources to devote to the Web.

Associations

The Web provides a means by which members of various aviation associations and interested visitors can learn about the latest developments regarding the association. One of the most comprehensive sites is offered by the National Business Aviation Association (NBAA). Launched in 1995, it has seen a dramatic increase in member use. It offers an online discussion forum where members can chat with each other via e-mail and on the site itself. Users can subscribe to any or all categories, which include sections for flight department managers, pilots, schedulers and dispatchers, maintenance personnel, and flight attendants, as well as topical sections on taxes, jobs, and even fractional ownership.

The main reason for conducting business online is to increase revenues and reduce transaction costs. E-commerce, used correctly, can strengthen the relationship between a company and its customers. Consumers benefit from being able to use their computers to enhance the overall buying experience. For example, customers can track the status of orders they have placed, get quick answers to technical questions, swiftly compare prices between multiple vendors, search online catalogs with ease, and solve product warranty issues. In short, the onus is on the seller to create a business environment that makes the buyer's job simple. With the right interactive programming, an aviation Web site can be transformed into a sophisticated marketing and sales tool that offers every visitor a highly personalized and responsive experience.

GENERAL AVIATION WEB SITES

The following listing of general aviation Web sites contains nearly 500 entries, which are broken down into 20 categories for quick reference by company or organization. It provides a fairly comprehensive listing of firms and organizations that fall within the scope of the GA industry. However, no attempt was made to make it all-inclusive. Savvy users of the Web are encouraged to utilize various search engines to find other sites of interest.

Airframe Manufacturers

AASI: www.aasiaircraft.com
Airbus: www.airbus.com
American Utilicraft: www.utilicraft.com
BAE Systems: www.baesystems.com
BellAgusta Aerospace: www.bellagustaaerospace.com
Bell Helicopter Textron: www.bellhelicopter.textron.com
Boeing Business Jets: www.boeing.com/bbj
Bombardier: www.aero.bombardier.com
Britten-Norman: www.britten-norman.com
Century Aerospace: www.centuryaero.com
Cessna: www.cessna.com
Cirrus: www.cirrusdesign.com
Commander: www.commanderair.com
Dassault Falcon Jet: www.falconjet.com
EADS: www.eads-nv.com
Eclipse: www.eclipseaviation.com
Embraer: www.embraer.com
Enstrom: www.enstromhelicopter.com
Eurocopter: www.eurocopter.com
Explorer Aircraft: www.exploreraircraft.com
Fairchild Dornier: www.fairchilddornier.com
Farnborough Aircraft: www.farnborough-aircraft.com
Groen Brothers Aircraft: www.gbagyros.com
Gulfstream: www.gulfstream.com
HondaJet: www.hondajet.honda.com
Ibis Aerospace: www.ibisaerospace.com
Kaman: www.kamanaero.com
Learjet: www.learjet.com
MD Helicopters: www.mdhelicopters.com
Mooney: www.mooney.com
Pilatus: www.pilatus-aircraft.com
Piper: www.newpiper.com
Robinson: www.robinsonheli.com
Saab: www.saabaircraftleasing.com
Scaled Composites: www.scaled.com
Sikorsky: www.sikorsky.com
Sino Swearingen: www.sj30jet.com
Socata: www.socata.com
Soloy: www.soloy.com

Aircraft Sales

Aeroprice: www.aeroprice.com
Aircraft Dealers Network: www.aircraftdealers.net
Aircraft Sales Corp.: www.aircraftsalescorp.com
Aircraft Services Group: www.yourjet.com
Aircraft Shopper Online: www.aso.com
Bidjet.com: www.bidjet.com
Bizjet: www.bizjet.ch
Executive Controller: www.aircraft.com
HelicopterBuyer .com: www.helicopterbuyer.com
JB&A Aviation: www.jbaaviation.com
Mesinger Corporate Jet Sales: www.jetsales.com
MyPlane.com: www.myplane.com
National Aircraft Resale Association: www.nara-dealers.com
Peregrine Aviation: www.peregrineaviation.com
Trade-A-Plane: www.trade-a-plane.com
Vance & Engles: www.vanceengles.com
Welsch Aviation: www.welschaviation.com

Associations

Aerospace Industries Association: www.aia-aerospace.org
Aircraft Electronics Association: www.aea.net
Aircraft Owners and Pilots Association: www.aopa.org
Air Line Pilots Association: www.alpa.org
Air Transport Association: www.air-transport.org
Allied Pilots Association: www.alliedpilots.org
American Association Of Airport Executives: www.aaae.org
American Helicopter Society: www.vtol.org
Aviation Insurance Association: www.AIAweb.org
Canadian Business Aircraft Association: www.cbaa.ca
Corporate Aircraft Association: www.corpaa.org
Corporate Angel Network: www.corpangelnetwork.org
European Business Aviation Association: www.ebaa.org
European Regions Airline Association: www.eraa.org
Flight Safety Foundation: www.flightsafety.org
Helicopter Association International: www.rotor.com
International Business Aviation Council: www.ibac.org
National Air Traffic Controllers Association: www.natca.org
National Air Transportation Association: www.nata-online.org
National Business Aviation Association: www.nbaa.org
The Ninety-Nines: www.ninety-nines.org
Professional Aviation Maintenance Association: www.pama.org
Regional Airline Association: www.raa.org
Royal Aeronautical Society: www.raes.org.uk
Society of Automotive Engineers: www.sae.org

Women in Aviation, International: www.wiai.org
Women in Corporate Aviation: www.wca-intl.org

Avionics

AirCell: www.aircell.com
Airshow: www.airshowinc.com
Archangel: www.archangel.com
Arinc: www.arinc.com
Avidyne: www.avidyne.com
Avionics Zone (Honeywell): www.avionicszone.com
Ball Aerospace: www.ballaerospace.com
Becker Avionics: www.becker-avionics.com
BendixlKing: www.bendixking.com
Century Flight Systems: www.centuryflight.com
EMS Technologies: www.ems-t.com
Eventide: www.eventide.com
Garmin: www.garmin.com
Honeywell: www.honeywell.com
Icarus Instruments: www.icarusinstruments.com
IEC International: www.iecinternational.com
Innovative Solutions & Support: www.innovative-ss.com
Intheairnet: www.intheairnet.com
Kollsman: www.kollsman.com
Meggitt: www.meggitt.com
Narco: www.narco-avionics.com
Northstar Technologies: www.northstarcmc.com
Ryan International: www.ryan-tcad.com
Safe Flight: www.safeflight.com
Sigma Tek: www.sigmatek.com
S- TecJMeggitt: www.s-tec.com
Teledyne Controls: www.teledyne-controls.com
UPS Aviation Technologies: www.upsat.com

Charter Reservations / Price Quotes

Aircharter.com: www.aircharter.com
Air Charter Guide: www.aircharterguide.com
Air Charter Online: www.aircharteronline.com
AirCharter World: www.acworld.com
BidjetCharter: www.bidjetcharter.com
CharterX: www.charterx.com
Corporate Jet Link: www.corporatejetlink.com
Daimler Chrysler Automotive Air Charter: www.automotive air.com
EBizJets: www.ebizjets.com
FlightTime: www.flighttime.com
Jet Aviation Charter: www.jetaviation.com/charter
Sky Jet: www.skyjet.com
Transjet: www.transjet.com

Completion Centers

AAR Aircraft Services: www.aarcorp.com
ADI Interiors: www.flyadi.com
Air Methods: www.airmethods.com
Atlantic Aviation: www.atlanticaviation.com
Aviation Concepts: www.aviationconcepts.net
Avmats: www.avmats.com
B/E Aerospace: www.beaerospace.com
Bizjet International: www.bizjetinternational.com
Bombardier Completions: www.aero.bombardier.com
Byerly Aviation: www.byerlyaviation.com
Capital Aviation: www.capitalaviation.com
Commuter Air Technology: www.commuterair.com
Duncan Aviation: www.duncanaviation.com
Eagle Aviation: www.eagle-aviation.com
Elliott Aviation: www.elliottaviation.com
Flying Colours: www.flyingcolourscorp.com
Garrett Aviation Services: www.garrettaviation.com
H.A.S. Corporation: www.has-corp.com
Innotech-Execaire: www.innotech-execaire.com
International Jet Interiors: www.intljet.com
Jet Aviation: www.jetaviation.com
JetCorp: www.jetcorp.com
Lufthansa Technik: www.lufthansa-technik.com
Mena Aircraft Interiors: www.aircraft-interiors.com
Midcoast Aviation: www.midcoastaviation.com
Rose Aircraft Interiors: www.roseaircraft.com
Sierra Industries: www.sijet.com
Stevens Aviation: www.stevensaviation.com
Trace Aircraft Completions: www.traceww.com
Vee Neal Aviation: www.veeneal.com
West Star Aviation: www.weststaraviation.com

Engine Manufacturers

Agilis: www.agilis.com
CFM International: www.cfm56.com
GE Aircraft Engines: www.geae.com
Honeywell: www.honeywell.com
Orenda Recip: www.orenda.com
Pratt & Whitney: www.pratt-whitney.com
Pratt & Whitney Canada: www.pwc.ca
Rolls- Royce: www.rolls-royce.com
Turbomeca: www.turbomeca.com
Williams International: www.williams-int.com

FBO Chains/Fuels Suppliers/Cards

Air BP: www.airbp.com
Avcard: www.avcard.com
Avfuel: www.avfuel.com
Chevron: www.chevronaviation.com
Exxon Card Services: www.airworld.com
ExxonMobil: www.exxon.mobil.com/em_aviationfuels
Irving Aviation Service: www.irvingaviation.com
Jet Aviation: www.jetaviation.com
Mercury Air Centers: www.mercuryaircenters.com
Midcoast Aviation: www.midcoastaviation.com
Million Air: www.millionair.com
Shell Aviation: www.shell.com/aviation
Signature Flight Support: www.signatureflight.com
Skyservice: www.skyservice.com
Stevens Aviation: www.stevensaviation.com
TAC Air: www.tacair.com
TAG Aviation: www.tagaviation.com
Uvair: www.uvair.com

Federal Government

Bureau of Transportation Statistics: www.bts.gov
Federal Aviation Administration: www.faa.gov
Int'l Civil Aviation Organization: www.icao.org
National Transportation Safety Board: www.ntsb.gov
U.S. Dept. of Transportation: www.dot.gov

Financial Services

AirFleet Capital: www.airfteetcapital.com
Cessna Finance: www.cfcloan.com
CIT Group: www.citgroup.com
Finova: www.finova.com
First Equity: www.firstequity.com
GE Capital Aviation Services: www.gecas.com
GE Capital Corporate Aircraft Group: www.gecorporateaircraft.com
TFC Textron Business & Charter Aircraft: www.tfcaviation.textron.com

Fractional Aircraft Providers

Bombardier FlexJet: www.flexjet.com
Citation Shares: www.citationshares.com
NetJets: www.netjets.com
Flight Options: www.flightoptions.com
PlaneSense: www.planesense.org
PlaneSmart: www.planesmart.com

Flight Planning

AirNav: www.airnav.com
Airport Taxi Diagrams: www.aopa.org/asf/taxi
Air Routing International: www.argis.com
Air Routing's Flight Manager: www.flightmanager.com
Baseops International: www.baseops.com
FltPlan.com: www.fltplan.com
Jeppesen Corporate Flight Services: www.jeppesen.com
Ultra-Nav Aviation: www.ultranav.com
Universal Weather & Aviation: www.universalweather.com

Information Resources

100 Low Lead.com: www.100LL.com
Ac-U-Kwik: www.acukwik.com
Aerolink Global Aviation Infosource: www.aerolink.com
Aeroseek: www.aeroseek.com
Aerospace Mall: www.aerospacemall.com
Aircraft Technical Publishers: www.atp.com
Air Security's World Watch Online: worldwatch.airsecurity.com
Amstat: www.amstatcorp.com
ARGIUS: www.aviationresearch.com
AvCrew: www.avcrew.com
Aviation Employee Placement Service: www.aeps.com
Aviation Jobs Online: www.aviationjobsonline.com
The Aviation Search Engine: www.aviationsearchengine.com
Avjobs: www.avjobs.com
BizjetPilot.com: www.bizjetpilot.com
Conklin & de Decker Associates: www.conklindd.com
Corporate Aviators, Inc.: www.corporateaviators.com
Corporate Jet Link: www.corporatejetlink.com
Corporate Pilot.com: www.corporatepilot.com
Executive Jet Aviation Pilot's Information Site: www.ejapilots.com
FBOweb.com: www.fboweb.com
Fillup Flyer Fuel Finder: www.fillupfiyer.com
Find-a-Pilot Online Resume Service: www.findapilot.com
Global Aviation Navigator: www.globalair.com
JetLinks: www.jetlinks.com
Landings: www.landings.com

Insurance

Aircraft & Marine Insurance Group: www.aircraft-marine.com
Aircraft Insurance Group: www.aigltd.com
Aircraft Underwriters: www.aircraftund.com
Associated Aviation Underwriters: www.aau.com
Avemco: www.avemco.com
CS&A Aviation Insurance: www.aviationinsurance.com

Dorr Aviation: www.dorraviation.com
LL Johns & Associates, Inc.: www.lljohns.com
USAIG: www.usaig.com

Maintenance/Modifications

Aerial View Systems: www.aerialviewsystems.com
Aeromech: www.aeromechinc.com
Aerospace Lighting (BIE Aerospace): www.aerospacelighting.com
Aircraft Belts: www.aircraftbelts.com
Aviation Fabricators: www.aviationfabricators.com
Aviation Partners: www.aviationpartners.com
A vquotes: www.avquotes.com
Avtec: www.avtec-inc.com
Banyan Air Service: www.banyanair.com
BBA Aviation: www.bba-aviation.com
BIE Aerospace: www.beaerospace.com
Bizjet: www.bizjetinternational.com
CAMP: www.campsys.com
Dallas Airmotive: www.dallasairmotive.com
DeVore Aviation: www.devoreaviation.com
EV AS Worldwide: www.evasworldwide.com
FR Aviation: www.fraviation.co.uk
Garrett Aviation: www.garrettaviation.com
Hartzell Propeller: www.hartzellprop.com
Innotech- Execaire: www.innotech-execaire.com
King Aerospace: www.king-aerospace.com
Magellan Aerospace: www.malaero.com
Messier-Buggati: www.messier-bugatti.com
Messier Services: www.messierservices.com
Nordam Group: www.nordam.com
Really Quiet: www.reallyquiet.com
Sabreliner: www.sabreliner.com
Securaplane: www.securaplane.com
Signature RMC: www.signatureflight.com
Standard Aero: www.standardaero.com
Stevens Aviation: www.stevensaviation.com
West Star: www.weststaraviation.com

Online Publications

AIN Online: www.ainonline.com
Air & Space Smithsonian: www.airspacemag.com
Aviation Week and Space Technology: www.aviationweek.com/aw
AvWeb: www.avweb.com
Business & Commercial Aviation: www.aviationnow.com/bca
FAA Aviation News: www.faa.gov/avr/news/newshome.htm
Flight Global: www.flightglobal.com
Professional Pilot: www.propilotmag.com

Parts, Suppliers and Locators

Aerospace Products International: www.apiparts.com
Aircraft Parts Locator Service: www.apls.com
Avgroup: www.jetparts.com
Aviall: www.aviall.com
Aviation Online Network: www.airparts.com
Avsupport Online: www.avsupport.com
Corporate Rotable & Supply: www.corporaterotable.com
Inventory Locator Service: www.ilsmart.com
Parts Base: www.partsbase.com
Parts Logistics: www.partslogistics.com
TradeAir.com: www.tradeair.com

Pilots Only

Aviation Employee Placement Service: www.aeps.com
BizjetPilot.com: www.bizjetpilot.com
Fractional Operations Information: www.fracstats.com
IPilot: www.ipilot.com
Minority Pilots Association/Academy: www.minoritypilot.org
Professional Pilot's Rumor Network: www.pprune.org

Training

Aerolearn: www.aerolearn.com
CAE: www.cae.com
Facts Training International: www.facts-aircare.com
FlightSafety International: www.flightsafety.com
Pan Am International Flight Academy: www.panamacademy.com
University Aviation Association: www.uaa.aero

Weather Resources

Accuweather: www.accuweather.com
FlightBrief: www.flightbrief.com
GTE Duats: www.duat.com
National Weather Service (NWS): www.nws.noaa.gov
Pilotweather.com: www.pilotweather.com
Unisys: www.weather.unisys.com
Universal Weather & Aviation: www.universalweather.com
Weather Channel: www.weather.com/aviation
Weather Services International: www.pilotbrief.wsicorp.com
WeatherTap (Trade-a-Plane): www.weathertap.com
Weather Underground: www.wunderground.com
WSI's Intellicast: www.intellicast.com

KEY TERMS

Aerial Application
Aerial Observation
Aerial Other
Sightseeing
Air tours
Air taxi
External load Medical
General aviation
Primary use category
Public use
Executive/corporation transportation
Business transportation
Personal flying
Instructional flying
Fixed Base Operator (FBO)
Instrument Landing System (ILS)
Air route traffic control centers (ARTCCs)
Flight Service Station (FSS)
Other flying
Publicly owned airports
Private use airports
Very-high frequency omnidirectional range (VOR)

REVIEW QUESTIONS

1. Define "general aviation." General aviation aircraft have traditionally represented what percent of the total active aircraft in the United States? What are the 14 FAA primary use categories? Approximately how many active general aviation aircraft were there in the United States in 1999? What is the dominant type aircraft?
2. Give some examples of public use aircraft. What is the preponderance of helicopters used for? What is the difference between executive/corporate transportation and business transportation? How many turbine aircraft are operated by business aircraft users? Give several reasons that businesses use their own aircraft.
3. Personal flying is primarily for wealthy individuals who want aircraft for recreation. Do you agree? Why? Discuss the importance of instructional flying. Distinguish between aerial application, aerial observation, and aerial other. Give several examples of each. Distinguish between sightseeing, air tours, and air taxi. What is the big advantage of chartering an aircraft? Describe several uses of aircraft for carrying external loads and medical flying. What is included in the other flying category?
4. Approximately how many publicly owned airports are in the United States? How many are reserved by the scheduled air carriers? Describe the important economic role played by general aviation airports. Why is the growth in the number of student and private pilots so important to the continued health of the general aviation industry?
5. Describe several services provided by the FAA for general aviation pilots. What is the purpose of flight service stations? What has been the trend in general aviation aircraft manufacturing since 1980? Identify some single- - and multi-engine aircraft available in the United States. What is the significance of pilots to aircraft manufacturing? Identify several sources for general aviation forecasts.
6. Describe the importance of the Internet and Web sites to marketing and sales of general aviation aircraft, components, and services. How are airframe manufacturers using their Web sites to service operators? How has the aircraft sales process been changed by the Internet? What is some of the information pilots can obtain online? How are flight training organizations using their Web sites? What is the main reason companies and their customers are conducting business online?

PART TWO:
OPERATING AN FBO

Chapter 3
The Fixed Base Operator

OUTLINE

OBJECTIVES

At the end of this chapter you should be able to:

- Describe the principal services provided by an FBO.
- Describe the size and scope of the FBO industry, including the various categories. Discuss several current trends in the FBO industry and the future outlook for the industry.
- Choose the correct legal structure for a new FBO.
- Identify and highlight the factors which go into the analysis of the market and selecting a location for an FBO.
- List the basic facilities and equipment needed in establishing an FBO.
- Discuss some of the advantages and disadvantages of joining an FBO chain.
- Describe some of the important practices and procedures designed to improve service to customers in the following areas: ramp, ground personnel, aircraft, and flight personnel.

Introduction

In the early days of aviation, most individuals who made their living by flying went from field to field putting on air shows, giving rides, and providing maintenance services for other operators. These barnstormers, as they became known, did not have a fixed base of operation and were not highly regarded from the standpoint of dependability or business acumen. Some, however, became successful aviation business people and established airport facilities to base their aviation service operations. These respected, down-to-earth, here-to-stay stalwarts became know as *fixed base operators.* Although attempts have been made to rename FBOs as flight support operations or aviation service businesses, the term is now widely used all over the world. FBOs are FBOs even in France.

Today, fixed base operators (FBOs) are to the general aviation industry what service stations, repair garages, engine specialists, body and fender shops, paint shops, tire sales outlets, driver training schools, taxicabs, new and used automobile dealers, and auto supply stores are to the automobile industry. By the very nature of the aviation business, all of these services must be concentrated on or close to a designated airport, and usually at one or two locations on an airport, in many cases sharing the airport with air carrier operations and military operations.

Size and Scope of the FBO Industry

It has been estimated that there were as many as 10,000 FBOs during the late 1970s. A study in 1992 counted 4,099. Recent estimates indicate that the number is somewhere between 3,440 and 3,900. Of those, about 12 to 15 percent have the facilities and location to specialize in servicing turbine-powered business aircraft and their passengers. NATA defines an FBO as an organization that has a specific lease with an airport-owning entity and offers a minimum of two of the major services provided by FBOs.

At the start of 2006, there were 5,270 public-use airports in the United States, of which 575 were certificated under FAR Part 139 to serve air carriers, as well as general aviation. Of the remaining 4,695 airports, which might be called general aviation airports, plus several hundred privately-owned airports open for public use, not all are attended or have service all the time. Many are attended seasonally (summer resorts, for example), and many are attended only during daylight hours. On the other hand, many offer services 24 hours a day, and many large airports have several FBOs competing for aviation business.

FBOs fall into three major categories:

1. **Major fixed base operators.** These are located on major commercial-service airports and are fully equipped to handle the servicing and maintenance of all types of aircraft from the large air carrier types used by the airlines and major corporations to the single engine aircraft that use the airport. Many of these full-service FBOs have multiplex operations as do some of the medium size FBOs, but most major operators have a single operations base. Their investments run into hundreds of millions of dollars, including leaseholds and equipment.
2. **Medium-sized fixed base operators.** The difference between major and medium-sized operations is chiefly the amount of investment, for most medium-sized operators are located at airports where air carriers are also served. FBOs must be able (by contract with the lessor) to remove and repair any aircraft that may be expected to use their facilities in the event that such aircraft becomes disabled on the ramps or runways. The investment in a medium-sized FBO may run as high as $50 million and sales volumes may run into the multimillion dollar figure annually, principally on aircraft sales, fuel sales, and maintenance.
3. **Small fixed base operators.** It is estimated that two-thirds of FBOs fall into the small category. Many are small firms doing business on a shoestring budget, using the cash drawer system. At the beginning of the year there is so much money in the till; during the year some goes out and some comes in, and at the end of the year, whatever is left is "profit." The vulnerability of such operations in the modern business environment is too clear to require comment.

The vast majority of the small operators have no business training. A small FBO is started by a person who is an aeronautical specialist, a pilot or a mechanic, an artisan such as an engine rebuilder, a radio expert, or a sheet metal fabricator, because of love for aviation. Then the operation grows in size to meet the increasing demands of the aviation public.

Beginning with a flight instruction or repair facility, the small operator attracts a clientele, and as the flying public learns of the operation, expands services to include fueling, hangarage, and tie-downs. In a short time the specialist becomes a generalist and blossoms into a classic multi-service fixed base operation, with many employees and increased investments—an aviation shopping mall—which the specialist/ generalist is often not educationally equipped to manage on a businesslike basis.

Recognizing that the fixed base operator is the major contact between the manufacturers and the general public for the sale of new aircraft and for flight instruction, it can be seen that there is a fragility in the general aviation industry that must be corrected if general aviation is to continue, not only to grow, but to exist as a transportation form of value to the nation.

In addition to the three main categories of FBOs, specialized aviation service businesses includes extremely specialized aviation operations found on public airports that do not qualify as a fixed base operation, but are nevertheless totally involved with and dependant upon general aviation. This includes engine manufacturers and remanufacturers, avionics specialists, propeller specialists, aircraft painting, interior retrofit and upgrades, and certain flight training specialists who do nothing but recurrent flight training for professional or semiprofessional pilots of high performance aircraft. These operations are separate from and not competitive with true fixed base operators at the same airport, but fall within the category simply because they are located at the same airport.

General aviation air transportation cannot exist without a nationwide system of fixed base operators to support it. Not only is the FBO the interface between the manufacturing business and the public, as well as the principal outlet for aircraft sales, it also typically provides the fueling, routine (and major) maintenance, inspection and relicensing facilities, storage, and general aviation buildings. No one can plan a trip by general aviation aircraft unless such support facilities, at least fueling capabilities, are available at both departure and arrival airports.

Recent Trends in the FBO Industry

It was mentioned earlier that the FBO industry went through a transitional stage from the early 1980s through the mid1990s wherein mergers and failures were the rule. By the mid1990s, NATA statistics showed a drop in FBOs from a high of more than 10,000 to fewer than 5,000 with dire predictions of "2,000 in 2000" if something did not change. But something did change. The U.S. economy remained strong during the latter half of the 1990s. The General Aviation Revitalization Act (GARA) was passed; Cessna resumed production of single-engine aircraft; new models entered the market; and fractional ownership all served to increase aircraft sales. These factors have led to a stabilization in the FBO industry with the number now between 3,440 and 3,900.

Historically, FBOs have been driven by the rate of new aircraft deliveries. The explosive growth in FBOs and other industry segments during the 1970s was led by new aircraft sales. The contraction in the number of FBOs in the 1980s and early 1990s again reflected the rate of new aircraft sales. Present, but not visible in new aircraft delivery statistics, was a growing trend on the part of airframe manufacturers to seek after-market work such as repair, overhaul, and maintenance including refurbishing, painting, interior, and avionics work. In the past, this work was almost entirely the province of independent FBOs, modification centers, and maintenance facilities. This trend began in the early 1980s as aircraft sales declined and manufacturers looked to other markets to supplement declining revenues and profits.

Complying with the myriad federal, state, and local regulations has also added to the cost structure of many FBOs. Some of these costs include those arising from security requirements, fuel flowage fees, and Superfund. Many FBOs also incur costs in order to conform to EPA underground storage tank regulations. Added to these fees and charges are the rising product costs, including large increases in Jet-A and 100 low-lead fuels in recent years. Insurance premiums have also begun to rise since the fiercely competitive rates offered during the late 1980s to mid1990s. These trends may add such incremental costs to smaller or marginally profitable FBOs that they will fail. The larger FBOs, by their very nature, capital base and size, are better able to absorb these costs.

The entry of airframe manufacturers has impacted those FBOs that in the past had derived significant income from completions, modifications, maintenance, and parts. New aircraft completions were profitable business with significant margins available on material content and with somewhat lower margins on interior and paint. Now virtually all of the business jet manufacturers have in-house completion capability. At the same time, manufacturers have been able to extend warranty periods due to improved quality. Some manufacturers now offer inclusive long-term maintenance and parts packages with the purchase of the aircraft. This further erodes one of the FBO's traditional market opportunities.

Another trend has been the move towards corporate self-fueling. Information collected by *FBO Magazine* shows that close to 40 percent of the airports surveyed permit self-fueling and over 20 percent of the airports surveyed actually use self-fueling. Because most FBOs derive the highest percentage of their income from fuel service activities, this trend is very alarming. Corporate self-fueling is justified by the corporate operator because their into-plane "cost" may be less than 50 percent of their neighboring FBO's retail fuel price. Ironically, that same corporate operator, when a transient, expects their destination FBO to have ground transportation, catering service, fuel trucks, line persons, lounges, telephones, and other services ready 24 hours a day. The host FBO now depends on retail fuel sales to pay for these services even if the transient purchases little or no fuel. These market forces will lead to a diversification of services on a pay-as-you-go basis. The purchase of fuel cannot remain the sole currency of the transient aircraft. Actually, this may be beneficial for both buyer and seller. A fairly priced menu of services allows the FBO to recognize and deal with the consequences of tankering, self-fueling, and fuel discounting. It also allows customers to buy what they need while not appearing to subsidize other transients.

Establishing an FBO

The simplest form of a fixed base operator is the flight instructor who owns an airplane and is in business independently. The only reason this person is in business at all is due to enthusiasm about flying. Then, take the single flight instructor operation, add satisfied customers, and let the business grow and expand. A second aircraft is added. The instructor has the start of a "fleet." While the instructor is flying one plane, the other remains on the ground. At this point, another pilot should be hired as a part-time instructor. Even with such simple acquisitions, business is suddenly becoming more complex. Now there is a payroll with tax deductions, additional insurance for the second plane, cost of maintenance of both planes, and hangar or tie-down charges.

The flying business, however, keeps both pilots and planes busy. The instructor begins to think further. By leasing a hangar and hiring a mechanic, the operation could handle its own maintenance, and then take in other work for additional income. Soon, in this oversimplification of FBO growth, the enterprise is generating more work for more people, and paying wages that directly or indirectly contribute to the economy of the community.

Another example is the FBO at a major airport with an executive aircraft terminal which is the base for general aviation aircraft, as well as scheduled and charter air carriers. Computerized weather information and direct phones to flight service for additional briefing and the filing of flight plans are available. Pilot lounges have high-speed Internet, printers, and multifunction fax/copy/scan machines.

The firm has contracts with some scheduled airlines for fueling, cleaning, and supplying turbine-starting equipment to jet-powered aircraft. It operates a helicopter for charter/lease, and light aircraft for air taxi. Aircraft maintenance is offered by the same operator, as well as avionics services, and an aircraft interior shop. The owner-manager holds FAA repair station certificates for various categories of large and small aircraft.

The operation described here is obviously on a large scale. However, it was developed rather speedily at a time when the airport had decided to expand and upgrade its facilities.

Regardless of whether an FBO starts on a small or a large scale, its success will largely depend on how it plans for the future and responds to changing conditions. As the scope of services offered by the typical fixed base operator grows, technical aviation knowledge will continue to be important, but will become secondary to other qualifications needed to manage any successful enterprise. Management will have less direct contact with the aviation activities, and concern with running the FBO and problem-solving activities which accompany the growth of any business.

Legal Structure

The manner in which these various FBOs can be organized also varies. By selecting the correct legal structure, the owner(s) of the FBO can enjoy tax savings and increased profit, provide for orderly growth of the business, and plan for eventual ownership changes. Although the three main types of organization are discussed below, it is prudent to consult on any business start-up issues with competent attorneys and tax advisors. A business can be organized using one of three main forms: (a) Sole proprietorship, (b) Partnership, and (c) Corporation.

Sole Proprietorship

The Sole Proprietor is an individual who owns and operates the business. In community property states, the spouse also has an ownership interest.

Advantages include:

- Ease of formation and dissolution
- Sole ownership of profits
- Control and decision making vested in one owner
- Flexibility
- Relative freedom from regulation and special taxation

Disadvantages include:

- Unlimited personal liability for business debts and liabilities
- Unstable business life, solely dependent on the health of the sole owner
- Difficulty in acquiring capital
- Relative lack of additional expertise and alternative perspectives

Partnership

A Partnership is an association of two or more individuals for business purposes. In a best effort to avoid the typical conflict associated with numerous partners, it is best to execute a written Articles of Partnership prior to legally creating the business. These articles will typically address the duration of the agreement, nature of the partner's involvement with the business, how capital and ongoing expenses will be handled, the manner in which losses and profits will be shared, and the manner in which disputes will be settled. It is also recommended that each partner be subjected to an intensive background, credit, and character investigation to minimize any potential problems with this form of organization.

Advantages include:

- Relative ease of organization
- Minimum capital required
- More capital available
- Broader management base and continuity

Disadvantages include:

- Conflicts between partners
- Less flexibility due to need for agreement among partners
- Unlimited liability, as with sole proprietorship
- Size limitations
- Capital restrictions
- Firm bound by actions of only one partner
- Difficulty of transferring partnership interest

Corporation

The corporation has a separate and distinct legal life from its members and is an artificial being existing only in contemplation of the law. Corporations are typically formed under the authority of state governments. Although the state requirements vary, the formation of a corporation usually begins by filing an Articles of Incorporation with a state's Division of Corporations. Some states are more corporation-friendly; thus, Delta Air Lines is incorporated in the state of Delaware, even though the corporate offices are in Atlanta, Georgia. A company must have a registered agent in each state in which they conduct business.

There are two main options available for forming a corporation. A company may be formed as either a C corp or an S corp. These are differences recognized by the Internal Revenue Service (IRS) and allow smaller corporations the opportunity to experience tax advantages by avoiding the double taxation associated with C corporations. Double taxation occurs when corporate net income is taxed and then stock dividends and individual salaries are also taxed. The S corp can avoid this and allow shareholders to offset business losses against other income by forming as a Subchapter S corporation with the IRS. Not all corporations are eligible, however. The corporation must have fewer than 10 shareholders, all of whom are individuals or estates, there must not be nonresident alien shareholders, there must be only one class of outstanding stock, all shareholders must consent to filing as a Subchapter S corp, and a specific portion of the corporation's income must be derived from active business rather than from enumerated passive investments.

Advantages of incorporating include:

- Limitation of the stockholder's liability to the amount invested, with respect to business losses
- Ownership is readily transferable
- Separate legal existence, even with the demise of all current owners
- Relative ease of obtaining capital
- Tax advantages
- Permits large size
- Easy expansion
- Delegated authority
- Potentially broad management base

Disadvantages include:

- Close government regulation
- Cost and complexity to set up
- Activities limited by charter
- Manipulation of minority stockholders
- Double taxation—once on corporate income and again on individual salaries and stock dividends

A final form of legal structure is the LLC. Although many consider this a Limited Liability Corporation, it actually refers to a Limited Liability Company. It offers limited liability to its owners, is similar to a corporation, and is often a more flexible form of ownership, especially suitable for smaller companies with a limited number of owners. Unlike a regular corporation, a limited liability company with one member may be treated as a disregarded entity by the IRS. A limited liability company with multiple members may choose, generally at the time that the new entity applies for a US federal taxpayer ID number, to be treated for U.S. federal taxation purposes as a partnership, as a C corporation, or (if it is otherwise eligible) as an S corporation. An LLC can elect to be member-managed or manager-managed (information from http://www.irs.gov and http://en.wikipedia.org).

Advantages of an LLC include:

- Much less administrative paperwork and record keeping than a corporation.
- Avoid double taxation.
- Limited liability, meaning that the owners of the LLC, called "members," are protected from some liability for acts and debts of the LLC, but are still responsible for any debts beyond the fiscal capacity of the entity.
- An LLC can elect to be taxed as a sole proprietor, partnership, S corporation, or C corporation, providing much flexibility.

Disadvantages include:

- Many states levy a franchise tax or capital values tax on LLCs for the privilege of that company having limited liability.
- It may be more difficult to raise financial capital for an LLC as investors may be more comfortable investing funds in the better-understood corporate form with a view toward an eventual IPO.
- The LLC form of organization is relatively new, and as such, some states do not fully treat LLCs in the same manner as corporations for liability purposes.
- The principals of LLCs use many different titles—e.g., member, manager, managing member, managing director, chief executive officer, president, and partner. As such, it can be difficult to determine who actually has the authority to enter into a contract on the LLC's behalf.

Analyzing the Market and Selecting a Location

Once the legal structure is selected, and before deciding upon a location for a fixed base operation, a study of the potential market is needed. The process of studying the market is called market analysis. Information sought in a market analysis for a fixed base operator (or any kind of business) includes the number of potential customers, where they are located, and what kind and what quantity of business they are likely to bring to the firm.

In studying the potential market, it is necessary to recognize that the aviation industry as a whole has been undergoing tremendous and rapid change. The introduction of Very Light Jets (VLJs), Light Sport Aircraft (LSA), and other innovative technologies have affected the kinds of products and services the flying public has come to expect.

One of the first questions in analyzing the potential market is what the firm has to offer the flying public to meet current demand. In other words, why is another FBO needed? Next, the firm must consider how useful and how popular its offerings are going to be with the people in the community in which it plans to locate.

Other important market factors to be considered are population, weather conditions, income levels, the social and economic nature of the community, ground facilities to support efficient use of the aircraft, industrial developments and trends of the community, agricultural activities, traffic problems, and other ground transportation problems in the area. For example, weather conditions are important to any flight-related business. Is the area subject to snow on the ground for several months during the year? Does it rain almost steadily for months at a time? Will fog close the airport for long periods? These are important questions which must be considered by prospective FBO owners. A check with the FAA and National

Climatic Data Center can determine the prevailing weather and the number of flying days in the past five years, which would indicate the number of business days the FBO can expect during an average weather year.

The Community

The characteristics of the community will affect an operation. Is general aviation an established fixture of the community, or is it still considered a rich man's pastime? Is the airport on established commercial routes? Will there be an opportunity for charter flights to neighboring communities? These and other questions concerning the community should be answered in any complete market analysis.

Activities such as agriculture, aerial survey, and aerial exploration are also covered in a market analysis. Occupations and activities such as these provide increased opportunities for charter operations. On the other hand, if such activities are not carried on to any extent, a firm must determine whether the other business opportunities are such that they compensate for this deficiency.

Industrial and business activities constitute another area to be examined in the market analysis. Many businesses use the airplane as a daily part of their operations, while other corporations fly personnel to and from conferences to conserve time. If these business practices do not exist in the location under consideration, it may be a sign that the firm will have to depend upon other sources of revenue.

The market for an FBO is not just one group, but many segments, and each requires a separate analysis. Major segments include, but are not limited to, the following:

1. Business and corporate market
2. Private or pleasure market
3. Agricultural market
4. Government aircraft sales and service market
5. Transient potential
6. Other operations or airline markets

Each of these areas should be thoroughly explored before a location is selected, and regardless of the size of the FBO, possible sources of business must be considered regarding their potential. A large percentage of these possibilities should look promising or the chances for success will be slim.

Site Selection

The process of site selection should start with the choice of a geographical area. Having decided on a general area, the next step involves the selection of a specific airport. In making this choice, it is important to survey the competition of other FBOs and find out how well they are doing. A firm must also determine whether to locate on a private or publicly owned field.

In comparison with most other businesses, site selection for a fixed base operator can be a difficult process because suitable locations are limited. A firm must think in terms of the entire airport and its future development plans. Moving into an existing facility has good and bad points. Choosing an established facility is certainly beneficial, but if the airport master plan calls for relocation of the center of activities, leaving the FBO isolated, the result could be disastrous. Additionally, the firm must consider why the established facility is currently vacant. The location on the airport has a significant effect on business both immediately and in the future. A few key factors include the distance to fueling facilities (if this service is not provided); distance to the main terminal area (especially if no restaurant is available); distance from the nearest competitor (to avoid customer confusion); and ease of access to and from public roads. Consider also that the operator of an airport may not desire or have space for a new FBO. A firm often must consider whether to buy or rent the facility site. Do financial arrangements make it advisable to own the property, or is it more desirable to lease? The firm must consider whether or not the site is likely to be permanent. Being forced to vacate on short notice could be a great inconvenience. These terms would be negotiated and spelled out in the lease agreement.

Another consideration in deciding whether or not to buy an existing facility is the matter of who the predecessors were. If a similar fixed base operation existed, what was its reputation? A firm must consider whether its reputation will be favorably or unfavorably affected by the former tenant.

Getting Assistance

Individuals considering the establishment of an FBO typically need two main forms of assistance: (a) informational and (b) financial. Informational assistance can obtained from a number of sources including local chambers of commerce, airport boards and local airport advisory committees, Aircraft Owners and Pilots Association (AOPA), Federal Aviation Administration (FAA), Internal Revenue Service (IRS), National Air Transport Association (NATA), National Association of State Aviation Officials (NASAO), and the Small Business Administration (SBA). Local chambers of commerce typically provide detailed information on the local economy and businesses in the local area. The airport governing board and any airport advisory committee and their past meeting minutes will prove helpful in learning more about the airport's business and any concerns that the community voices about the airport and/or businesses operating on the airport. AOPA is the main voice for GA aircraft owners and pilots and this organization is a wealth of information on issues affecting the GA industry. Likewise, the FAA and its Advisory Circulars associated with issues such as minimum standards, aircraft fueling, and towing will be quite helpful sources of information for individuals starting an FBO (see Appendices). Additionally, various services can be rendered by the FAA, including those of the FAA District Airport Engineer. However, because of the small staff of the airport district offices, its services are usually limited to preliminary discussions and advice and do not include the solution of complex operational problems. The Internal Revenue Service has many publications geared toward small businesses, which will assist entrepreneurs with issues such as establishing their legal structure and filing appropriate taxes. The National Air Transportation Association is an organization with a heart for corporate aviation. This organization makes available a large number of resources to members and nonmembers. Most helpful to FBOs is the Safety First line service training program. NASAO will assist with providing contact information for state aviation officials, which will be specifically knowledgeable on state aviation issues. Frequently, it may be necessary to obtain certification for a new FBO from the state aviation office. The airport manager or owner will, of course, have valuable information concerning the airport—statistics on aircraft movements, plans for future expansion of the facility, and much more information that will directly affect any proposed business. Lastly, the Small Business Administration provides a great deal of guidance to those establishing small businesses.

The second, and typically most important, type of assistance needed by those establishing an FBO is financial assistance. This is discussed in detail in chapter 14, Financial Planning. For now, the reader should understand that debt and equity are the two possible sources of start-up capital. Also known as seed funding, sufficient start-up capital is imperative for the business to have a chance at success. Debt (in the form of loans, bonds, lines of credit) must be paid back, whereas equity does not. Why wouldn't everyone use equity financing to fund a new business? Equity is oftentimes difficult to secure, but also, the return for investors providing equity capital is a share in the ownership of the business. The individuals establishing an FBO must thoughtfully consider these two forms of financial assistance and make a strategic choice.

Facilities

After considering all airport requirements, the firm can narrow its sights to specific facilities for its own operation. While the facilities chosen will largely depend upon the size of the FBO and services offered, there are three categories: aircraft storage areas, customer or public areas, and employee or work areas.

In a small operation, these facilities can easily be grouped together in one multi-purpose structure. Often, a hangar can be converted, by a little simple carpentry, into office space, as well as storage and work areas. If the firm is planning a larger operation, it may have several large hangars, 20 or 30 smaller T-hangars, equipment and maintenance hangars, and a separate office building.

Aircraft Storage Areas

1. **Outdoor tie-down area.** Is the area adequate for the expected number of aircraft to be based at the airport as well as for transient aircraft? Are the tie-downs spaced properly? Are the parking spaces clearly marked? Can the area be policed and kept clean easily? These are just some of the questions that must be considered regarding this important category.
2. **T-hangars, design, and site.** There are literally hundreds of designs and types of T-hangars available to meet a particular FBO's needs. Consideration must also be given to having an adequate number placed in good locations convenient for customers.
3. **Large hangar storage.** A large hangar is one that can hold many aircraft and can also be a combination hangar—both for storing aircraft and for maintenance work.

Customer (or Public) Facilities

These facilities are designed primarily for customer use and should always be kept neat and clean. The first requirement is the reception area, with a place for registration if necessary, and a pilots' service desk. Next is the pilot ready room, with maps, weather information, phones, and Internet. Although this need not be a completely separate room, having separate room is always an attractive feature. It must be fully equipped and functional from the pilot's standpoint. The exact location of maps, forms, weather information, and assorted pilot aids should be carefully planned. Adequate space must be provided for pilots to spread out sectionals, approach plates, and other items to properly plan a trip.

Other facilities include:

1. **Pilot or crew sleeping quarters.** This may be considered a luxury facility, but is certainly important if the firm expects to attract corporate business.
2. **Rest rooms.** Clean and modern rest-room facilities including showers and a dressing area with lockers are a decided plus factor.
3. **Waiting lounge.** People are always waiting for other people at any transportationfacility, and airports are no exception. Whether traveling by airline or business aircraft, individuals appreciate a comfortable waiting area or lounge.
4. **Classroom(s).** Providing classroom(s) is important, especially if offering flight instruction. This facility should be neat and well equipped.
5. **Visitors' conference room.** The larger corporate aircraft

are actually flying offices. Conferences and meetings are often held while the plane is en route. For firms using intermediate-sized business aircraft or for those firms meeting customers, a conference room can be a real asset. This facility can also be used by the FBO for meetings with employees and customers when it is not scheduled to be used by corporate aircraft users.

6. **Recreational facilities.** Consideration should be given to whether outdoor or indoor recreational facilities would be appropriate for the kind of customer the FBO expects to attract.
7. **Display case or room.** Whether it is simply a display case or an entire room devoted to pilot supplies and accessories, this can be a highly profitable area for an FBO.

Employee (or Work) Facilities

The principal areas used by employees are as follows:

1. **Offices as required.**
2. **Line crew ready room.** This room should have a view of and be easily accessible to the transient aircraft ramp area.
3. **Maintenance shops.** This area should include at least one small office for mechanics to order parts, write up job tickets, and talk to customers.
4. **Parts and supply storage.** Parts and supplies require adequate shelves for access and inventory purposes. A separate storage area should be provided to place cartons, damaged parts, and other materials that can clutter up the main part of the hangar.
5. **Fueling facilities.** Normally, this is one of the easiest of all facilities to plan because of the readily available assistance from the oil companies. The major decision here is whether to have trucks or a fixed fueling facility. Both have advantages but this decision largely depends upon the FBO's location on the airport and the airport's minimum standards.

Mobile equipment has the advantage of being more flexible in allowing the line personnel to reach aircraft at various locations on the ramp area. Generally mobile equipment enables an FBO to stock a greater variety of octanes or jet fuel, if these are required.

On the other hand, the initial cost and the maintenance cost of mobile equipment is higher than that of fixed fueling equipment. Moreover, with mobile equipment, there is always the possibility of accidents, for which insurance must be carried. Also, evaporation and stock losses are higher with mobile equipment. For the average FBO, stationary facilities are dependable and economical to install and also require less personnel to operate.

6. **Wash ramp.** A specific site with good drainage should be provided for washing aircraft. The size of the area largely depends upon the expected size of the aircraft to be washed and specific airport environmental requirements.
7. **Vehicle storage areas.** Gasoline trucks, courtesy station wagons, even scooters can get in the way and cause accidents unless they are parked in a designated area.
8. **Employee showers and locker room.** This may seem like a luxury facility but it is found at many successful FBOs and greatly enhances employee relations.

Equipment

The equipment needed is related to the services provided, but the following list gives an idea of the major items included.

1. **Fueling trucks.** The number of trucks and type of fuel required will depend entirely on the nature and volume of business expected. Typically, a minimum of one Avgas and one Jet-A truck would be expected.
2. **Other vehicles.** These include station wagons, utility trucks, scooters, and trailers or carts.
3. **Housekeeping needs.** Buckets, mops, brooms, carpentry tools, ladders, rags, and dust equipment fall into this category.
4. **Shop tools.** The type of aircraft to be worked on will determine the shop tooling needs. Appropriate cabinets and hanging devices for storing tools must also be considered.
5. **Supplies.** This area includes those items intended for resale and operating supplies used exclusively by the FBO.
6. **Office equipment.** Included are desks, chairs, word processors, file and storage cabinets, copying equipment, and desk supplies.

Aircraft

Certainly one of the most important areas to consider is the type and quantity of aircraft in inventory. This may include aircraft intended for sale or operation, or both. The operational inventory would include aircraft to be used for charter, flight training, and other commercial work. Obviously, this category can prove expensive and may benefit from a staggered or multi-year phased plan for growing the aircraft inventory. For instance, an FBO may purchase two single-engine piston aircraft for flight training in the first year, add a twin-engine aircraft for flight training the following year, and add a turboprop for charter purposes in year three.

Chains Versus Independents

To many FBOs, the question of remaining independent or becoming affiliated with a chain is an important decision to be made during the 2000s. Which of these choices can increase the odds for surviving in today's industry?

The best year for the general aviation industry from an aircraft sales standpoint was 1978, when 17,811 general aviation aircraft were sold. From an FBO-industry historical perspective, of the very prosperous FBO industry years during the 1970s and early 1980s, any lack of attention or responsiveness to a specific problem area within the industry, or within an individual organization, would not necessarily have been catastrophic. During this period, an FBO could easily compensate for oversights in any one problem area by increasing product or service margins, or increasing volume.

This all changed from the early 1980s through the mid 1990s. It was a different marketplace and operating environment in which there were dramatic declines in aircraft sales, fuel revenues, aircraft maintenance income, and revenues from the ancillary services provided by FBO organizations. During recent years, many FBOs have realized the importance of becoming part of a larger organization.

The most significant motivation for an FBO to become affiliated with a chain is the benefits and cost savings derived from marketing and identity and the resulting economies of scale inherent to such an organization. Belonging to a national or international chain is not for all FBOs. The chains are very selective, as are many independent owner/operators. The cost/benefit relationship may not be viable for some smaller FBOs. The approach of most chains is to support an individual operator as an independent business that has access to a well-financed and professionally developed marketing and identity program. This offers the best of both worlds as operators receive assistance from the chain in marketing, while making their own decisions regarding operation of FBOs.

The question of independence or affiliation can be a difficult decision for many FBO operators because of self-esteem issues that founders and/or operating management have developed from having survived and even prospered during the previous tenuous periods in the evolution of the industry. For the most part, the strength and determination of many FBOs have given them the feeling that they can go it alone; however, this approach may not always be the most prudent.

By examining some of the basic issues when evaluating the affiliation or independence question, readers can draw their own conclusions. Some considerations for remaining independent include the following:

1. A desire to continue to operate as an independent business, thereby ensuring control when making marketing, management, and operational decisions.
2. Operating an FBO that has a sound reputation for quality services and support, and a highly established and recognizable identity/image.
3. Established and profitable FBOs that would have little or no potential incremental revenue impact from increased marketing exposure or networking with affiliated organizations.
4. Operating an FBO in a strong geographical location or established destination marketplace which would not benefit from increased network exposure.

Conversely, the process for deciding if a program of affiliation would be desirable for an FBO would include the examination of these same issues from a slightly different perspective:

1. The desire to operate with the support of a larger organization and to have access to a variety of resources and expertise.
2. Limited advertising budget and the need to gain national exposure to increase market share and sales volumes.
3. Being located in an underexposed geographical area. Need for national marketing and networked transient clientele, with additional high cost/benefit exposure to the marketplace to develop a larger customer base.
4. Desire to work with other FBOs with similar interests and operating objectives who are also affiliated with the franchise organization through an advisory counsel approach.

Although they are not franchise organizations in the literal meaning of the word, several oil companies also offer marketing programs for their dealers to stress the advantages of their programs for promoting their brand products. Exxon/Mobil—with close to 50 locations in the U. S. and Canada—was the first to develop this concept over 20 years ago and continues to add new designated dealers each year. Phillips also has its "super dealer" program called Aviation Performance Center (APC). About 80 of the 900 Phillips dealers are APCs. Therefore, it stands to reason that FBOs seeking broader identity or deeper market penetration for their fuel products and services may be well served to consider the support available as an authorized franchisee or specialized dealer.

Signature Flight Support, a BBA Aviation company, is the world's largest fixed base operator and distribution network for business aviation services. Headquartered in Orlando, Florida, Signature currently operates at more than 80 locations in the United States, Europe, South America, Africa and Asia. Signature Flight Support's vision and mission are accomplished through the following core values: integrity, responsibility, safety, service, people, and performance (information from http://www.signatureflight.com).

Million Air, a very successful chain with over 30 locations, identifies five primary benefits in joining a chain. They are (1) name recognition, (2) image enhancement, (3) value for advertising dollars spent (when cost of franchising is considered advertisement), (4) consistent service levels and product quality, and (5) standardized training and the potential to attract higher quality employees.

In any organized marketing program such as Signature's, Million Air's, or Exxon/Mobil's Avitat network, there is a large pool of ideas from which to draw, all within the same organization, all having the same objectives. There is no question that the chain concept has not only improved the outward appearance and perception of Million Air FBOs, but has markedly improved market share and sales volume for these operators as well.

The success enjoyed by Million Air franchisees is basically the same as that of any high-quality FBO. Operators are allowed maximum decision making in running their businesses. However, in order to maintain the integrity of the system, there are specific requirements for standardized identity signage and uniforms, and certain other operations and procedures are mandatory from a customer service standpoint.

By comparison, participants in the Avitat, APC, and other similar branding programs also have to meet the personnel and graphic identity standards similar to those required in the Million Air program—and all enjoy the benefit of cooperative advertising and network identity.

Regardless of an operator's decision concerning independence or affiliation, these challenging economic times mandate innovative and nontraditional approaches for increasing revenues in today's declining marketplace.

The theory of maximum competition within the FBO industry was once held as indisputable dogma by the FAA and many airport management communities. However, this theory is being challenged everyday on the basis of pure economic survival. Competitors today may become partners tomorrow. The decision to remain independent or align with an external support program and identity (franchise) system may be clearer as dollar/valuc tradeoffs become more important.

In many business dilemmas, quick fix solutions, while appealing at first, may ultimately result in having to return to the basics of the business. Nevertheless, from a fundamental perspective, the decision of independence or affiliation may apply now more than ever.

An individual operator's choice to remain independent or align with some form of franchise or other affiliation structure is an important decision. However, one thing is clear: the once thriving dynamo of general aviation after-market sales has virtually ceased to produce the dramatic annual increases in sales volumes for products and services that the industry witnessed during the 1970s and early 1980s.

KEY TERMS

Major fixed base operators
Medium-sized fixed base operators
Small fixed base operators
Specialized aviation service businesses
Corporate self-fueling
Sole proprietorship
Partnership
Corporation
Market Analysis
Site selection
FBO chain

REVIEW QUESTIONS

1. How was the term "fixed base operator" coined? What are FBOs similar to?
2. Approximately how many FBOs are there in the United States? How are they categorized? Discuss some of the problems experienced by small fixed base operators. What are specialized aviation service businesses?
3. Discuss some recent trends affecting FBOs.
4. In establishing an FBO, what are the advantages and disadvantages of the three main forms of legal structure? Describe the importance of analyzing the market and selecting a location. What is market analysis? Discuss the importance of the community. Describe the factors which must be considered in selecting a site for an FBO. Where can a prospective FBO get assistance?
5. List the basic facilities found in the following areas: aircraft storage, customer (or public) facilities, and employee (or work) facilities. List the basic equipment needed to get started.
6. What specific facilities and equipment are needed for an FBO?
7. Why have many independent FBOs joined a chain? Why would an FBO choose to remain independent? Give some advantages and disadvantages of joining a chain.

REFERENCES

Cohen, David. *Fixed Base Operator's Management Handbook.* Basin, WY: Aviation Maintenance Publishers, Inc., 1980.

Rodwell, J. F. *Essentials of Aviation Management: A guide for aviation service businesses* (6th ed.). Dubuque, IA: Kendall Hunt Publishing Co., 2003.

SCENARIOS

1. Your FBO is located at a small GA airport and is currently the only FBO on the field. At present, you do not offer Jet-A fuel. Your AvGas sales have always been your highest source of revenue, and your airport generally sees very little, if any, turbine (jet or turboprop) traffic. This is

mainly due to your airport's short, single runway (3,000 feet). However, you have been reading about the new Very Light Jets (VLJ) and recently observed a presentation by a new air taxi operator utilizing Eclipse 500 VLJs. This operator indicated they would begin serving airports in your state in the near future. However, your FBO is not currently prepared to handle these VLJs (mainly because you do not have Jet fuel). How do you evaluate the need to begin offering Jet fuel? What must you consider? In essence, will your FBO choose to cater to VLJs?

2. Your best friend and you decide to start an FBO together. A Request for Proposals (RFP) was recently issued by a local GA airport to find an FBO operator to take over the existing airport-managed FBO on the field. You closely examine this opportunity, realize that it is the only FBO on the field, has a solid customer base, and is located in a growing area and at a popular GA airport. As you both work on your Proposal, you must consider how you will legally structure your business. Which of the three forms of business structure will you choose and why?
3. You have been working at an FBO for five years. You started out in line service and then spent time in Administration as the Director of Line Service. You feel you know the FBO business inside and out. Thus, you have decided to start your own FBO. After analyzing the market, you have decided upon two possible locations for your FBO. The first location is at a small GA airport where there is currently no FBO. This airport is not very active and only has 10 T-hangars, but you feel there is potential for an FBO to offer fueling, aircraft rental, and flight instruction. Your second option is to join an existing FBO at a larger GA airport where there are 60 based aircraft, and an active GA pilot community. Of course, if you select this location, you'll have direct competition starting on the first day of business. Which location do you choose and why? The smaller GA airport with fewer tenants, but with possibly greater growth potential, or the larger GA airport with many more tenants, but also with direct competition?
4. You recently prepared a bid to operate an FBO at a busy GA airport near your hometown. Your firm was selected and you are excited as you and a long-time friend begin this venture together. Fortunately, you'll be housed in an existing terminal building, which has a community hangar. What additional facilities and equipment might you need? You do plan to offer flight instruction (as your friend is a CFII), but how many and what typre of aircraft should you acquire? What type of customer/public facilities will you need? What about employee facilities?
5. You have owned a small FBO for the past 10 years. It has been successful, but you feel revenues could always be higher. You are considering adopting an aggressive marketing campaign when you are approached by a nationwide FBO chain. They would like you to consider joining their chain. This would require you pay franchise fees and sacrifice a percentage of your gross revenues. At the same time, however, you would have access to their name (brand recognition) and national marketing, as well as standardized procedures and improved efficiencies. Do you remain independent or become part of the chain?What is your thought process in making this decision?

Notes

Chapter 4
Line Service

OUTLINE

OBJECTIVES

At the end of this chapter, you should be able to:

- Identify the role of a line service specialist.
- Understand the importance of safety for the line service specialist.
- Provide directions from the pilot's point of view.
- Convert Local time to Zulu time.
- Recite the phonetic alphabet.
- Describe the components of an aircraft.
- Describe the various classes of fires and properly use a fire extinguisher.
- Understand the refueling process for piston, turboprop, and jet aircraft.
- Describe various types of fuel contamination.
- Describe the types of aviation fuel and their colors.
- Discuss the proper manner in which to tow an aircraft.
- Recognize proper marshalling signals.
- Describe the many possible services of the line service specialist.

Most Visible Aspect of FBO

The most visible and important aspect of the operation of an FBO can be characterized simply as "line service." The "line" refers to the aircraft flight line, which is active with aircraft taxiing inbound and outbound, passengers and pilots walking to and from aircraft, aircraft being towed, aircraft being fueled, and aircraft being marshaled to their parking area. When you visit an FBO and take a look out the terminal building window, you are looking at the line; this is the most visible aspect of operating an FBO. It is imperative for the beginning FBO manager to fully understand the line before being tasked with managing this aspect of an FBO's operation.

Role of Line Service Specialist

The role of the line service specialist cannot be overstated. Indeed, these individuals are typically the first contact a flight crew has with an FBO. As such, these individuals must be well-trained and act with professionalism at all times. Specifically, they must place a high priority on safety. If the FBO is not operated in a safe manner, financial difficulty will likely result. Additionally, the line service specialist must display positive work habits and treat everyone, whether the pilot of a Cessna 152 or a Cessna Citation, with courtesy and respect. A wise line service specialist realizes that the weekend pilot of a Cessna 152 may be the Chief Pilot for a large corporation.

Although it may not be obvious to the beginning line service specialist, this position plays a large role in supporting the overall health of the FBO. First, the line service specialist pumps many gallons of fuel on a daily basis. Fuel sales, for many FBOs, are the largest single revenue source. The safety posture exhibited by line service specialists leads to a safer FBO, fewer incidents, and lower insurance premiums.

Lastly, line service specialists are the front door to most FBOs, which allows these individuals to single handedly make a positive or negative first impression on customers flying into the facility.

Knowledge Base

As with any position within the aviation industry, it is imperative that line service specialists posses the knowledge necessary to successfully perform their job. The FBO employing line service specialists without this specialized knowledge is making a mistake which may have serious consequences. On the other hand, wise FBO managers realize the specialized nature of the business and insist on hiring line service specialists with at least basic aviation knowledge and then utilizing the resources necessary to provide additional on-the-job training. In this way, individuals in these positions feel more competent and are able to positively contribute to the success of the organization.

Safety

Prior to first stepping onto the ramp, the line service specialist must be fully aware of the hazards involved. Airport ramps contain jet blast, spinning propellers, helicopter main and tail rotor blades, tie down cables, chocks, protruding aircraft parts, high levels of noise, and vehicles moving in all directions. Lives have been lost due to careless behavior on the ramp. First and foremost, safety must be a way of life for the line service specialist. Keep your head up and your eyes moving. Many airport employees are taught to keep their "head on a swivel" to allow the early detection of an oncoming hazard. This is good advice and practiced by the experienced line service specialist. Line service specialists must also protect themselves with gloves, hearing protection, and proper clothing. Line service specialists in many parts of the country would likely add sunscreen, a cap, and sunglasses to that list as well. Safe line service specialists don't rush into performing a task. Although time will be of the essence, it is more important to be safe and perform a task properly than to speed things up and make mistakes. Lastly, a beginning line service specialist will ask his supervisor if he has questions about any task. Accuracy is important and verification of instructions may be necessary.

Directional Terminology

One of the most basic pieces of knowledge with which a line service specialist must be armed is that of directional terminology. For instance, if the pilot requests to have maintenance check on the oil pressure in the number one engine, what must be done? Which is the number one engine? Aircraft engines are numbered from the pilot's point of view, left to right. Thus, the number one engine is the engine to the pilot's left as he or she is seated in the cockpit. On a Boeing 747, engine number one is the outboard engine to the pilot's left, while engine number four is the outboard engine to the pilot's right. Don't be mistaken, FBOs may actually serve a B747 on a charter operation. Air Force One (usually a B747) typically utilizes an FBO to ensure a more secure operation away from commercial airlines and their passengers.

All directional terminology is oriented from the pilot's point of view from the cockpit. For instance, the left wing is always the wing to the pilot's left. If a pilot calls inbound to ask for directions to the FBO, these directions must be provided from the pilot's point of view. By explaining that the FBO is "on the right as you taxi off the runway," the employee providing directions must be certain that this takes into consideration the active runway and the pilot's point of view.

Coordinated Universal Time

Yet another unique aspect of the aviation industry is the need to coordinate time on a worldwide basis. As one flight leaves New York and flies to London, it departs from one time zone, flies through several other time zones, and then lands in yet another. If time were not coordinated, this would really wreak havoc on flight times and on the job of the airline dispatcher. As a result, the aviation industry operates under coordinated universal time (UTC). Also designated as Greenwich Mean Time or Zulu time, this is the time at the meridian of the globe or zero degrees longitude, which passes through Greenwich, England.

To covert either from local time to UTC or vice versa, the rules shown in Table 4-1 must be followed. For example, if an airport is located in the Central Daylight Time zone, five hours must be added to local time to arrive at UTC. If it is 8:00AM local time, the addition of five hours results in 1:00PM, or more accurately, 1300(Z). As shown in this example, the aviation industry also operates on a 24-hour clock. Familiar to those in the military, the 24 hour clock contributes to the effectiveness of UTC. In order to convert regular time to the 24 hour clock, simply add the PM time to the 12:00. For instance, 6:00PM local time, when added to 12:00, results in 18:00. In aviation, times are typically represented without the colon or AM or PM, which also signifies the 24 hour clock. Additionally, the letter in parentheses after the numbers will signify whether the time refers to local time (L) or Zulu (Z) time.

Phonetic Alphabet and Numbers

In addition to the unique way to signify time, aviation also has a unique alphabet, known as the phonetic alphabet. It is easy to discern if someone is in aviation when they say "B, as in Bravo." Otherwise, you'll likely hear, "B, as in Boy." It is

Table 4-1
To Convert to Coordinated Universal Time (UTC) from:

Atlantic Standard	Add 4 hours
Eastern Daylight	Add 4 hours
Eastern Standard	Add 5 hours
Central Daylight	Add 5 hours
Central Standard	Add 6 hours
Mountain Daylight	Add 6 hours
Mountain Standard	Add 7 hours
Pacific Daylight	Add 7 hours
Pacific Standard	Add 8 hours
British Columbia Daylight	Add 7 hours
British Columbia Standard	Add 8 hours
Alaska Daylight	Add 8 hours
Alaska Standard	Add 9 hours
Hawaii Standard	Add 10 hours

imperative for all line service personnel to memorize the phonetic alphabet. If not, it will likely lead to a recognition by others that an individual is not very knowledgeable of aviation and possibly lacks the skills and knowledge necessary to effectively perform the job of a line service specialist.

As shown in Table 4-2, each letter of the alphabet has a word associated with it. The use of this alphabet plays an important role in preventing miscommunication among pilots and air traffic control (ATC), pilots and FBO staff, etc. Typically, ATC and pilots will refer to their tail number (discussed next) as "November One Three Charlie Bravo Kilo." Without knowledge of the phonetic alphabet, this will leave an individual scratching her head. However, once the phonetic alphabet is memorized, it becomes a second language and is very effective at improving communication in aviation.

Likewise, a knowledgeable line service specialist will effectively communicate numbers (Table 4-2). A few rules are applicable. First, each number must be enunciated clearly. The number nine is spoken as "niner," and zero is spoken as "zero" rather than "oh." Numbers above 9,900 are spoken by saying each digit before the word "thousand." For instance, 13,000 is spoken as "one three thousand."

Tail Numbers

Every aircraft is registered in its country of ownership by the country's equivalent to the Federal Aviation Administration (FAA). As part of this registration, each aircraft has a given tail number, referred to as such because it is typically painted on the tail of the aircraft, either on the vertical stabilizer or the engine. As expected, whether it includes numbers

Table 4-2
International Phonetic Alphabet

Character	Telephony	Phonic (Pronunciation)
A	Alfa	AL FAH
B	Bravo	BRAH VOH
C	Charlie	CHAR LEE or SHAR LEE
D	Delta	DELL TAH
E	Echo	ECK OH
F	Foxtrot	FOKS TROT
G	Golf	GOLF
H	Hotel	HOH TEL
I	India	IN DEE AH
J	Juliett	JEW LEE ETT
K	Kilo	KEY LOH
L	Lima	LEE MAH
M	Mike	MIKE
N	November	NO VEM BER
O	Oscar	OSS CAH
P	Papa	PAH PAH
Q	Quebec	KEH BECK
R	Romeo	ROW ME OH
S	Sierra	SEE AIR RAH
T	Tango	TANG GO
U	Uniform	YOU NEE FORM or OO NEE FORM
V	Victor	VIKTAH
W	Wiskey	WISS KEY
X	Xray	ECKS RAY
Y	Yankee	YANG KEY
Z	Zulu	ZOO LOO
1	One	WUN
2	Two	TOO
3	Three	TREE
4	Four	FOW-er
5	Five	FIFE
6	Six	SIX
7	Seven	SEV-en
8	Eight	AIT
9	Nine	NIN-er
0	Zero	ZEE-RO

Adapted from FAA Aeronautical Information Manual.

Table 4-3
Country Registration Prefixes

Algeria	7T
Angola	D2
Antigua	V2
Argentina	LQ,LV
Aruba	P4
Australia	VH
Austria	OE
Bahamas	C6
Bahrain	A9
Bangladesh	S2,S3
Barbados	8P
Belgium	OO
Benin	TY
Bermuda	VRB
Bolivia	CP
Bosnia-Herzegovina	T9
Botswana	A2
Brazil	PP,PT
Brunei	V8
Bulgaria	LZ
Burkina Faso	XT
Burundi	9U
Cameroon	TJ
Canada	CF,CG
Cayman Islands	VR-C
Chad	TT
Chile	CC
Colombia	HK
Comoros	D6
Congo Republic	TN
Costa Rica	TI
Croatia	9A
Cyprus	5B
Czech Republic	OK
Denmark	OY
Djibouti	J2
Dominican Republic	HI
Ecuador	HC
Egypt	SU
Eire	EI
Eritrea	ER
Ethiopia	ET
Finland	OH
France	F
Gabon	TR
Germany	D
Ghana	9G
Greece	SX
Guatemala	TG
Guinea	3X
Honduras	HR
Hong Kong	VR-H
Hungary	HA
Iceland	TF
India	VT
Indonesia	PK
Iran	EP
Iraq	YI
Israel	4X
Italy	I
Ivory Coast	TU
Jamaica	6Y
Japan	JA
Jordan	JY
Kazakhstan	UN
Kenya	5Y
Kuwait	9K
Lebanon	OD
Liberia	EL
Libya	5A
Lithuania	LY
Luxembourg	LX
Macedonia	Z3
Madagascar	5R
Malawi	7Q
Malaysia	9M
Malta	9H
Mauritania	5T
Mexico	XA,XB,XC
Monaco	3A
Morocco	CN
Mozambique	C9
Myanmar	XY
Namibia	V5
Netherlands	PH
Netherlands Antilles	PJ
New Zealand	ZK
Niger	5U
Nigeria	N
Norway	LN
Oman	A4O
Pakistan	AP
Panama	HP
Papua New Guinea	P2
Paraguay	ZP
Peoples Republic of China	B,HY
Peru	OB
Philippines	RP
Poland	SP
Qatar	A7
Romania	YR
Russia	RA
Sao Tome	S9
Saudi Arabia	HZ
Senegal	6V
Singapore	9V
Slovakia	OM
Somalia	S5
South Africa	ZS
South Korea	HL
Spain	EC
Sri Lanka	4R
Sudan	ST
Swaziland	3D
Sweden	SE
Switzerland	HB
Syria	YK
Taiwan	B
Tanzania	5H
Thailand	HS
Togo	5V
Turkey	TC
Turkmenistan	EZ
Uganda	5X
Ukraine	UR
United Arab Emirates	A6
United kingdom	G
United States of America	N
Uruguay	CX
Venezuela	YV
Vietnam	VN
Yemen	7O
Yugoslavia	YU
Zaire	9Q
Zambia	9J
Zimbabwe	Z

or letters, the tail number is referred to using aviation speak (phonetic alphabet and numerals). Although tail numbers in the United States are referred to as "N-numbers," this is not true for any other country. Table 4-3 presents the registration prefixes from other countries. For instance, Canada, rather than having "N-numbers," has "CF-numbers."

Aircraft Components

It is also important for a line service specialist to fully understand the typical components of an aircraft. Although most anyone interested in aviation has a basic understanding of these components, they are presented here for clarification purposes.

Engine or Powerplant

The engines or powerplants on an aircraft are the driving force behind powered flight. These may consist of an engine-propeller combination, or in the case of jet aircraft, just the engine itself. In addition to the engine, propeller-driven aircraft have a cowling (used to enclose the engine and provide cooling by ducting the air around the engine) and a nacelle (providing protection, as well as improved aerodynamics, and located aft of the engine).

The three types of engines typically encountered at an FBO include the reciprocating piston, the turboprop, and the jet. Common to a large majority of single-engine aircraft and light twin-engine aircraft, the reciprocating piston engine is similar to an automobile engine and operates by moving pistons, which in turn move a crankshaft, which in turn spins the propeller. The turboprop engine, which is found in many large twins and commuter aircraft (such as the Beechcraft 1900), is actually a small turbine or jet engine which drives a propeller. Lastly, the true jet engine, which can be found in all corporate jet aircraft and many commercial air carrier aircraft, operates by compressing air, igniting it, and thrusting it out the rear.

Fuselage

The fuselage is that part of the aircraft which is most obvious. It is, in fact, the body or main structure of the aircraft. The fuselage serves as the attachment area for the wings and tail assembly, provides space for crew and passengers, and houses various flight controls and instruments. It also allows for a beautiful paint scheme and decals to truly make for a unique aircraft exterior.

Wings

The primary purpose of the wing, or airfoil, is to produce lift. Thus, wings are extremely strong and lightweight. On conventional aircraft, wings will contain most of the usable fuel on board. At the end of each wing and long trailing edge are ailerons, which control the roll and turning of the aircraft. Flaps are located on the inboard trailing edge and serve to increase descent without increasing airspeed and allow for improved lift at slower speeds of takeoff and landing. High performance aircraft may also have leading edge slats which may be extended during takeoff and landing. Vertical winglets, which may be found on the wingtips of higher performance aircraft, contribute to reduced drag and improved efficiency. Additionally, the leading edge of the wing may have inflatable boots for deicing or be heated using bleed air from the engines for anti-icing.

Undercarriage

The undercarriage of an aircraft primarily contains the landing gear or wheels. It may also include cowl flaps, landing lights, and antennas. Most aircraft have a tricycle gear configuration, allowing for a steerable nose wheel and two main wheels. Taildragger aircraft contain two main wheels and a tail wheel (such as found on a Piper cub or a DC-3). Complex aircraft have retractable landing gear, while lower performance (and most trainer) aircraft have fixed landing gear.

Empennage or Tail

The empennage or tail can be configured in one of several ways. Most common is the vertical stabilizer with an attached moveable rudder (controlling yaw or side-to-side motion) and the horizontal stabilizer with hinged, moveable elevators (controlling pitch or up and down movement). An aircraft may also have a pivoting, one-piece horizontal stabilizer referred to as a stabilator. Trim tabs are commonly found and consist of small hinged sections on the rudder and elevator.

When on the ramp, one may hear of a T-tail, V-tail, or canard. These unique configurations deserve special explanation. A t-tail aircraft is an aircraft with horizontal surface (typically the horizontal stabilizer) at the top of the tail, such as may be found on a Piper Turbo Arrow IV. A V-tail aircraft has moveable surfaces on the tail used in combination as both rudder and elevator (such as on a V-tail Bonanza). Lastly, a canard is actually an elevator assembly found at the front of an aircraft. Although unique in appearance, these work in the same manner as an elevator in a conventional tail assembly.

Fire Safety

Prior to handling any fuel, the line service specialist must be taught the importance of proper handling of fuels and the important of fire safety. An awareness of fire safety requires knowledge of the fire triangle (see Figure 4-1). This triangle contains the following three elements: heat, fuel, and oxygen. Remove any of these elements and the fire will be extin-

Figure 4-1

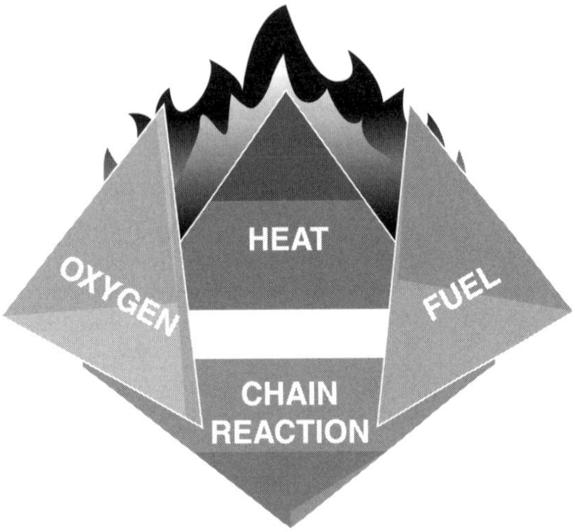

Figure 4-2

guished. In general terms, heat may be removed by cooling the fire, as is possible with the use of water on Class A fires. The fuel source may also be removed by eliminating the wood or paper fueling the Class A fire (such as making a fire break ahead of a forest fire). Oxygen can be removed by use of certain chemical fire extinguishers, such as carbon dioxide (which displaces oxygen). Although the fire triangle is appropriate for learning the components necessary to start a fire, the fire tetrahedron is necessary to learn how a fire continues to burn. The fourth side (as shown in Figure 4-2) is a chemical chain reaction. If uninterrupted, this chain reaction will maintain a fire. The chemical chain reaction can only be interrupted by application of certain extinguishing agents.

Prior to applying an extinguishing agent, however, the person fighting the fire must know which class of fire is involved. Class A fires are composed of ordinary combustibles (such as wood or paper). Class B fires are composed of flammable and combustible liquids (such as greases and gas). Class C fires are composed of energized electrical equipment. Class D fires are composed of combustible metals (magnesium and sodium). Water, which has a cooling effect, is used only on Class A fires. Carbon dioxide, which smothers the fire as it displaces oxygen, is effective on Class B or C fires. Dry chemical, which is a mixture of specially treated sodium bicarbonate, also deprives the fire of oxygen and is effective on Class B and C fires. Foam, also known as Aqueous Film Forming Foam (AFFF) is a blend of bicarbonate of soda and aluminum sulfate. AFFF effectively blankets a fire with a layer of foam, cooling the fire and starving it of oxygen. It is primarily used on Class B fires, such as on-airport fuel fires, but may also be effective on Class A fires. Foam, however, is not effective on vertical surfaces or pressure fires (such as a broken fuel line). Halon is a liquefied gas which breaks the chemical reaction by interrupting the supply of oxygen. Although it has negative environmental implications due to its ability to degrade the ozone layer, it is effective on Class B and C fires. For Class D fires, only specialized agents such as METL-X and G-1 powder are effective.

The principles used in fighting a fire begin with interrupting the fuel source if at all possible. If this is a fuel fire, this can be done with an emergency fuel shutoff or the releasing of a deadman control. Before reaching for the proper fire extinguisher, one must evaluate the fire to determine if the fire is of a small enough size to extinguish. If not, 911, the Airport Fire Department, or a supervisor must be notified. If so, the proper fire extinguisher is selected, the individual positions himself upwind, and approaches the fire. Next, the fire extinguisher safety seal must be broken, the pin must be removed, and the nozzle must be pointed at the base of the flame. Next, the nozzle trigger is pulled to begin releasing the agent, while the extinguisher is moved with a rapid sweeping motion and the individual fighting the fire steadily advances toward the flame. "PASS" is an acronym used to aid in remembering this process: Pull, Aim, Squeeze, Sweep.

Certain measures should be taken to regularly minimize the risk of fire. Keep in mind that liquid fuels, such as AvGas and Jet-A, emit vapors that can ignite when the flashpoint is reached. The flashpoint of AvGas is -50 degrees Fahrenheit, while Jet-A has a 100 degree Fahrenheit flashpoint. As a result, the vapors released from these two fuels will be at or above the flashpoint in almost every circumstance in which they'll be handled. The first measure that should betaken is to ensure the engines of all mobile fuelers be equipped with air filter/flame arrestor equipment and a leak-free exhaust system which terminates into a standard baffle muffler at the front of the vehicle. Next, line service personnel should only wear clothing composed of 100 percent cotton. Fabrics such as silk, polyester, nylon, and wool generate static, which can produce a spark that may ignite fuel or fuel vapors. Additionally, refueling personnel should not carry any type of igniting device on their person or within 100 feet of any fuel tank or refueler. Next, plastic funnels or buckets should not be used to handle fuel. Rather, a high quality non-galvanized metal funnel should be used. Bonding is also extremely important during fueling procedures. Static can build up on an aircraft during flight and while fuel is flowing through a hose and nozzle. Thus, bonding is necessary to equalize these charges and prevent an errant spark. Additional ignition sources include hot brakes, hot engine surfaces, jet engine exhaust, thunderstorms and lightning, portable electrical devices, fixed electrical equipment, and exposed light bulbs.

Even with proper measures in place, a spill may occur. Typically, fuel spills may occur if a fueler has been filled beyond its capacity at the fuel farm, an aircraft has vented a significant amount of fuel, or a fueler has been moved while connected to an aircraft or fuel farm. If a spill does occur, one must first stop the flow of fuel. If possible, a fire extinguisher must be placed upwind of the spill. Next, a supervisor or the Airport Fire Department must be notified. Third, one must not move a fueling vehicle or start or turn off any equipment (due to a possible backfire). If trained and properly equipped, one may begin cleaning up the spill. Typically a spill cart will need to be brought on scene to enable proper clean up of the spill. It is important to have ARFF or fire extinguishers standing by, as the vapors may ignite.

Aircraft Refueling

A major aspect of the line service specialist's job is to perform aircraft fueling. Indeed, the sale of aircraft fuel is the lifeblood of many FBOs. Learning how to properly fuel an aircraft is most effectively conducted through on-the-job training at the FBO. However, the beginning line service specialist should be aware of the basic terminology and procedures utilized when fueling aircraft.

Piston Aircraft

Piston aircraft have reciprocating engines, which is nothing more than an internal combustion engine with pistons that move back and forth, or reciprocate. This reciprocating motion spins a crankshaft that is connected to the propeller, which produces the thrust to propel the aircraft. Although some higher performance piston aircraft may use a turbocharger to increase manifold pressure, and thus high altitude performance, be aware that this remains a piston aircraft utilizing avgas and should not be confused with a turboprop aircraft. Thus, the line service specialist must use caution when fueling aircraft such as a Turbo Arrow.

There are three types of aircraft fuel filler caps. First, with a simple twist-off surface-mounted cap, the grip must remain parallel to the airflow. A second type has an inner cap located under a secure access door. A pop-up lever releases the cap for removal. The most common type involves a flush-mounted filler cap with a pop-up tab which must be rotated counterclockwise for removal. Regardless of the type, the line service specialist must ensure that the cap is properly secured at the completion of fueling.

The entire process of refueling a piston aircraft can be summarized in the following 11 steps:

1. Understand the service order.
2. Choose the correct refueler.
3. Properly position the refueler.
4. Review the service order.
5. Set up to refuel.
6. Refuel the aircraft (see below).
7. Check the oil.
8. Clean the windshield.
9. Stow and check.
10. Complete paperwork.
11. Perform a final visual check.

Step 6, which involves actually refueling the aircraft, has additional steps. First, protect the wing's leading edge by placing the appropriate wing mat. Additionally, be sure to touch the nozzle to the filler cap. This will discharge any remaining static electricity prior to beginning the fueling process. Next, as the nozzle is inserted into the tank, remember not to insert the nozzle deeper than 3 inches and to maintain contact with filler neck and nozzle. As you begin the flow of fuel, maintain vigilance so as not to allow contaminants into the tank (such as pens or sunglasses). Once complete, replace the filler cap immediately to avoid any contaminants from finding their way into the tank. Be aware that during the summer, the service order may request fuel to be at a level below a full tank to allow room for fuel to expand. If refueling a multi-engine aircraft, the process is essentially the same, albeit with additional filler locations.

If refueling a reciprocating engine helicopter, care must be exercised around the rotor blades. Specifically, always park the refueler outside the circle of blade rotation even if blades are not turning. Also, never walk behind a helicopter. Remain in the pilot's field of vision away from the tail rotor. Refueling of helicopters "hot," or while the blades are turning, is not recommended. Due to the large amount of static generated by helicopter blades, several minutes must pass for static to dissipate after bonding the refueler to the aircraft. Lastly, as with refueling piston aircraft, always touch the refueler nozzle to the filler cap prior to opening the fuel tank.

Turboprop and Jet Aircraft

Turboprop refers to an aircraft with propellers, but also equipped with a jet engine or turbine, and as a result, requires Jet fuel. A turboprop engine takes in air, which is routed through a series of spinning turbine blades. This process compresses the air, which is then mixed with jet fuel and ignited.

Gasses are produced, which spin a shaft that is attached to the propeller. Similarly, once the air is compressed within a jet engine, it is mixed with fuel and ignited, which produces a jet blast which propels the aircraft forward. The most common type of fuel for these aircraft is Jet-A.

Fuel additives, including those specifically intended to prevent icing, may be called for. These additives are either pre-blended by the manufacturer or supplier, injected through a closed system on the refueler, or delivered over the wing via an aerosol spray can during refueling. If using an aerosol spray can, certain steps must be followed to ensure proper mixing of the additive. One must start the flow of fuel before beginning the flow of additive and then shutoff the flow of additive before refueling is completed. This process will ensure proper mixing and avoid any areas of concentration of the additive in the fuel.

Jet fuel refuelers typically have larger tanks and additional fuel hoses, nozzles, and meters. There are three delivery hoses: two over wing hoses and nozzles and one single point (pressure) hose and nozzle. The over wing nozzles will have a J spout, which will prevent inadvertent delivery of Jet-A into a piston engine aircraft. Refuelers providing jet fuel will have both types, as any aircraft with a single point refueling system will also have overwing filler caps to be used if the pressure system is inoperational. Single point systems, which are common on many business jets, are easy to use, safe, and more efficient than over wing refueling, as they produce a closed, pressurized system which should reduce the opportunity for fuel spills. These systems have an automatic shutoff which terminates the flow of fuel when the tanks are full. Unique to the single point system, the deadman control allows delivery of fuel from a position slightly away from the aircraft and will only start the flow of fuel when the deadman control is held open. When released, the flow of fuel stops.

The single point is typically located in the vicinity of the wing root, either fore or aft, and either above or below wing. A fuel control panel will have the master fuel power switch, tank valve on/off switches, refuel/defuel switches, fuel tank configuration diagram, and possibly fuel quantity gauges. The closed, single point system must also have a way for air to escape that is being displaced by fuel in the tanks. This is accomplished through a fuel vent system. Vents are commonly located on outboard, underside sections of wings, near the wingtips. Connecting a single point nozzle simply involves making contact at the appropriate connection point and rotating the handles of the nozzle clockwise for proper connection. Once refueling is complete, the nozzle is removed by rotating handles counterclockwise.

Special precautions must be taken when filling aircraft with tip tanks. A prime example is the Mitsubishi Mu-2. The aircraft's wingspan is 39 feet, 2 inches, yet the wheelbase in relation to the wingspan is slightly less than 4 feet wide. This makes the aircraft susceptible to a tip over if the aircraft is improperly refueled, resulting in an unbalanced situation. The proper procedure to refuel a Mitsubishi Mu-2 is to approach the aircraft from the nose in a safe manner (generally approaching the aircraft parallel with the wings and waiting until the aircraft's engines have ceased operating before approaching). Next, line personnel should attach the bonding (ground) cable to the designated grounding point. After the bonding cable is secure, proceed to locate the left inboard tank to begin refueling operations. Line personnel must start with the left inboard tank, due to the aircraft's baffling within the wing. After refueling the left inboard tank, the line personnel should proceed to refuel the aircraft via the right inboard tank, followed by the right outboard tank, followed by the left outboard tank. Once the main wing tanks have been fueled, the line personnel should proceed to the left tip tank. The Mitsubishi Mu-2's tip tanks are different than the inboard/outboard wing tanks on the aircraft. The tip tanks are pressurized, meaning the line personnel refueling the aircraft should take great care in opening the tank's filler cap, to prevent personal injury, as well as damage to the aircraft. A good general rule of thumb is to pull the filler cap's tab, and wait for the pressure to stabilize before removing the cap completely. When filling the Mu-2's tip tanks, it is important to remember that the tanks cannot exceed more than 45 gallons per tip tank (maximum capacity is 90 gallons), in order to keep the aircraft from tipping over. To properly complete the refueling procedure, the line personnel must move from the left tip tank (after adding no more than 45 gallons) to the right tip tank (again taking care to depressurize the system), adding the desired amount of fuel. After the right tip tank is fueled, the left tank can be completed, unless the desired amount of fuel in the tip tanks is less than 45 gallons; in which case, the left and right tip tanks are now finished. After refueling, remove the bonding cable from the aircraft, and proceed away from the aircraft to complete the process. It is important to understand also that the Mitsubishi Mu-2's wings have a tendency to flex downward, or droop, under the added weight of the fuel. The wings have been known to flex anywhere from a few inches to roughly a few feet. This is important because if line personnel place an access ladder underneath the wing, the wing itself could flex and lodge itself onto the ladder, making it impossible to remove the ladder without transferring the fuel load, and making the wing flex yet again. Of course, the best scenario when it comes to the refueling of a Mitsubishi Mu-2 is to have two line personnel, each with a separate refueling hose, working independently on each side of the aircraft. This scenario makes refueling the aircraft faster, more efficient, and less likely to become involved in an unbalanced situation.

Additionally, when refueling an aircraft that appears to be unbalanced, use extreme caution in opening filler caps on the lower wing, as fuel may rush out, resulting in a fuel spill.

Fuel Farm Management

Fuel farms are areas where fuel is stored in bulk at airports. It may indeed appear to be a "farm," as there are typically several above-ground storage tanks containing AvGas and Jet-A fuels. Pilots expect high quality fuel that is of the correct type and grade and free of any contamination. As a result, the fuel farm must be properly managed to ensure the delivery of quality fuel meeting these standards.

Fuel is regularly checked for contaminants. Different types of contaminants may exist in fuel. Water, which appears as a cloud, haze, or droplets at the bottom of the fuel sample, must be eliminated by draining, extracting with a sump pump, or through the use of monitor elements and filter separators. Free water can cause many complications for an aircraft. It can freeze in fuel lines and filters, stimulate the growth of microorganisms which can block fuel lines and filters, or if severe enough, can cause engine shutdown or flameout. In contrast to free water, fuel can contain dissolved water, referring to water occurring in such trace amounts that fuel is not considered contaminated. Next, solids, such as sand, fiber, particles, and metal shavings can contaminate fuel and may result from damaged filters and rust and scale from storage tanks, hatches, pipes, and nozzles. Solid contaminants such as these are best removed by micron filters, monitors, and filter separators. Yet another form of contamination is microorganisms, including bacteria, fungi, and yeast. These can damage or obstruct fuel filters, corrode engine components, and cause fuel deterioration. The most effective way to minimize the presence of microorganisms is to eliminate free water in the fuel. Surfactants, such as soap, can enter the fuel system through inadvertent chemical contamination, such as improperly cleaned tanks or motor gasoline residue. Finally, mixing of different types and grades of aviation fuels is also a form of contamination. This can be prevented by segregating each type and grade of fuel and properly marking tanks and fueling trucks. To ensure high quality fuel, filtration is performed at three stages: as it is loaded into storage tanks, when loaded onto the refueler, and when fuel is delivered to the aircraft.

Each type and grade of aviation fuel has a unique color. AvGas may be in 80/87 octane (red in color), 100/130 (green in color), or 100 Low Lead (blue in color). Although 80/87 octane is used in lower-powered piston engines, and 100/130 is used in high piston performance engines, 100 LL is most common, compatible with all reciprocating engines, and offered by the majority of FBOs. Jet fuel, most commonly in the form of Jet-A, is clear or occasionally straw in color. Additionally, each fuel has a universal marking and coding system. All tanks, pipelines, filter vessels, valves, and fittings must be marked with the appropriate grade, ID, and color banding. AvGas has white letters on a red background. Additionally, 100LL has a blue band, 80 octane has a red band, and 100 octane has a green band. If the entire system is painted the appropriate color, no colored banding is required on the valves and fittings. Jet-A has white letters on a black background, next to a single black band. The entire Jet-A system may be painted white silver or aluminum with black joints, fittings, and valves.

Fuel at fuel farms may be stored in either underground tanks or above-ground tanks. Although there are strict requirements for underground storage tanks (including LUST), there are some advantages to locating tanks underground, including minimizing sabotage. Typically, however, FBOs have above-ground tanks at their fuel farms. All successful FBOs have accurate record-keeping and clean, well-maintained fuel farms. Security is also important to protect the fuel farm area. Most commonly, this is in the form of chain-link fencing with three strands of barbed-wire on top. Additionally, "No Smoking" and "Flammable" signs should be posted. Emergency shutoff controls must be properly marked, fire extinguishers must be present, and bonding cables must be available at all loading and unloading locations.

To ensure high quality fuel, periodic testing and monitoring must be performed. There are five main types of tests that are performed. First, the "clear and bright test" is utilized for both jet fuel and avgas to determine clarity and the presence of particulates or water in the fuel. Also, the proper color of the fuel can be verified. Next, the "white bucket test" is used for testing jet fuel and provides the ability to identify water, particulates, and microorganisms in the fuel. A water finder and sump check may be used to detect water in fuels. Water is heavier than aviation fuel and will settle to the bottom of all storage tanks and piping. The "millipore test" is used to evaluate particulate contamination of aviation fuels. Fuel is drawn through a filter membrane with a pore size of 0.8 microns. Of these, the "colorimetric test" is most common and allows a comparison of the color and intensity of the membrane to established standards. Lastly, the "differential pressure check" is conducted by measuring the difference between the inlet pressure and the outlet pressure with fuel flowing through the filtration vessel. A drop between inlet and outlet pressure is normal with a new filter, ranging from 2-7 psi. However, as fuel flows through the filter and collects contaminants, the differential pressure will increase. The filter elements need replacing when the corrected differential pressure equals or exceeds 15 psi, a drastic drop in differential pressure is experienced, no differential pressure is shown, and when free water is found downstream of the filter vessel.

Daily fuel farm checks consist of:

Storage tanks

- Clear and bright test on avgas
- White bucket test on jet fuel
- Water detection test on each storage tank

Filter separators

- Clear and bright or white bucket test on each filter separator sump drain
- Monitor differential pressure on the direct reading gauge

Overall

- Fuel tank quantity, tank vents and hatches, bonding wires, hoses and connections, pumps and motors, overall storage area, fire extinguishers

Weekly fuel farm checks consist of:

- Emergency shutoff and deadman controls
- Floating suction on storage tanks
- Signage and placards

Monthly fuel farm checks consist of:

- Millipore/Membrane testing
- Hoses (working pressure test)
- Pumps, reels, and motors (oil level)
- Water slug test (if so equipped; water slug shutoff valves)
- Month end fuel inventory
  - A full inventory of fuel ordered and delivered is compared to the fuel levels in each storage tank and each refueler. Keep in mind that fuel consumed in testing may have an impact on monthly inventory.

Towing

Towing is the movement of an aircraft with a specialized vehicle. This task requires hand-eye coordination and skills that are developed with practice. Prior to towing any aircraft, however, the line service specialist must be aware of proper aircraft care and handling. All aircraft components can be delicate and subject to damage if they come into contact with any ground equipment, other aircraft, or objects. What appears to be minor damage can cause catastrophic failure in flight. Therefore, it is important to notify your supervisor of any aircraft damage, no matter how insignificant. Keeping quiet in hopes of avoiding negative consequences is not an option.

When moving aircraft, the line service specialist must be certain of clearances. If in doubt, one must stop the vehicle and check clearances. If there is concern about the amount of clearance, the use of wing walkers is highly recommended. Wing walkers assist on each wingtip in ensuring proper clearance. Remember, it is the line service specialist's job to ensure the safety of a customer's aircraft.

Tow vehicles include tugs, tractors, electric towing units, gas-powered walk-behind units, remote-controlled units, handheld towbars, towbar-less vehicles with nose cradles, and may be operated from a standing, seated, or remote position. Tugs which allow the driver to be seated are typically the most common tow vehicle in use at FBOs.

Tugs connect at either the nosegear (for tricycle gear aircraft) or the tailwheel (for taildragger aircraft). The connection point may be the nose gear wheel axle, nose gear shear pins, or tow bar connection points. Prior to towing, the proper tow bar (if required) must be selected. Options include a universal-fit tow bar or custom tow bars. Typically, larger turboprop and jet aircraft require use of a unique tow bar head. Be aware that once underway, aircraft develop momentum that can cause difficulty in stopping. Larger corporate jet aircraft can weigh 35 tons. Thus, speed must be kept to a minimum, with plenty of space to bring the aircraft to a complete stop. Likewise, if an aircraft becomes disconnected from the tow vehicle during a towing operation, move the vehicle away from the aircraft and allow the aircraft to stop on its own. Never attempt to stop the moving aircraft.

What is the typical manner in which to tow an aircraft? First, one must determine the preferred route of travel. This should be the safest and most direct route available. After performing a vehicle safety check (including making sure the correct towbar is available), the tug is started and the brakes are tested as the front of the (tricycle gear) aircraft is approached. Once in position, one must turn off engine and set the parking brake. Next, the tow bar is attached to the aircraft. One must be sure to check for any turning limit markers on the nosegear. Next, the tow bar is connected to the tug. Prior to towing the aircraft, one must perform an aircraft walk-around. Are chocks removed? Are the aircraft tie-down cables removed? Is the aircraft parking brake off? As the tug is started, one must check for clearance around the aircraft and in the intended direction of travel, slowly and smoothly beginning to move the aircraft. While towing, the driver must stay alert and keep her eyes moving. When pulling the aircraft into position, the driver must slowly and smoothly come to a stop. The tug is placed in park, the engine is turned off, and the parking brake is set. Chocks are positioned to secure the aircraft and the towbar is disconnect from the tug first and aircraft next. Safe line service specialists know to never remove the towbar without first securing the aircraft with chocks; otherwise, the aircraft may roll into the tug.

When towing into a hangar, additional considerations apply. In these confined areas, hazards such as wing clearances, tail height and ceiling limits, hangar door openings, and various obstructions must be considered. Wing walkers are important when moving aircraft in or out of a hangar. The wing walker and tug driver should always maintain eye contact to ensure a successful operation. When pushing an aircraft back, the driver always steers the tug in the same direction intended for the aircraft. When moving the aircraft over hangar door tracks, one must avoid stopping the aircraft while the landing gear wheels are over the tracks. Further, the hangar door should be approached so that both wheels cross over the track at the same time. An aircraft with a red maintenance tag on the nose gear should never be moved. Also, avoid overlapping wing surfaces in a hangar. If a landing gear strut collapses, substantial damage may result. Also, avoid parking aircraft within the propeller arc of another aircraft. By following these guidelines, the line service specialist can ensure a safe towing operation within the hangar environment.

Marshalling

Yet another role of the line service specialist is the marshalling of aircraft. Pilots need assistance in knowing where to park at unfamiliar FBOs. The role of the marshaller is to provide this direction and ensure adequate wingtip clearances with common hand signals (shown in FAA Advisory Circular 00-34A). When acting as a marshaller, the individual is considered an extension of the pilot and is there for the pilot's benefit. A marshaller has an unobstructed view and better perspective than the pilot sitting in the cockpit.

Marshallers are typically located in front of the aircraft nose and in full view of the pilot. If the marshaller can't see the pilot, the pilot will not be able to see the marshaller. The marshaller must also wear hearing protection and have illuminated wands for night operation. Orange wands are typically used during daytime operations to enhance visibility of hand signals. The following is a list of typical safety procedures utilized by marshallers.

1. Always remain visible to the pilot.
2. Use standard aviation hand signals
3. Fully extend arms and provide clear signals
4. When directing arriving aircraft to a parking position, establish and remain in the proper position prior to the aircraft arriving on the ramp.
5. Be aware of pilot's reaction and adjust hand signal if necessary.
6. Use additional personnel to assist in congested areas or provide additional clearance guidance.
7. Never position a small aircraft where it will be in danger of jet blast.
8. Remain clear of props and rotors.
9. Secure the aircraft using appropriate chocks and tie-downs.

Aircraft Storage

Fixed base operators also have facilities for storing planes. Several storage options are usually available for based and transient aircraft and they can be divided into two categories: hangar and tie-down. Hangars, offering protection from the elements, are often available for an individual to rent and can be found in a variety of sizes from those designed for a small single-engine airplane to large buildings that can house a corporate fleet. Also, many aviation businesses offer storage options in a general or community hangar. This is usually where any transient aircraft will be kept and can be less expensive than a single-user hangar. A tie-down space is generally less expensive than hangar storage. These are open areas on the airport ramp that allow an airplane to be secured to the ramp via ropes, chains, or other means. [See FAA Advisory Circular 20-35C, for guidance on aircraft tie-down.]

Additional Line Services

Additional services a line service specialist may perform include foreign object debris (FOD) removal, ground power unit operation, windshield cleaning, interior and exterior aircraft cleaning, lavatory servicing, and potable water servicing. Although not necessarily a specific task, the line service specialist must always be aware of and on the lookout for FOD on the line and the ramp. FOD (also known as foreign object damage) can cause severe damage to aircraft and persons on the ramp as objects are picked up by jetblast or propwash and propelled into the air or ingested into the engine. As a result, persons on the ramp must always be on the lookout for pieces of metal, trash, etc., that simply don't belong. Expecting someone else to pick up this debris is an employee attitude that a successful FBO simply cannot afford to have. An example of the effects of FOD (although on a runway) occurred on July 25, 2000. On this unfortunate day, a piece of titanium from an earlier departing aircraft remained on the runway and was rolled over by the Concorde on its departure roll. A tire blew, spraying the fuselage with pieces of rubber, which then shattered a fuel tank and eventually brought down the aircraft, resulting in the deaths of 100 passengers and nine crew members on board and four people on the ground. Obviously, the role of the line service specialist in detecting and retrieving FOD cannot be overstated.

Another service provided by the line service specialist is ground power unit (GPU) support. The GPU is used to provide a source of electricity to power aircraft systems while the aircraft is on the ramp without engines running. GPUs are typical at FBOs, although much less so at main air carrier terminals because a 400 Hz power cord is usually provided which may be connected to the aircraft to provide a power source. GPUs can be used for starting engines and provide a power output of 12, 28, or 115 volts. Caution must be exercised, as delivering the wrong voltage to an aircraft will damage the aircraft's electrical system. The procedures for using a GPU are as follows:

1. Determine aircraft power requirements and select proper GPU.
2. Position power unit at rear of aircraft.
3. Do not position within 10 feet radius of fuel tank vents.
4. Set GPU parking brake.
5. Start GPU engine and allow it to warm up to normal operating temperature.
6. Verify generator switch is off and connect the cable to the aircraft. Never connect the GPU to the aircraft with the generator running as a dangerous electrical arc may occur.
7. Once the pilot is ready, bring the GPU up to operating speed, check voltage and amperage, and switch generator on.
8. Remember to switch the generator off prior to disconnecting the cable from the aircraft to avoid an electrical arc.

Another service provided by line service is windshield cleaning. Although this sounds fairly basic, there are rules which must be adhered to that are unique to aircraft. Whether cleaning a glass or Plexiglas windshield, never use shop rags, as small metal particles may be present which could scratch the windshield. Most cleaners are designed for either glass or Plexiglas, but not both. Additionally, use plenty of solution and wipe in the direction of airflow (never in a circular motion).

A clean aircraft is an aircraft that is more likely to hold its value, be more efficient in flight, and provide a pleasing experience for both passengers and crew. Therefore, the line service specialist may be called upon to clean either an aircraft exterior or interior. The aircraft exterior is typically washed as one would wash an automobile, using special cleaning solutions and drying the aircraft after washing. A clean exterior is critical to maintaining efficiency in flight, as a clean surface produces less drag than a dirty surface. More likely, the line service specialist will be asked to clean the interior of an aircraft. Interior cleaning includes vacuuming the interior, washing galley and lavatory surfaces, removing trash, and straightening seat belts. One must never enter the cabin without flight crew permission, however. Prior to cleaning, the attendant will make sure to have proper supplies and protection (including gloves), and have clean shoes (rather than oily boots). It is important to be efficient, yet thorough, to please passengers and crew.

Aircraft arriving into an FBO may be equipped with a lavatory on board. Whether a portable lift-out system or a permanently installed internal system, the lavatory may likely need servicing. Prior to servicing any lavatory, one must wear protective gloves and goggles to prevent inadvertent exposure to bacteria and disease. Portable systems can be lifted out and taken to a remote fill and disposal location. These systems should be flushed and refilled with clean water. It is best to wait until the unit is reinstalled in the aircraft prior to adding blue deodorant tablets. If not, a spill upon entering the aircraft may result in blue water being spilled inside the cabin.

Fixed internal lavatory systems may also need to be serviced. These systems must be serviced with a lavatory service truck or a service cart. Servicing these systems involves connecting a discharge hose and water fill line to the aircraft. Once the waste is discharged and the system is flushed, blue deodorant water is pumped into the holding tank to the recommended fill level. The flight crew should be notified of any leaks and the waste should be disposed of at approved locations.

Lastly, potable water servicing may also be necessary. Potable water is the term given to sanitary drinking water. Aircraft with potable water on board will have one of two systems. A portable lift out container is serviced from a potable water faucet at the FBO. An installed tank is filled from a remote location outside the aircraft and is serviced with a water truck or pull-behind cart.

In recent years, with the growth of the regional airlines, many FBOs have established contractual services with the air carriers, including fueling, exterior cleaning, interior cleaning, deicing, turbine starting, minor maintenance, and even baggage handling and screening and passenger screening in some cases. Thus, line service specialists are increasingly called upon to fulfill these requests for additional services. Rather than from detracting from the line service profession, this simply enforces the importance of line service at FBOs.

KEY TERMS

Line service specialist
Coordinated Universal Time
Phonetic Alphabet
Tail Number
Engine
Fuselage
Wings
Undercarriage
Empennage
Fire triangle

Fire tetrahedron
Class A fire
Class B fire
Class C fire
Class D fire
Piston engine aircraft
Turboprop aircraft
Jet engine aircraft
Over the wing fueling
Single point fueling
Fuel Farm
Towing
Marshalling
Tie down
FOD
GPU

REVIEW QUESTIONS

1. What is the most visible aspect of an FBO?
2. What is the role of the line service specialist?
3. What makes up the knowledge base for a line service specialist?
4. Why is fire safety important for the line service special ist? What are the four classes of fires? What principles are used in extinguishing a fire? What measures should be taken by FBOs to minimize the risk of fire?
5. What are the three types of aircraft fuel filler caps? What are the proper steps in refueling an aircraft?
6. Explain the three different types of aircraft engines a line service specialist would expect to service.
7. Describe the types of fuel contamination.
8. What are the different types and colors of aviation fuel? Which two types are most common?
9. What is the procedure to be followed in towing an aircraft?
10. What are the safety procedures typically utilized by marshallers?
11. What are two categories of aircraft storage?
12. What services, in addition to fueling, may a line service specialist be expected to carry out?

REFERENCES

FAA Advisory Circulars.
FAA Aeronautical Information Manual.
NATA Safety 1st Program.

SCENARIOS

1. An MU-2 aircraft just taxied into your ramp and requested to be "topped off." As you approach the aircraft, it appears to be leaning toward one side. What do you do?
2. This is only your second day as a line service specialist at a full-service FBO. The line service manager, who has been quizzing you on various aspects of line service, recently handed you a quiz. You were instructed to answer the following questions and have it back to her be fore lunch.
   a. What color is 100LL?
   b. If it is 1400(L), and we are in EDT, what time in Zulu is it?
   c. A pilot in a King Air just called in and requested maintenance to look at the oil pressure in the number two engine. To which engine is he referring?
   d. Your co-worker just rushed in to say there was a fire behind the hangar. Upon arriving on the scene, you see some cardboard burning. What class of fire is this and what is the preferred extinguishing agent?
   e. What is a J-spout?
3. You are underway towing a Piper Seminole toward the hangar. As you near the hangar door, you realize that it will be a tight fit getting between two aircraft parked near the entrance. What do you do?
4. A pilot that just arrived on the ramp is concerned about your ability to correctly fuel his aircraft. He starts quizzing you to determine your level of knowledge. "What types of testing do you do for quality control at your fuel farm?" If your FBO followed the guidance in this chapter, what would you tell him?
5. You have three years of experience as a line service specialist. Your FBO just hired a new line service specialist whom you've been instructed to train. After fueling a King Air, the new employee asks," Why didn't you put AvGas in that aircraft? It has props just like that Seminole you fueled over there." How do you answer him and explain the differences?

Notes

Chapter 5
FBO Services

OUTLINE

Introduction
Maintenance
- Overview
- FAR Part 1
- FAR Part 21
- FR Part 23
- FAR Part 39
- FAR Part 43
- FAR Part 65
  - Airframe and Powerplant
  - Privileges and Limitations
  - Inspection Authorization
  - Repairman Certificate
- FAR Part 91
  - Annual Inspection
  - 100 Hour Inspection
- Progressive Inspection
- Continuous Inspection Program
- Avionics
  - Altimeter and Static System
  - Transponder
  - Emergency Locator Transmitter
- FAR Part 145

Flight Operations
- Flight Instruction
- Aircraft Rental
- Aircraft Charter

Sales
- Aircraft
- Aircraft Parts and Aviation Supplies

Corporate Flight Service
Other Specialized Commercial Flight Services

OBJECTIVES

At the end of this chapter, you should be able to:

- Discuss the benefits of having a maintenance department at an FBO.
- Discuss the many FARs applicable to aircraft maintenance.
- Realize the differences between a technician possessing airframe, powerplant, A&P, and IA.
- Explain what a 100 hour and annual inspection is.
- Explain what a progressive inspection program and a continuous inspection program are.
- Discuss the avionics typically requiring inspection.
- Discuss the benefits and considerations in offering flight instruction, aircraft rental, and charter services.
- Discuss the aircraft sales process and considerations necessary in forming an aircraft sales division at an FBO.
- Discuss the sale of aircraft parts and supplies.
- Discuss corporate flight service and other specialized flight services that an FBO may offer.

Introduction

As noted in chapter 4, the principal business of fixed base operators is line service, which includes the retail sales of fuel and oil, minor repairs, emergency service, and other flight continuation services for general aviation aircraft. In addition to line service, FBOs also maintain storage facilities for private airplanes, provide continuing maintenance and overhaul services, and usually have small or medium-sized planes available for charter. Some of the larger FBOs are active in selling new and used airplanes, and some also operate flying schools. A few of the larger operators are equipped to offer complete flight service arrangements for business firms, including supplying both aircraft and crews.

Maintenance

Overview

The proper maintenance of aircraft is necessary so that aircraft can be maintained in an airworthy condition, as required by the Federal Aviation Regulations (FARs). The aircraft owner/operator is responsible for ensuring that maintenance personnel, upon completion of necessary maintenance, make appropriate entries in the aircraft maintenance records indicating the aircraft has been approved for return to service. It is the responsibility of the owner and operator to have maintenance performed that may be required between scheduled inspections.

Inspection of airframes, powerplants, propellers, and appliances is the single most effective way to identify potential problems with aircraft and ensure safe operations. The FAA requires aircraft and their associated components to be inspected at regular intervals. The frequency of these inspections varies depending on the types of aircraft, its primary use, and components installed. As a result, inspections, maintenance, and repairs can be a primary business function of an FBO.

Although corporately owned aircraft may be maintained by an in-house maintenance department, there are many aircraft owners that utilize FBOs for aircraft maintenance. FBOs presenting a complete offering of services will include maintenance in those services. At a minimum, these maintenance services will include piston engine aircraft. Larger FBOs with the proper equipment and personnel will also maintain larger aircraft maintenance departments that are capable of maintaining turboprop and jet aircraft.

Any maintenance performed on an aircraft today must comply with the FARs. When it becomes necessary to implement a new rule or change an existing FAR, the FAA creates a statement of reason and support called a *Notice of Proposed Rule Making* for publication in the *Federal Register*. After a predetermined period for public comments, proposals are adopted in *Title 14 of the Code of Federal Regulations* (14 Title CFR) thus becoming a federal statute. The FARs are organized into separate sections or parts. For example, 14 Title CFR Part 65 describes the requirements, privileges, and limitations for certification of airmen other than flight crewmembers, which includes aviation maintenance technicians and repairmen.

There are numerous regulations that are of vital importance to the aircraft maintenance industry, whether experimental, private, commercial, or air cargo. Several of the regulations that specially concern general aviation are listed and discussed below:

1. **FAR Part 1:** Definitions and Abbreviations
2. **FAR Part 21:** Certification Procedures for Products and Parts
3. **FAR Part 23:** Airworthiness Standards, Normal, Utility, and Acrobatic Aircraft
4. **FAR Part 39:** Airworthiness Directives
5. **FAR Part 43:** Maintenance, Preventive Maintenance, Rebuilding, and Alteration
6. **FAR Part 65:** Certification: Airmen other than Flight Crewmembers
7. **FAR Part 91:** General Operating and Flight Rules
8. **FAR Part 145:** Repair Station

FAR Part 1

FAR Part 1 is an official listing containing the definitions of words, their abbreviations, and associated symbols. Maintenance personnel utilize FAR Part 1 terminology to distinguish between types of maintenance performed, such as maintenance (inspection, overhaul, repair, replacement of parts, and preservation) and preventive maintenance (oil and filter changes, and the replacement of small standard parts such as brakes, tires, or tubes).

FAR Part 21

FAR Part 21 details the requirements for establishing and maintaining the certification of aircraft and components. When an aircraft is assembled and test flown, an authorized representative must decide if it conforms to the appropriate model's FAA approved type certificate. The type certificate lists all the essential information about the aircraft and its accessories. If the aircraft is in conformity to the type certificate for safe and reliable operation, it is then issued an airworthiness certificate, signifying the aircraft meets acceptable standards for service. The airworthiness certificate remains with the airplane during is service life regardless of owner. However, proper and timely maintenance must be performed on the aircraft for the airworthiness certificate to remain valid.

FAR Part 23

FAR Part 23 describes the precise performance characteristics aircraft and their related systems must demonstrate to be considered airworthy. It details the requirements for every component and system installed on the aircraft, down to the slightest detail. For example, whenever a cockpit instrument is repaired or replaced, technicians installing the instrument must ensure that the range markings on the instrument dial are correct according to the FAA-approved aircraft flight manual.

FAR Part 39

Whenever an unsafe condition develops on an aircraft, engine, propeller, or accessory and is likely to exist in other products of a similar design, the FAA issues an airworthiness directive to notify concerned parties or aircraft owners of the condition. FAA's airworthiness directives are legally enforceable rules for anyone who operates a product for which an airworthiness directive applies. Airworthiness directives specify inspections the aircraft owner or operator must carry out, conditions and limitations that must be complied with, and any other actions that must be taken to resolve the unsafe condition. Airworthiness directives are part of the 14 Title CFR, but are not published in printed editions. The FAA publishes airworthiness directives in full in the Federal Register as an amendment to FAR Part 39.13. Consequently, anyone who operates a product that does not meet the requirements of an applicable airworthiness directive is in violation of the FAR.

FAR Part 43

FAR Part 43 outlines the fundamental standards for general aviation aircraft inspection, maintenance, and repair, as well as all record keeping requirements. A repair is an operation that restores an item to a condition of useful operation or to original condition, whereas an alteration is a change in the configuration or design of an aircraft. Under FAR Part 43, the FAA divides aircraft repairs and alterations into two categories: major and minor. A major repair is one that, if performed incorrectly, may significantly affect weight, balance, structural strength, flight performance, powerplant operation, or other airworthiness factors. A major alteration is any change or alteration not listed in the aircraft, powerplant, or accessory specifications that might affect the product's performance in a fashion similar to a major repair. FAR Part 43 defines minor repairs and alterations as those that are not considered major repairs or alterations. Since this definition is not very specific, it is sometimes difficult to distinguish in which category a repair or alteration is considered.

Preventive maintenance consists of preservation, upkeep, and the simple replacement of small parts. In some situations, the FARs allow licensed airmen other than maintenance technicians to perform preventive maintenance tasks. For example, if an aircraft owner holds at least a private pilot certificate, the owner can, among other things, change the aircraft's engine oil and replace a landing gear tire. A comprehensive list of items that are considered preventive maintenance are included in Appendix A of FAR Part 43.

FAR Part 43.15 catalogs the performance criteria for performing inspections on most general aviation aircraft types, and specifically states that a checklist which meets the minimum requirements listed in FAR Part 43 Appendix D must be used for all annual and 100-hour inspections. This does not preclude the operator developing a more comprehensive checklist or using one prepared by a repair station or manufacturer. As long as the checklist covers all the items in Appendix D, and is approved by the local FAA office, it may be used. Most aircraft, powerplant, and propeller manufacturers provide inspection checklists for their equipment types. These forms are readily available through the particular manufacturer and often include references to service bulletins and information letters that contain important product service and improvement information.

FAR Part 65

Airframe and Powerplant

FAR Part 65 discusses the certification requirements, as well as the privileges and limitations, for aviation maintenance technicians. Under current regulations, there are two certificates for maintenance personnel described in Part 65, each with different privileges and limitations: the mechanic certificate and the repairmen certificate. In addition, there are two ratings issued to certificated mechanics: the airframe rating and the powerplant rating.

The FAA requires at least 18 months of work experience for an airframe, or powerplant technician's certificate. For a combined A & P certificate, at least 30 months of experience working with both engines and airframes is required. Many applicants complete an aviation maintenance technician program at an FAA approved FAR Part 147 Aviation Maintenance School. Current FAA standards require that these approved aviation maintenance schools offer students a minimum of 1,900 actual class hours. All applicants must be at least 18 years old, able to read, write, speak, and understand English. In addition, they must pass a series of written and oral tests, as well as a practical examination to demonstrate that they can perform the work authorized by the A&P certificate.

An Airframe and Powerplant Mechanic Certificate remains in effect until it is surrendered, suspended, or revoked. However, FAR Part 65 also requires current experience to keep the A & P certificate valid. Appropriately rated technicians must have at least 1,000 hours of work experience in the previous 24 months or take a refresher course.

Privileges and Limitations

A certificated mechanic may perform or supervise the maintenance, preventive maintenance, or an alteration of aircraft, appliance, or part for which a technician is appropriately rated. A mechanic certificate with an airframe rating allows a technician to approve and return to service an airframe, or any related component or appliance, after performing, supervising, or inspecting its maintenance or alteration. An airframe-rated technician can perform 100-hour inspections on airframes and related parts or appliances and approve them to service. However, a technician with an airframe rating may not inspect or return to service an airframe or related part or appliance that has undergone a major repair or alteration.

A technician holding a powerplant rating can approve

and return to service powerplants, propellers, and accessories after performing, supervising, or inspecting its maintenance or alteration. A powerplant-rated technician is allowed to perform 100-hour inspections on powerplants and propellers and return them to service. However, like the airframe rating, a powerplant rating does not permit a technician to inspect or return to service a powerplant, propeller, or accessory that has undergone a major repair or alteration.

Technicians that possess both airframe and powerplant ratings can perform minor repairs and alterations to airframes, powerplants, propellers, and components and approve these items for return to service. In addition, an A & P can perform major repairs and alterations to airframes, powerplants, and components. However, an A & P cannot perform major repairs or alterations to propellers, or perform any type of repairs or alterations to instruments. An A & P can, however, perform 100-hour inspection procedures on airframes, powerplants, propellers, accessories, and instruments and approve them for return to service. It is important to note that an A & P cannot delegate his inspection duties while performing a 100-hour inspection. In addition, an A & P cannot perform annual inspections. However, they can correct discrepancies an authorized inspector discovers during an annual inspection.

Inspection Authorization

Technicians who have held a mechanic certificate with both an airframe and powerplant rating for a minimum for three years and who have been actively involved in maintaining general aviation aircraft for at least two years can apply for an Inspection Authorization (IA). In addition to all the privileges of an airframe and powerplant rating, an IA permits a technician to perform an annual inspection on aircraft and approve it for return to service. Furthermore, an IA can perform major repairs and alterations made on airframes and powerplants and approve the work for return to service. However, an IA cannot perform major repairs and alterations to propellers, or make repairs or alterations of instruments. Under current federal regulations, these tasks must be performed by an appropriately rated repair station.

Unlike an A & P rated technician, an IA's privileges expire on March 31 of each odd-numbered year. To renew the rating, the FAA requires that the IA achieve certain recurrence levels on an annual basis. For an IA's certificate to remain active, evidence must be shown that the IA has performed at least one annual every 90 days, inspected at least two major repairs or alterations every 90 days, performed or supervised at least one progressive inspection, completed an approved IA refresher course, or passed an oral test given by an FAA inspector.

Repairman Certificate

Many aircraft repair facilities work on aircraft components, accessories, and instruments. Technicians employed in these facilities performing maintenance-related activities such as component overhaul and rebuilding do not require the broad training an airframe and powerplant is required to achieve. However, the FAA does require training on the specific duties they are expected to perform. Once a person satisfactorily completes the appropriate training, they can be issued a repairman's certificate. FAR Parts 65 and 145 identify the requirements for repairman's certificate for technicians performing specialized maintenance functions at certificated repair stations.

The holder of a repairman's certificate can perform and supervise the maintenance, preventive maintenance, and alteration of an aircraft or its components for which the employer is certified. The repairman's certificate is issued to a technician for the repair station at which they are employed. Therefore, if a repairman leaves the employment of the designated repair station, the certificate is surrendered.

FAR Part 91

Annual Inspection

One segment of aircraft operations, known as general aviation, is conducted under FAR Part 91. As previously discussed, general aviation refers to all aviation other than commercial (scheduled and nonscheduled) airline operations and military aviation. Although general aviation usually involves small aircraft, the definition depends on the nature of the operation, not the size of the aircraft. The FAA requires aircraft and their associated components to be inspected regularly. The frequency of these inspections depends on the type and use of the aircraft or component.

FAR Part 91 states that all general aviation aircraft must go through an annual inspection to remain airworthy. Annual inspections are based on calendar months; therefore, annuals are due on the last day of the twelfth month after the last annual was completed. For example, if the preceding annual was completed on July 8, 2008, the next annual inspection would be due by July 31, 2009.

Annual inspections must be performed regardless of the number of hours flown in the preceding year. Annual inspections may only be performed by airframe and powerplant technicians possessing a valid Inspection Authorization. If the person performing the annual inspection finds a discrepancy that makes the aircraft un-airworthy, the technician is required to provide the aircraft owner with written notice of the discrepancy. Additionally, the defect must be corrected before the aircraft is approved for return to service. In special situations where the aircraft needs to be flown to a different location for repairs to be made, a special flight or ferry permit may be obtained to fly the aircraft to the place for repairs to be made.

100-Hour Inspection

General aviation aircraft operated for flight instruction or hire must be inspected every 100 flight hours. For most types of general aviation aircraft, the 100-hour inspection is in addition to the annual inspection check and often covers the same parameters as the annual inspections. A major difference between the 100-hour and annual inspections is that an A & P technician may perform a 100-hour inspection.

As the 100-hour inspection implies, actual flight hours are the primary consideration for determining when a 100-hour inspection is due. Simply, a 100 hour is required in 100-hour increments after the last 100-hour inspection was completed, regardless of the calendar date. If the aircraft is away from the place where its regular maintenance is performed, there is a provision for extending the 100-hour interval up to 10 hours to allow the aircraft to be flown to its base. However, whenever this is required, the numbers of hours in excess of the 100-hour interval are deducted from the next inspection interval. For example, if it is necessary to fly the aircraft to a facility where a 100-hour inspection can be performed and the flight takes five hours to complete beyond the 100-hour interval, the next 100-hour inspection is due in 95 hours. Simply, the next inspection interval is shortened by the exact amount of time the previous inspection was extended.

Progressive Inspection

A Progressive or Phase Inspection Program is an option for aircraft owners or operators routinely flying more than 400 hours yearly and who do not wish to have their aircraft out of service for several days to complete a 100-hour or annual inspection. A Phase 1 would require an in-depth inspection of the engine and propeller and a brief inspection of the rest of the aircraft. After a specified amount of hours or calendar months, the next phase would do a quick inspection on the engine and fuselage, but require a detailed inspection of wings and landing gear, and so on until the whole aircraft has had a detailed inspection. Usually, a progressive or phase inspection program requires the entire aircraft and all components be inspected within 12 calendar months.

Continuous Inspection Program

A Continuous Inspection Program is designed for operators of large commercial aircraft currently in use by a person holding an air carrier operating certificate or an operating certificate issued under FAR Part 121 or 135. Like the Progressive Inspection program, the Continuous Inspection Program must be approved by the FAA, and allows the owner/operator to maximize aircraft availability and reduce maintenance costs by dividing inspection requirements into regularly scheduled blocks.

Avionics

Modern aircraft navigation and communication systems are a complex mix of computers, sensors, actuators, and control and display units interconnected with many aircraft flight control and other systems. As aircraft systems have increased in sophistication, the avionics component accounts for an increasing proportion of the value of the aircraft. As part of an FBO's aircraft maintenance services, several important avionics checks and inspections must be performed:

Altimeter and Static System

PAR Part 91.411 requires the periodic altimeter and static checks for aircraft that operate in controlled airspace under instrument flight rules. These checks must be completed in accordance with the guidelines of FAR Part 43, Appendix E, and performed every 24 months. Additionally, tests must be performed any time the static system is opened or otherwise disturbed.

Transponder

A transponder is an electronic device that detects incoming radar signals and broadcasts an encoded radio signal to the air traffic control system, providing aircraft identification, altitude, airspeed, and destination. Because of their critical safety role, transponders must be checked every 24 months. Transponders checks are complied with under FAR Part 91.413 in accordance with FAR Part 43, Appendix E.

Emergency Locator Transmitter

Emergency locator transmitters (ELTs) are essential safety devices that have been used in airplanes for decades. When activated, these distress beacons send a signal to FAA air traffic control centers and towers that can pinpoint an aircraft's location. ELTs are automatically activated when the aircraft impacts the ground or water above a certain g-force or can be manually activated by the pilot. FAR Part 91.207 requires that all U.S. aircraft be equipped with an ELT. These devices must be inspected every 12 calendar months for proper operation of the crash sensor, battery condition, and radio strength.

FAR Part 145

FBOs situated at major airports are often affiliated with aircraft manufactures to provide aircraft maintenance and other services such as painting, interior improvements, or engine and component overhauls. In addition to providing flight training, fuel, and crew rest facilities, many FBOs also hold Repair Station Certificates issued by the FAA under FAR Part 145. These certificates are the industry's "license to do business." They authorize repair stations to perform maintenance and alterations on civil aircraft including engine overhauls and propellers, and on the component parts installed on these products. These repair stations can also perform maintenance for airlines and air taxi or charter operators.

Today, many low-cost air carriers do not perform their own heavy maintenance on their respective aircraft fleets. As a result, several large repair stations have emerged or existing repair stations have expanded to accommodate the increased work from these air carriers. In an effort to reduce work force numbers and expenses related to heavy maintenance work, there has been a trend for established air carriers to contract out heavy maintenance work to overseas repair stations that can perform the necessary procedures at substantially reduced costs.

To operate in the civil aviation maintenance industry, certificated repair stations must demonstrate to the FAA that they possess the facilities, equipment, personnel, technical data, and quality control systems necessary to perform maintenance in an airworthy and safe manner. A repair station is rated to perform certain types of maintenance on specific aircraft, engines, or propeller types and components such as generators or governors. Not all repair stations are alike and their capabilities can vary significantly. Some repair stations provide line maintenance, routine work necessary to keep an aircraft operating safely. Some perform substantial maintenance, which includes more comprehensive or progressive inspections and repairs on airframes and overhauls of aircraft engines. Some repair stations offer specialized services such as fuel cells, landing gear overhauls, or aircraft paint.

Flight Operations

In addition to providing maintenance, FBOs are also obviously involved in various aspects of flight operations. Without flight operations, FBOs may only fuel and maintain aircraft. However, the heart of the GA industry gets its start at FBOs in the form of flight training. Even the smallest of FBOs tend to offer flight instruction and aircraft rental. Additionally, some FBOs also offer charter services. Regardless, flight operations, in one form or another, allow an FBO to capitalize on another area of demand and diversify service offerings.

Flight Instruction

Flight instruction is offered by many FBOs, although this tends to be concentrated at smaller FBOs which lie outside busy Class B airspace. This is due to the inherent problems with conducting flight training at busy commercial service airports. Although learning about wake turbulence is important, a first-hand experience behind a B747 will likely be more than a student bargained for!

The offering of flight instruction is critical to continued growth of general aviation. This instruction includes training new pilots and retraining experienced pilots. There are two types of flight training programs, FAR Part 61 and Part 141. The major difference between the two is the amount of structure present in training. Part 141 schools are certificated, as businesses, by the FAA and are periodically audited by the agency. These schools must have a detailed, FAA-approved course curriculum and their students must meet certain minimum performance standards. In contrast, Part 61 schools allow more flexibility to rearrange lesson content and sequence to meet the needs of the student. Depending on the student's overall goals, either type of training may be better and many flight schools offer training under both regulations. Regardless of the governing regulation, all flight training must be provided by FAA-certificated flight instructors (CFI), and, if advanced certificate training is offered, instrument (CFII) and/or multiengine (MEI) instructors are needed, as appropriate.

Aircraft Rental

Most fixed based operators, even the relatively small ones, own at least a few planes that can be rented for short periods of time. Most facilities offer several single-engine piston aircraft with varying degrees of complexity, from the basic two-seat trainer to larger airplanes with retractable gear and an adjustable propeller. Some FBOs offer multiengine aircraft as well. A rental agreement and inspection of the pilot's certificate and currency are always required. Many businesses also require a "check-out" before renting. In an aircraft check-out, one of the school's flight instructors reviews the performance aspects of the aircraft with the renter and then conducts a flight to evaluate the renter pilot's ability to operate the aircraft safely. Aircraft can be rented by the hour, day, week, or for specific trips. Typically, overnight trips require the renter to pay for a minimum number of hours per day (typically four), whether or not the aircraft was actually used. In this way, the FBO is able to ensure a minimum number of rental hours per day (with subsequent revenue) even if the aircraft is away for an extended period.

Aircraft Charter

Other FBOs have a more complete line of aircraft available for chartering. These operators provide a variety of services to the public, including personal aircraft charter, cargo transportation, emergency medical flights, and air tours. Accordingly, a wide range of aircraft is necessary to complete these missions and includes single-engine piston to large, turbine-powered planes, corporate aircraft to helicopters.

Many business firms, including quite a few that own their own planes, utilize chartering services regularly. Some companies prefer to own only one or perhaps two planes and to charter additional aircraft as necessary for special occasions or periods of peak load. Some firms chartering aircraft use only their own crews, but some of the fixed base operators provide crews, if desired. [See chapter 11 for an in-depth discussion of chartering.]

There are over 3,000 on-demand air charter operators nationwide. All operators must hold an Air Carrier Operating Certificate, issued by the Federal Aviation Administration (FAA) and are regulated under FAR Part 135, which sets forth operational, maintenance, training, and other safety requirements. Additionally, pilots and management personnel are subject to minimum qualification standards. A series of regular inspections, spot inspections, routine surveillance and in-depth inspections are all performed by the FAA to ensure compliance with applicable regulations.

Sales

The sales of aircraft, parts, and supplies are yet another form of revenue stream for FBOs. Although new aircraft are in demand and could be sold at an FBO, one typically finds only used aircraft available for sale. The used aircraft market remains strong because used aircraft are more affordable. Additionally, aircraft parts and supplies may be made available for sale at an FBO. FBOs with maintenance services tend to make aircraft parts available for sale as this becomes part of the necessary support for aircraft maintenance, especially if much repair work is done. Supplies may include a number of items, from aircraft supplies to pilot supplies. Typically, if flight instruction is offered, a number of pilot supplies will also be made available for sale.

Aircraft

The addition of an aircraft sales division to an FBO can create many new and different opportunities for enhancing revenue. A sales department typically has the best overhead-to-profit ratio of the entire company. The reason is that there is no need for a large staff or expensive equipment and materials. The salespeople are typically all commission-based, and basic office supplies and some initial marketing money are the main costs involved with the startup. This allows an FBO to grow a sales department from one current employee performing the task on the side, to a department that moves millions of dollars in inventory per year.

The benefits of having a sales department fall into two main categories. The first category consists of the ways in which a sales department functions as its own profit center. The second category relates to the many ways in which the activities of the sales department are able to feed all of the other FBO divisions.

Table 5-1
Typical Aircraft Brokerage Commissions

Price of Aircraft	Brokerage Fee
0 - $500,000	8% - 10%
$500,000 - $1,000,000	6% - 8%
$1,000,000 - $3,000,000	4% - 6%
$3,000,000 - $4,000,000	3% - 4%
$4,000,000 - $5,000,000	2% - 3%
$5,000,000 and Up	1% - 2%

One of the best ways to understand how aircraft sales works as its own profit center is to compare it to the more commonly known business of real estate. Real estate companies acquire listings on houses, sell houses, find houses for people, and even purchase property for investment purposes. The reason people go through a real estate agent is that they are experts in the market, know about the pitfalls in buying a house, advise prospective home buyers on their best course of action, and orchestrate a smooth transaction. For each type of transaction, a percentage of the closing sales price is paid to the real estate company as a fee for professional services rendered. The business of aircraft sales works the same way, only with aircraft.

The percentage of commission on an aircraft deal varies with the price of the aircraft. All percentages are negotiable, but Table 5-1 provides a general breakdown of the fees associated with selling an aircraft.

These percentages charged by the aircraft sales department will vary, based on different situations. For example, if there is competition over an exclusive brokerage on a $6,500,000 Citation, it may be wise to offer brokerage services at one percent instead of two percent that might typically be charged, in that a $65,000 profit, minus expenses, will still be well worth the resources required to make the sale. Ultimately, a sales department exists to create lucrative deals using the best strategy for the given scenario. Skilled negotiation combined with this ability to find the profit in any deal, are the ingredients that can turn an aircraft sales department into the most lucrative profit center within an FBO.

In addition to being a very lucrative profit center with relatively low overhead, a sales department creates an increase in the revenues of all other profit centers of the FBO. The number of ways that an aircraft sales department can create revenue for an FBO are almost endless. In fact, one would be hard pressed to think of an area of an FBO's business that could not benefit from the activities of the sales department.

The maintenance department typically benefits the most as an aircraft transaction provides opportunities for performing log reviews, inspections, squawk repairs, and many different upgrades. Often, deals will hinge on what the potential buyer can be provided concerning their maintenance. Many long-term relationships are created with an FBO's maintenance shop as a direct result of an aircraft purchase.

Speculative purchases of aircraft are another way that an aircraft sales department can help create revenues. The sales department's ability to locate aircraft well below retail price can be lucrative investments for the FBO, as the sales department can sell the aircraft to create profit for the FBO as well as sales. This scenario can be taken a step further with purchasing a group of aircraft that are in need of maintenance at a very good price. This would provide the maintenance department with income, the sales department with income, and the FBO as whole with income.

Charter departments can also benefit, as a sales department can encourage the buyer of an aircraft to place the aircraft into the charter fleet of the FBO to offset expenses. This creates a low risk scenario for the charter department since there is less risk in chartering another's aircraft versus one owned by the FBO. This increase in charter increases traffic through the FBO, creating more opportunity for selling other services.

As an FBO considers offering aircraft sales, a few considerations must be kept in mind. First, is the FBO simply going to offer aircraft brokering or will it also sell aircraft from its own inventory? FBOs can make money on aircraft sales by simply serving as the broker (buyer's agent/seller's agent) of someone else's aircraft. They may also choose to be a dealer and purchase aircraft for their own inventory to sell. Another consideration is that the aircraft sales business is completely unregulated. Anyone claiming to be an aircraft broker or acquisition specialist can perform those services without any training or knowledge of the aircraft sales process. Therefore, FBOs must be cautious in hiring individuals to staff a new aircraft sales division. Experience and references come into play here.

If an FBO decides to offer aircraft sales, what are the keys in selling an aircraft to a client? First, the salesperson must spend a great deal of time understanding client needs, travel history, missions, and the amount of money budgeted for the purchase. A reputable broker will also encourage the buyer to build a team of professionals, including a CPA or tax specialist, attorney for LLC formation and asset protection issues, insurance professional, escrow agent, banker/lender, inspection facility to conduct prepurchase inspections, and possibly pilot(s) to perform a thorough evaluation of the aircraft in-flight. The broker will also assist the buyer in answering the following preliminary questions:

- What is the primary purpose for the aircraft?
- Do you have an aircraft in mind?
- What is your mission?
  - How many passengers typically?
  - Going how far?
  - Which cities/airports?
  - How long will you stay?
  - How often?
- Will the aircraft you're considering work on 80-90% of your missions?
- What is your budget?
- Will you be the pilot or the passenger?
- Will you hire your own crew and manage your own aircraft or hire a professional management firm to manage aircraft for you?
- If the plane will be used for both business and pleasure, in what percentage for each?
- Are you trading an aircraft?
- When would you like your new aircraft to be in service?

Buyers must also be encouraged to "think outside the box." For instance, maybe two smaller aircraft will make more sense than one larger aircraft. Chartering the right aircraft for those few trips the new plane is not well suited for may be a good alternative. Even the largest companies find that alternative methods for supplemental lift may make more sense than a larger plane or larger fleet. Lastly, flying on a major air carrier should also be considered an option if necessary.

Aircraft Parts and Aviation Supplies

In addition to the sale of aircraft, the sale of parts and accessories is an important segment of business for most fixed base operators. The items carried by a well-stocked operator include engines, airframe parts, tires, and avionics components, as well as a wide variety of accessories. All parts are subject to strict FAA standards for tracking, storage, sale, and installation to prevent the introduction of fraudulent parts into the market.

As discussed earlier, offering aircraft parts and aviation supplies can significantly contribute to a diverse revenue stream for an FBO. Aircraft owners/operators will oftentimes not have a choice in having non-scheduled maintenance performed at an FBO, but others will choose to have scheduled maintenance performed if the facilities are clean and modern, if the timeframe for having the work performed is reasonable, and if the price is right. Many FBOs become known in their local areas as being the experts in certain aircraft (Cessna, for instance) and word of mouth will assist these FBOs in continuing to gain more maintenance work on these aircraft. Pilots will purchase aviation supplies if prices are competitive simply due to the convenience of having these items available at the FBO. The FBO must remain competitive with Internet and mail-order sources such as Sporty's Pilot Shop.

Corporate Flight Service

Many of the larger fixed base operators offer a complete corporate flight service for business customers. Under such an arrangement, the owner or FBO supplies the aircraft and the FBO provides the flight, maintenance, and administrative personnel, and is responsible for conducting flight operations, performing maintenance, and handling administrative matters. Thus, the owner is relieved of the responsibilities of running an aviation department and all of the workload associated with it. The client company normally is billed monthly for the actual cost of the service, plus an agreed-upon management fee, which is usually a specified percentage of the cost of the service rendered.

The fixed base operator makes arrangements to acquire the plane or planes to be used by the company and supervises the installation of the appropriate avionics and passenger cabin accommodations. The FBO obtains the hull and liability insurance coverages on the aircraft in accordance with minimums of liability coverage that are normally specified by the operator. The operator handles the assignment of pilots and copilots, either selecting crews from among its own personnel or hiring new personnel especially for the customer's operation. In either event, the flight crews are assigned to the customer company full time, though they remain the employees of the FBO. The operator is responsible for checking out pilot and copilot qualifications, seeing that they receive the appropriate recurrent flight and ground school training, and arranging for the periodic medical examinations required.

The FBO is completely responsible for flight operations, maintenance, and whatever administrative services and personnel are required to provide full service. Responsibility includes establishing safe operational standards for the aircraft and crews regarding such factors as aircraft performance, weather conditions, airport facilities, and crew duty times, as well as providing employees to handle scheduling, clerical, and secretarial duties. Office space is also provided, with furnishings and equipment for the use of the flight and administrative personnel and the customer company's passengers. Maintenance supervision is provided in the typical contract, though the supervisor usually does not work full time for a customer unless the size of the customer's fleet warrants such full-time assignment.

Other Specialized Commercial Flight Services

Some FBOs have arrangements with private and public organizations to provide various specialized commercial flight services. These include aerial advertising, aerial photography, fire fighting, fish spotting, mosquito control, pipeline and powerline surveillance, and wildlife conservation.

Not all FBOs perform all the functions set forth above; indeed, some FBOs may elect to participate as specialists in only one or two categories. However, it is normal for FBOs to perform at least four of the services listed, either as part of their own business or by leasing space to specialists who perform the functions on their own (or leased) premises. A fixed base operator has been compared to a shopping mall manager who is charged with making a profit on each of the many widely diversified individual businesses within the orbit of the overall operation.

KEY TERMS

Maintenance
FAR Part 1
FAR Part 21
FAR Part 23
FAR Part 39
FAR Part 43
FAR Part 65
Airframe Technician
Powerplant Technician
A&P Technician
Inspection Authorization
Repairman Certificate
FAR Part 91
Annual Inspection
100-Hour Inspection
Progressive Inspection
Continuous Inspection Program
Avionics
Altimeter and Static System
Transponder
Emergency Locator Transmitter
FAR Part 145
Flight Instruction
Aircraft Rental
Aircraft Charter
Broker
Commissions

Aircraft Parts
Aviation Supplies
Corporate Flight Service
Other Specialized Commercial Flight Services

REVIEW QUESTIONS

1. Why is maintenance necessary for aircraft? Explain what FARs concern aircraft maintenance.
2. What are the privileges and limitations of aircraft maintenance technicians under FAR Part 65?
3. What is an A&P technician? What is required to become one? What is an IA? What is required to become one?
4. Explain why an annual inspection and 100-hour inspection are necessary.
5. Why would a progressive inspection program or a continuous inspection program be adopted?
6. What avionics require regular inspections?
7. Explain the difference between FAR Part 61 and 141 flight programs.
8. Explain why the addition of an aircraft sales department to an FBO can be beneficial.
9. What are typical commissions charged by aircraft brokers?
10. What must be considered in assisting a buyer with purchasing an aircraft?

SCENARIOS

1. As Manager of the Maintenance Department at a full-service FBO, you are constantly seeking ways in which to cover costs, make a profit, and still price repair and maintenance services competitively with a competing FBO on the field. What are some ideas to accomplish these objectives?
2. It is true that not all FBOs provide aviation maintenance services. Of those that do, however, a number of Federal Aviation Regulations must be complied with. You are currently starting an FBO at a GA facility with no aviation maintenance services currently available. Do you feel it is in your best interest to include aviation maintenance in your start-up plans? If so, what are some considerations you must keep in mind in opening an aviation maintenance shop?
3. In deciding to offer flight instruction at your FBO, you must consider whether to offer these services under FAR Part 61 or FAR Part 141. What are the pros and cons of each? Which will you choose?
4. You were recently hired by FastFlight FBO as an Aircraft Sales Associate. What process would you use in assisting someone with their first purchase of an aircraft? What types of questions would you ask? What commission would you charged based on their budget and preferred aircraft? How would you see the sale through to completion?
5. As the new manager of a small, but growing FBO, you have decided to diversify your offerings. Specifically, you feel that aviation supplies need to be offered for sale. What types of supplies will you offer and how will you cater to your existing customers?
6. Quality control is a necessary component of a good FBO maintenance facility. At a minimum, the FARs must be complied with. However, as an FBO Manager trying his best to control costs, you're hesitant to spend a great deal on quality control. When is it advantageous to adopt various quality control procedures? Is it possible to spend more on quality control than you receive in either direct or indirect benefits?

Chapter 6
Customer Service

OUTLINE

OBJECTIVES

At the end of this chapter, you should be able to:

- Identify internal and external customers.
- Describe methods of effective customer service.
- Properly handle complaints received via the telephone, radio, and face-to-face.
- Discuss the attributes of a good FBO and a bad FBO.
- Highlight various customer service initiatives.
- Discuss the components of an FBO Customer Services Checklist.
- Propose how an FBO in your community could enhance their customer service.

Customers

At the core of every business, FBOs included, are customers. As discussed in this chapter, customers can be internal and external. They can experience the best a business has to offer, or unfortunately, the worst as well. Customers are the group to which FBOs owe their success, for without them, there is no reason to offer services and truly no demand to meet. At the same time, customers can be quite particular regarding their needs and desires. At times, it may seem impossible to meet the needs of every customer. As stated in the past, "You can't be all things to all people." Just as an FBO doesn't cater to every individual in the local area, this quote also provides some insight into the difficulty in attempting to please every customer that walks through the front door of an FBO.

Customer service, and the goal of complete customer satisfaction, is truly an art. Customer service is more than just being nice or smiling. The commitment to customer service is an important component of an FBO's success. Many of us have either directly experienced or heard of poor examples of customer service, including not meeting customer needs, not being knowledgeable about the products available, or simply lacking a professional attitude and courteous manners. News of these negative experiences spread fast in any industry, and this includes aviation. Pilots speak to each other and word will quickly spread about an FBO's lack of customer service and poor customer satisfaction. It is probably even easier to recall personal experiences of poor customer service than positive experiences. Whatever the reason, all FBO managers must be aware of this and realize it is much more efficient to retain a customer than acquire a new one. Retaining a customer begins with a proactive focus on customer service.

Internal

When considering the typical customer of an FBO, we likely picture pilots taxiing their aircraft to the ramp upon landing. While this is true, there is another important customer base as well: internal customers. This customer group includes the individuals working within the company; more specifically, those working by your side and in other departments. Consider this: A&B FBO has three main departments: Flight Operations (which includes line service, charters, maintenance, and flight instruction), Aircraft Sales, and Administration (which includes Finance, Marketing, and Public Relations). Flight Ops does a good job of handling their daily tasks and earning revenue for the company. The aircraft sales division does a great job of enhancing revenue, but rarely communicates with the Flight Ops department. Lastly, employees in administration (including the FBO manager) usually stay on the second floor of the terminal building all day and rarely communicate with the department directors or shift supervisors. In fact, corporate communication is lacking and Flight Ops doesn't understand why they have to fire two flight instructors and delay their acquisition of another training aircraft. The Aircraft Sales Department feels things are great, but has recently been told they must increase gross sales 10 percent next fiscal year. Over time, this FBO begins experiencing major problems internally simply due to lack of communication and lack of internal customer service.

Internal customers are as important as external customers, because if the business does not communicate effectively, with all departments working toward the same goals and objectives, the business will suffer. Employee morale will decline, employee productivity will suffer, and the achievement of company goals will be delayed, if not sidelined altogether. As this occurs, it will become obvious to external customers and prove extremely difficult to offer superior levels of customer service to these external customers. In essence, people make up the industry. They fly the planes, they travel on the planes, they service the planes, and they maintain the planes. Therefore, without a clear, concerted effort to focus on people (customer service, in other words), any FBO, or any company, will likely experience financial difficulty as a result.

External

In addition to the internal customers of an FBO, external customers are important. In fact, it is sometimes easier to focus on external customers because they are the typical customers for which the FBO operates. The two main customer groups of an FBO are pilots (or flight crews) and their passengers. These external customers serve as the core customer base for an FBO. If one thinks of instances in which they experienced either positive or negative customer service, they most likely were the external customer that company was interacting with.

Let's consider a negative customer service experience at an FBO—Bob's FBO, for the sake of discussion. You just landed and are taxiing your Cessna 172 up to the only FBO on the field. You don't see a line service specialist and really have no idea where to park. You look up the FBO frequency and give them a call on the radio. No answer. You call ground control and are told, "They're hardly ever there. Just park wherever." Disappointed, you taxi a bit further and pull into a tie-down spot on the ramp. Just as you shut down your engine and are about to exit the aircraft, a line service specialist runs up to your aircraft and says, "You should have parked over there!" As he points to another tie-down spot, you can't help but wonder how you were supposed to know this. After all, they didn't answer your radio call and had no one on the ramp to direct you to a proper parking spot. This first impression of this FBO is obviously a negative one. What do you do? You tell your pilot friends, "Stay away from Bob's FBO."

As an important external customer, you were poorly treated and will likely not return to this FBO. However, the wise FBO manager realizes how important external customers are and will focus a great deal of effort on continuously improving customer service to meet the needs of these customers. Without positive customer service, an FBO may see the number of based aircraft decline, hangar rentals not renewed, fuel sales decline, employees resigning, and a number of other consequences of poor customer service. Customer service, and specifically, external customer service, is becoming one way in which successful FBOs are able to differentiate themselves from the competition. In fact, *Aviation International News* regularly conducts an Annual FBO Survey which includes areas such as line service, passenger amenities, pilot amenities, and facilities. Interestingly, when examining the results and specific comments received from survey participants, much of the ratings center around customer service. It is clear that the highly-rated FBOs offer excellent customer service and place an emphasis on their external (and likely internal) customers. Likewise, FBOs with poor customer service are not highly rated in this annual survey.

What are the main external customer groups of an FBO? Obviously, pilots and their passengers are the largest group. This group will expect aircraft fueling, aircraft marshalling, aircraft cleaning, catering, clean and convenient facilities, and information. Specifically, upon arriving on the ramp, flights crews think:

- "Will anyone be available to show me where to park?"
- "Will ground transportation be waiting?"
- "Will anyone be available to assist with offloading baggage?"
- "Will the catering be available for the departing flight?"
- "Will the line service specialists have knowledge in handling my aircraft and taking care of my servicing needs?"

The successful FBO will anticipate these questions and meet these needs without delay. Yet another group of customers with which an FBO may interact are potential flight training students. These are individuals who are interested in aviation and have decided (or are considering) to start flight instruction. They may be apprehensive about the financial requirements, their abilities, and the physiological effects of flight. Therefore, these customers must be treated with respect and taught about aviation as they are entering the process of flight instruction. They will expect clean, modern aircraft, competent and friendly flight instructors, and clean and adequate facilities. Yet another external customer group is the potential aircraft sales customers. These individuals (or organizations) will be in the market for an aircraft and will demand knowledgeable salespeople, well-priced and well-maintained aircraft, and the ability to investigate their many options without being hassled or pressured into making a premature purchase.

Clearly, the wise FBO manager realizes the diverse customer groups and their many needs. This person will understand the importance of customer service (both internal and external) and conduct training classes for employees. Some FBOs have utilized the Walt Disney Co., Ritz-Carlton, or Dale Carnegie for specific customer service training. This training is beneficial in that it requires employees to consider the importance of customer service and learn the skills necessary to provide exemplary customer service within the FBO environment. Training will seem ineffective, however, if management does not model appropriate customer service skills. Management should be aware of the internal and external customers of the FBO and focus on providing excellent customer service to these two customer groups. Additionally, it will seem ineffective if employees are not empowered to exceed customer needs. Employees should be given the ability to think outside the box and, within reason, utilize company resources to address customer concerns and exceed expectations. Most likely, this will require guidance so that employees understand the boundaries of this empowerment. However, once empowered, the manager will be surprised at the ability of employees to resolve concerns and complaints before they ever reach the desk of the FBO manager.

Methods of Effective Customer Service

Just as there are proper ways to fuel an aircraft, there are also proper ways to interact with customers to ensure a delightful experience. While some of these methods may seem obvious, it is amazing how many companies today lack employees who exhibit these basic customer service skills. As stated before, companies without a proactive position on customer service will likely see sales and customers decline. This can be so severe that the FBO is unable to prosper and eventually goes out of business.

Telephone Procedures

As with many businesses, the first point of contact with an FBO may be via a telephone call. Thus, it is extremely important that those answering the phone do so in a professional and courteous manner. Although this may seem obvious, the wise FBO manager does not assume that every employee answers the phone properly. Indeed, training in telephone procedures is recommended.

First, employees must be taught to answer the phone professionally and with a smile in the voice. How does one smile through the telephone? In simple terms, they speak in an upbeat manner with a positive tone in their voice. It is easy to tell if someone is having a bad day just by speaking to them on the phone. Obviously, even if an employee is not having the best day, this should not be obvious in their voice.

Next, in answering the telephone, the employee should identify their company and themselves. You have likely called a business before only to find yourself asking, "Is this Bob's Pizza Palace?" If the employee had answered the phone properly, there would have been no question. Thus, the proper manner in which to answer the telephone is as follows: "Hello. Thank you for calling Expert FBO. This is Wendy." The employee may also offer assistance to the caller, but should avoid speaking a paragraph as they answer the phone. In busy times, the employee answering the phone may find herself saying, "Expert FBO. This is Wendy." Even so, she has followed proper telephone protocol by identifying the company and herself.

While on the telephone, it may be helpful to take notes. This is especially important if the caller is giving specific directions or making a long request that may be difficult to remember. With experience, one will develop a shorthand method to use in copying down the most pertinent information in each phone call. Although jotting down a few notes takes time and may take the employee away from other duties, one must avoid the tendency to check e-mails or listen to another employee while listening to a customer on the telephone. These distractions will make it obvious to the caller that they are not important, and will be perceived as poor customer service.

Additionally, one must use caution when receiving another phone call while currently on the phone. It is best to ask the caller if they can hold, greet the second caller and ask them to hold, and then return to the first caller and finish the conversation. In this way, the second caller won't be lost (unless the hold time grows much longer than one minute), and the first caller will likely not be offended.

In summary, proper telephone procedures require a positive mental attitude, good listening skills, an enthusiastic and knowledgeable employee, and a customer focus. Clearly, the employees answering incoming telephone calls can have a positive impact on the company image. Conversely, if these employees don't follow proper telephone procedures, they may have a substantial negative impact on the company. Thus, FBO managers must educate employees about proper telephone etiquette and explain that current and potential customers can be won or lost on the telephone.

Radio Communications

In addition to interacting with current and potential customers on the telephone, FBO personnel will likely also interact with customers (both internal and external) via a radio. This includes company radio, Air Traffic Control (ATC) ground radio, and air to ground radio. Company radio will be used most often to communicate with fellow employees. This is especially useful in the ramp environment as line service specialists are busy fueling aircraft and towing aircraft. Occasionally, a line service specialist may need to communicate with the ATC ground control. Normally, if the line service specialist has the need to be on the movement area (to retrieve a disabled aircraft, for example), an escort would be provided by Airport Operations, who would also make all necessary ATC radio calls. Most often, the air to ground radio will be used. This allows people on the ground to communicate directly with an aircraft in flight. This is initiated by the flight crew in advance of their arrival to express their needs and coordinate servicing.

The key to effective radio communication is to relay information with a minimum number of words. Lengthy requests only create frequency congestion, which only interferes with others attempting to speak on the same frequency. Prior to speaking, it is important to listen momentarily to avoid "stepping on" another conversation. The following is a typical radio conversation one would expect to hear at an FBO:

Pilot: "Tampa Jet Center, this is Eclipse 586 golf hotel."

FBO: "586 golf hotel this is Tampa Jet Center."

Pilot: "586 golf hotel will be landing at Tampa International in 15 minutes and we will need fuel and a courtesy car. Our passenger states he has your boardroom reserved as well."

FBO: "586 golf hotel, understand 15 minutes to arrival and we'll be ready with fuel and courtesy car. Boardroom is reserved for Mr. Hanes."

Pilot: "Roger, 586 golf hotel."

This radio transmission is typical, and although the actual requests may vary, you can see how a great deal of information was relayed in a short period of time by using few words and focusing on pertinent information.

Handling Complaints

Inevitably, regardless of the superior level of customer service being provided, customers may complain about something. These complaints, no matter how trivial, must be treated seriously and with the utmost professionalism. Often, a customer may simply be having a bad day and may be angry with circumstances that are completely out of the employee's control. Sometimes the complainant may be quite agitated and confrontational. The FBO employee should never place himself in a dangerous situation. If necessary, assistance should be requested. By listening to customer needs and striving to satisfy those needs, the employee can effectively resolve complaints and maintain high levels of customer relations. Complaints may be received in the form of verbal or written communication.

If the complaint is received via verbal communication (most likely the telephone), it is best to simply listen and do so carefully. As mentioned, the complainant may simply need to blow off some steam. By simply listening, the customer will be allowed to vent his frustrations. While doing this, the individual answering the call should be taking some notes. This will enable a specific response to the caller's concerns, rather than saying, "I know how you feel," (which, most likely, isn't true). This leads to the need to show empathy. The employee must put herself in the caller's shoes, but should not claim to know how the caller feels to have aircraft flying over his house every few minutes, for example. Also, one must avoid placing blame. "It's not our fault, it's the pilots'" is not a satisfactory response. The FBO personnel answering the complaint are not there to place blame. Rather, they are there to listen to the complaint and resolve it as best as possible. In particular, one must avoid being defensive. The employee must remain calm and not take this personally. Once the caller has expressed the problem, the employee must clarify understanding of the actual complaint, thank the caller for bringing it to her attention and be sure to follow through on any agreed-upon solution or response to the situation.

An in-person complaint will be handled similarly to a telephone complaint, with minor differences. First, one must remember to maintain eye contact as he listens to the complaint. If able, one should take some notes, but not become preoccupied with this. If note taking seems excessive, the complainant will likely feel as if she is being ignored. That, of course, will simply make the situation worse. Actually, if responding to an in-person complaint, one has the advantage of using body language to positively impact the situation. A warm smile and non-defensive gestures will go a long way in easing the tension and positively resolving the complaint.

Going Above and Beyond

What does it mean to go above and beyond? It means doing more than what is expected of you, either by your manager or the customer. This is not easy to teach, as employees will likely feel that doing the minimum is all that is expected. Therefore, the wise FBO manager will create a corporate culture that supports going above and beyond in all situations. Although a manager may be tentative at first, if properly created, an environment such as this will positively impact the business and level of customer service offered by the business.

Several things are necessary to create a culture of going

above and beyond. First, employees must truly sense this culture by observing management model this behavior. If management is apathetic about the company or does the minimum to address employee concerns or customer concerns, employees will sense that the "above and beyond" talk is only that—talk. Therefore, managers and supervisors must model this high level of customer service for both internal and external customers.

Additionally, once employees understand the focus on going above and beyond, they need another tool. This tool is referred to as empowerment. Employees must know they are empowered to handle any situations that arise in their daily work. Even extraordinary circumstances should not derail a well-intentioned employee. This, of course, requires management trust and the confidence that employees are knowledgeable and well-equipped to provide such superior levels of customer service. Empowerment is more than simply telling employees to do whatever is necessary to please the customer. This may result in inappropriate use of company resources. For instance, an employee may decide to give a tenant free hangar rent for one month because the hangar was dirty upon move-in. Specifically, management must create guidance for employees so that any limits are known about the use of company resources. This guidance, typically in the form of a Standard Operating Procedure, will inform employees of the expectation by management that employees will handle and address most, if not all, customer concerns. It may give examples of ways to handle certain situations and give specific guidance on dollar amounts or maximum uses of company resources. It will likely also educate employees about the need to involve management if a customer cannot be satisfied within these boundaries.

Non-income Services

In addition to positively interacting with customers and effectively addressing customer concerns, customer service at an FBO can be enhanced by offering non-income services. In addition to income-producing services (such as fuel sales and aircraft rental), these non-income services create convenience and enhance the well-being of its customers.

Indeed, these services typically figure highly into the level of customer satisfaction at an FBO. Depending on location, market, and customer demands, any or all of these services may be available. One of the most rapidly emerging of these amenities is the provision of designated areas for business travelers. Many aviation businesses now offer private meeting rooms, phones, fax machines, photocopiers, high-speed Internet access, and plenty of electrical outlets to recharge the many electronic gadgets in use today. Conference rooms may also be made available to allow interactive presentations with clients. Wireless internet (Wi-Fi) is becoming more popular and allows customers to access the Internet from their laptops anywhere in the FBO.

Other commonly provided services are:

- Clean rest rooms and showers.
- Pilot lounges and sleeping quarters.
- Preflight planning rooms.
- Pilot supplies.
- Recreational facilities.
- Vending machines and/or a restaurant.
- Rental and/or courtesy cars.
- In-flight catering.
- Hotel accommodations.
- Tourist/visitor activities.

Clearly, these services cost the FBO money and yet don't directly bring in revenues. However, by spending money on these services, the FBO will likely attract additional customers and see an increase in revenues as a result. Specifically when referring to business/corporate aviation, the flight crew and passengers flying in a $20 million private aircraft will expect these services at an FBO. As such, non-income services are proving to be a major competitive factor among FBOs today.

What Makes a Good FBO?

Clearly, some FBOs do a much better job of meeting customer needs and going above and beyond customer expectations than others. What exactly makes a good FBO? The following comments were obtained by *Aviation International News* during their 2006 and 2007 FBO surveys.

FBOs are the transition point between ground and on-demand air transportation. Timely and efficient handling of the passengers first (if the boss isn't happy nobody's happy). Efficient and correct servicing of the aircraft. A comfortable place to wait for the crew and the passengers, and a comfortable way to get a good meal.

A good FBO is one that teaches its workers that they are not just employees, but are part of each flight department that comes in. They are my extended flight crew away from home.

Number one is customer service. The passengers aren't there very long, but the crew is. A good crew lounge with plenty of easy chairs.

Responsiveness, communication skills, follow-up and a thorough and pleasant demeanor. I need to feel confident that the FBO understands my requests, is operating as part of our team, and is willing to do what it takes to help us execute a successful trip.

A pilot is stressed enough without having to worry about the essentials such as fuel, passenger services, and so on. A good FBO takes care of the 'essentials' without me worrying about it.

Service, service, and service! Get the fuel in the tank in a timely manner. Ask me if I need anything else: ice, coffee, newspapers.... I don't mind paying more than average for good service.

Take care of the passengers, take care of the airplane, take care of the pilots, in that order.

Desk people who can keep a lot of balls in the air at the same time and still be friendly.

An operation that makes my job easier.

Prompt service, a warm greeting, and a good attitude. The best can't seem to do enough for you.

Line service awareness to flight crew servicing needs without having to track someone down.

An FBO that puts the customer first regardless of how much is spent.

The way you are received and treated; it shouldn't matter if you are first-time users or regulars.

Responsive, professional line service. Anything that makes my job easier.

Taking care of the passengers first. Once they are on their way and happy, attending to the needs of the crew. Fair pricing in services with a good attitude.

Smiles, smiles, smiles! It gets busy in the cockpit. At times the stress involved with our "trained for" job can get quite high, fighting ATC, passengersm and dispatchers. The problems FBO personnel are having should never interfere with the flight crew.

Safety must be the number one priority of employees.

Although these comments point to many things, the essence of most of the comments pertains to customer service. FBOs offering excellent customer service are those FBOs most preferred by customers and more likely to be rated very high in terms of customer satisfaction.

What Makes a Bad FBO?

At the same time, there are specific things that make a poor impression on customers and translate into being considered a bad FBO. The following comments were obtained by *Aviation International News* during their 2006 and 2007 FBO surveys.

Linemen who don't really care and are going through the motions. Customer service that comes across like they are doing me a favor. A place that charges premium prices and thinks it is doing a better job than they guy down the ramp.

One that doesn't understand that customer service and presentation are most important. They are the gateway to their communities in some cases, and the impression they show can make or break the experience.

If there is no place for the pilots to relax and take care of business (Internet and phone service), it makes for a very long day for a crew that has a several-hour layover.

Dumpy facility, indifferent service, poor flight planning amenities. Internet is nice to have for flight-planning these days, too.

One bad encounter with an FBO employee will stick in your mind for years, no matter how good the FBO has been in the past. Rude, unfriendly, and unhelpful associates will kill an FBO faster than anything. The FBOs that make you feel like you're the most important aircraft on the field are the ones I remember forever.

A rigid 'can't do' attitude. A cold, sterile, indifferent environment and an unwillingness to help the crew with their special needs coupled with poor crew facilities.

I go to great lengths to notify an FBO of my arrival and requests. If I get there and I seem to be a surprise, nobody is there to marshal me in and out, and/or I'm dealing with people who don't seem to know anything about aviation, then I get a bit disappointed.

Unfriendly CRSs, absentee line techs and unfulfilled requests are at the top of the list. At some FBOs, you'd think that it was their first time to fuel an airplane.

Poor supervision. You can't manage an FBO if you don't know what goes on outside your office.

Distracted CSRs (personal phone calls, issues, and so on) who delay transmittal of information to ramp personnel regarding needed crew/aircraft services.

Discounts only to large fleet operators while gouging smaller operators with exorbitant handling fees even if that operator doesn't use any of their facilities.

Not open at published hours, won't answer the radio, telephone long hold time, slow service, theft.

Requiring me to sign a hold harmless [agreement] before they will tow or store my aircraft.

A business that gives line people minimal training and turns them loose on the line by themselves.

Walking up to the counter and no one wanting to even look at you because they are chatting amongst themselves, and then after pulling themselves away with great effort (and usually a sigh), not even asking if I need something, or a hello or a greeting, only a blank stare.

Absence of safety.

Slow service, long faces, unclean facilities.

Although many complaints about FBOs concern high jet fuel prices, high ramp fees, and outdated and unclean facilities, most of the complaints stem from poor customer service. Clearly, it is a challenge for FBOs to hire and retain top-notch personnel. Yet, it is imperative if the FBO wants to experience success and high customer satisfaction. By reviewing the comments above, future FBO managers can learn what not to do, and instead focus on the correct things to do to ensure success.

Customer Service Initiatives

As indicated in the *Aviation International News* survey results, amenities are important among pilots, but service remains the most important factor among FBO customers. As one FBO manager said, "People make the biggest difference." As FBOs are trying to differentiate themselves in the comparative market, it is apparent that success stems from a proactive effort to enhance customer service. This effort, in the form of customer service initiatives, is increasingly important.

Excellent customer service begins with hiring the right employees. As discussed in chapter 15, this process can be time consuming, but very rewarding for the organization. As one FBO discovered, while being housed in temporary facilities and being able to increase fuel sales every month, business success is about the people and the service. How are FBOs able to continually improve in this area? An FBO may check rental and courtesy cars upon return to check for cell phones or other items left behind. This, in the words of one FBO manager, is about having "proactive customer service."

As any FBO manager would know, employees do not automatically begin providing excellent customer service the day they're hired. Thus, it is important for FBOs to train and educate employees in safety and customer service to ensure that this culture of positive customer service continues. There are companies that specialize in providing such training to FBOs. This training focuses on teaching employees how to focus on the customer and simplify the customer interaction. For example, rather than waiting on a customer to request something, employees are taught to be proactive and attempt to meet these needs before they're voiced. Whether contracting with a company specializing in service or conducting in-house training on this issue, successful FBOs realize that providing excellent customer service is a journey, not a destination. This requires continual training, education, and emphasis on the employee/customer interaction.

In addition to providing employees the resources they need to provide excellent customer service, it is imperative that an FBO gauge the level of customer satisfaction on a regular basis. Otherwise, how will an FBO manager know what level of customer service is being provided or if customers are satisfied with this level of service? One way to accomplish this objective is to employ mystery shoppers. This mystery shopper would generally fly into the airport, land, and taxi to the FBO just as a typical customer would. This person would also request services and "shop" like the typical customer, all the while paying particular attention to the level of customer service they are experiencing. This information would then be relayed to the FBO manager for data analysis to gauge the actual levels of customer service at his/her FBO. Another way to gauge customer service levels is to conduct surveys with customers. Similar to *Aviation International News'* nationwide survey, an FBO would conduct a local survey with customers and tenants to gauge levels of satisfaction and recognize areas for improvement. Typically, customers only voice comments if something needs to be improved, but a survey with all customers would allow both kudos and concerns to be voiced, which would allow the FBO to improve in certain areas and give praise in other areas.

FBO Customer Services Checklist

Exemplary service to customers is going to take on added significance for FBOs wishing to survive competition during the future. Whether the customer is a prospective student pilot seeking flight instruction, a business requesting a charter flight, or a corporate operator looking for a maintenance or line service facility, service becomes an important element in distinguishing competitors.

The following section provides a checklist of accepted practices and procedures designed to improve service to customers.

Ramp Area

A well thought out ramp area will not only enhance the appearance of an FBO, it will reduce the possibility of ramp accidents and increase the utilization of equipment. Good ramp planning can also improve fuel service and tie-down business.

1. Training aircraft should be parked for easy access from the flight office. Parking should be arranged to place the most active aircraft in the most accessible spots. There should be adequate room for students to taxi safely in and out of parking areas.
2. When possible, one-way, flow-through taxi routes should be provided. Lead-in stripes to guide aircraft into parking spots should be painted brightly. All obstructions close to taxi routes should be marked with high-visibility caution signs or symbols, according to standard airport markings and signage.
3. One-way, flow-through traffic paths to fuel islands should be used. A refueling parking spot for fuel truck operations should be designated so that it does not conflict with normal traffic flow.
4. If flood lighting is impractical or causes glare, a series of low (below wing level) ground illuminating lights should be considered. The refueling area should be well-lighted.
5. To attract transient aircraft, high visibility signs should be positioned to be seen from taxiways announcing transient fuel service. Lead-in signs and/or taxiway markings with lead-in stripes should indicate the route to refueling and parking areas.
6. The following items of ramp equipment should be provided in sufficient number, in good repair, and conveniently located:
   - Tugs
   - Tow bars
   - Ladders and stands
   - Power units
   - Jacks
   - Nitrogen, oxygen, and air tanks
   - Deicing equipment
   - Lavatory flush carts
   - Survival gear (life rafts, radios, etc.) at ports of debarkation
   - Avionics and component repair equipment to the extent that such service is offered or intended
   - Windshield cleaner and cleaning cloths
   - Oil wipe cloths
   - Chocks numbered to tie-down spots
   - Equipment lockers at strategic points on the flight line
   - Covered trash containers

Ground Personnel

The dispatcher and/or receptionist personnel should be responsible for the following areas:

- Complete understanding of and ability to explain:
  - Company rental policy and agreements
  - FAA pilot certificates, medical certificates, and Federal Communication Commission (FCC) radio license
  - Federal Aviation Regulations (FAR) currency requirements
  - Company insurance policies
  - Student enrollment procedures
  - Part 141 student record requirements
  - FAA, FCC, and Veterans Administration (VA) forms
  - Flight training and services fee schedule
  - Information regarding rental car service, hotel, or motel facilities including rates, discounts, and distances
- Familiar with all Unicom regulations, procedures, and responsibilities.
- Rescheduling customers after each flight.
- Calling customers who have become inactive.
- Training in telephone sales techniques.
- Use of an inquiry form to record the maximum amount of data from incoming phone inquiries.
- Assume duties that relieve flight instructors from routine tasks and allow more time for training.
- Monitor students' progress (ground school and flight training).

Line personnel are often the first interaction customers have with an FBO. As a result, they must be professional and well-qualified to perform their jobs. They should be responsible for the following areas:

- Thoroughly trained in the following aspects of line service (see chapter 4):
  - The nature, coding, and handling of all aircraft servicing materials

  - All aircraft servicing procedures
  - Aircraft towing and ground handling procedures
  - Ramp safety procedures
  - Aircraft spotting and parking techniques
  - All ramp signaling techniques
- Be in uniform or dress that is immediately identifiable to transient pilots.
- Develop a system of alert so that personnel are stationed where they can see incoming aircraft.
- Train personnel to respond to customer service requests immediately. All employees should be instructed on the importance of a safe, prompt, efficient, dependable, and courteous service attitude to all customers. Some larger FBOs employ a customer service representative to meet all incoming business aircraft, their passengers, and crews.

Aircraft

Aircraft must not only be airworthy, they must look airworthy. Nothing can add to the apprehension of a student or renter pilot more than an aircraft that looks unsafe to fly. The following list includes those items which demonstrate care and professionalism.

- A clean and polished exterior finish
- A clean engine compartment
- Tires in good condition and properly inflated
- Widows clean inside and out
- A clean interior (trash removed, seat belts straightened, etc.)
- All interior trim panels in good repair
- Carpeting clean and in good repair
- Instrument panel and anti-glare shield finish in good repair
- Upholstery clean and in good repair
- All knobs, levers, and switches in place and functioning
- All unused instrument cutouts, avionics bays, etc., properly covered or blanked out
- All loose equipment properly stowed and secured
- All checklists, frequency reminders, etc., professionally printed and durable
- All manuals and required paperwork on board and properly stowed or displayed

Flight Personnel

The demands on flight instructors should go far beyond pilot skills. The instructors must have ability in teaching, consulting, customer relations, and salesmanship. Flight instructors should be responsible for the following areas:

- Maintaining a professional attitude about teaching.
- Currency in the following:
  - All applicable FARs
  - All FAA recommended flight procedures and techniques.
  - Latest teaching techniques
- Many FBOs require instructors to attend revalidation seminars. Regularly scheduled meetings with instructors to review recent changes and developments are also utilized. Information bulletins explaining recent changes and developments are distributed on a regular basis.
- A system to standardize the following procedures and techniques used by instructors:
  - Teaching methods
  - Flight procedures and maneuvers
  - Semantics
  - Student evaluation
  - Flight and ground curriculum
- A program of standardization flights with the chief pilot can be established so that all instructors are teaching from the same syllabus.
- A policy to eliminate conflict between student instruction and charter flights. Some FBOs schedule a specific day for each instructor to fly charter. The manager or chief pilot can fly all charters that conflict with an instructor's training schedule.
- A plan for the continued upgrading of instructors' image and prestige. An area for student briefings and conferences (preferably including an office, cubicle or desk with nameplate). Some FBOs provide business cards for each instructor, as well as company shirts and/or jackets with the FBO logo and instructor's name. If aircraft use permits, one aircraft could be assigned to each instructor with the individual's name on the door.
- An incentive system to increase instructor remuneration. This might include incremental increases for such things as night instrument and multiengine training. A higher rate could be established for total hours after a pre-selected weekly minimum.
- An understanding of sales and customer relations. Some FBOs pay bonuses to instructors whose students complete an entire course. Finders' fees are sometimes paid to instructors who recruit students. A small override fee is often established for a student's solo time.

The responsibilities of the chief pilot vary depending on the size and complexity of the fixed base operation and whether the chief pilot is also the manager. However, the following responsibilities should apply to most operations.

- Maintaining a close relationship with local FAA personnel

- Developing flight and ground school curricula
- Conducting standardization flight for staff instructors
- Conducting student phase check flights
- Conducting regular instructor meetings to maintain standardization, review problem areas, and develop new methods
- Providing written information for instructors and students on operational techniques and procedures
- Maintaining student records and FAA reports
- Monthly status reports to management
- Maintaining a list of available local CFIs
- Maintaining an open door policy to listen to student or instructor problems
- Make regular checks on student attitudes
- Conduct introductory flights and tours of the facility
- Establish a program to recruit new students and improve attrition

Clearly, many things must be considered when committing to an environment of excellent customer service. Training, non-income services, and proper facilities all require financial commitments by the FBO, but are essential in maintaining a competitive position and ensuring "above and beyond" customer service well into the future.

KEY TERMS

Internal customers
External customers
Customer service
Telephone procedures
Radio communications
Complaints
Above and Beyond
Non-income services
Good FBO
Bad FBO
Customer Services Checklist

REVIEW QUESTIONS

1. What are the differences between internal and external customers? Are both groups important? Why?
2. What are some considerations in effectively answering the telephone?
3. What are some considerations when communicating via radio?
4. What are some considerations in handling complaints?
5. What does it mean to "go above and beyond"?
6. What are non-income services? Discuss their importance.
7. Summarize what makes a good FBO and a bad FBO.
8. Discuss some recent customer service initiatives adopted by FBOs.
9. What can an FBO do to improve efficiency and customer service in the ramp area? Describe some of the areas that ground personnel should be responsible for in carrying out their duties efficiently. Explain some of the little things that can be done to make aircraft look better.
10. The demands of flight instructors should go far beyond pilot skills. Explain.
11. Describe some of the responsibilities of the chief pilot.

REFERENCES

Aviation International News 2006 FBO Survey.
Aviation International News 2007 FBO Survey.
NATA Safety First Program.

SCENARIOS

1. As the manager of a full-service FBO at a large GA airport, you are aware of staying competitive. A pilot just taxied into your FBO and complained to the line service specialist that fuel prices were too high. He is about to purchase 500 gallons and is demanding a discount. How do you handle this?
2. You are working the front desk at the FBO you have been employed at for the past year. As you answer the phone, you hear, "These planes are driving me crazy! They are too noisy and I want you to make them stop! If not, I'll be calling Channel 10!" This is a typical day at your FBO and airport. How do you address this caller's concern and handle this complaint?
3. Your FBO manager recently held a customer service training class for all employees. In that class, he explained that the FBO is subscribing to a new standard of customer service: "Going above and beyond." In class, he presented some scenarios and asked you to explain how you would address each of the following situations:
   a. A long-time customer of your FBO, Mark Jenkins, is planning a trip out on Saturday at 0600 (L). Mr. Jenkins has a Lear 35 in your community hangar that will need to be out and ready to go. You and another coworker also remember that this Saturday is Mr. Jenkins' fortieth birthday. How could you "go above and beyond" for Mr. Jenkins?
   b. A pilot taxiing in calls on the radio and asks if a rental car could be reserved for his two passengers. You realize that a car is available and decide to go above and beyond in meeting this pilot's needs. How can you do that?

   c. Three passengers just arrived on a King Air and would like to use the FBO conference room to conduct some business. Unfortunately, the conference room is already in use by another customer. What are your options?

4. Your manager just asked you to develop some customer service guidelines for the line service division. He says, "Our crew is typically the first to interact with a customer on the ramp and we need some guidelines so each of these employees understands the value of customer service and knows what excellent customer service on the ramp looks like." What are some guidelines you could develop to assist these employees?
5. As an Assistant FBO Manager, you know how important excellent customer service is to your FBO. Recently, you have been studying the non-income services offered by a competitor and feel that your FBO needs to begin offering more non-income services for pilots and their passengers. However, your boss (the FBO Manager), feels these things are a waste of money. "If it doesn't make us money, we're not paying for it!" How do you persuade him of the need to adopt more non-income services to enhance your FBO's image and create more customer satisfaction?
6. While working the front desk, an irate customer (Chief Pilot of a Hawker 850XP) confronts you about lack of service personnel on the ramp. He has waited 30 minutes for jet fuel, and his departure will be delayed as a result. "I will never return to this FBO. Your lack of service is unacceptable," he states. As you listen to him, you formulate your response. What do you say?
7. The FBO at which you are the manager recently conducted a survey of based and transient customers. Overall, the results were disappointing. Particularly, customer service (in all areas) was ranked quite low. As FBO Manager, what is your next step?
8. You have been anxiously awaiting this day—the grand opening of your FBO. It's not going to be easy, though, because there is an established FBO already on the field. What can you do to differentiate your FBO from the competition?
9. In an effort to enhance the FBO you currently manage, you asked an aviation consultant to conduct an independent audit of your facility. In the report, it was noted that customer service could be improved upon. Specifically, the consultant stated that "employees are lacking customer service skills. Consequently, additional training and support is needed in this area." What are some of your options to address this?
10. You are the new manager of a full-service FBO that has a record of poor customer service. As part of your effort to improve in this area, you ask the employees about their ideas. Many say that they would do more, if only they could. They explain the former manager did not give them much latitude at all when it came to dealing with customers and handling their concerns/complaints. So, you say, the employees just need to be empowered. How do you do this?

Notes

PART THREE:
MARKETING AN FBO

Chapter 7
The Role of Marketing

OUTLINE

OBJECTIVES

At the end of this chapter, you should be able to:

- Trace the evolution of marketing through three distinct periods of development.
- Define the marketing concept and explain its importance to an organization's success.
- Define marketing.
- Explain the importance of determining objectives in quantifiable terms.
- Identify and highlight the steps in the process of segmenting the market.
- Differentiate the three approaches to target marketing.
- Describe each of the four Ps in the marketing mix.
- Discuss the factors involved in implementing and controlling marketing plans.
- Describe the uncontrollable variables that can affect a firm's marketing efforts.

Marketing Defined

Every day throughout the world an immeasurable number of goods and services trade hands. Why do individuals and businesses purchase particular products and services? Simply, marketing. The role of marketing in our modern society is much greater than many appreciate. Some even suggest that the price of products and services could be reduced by 30 percent to 50 percent if all marketing activities were eliminated. Is this elimination a viable alternative? Marketing is a powerful force in the world economy. Marketing is responsible for creating demand, goods and services, and jobs in many related fields like research, advertising, wholesaling, retailing, and transportation. Marketing has been a major factor in the increased quality of life enjoyed by developed countries throughout the world.

Contemporary marketing efforts are far different from those used in the past. The evolution of marketing can be traced through three distinct periods of development. The first period, known as the production era, covered the period of time from about 1870 to 1930. This era was characterized as a seller's market, where demand for products exceeded the supply. Firms concentrated on efficient production to offer products that were well made. This production thinking worked due to limited competition and the imbalance between demand and supply. During this production era, marketing was not needed. By 1930, however, technology had drastically changed and allowed manufacturers to produce more goods than they could sell. This created a buyers market, where supply exceeded demand, and was referred to as the sales era. During the sales era, manufacturers focused on aggressively selling the oversupply of their products. Their philosophy was to "sell what the firm could efficiently make, rather than making what the firm could sell." The initial marketing function that was introduced was one of aggressive sales tactics that often had the opposite of the desired effect because the customer was offended and refused to purchase the product. The sales era continued until the mid1950s when customers became more selective and demanded products that better fit their needs. The third and current era is best known as the marketing concept era and emphasizes customer need fulfillment and customer satisfaction. The marketing concept is a customer-oriented, integrated, goal-oriented philosophy for the firm. It means that a firm aims all its efforts at satisfying its customers—for a profit. Instead of just trying to persuade customers to buy what the firm is selling, a firm implementing the marketing concept tries to produce what customers need and want. Market research (discussed in chapter 9) plays an important role in assisting the firm to identify and monitor customer satisfaction. The three components of the marketing concept are (1) a customer orientation, (2) a total company effort, and (3) a profit, not just sales, as an objective.

Today, goods and services move through many different channels of distribution efficiently which allows consumers to satisfy their needs and wants on demand. The economic justification for a business firm today is that it has the ability to create utility or value for its customers. Utility is the want-satisfying ability of a good or service. From a marketing perspective, there are three forms of utility: time, place, and possession. Time utility involves making the goods available when the customer wants them. Having line service available 24 hours each day is an example of time utility. Place utility involves making products available where the customer wants them. Place utility helps bring buyers and sellers closer together. Locating an FBO at a preferred location may enable place utility for customers in that area. Possession utility involves transferring of title for a product between the parties. The use of trade credit among marketing intermediaries and credit cards with consumers have greatly enhanced this utility.

This chapter views marketing from a micro-perspective and will investigate the role of marketing in a firm and demonstrate how essential marketing is to the long-term survival of an organization. What does the term *marketing* mean? Most people mistakenly equate the term with selling and promotion. Marketing is much more than selling and promotion and is more commonly defined as "The performance of business activities or functions that direct the flow of products and services from the seller to the buyer in order to satisfy customers and accomplish the company's objectives."

Clearly, a variety of business activities must be performed to accomplish the overall objective of marketing, which is to develop exchange relationships with customers. The three categories of marketing activities are exchange, physical distribution, and facilitating functions. Exchange or transactional functions involve buying and selling on the part of various channel members, like wholesalers and retailers, and the final customer. Logistical or physical distribution functions help satisfy time and place utilities by efficiently combining the components of warehouse locations, inventory strategies, material handling, and transportation modes that provide a satisfactory service level for the customer. Functions that facilitate exchange include financing, risk-taking, providing information through market research, and standardizing and grading products. It is important to note that each of these functions must be performed for exchange to take place. Who performs these functions and how they are performed depends on the type of product, the type of customer, the geographical location, and the urgency of the need.

The second part of the definition deals with satisfying customers. Customer satisfaction is the ultimate objective of the marketing process. Marketing attempts to build stronger relationships with existing customers and to discover new target markets that fit well with the firm's expertise and objectives. Customers, not marketers, primarily determine what they need, want, and are willing to buy. It is the responsibility of marketing to identify and to satisfy customers' needs.

The final portion of the definition indicates that accomplishing the company's objective is an essential part of marketing. Just as the customers must be satisfied, the marketing plan must also achieve company objectives. The primary objective of the marketing plan is to make a satisfactory profit while meeting customers' expectations. Other objectives include increasing market share, expanding into the global market, introduction of new products, or increasing distribution efficiencies.

Marketing Management

Marketing management is a three-phase process that includes planning marketing activities, directing the implementation of the plans, and controlling these plans. This process is so central to the activities of most organizations that they formalize it as a marketing plan, which is a road map to guide the marketing activities for a specified future period of time, such as one year.

Planning

Marketing planning involves making decisions that commit the firm to actions in order to reach organizational and marketing objectives effectively. Planning includes determining objectives, segmenting the market, selecting target markets, and establishing a unique marketing mix aimed at the particular audience. The marketing mix includes the product or service, price, channel of distribution (place), and promotion (advertising, sales promotion, personal selling, and publicity). These so-called controllable variables are referred to as the "four Ps" of marketing. Although not generally taught, a fifth "P" could be referred to as passion. Another controllable variable, passion is the fifth ingredient in a successful marketing mix. Typically, passion is always present in the marketing mix of aviation businesses. Those in aviation are usually passionate about aviation and as a result, product, price, place, and promotion are more effective. Without passion, the "four Ps" lack a key component of the marketing mix.

Determining Objectives

Marketing objectives should complement and be set within the framework of the larger company objectives. For example, the firm's objectives might include increasing flight school revenues. A marketing objective would be to increase the number of students or to improve the student pilot retention rate. Because objectives are not equally important, a hierarchy of objectives should be specified for marketing personnel.

Marketing objectives should be quantified and stated in understandable terms. Ideally, the attitudes of upper management toward the achievement of these objectives should also be ascertained. Top management must guide each department manager of a product service area. For example, should a 20 percent increase in charter business be attained regardless of cost or only sought if return on investment is 18 percent or better? Even more important—but less quantifiable—should a 20 percent increase be obtained even if it requires high pressure selling, reduced availability or reliability, or other possibly unethical actions? Clearly, these costs would not be worth any potential benefits.

Each department manager is responsible for generating a certain amount of revenue so that the profit objective can be reached. The sales force has the objective of achieving a designated sales quota. Advertising has the objective of creating a level of awareness of product-service areas within the target markets. Prices must be competitive and achieve a specific market share or target rate of return. Marketing research must be completed on time and within budget.

Objectives at all levels of the firm should be operationally specified. Each department manager should understand what activities must be undertaken, and what operations must be performed in order to accomplish the objectives. Quantification is usually helpful here; "increase sales by 10 percent" is more precise than asking the department manager to get "more sales than last year." Managers should not focus their efforts exclusively on objectives that can be quantified, however. It is fairly easy, for example, to measure the cost savings of holding parts inventory to a minimum, but it is very difficult to determine the degree of customer dissatisfaction which might be created when that minimum inventory results in being out of stock of required parts which results in delayed repairs to a customer's aircraft.

Segmenting the Market

Market segmentation is the process of breaking down the total market into smaller, more homogeneous groups with similar needs that the firm can satisfy. A market segmentation approach aims at a narrow, specific consumer group (market segment) through one specialized marketing plan that caters to the needs of that segment. Market segmentation has emerged as a popular technique for FBOs with highly specialized products and limited resources. Market segments should be as similar as possible with respect to needs. There also should be significant differences among segments and the segments should be large enough to be profitable.

Segmenting assists the firm in deciding which market to target and also to plan marketing mixes. Here is a look at an approach to segmenting.

1. **Identify the product-service areas to be segmented.** The first step involves identifying all of the product-service areas presently offered by the firm. This might include:
   - Flight school
   - Aircraft sales
   - Rental: by Hour or by Trip
   - Charter:
     - Scheduled
     - Non-scheduled
   - Overhaul:
     - Major
     - Minor
2. **Identify all of the possible market segments.** This step includes an identification of all markets for the firm's product-service areas. These might include the following:
   - Pilots
   - Aircraft owners
   - High school students
   - High school graduates
   - Community college flight program students
   - Corporate fleet operators
   - Physicians
   - Engineers
   - Managers
   - Professionals

Table 7-1
Market Segmentation

Product-Service Areas		Pilots	Aircraft Owners	H.S. Students	H.S. Grads.	C.C. Flight Prog.	Corporate Fleet	Physicians	Engineers	Managers	Professionals	Proprietors	Salespeople	Commuter Airline
Flight School		O	O	X	X	X		X	X	X	X	X	X	
Airplane Sales		X	O		O		X	X	X	X	X	X	X	O
Rental:	Hour	X		X	X	X		X	X	O	X	O	O	
	Trip	X		O	X	X		X	X	X	X	X	X	
Charter:	Scheduled						X							O
	Non-Scheduled						X			X	X	X	X	
Overhaul:	Major		X				X							O
	Minor	O	X				O							
Hanger Rental		X				X								
Sale of Gas and Oil		X	X	X	X	X	X	X	X	X	X	X	X	X
Accessories:	Plane		X				X							O
	Pilot	X	X	X	X	X		X	X	X	X	X	X	X
Services		X	X	X	X	X	X	X	X	X	X	X	X	X

X = Major interest
O = Minor interest

Proprietors
Salespeople
Commuter airlines

At this point, it is helpful to develop a matrix as shown in Table 7-1. This table shows the product-service areas on the left side and possible target markets across the top. The table includes evaluations of each product-service area against each market with a judgment of whether that will be of major or minor interest to the firm.

Another helpful analysis in determining possible market segments is to compare product-service areas with competitors. In this case, product-service areas would be shown across the top of a sheet of paper and on the left side, a listing of the firm's chief competitors. Again, a matrix is formed in which the firm can rate competitors' strengths and weaknesses using a scale of one to five, with five being excellent and one being poor.

The ratings reflect how well each competitor delivers that product-service. The firms can also rate themselves. In order to check their findings, some firms poll customers who are familiar with the competitive operations to evaluate both the firm and its competitors. Customers may come up with completely different perceptions of the firm and its competitors for the various product-service areas.

The objective of these exercises is to try to identify possible target markets and also point out a firm's strengths and weaknesses. Too many FBOs fall into the trap of trying to be all things to all markets with the result of not excelling at anything. The better approach is to do fewer things but to do them well.

3. **List all needs for the possible market segments that have been identified.** This is a brainstorming step. For each of the product-service areas, it is now important to identify the needs for all of the possible market segments. For example, using the flight school as the product-service area, what are the particular needs of high school students? Their needs include availability of an evening ground school, instructor availability from 3 p.m. to 6 p.m., competitive prices, installment payment plan, college credit for attainment of the private pilot certificate, and counseling with parents.

The process of identifying segments and determining their accessibility necessitates focusing on customer needs. This, of course, is the essence of marketing management. It encourages the firm to track who buys its products—where, when, and how. Segmentation keeps the organization alert to changes in market conditions and competitors' actions. Competitive analysis may indicate which segments of the market are controlled by strong, entrenched competitors and which segments' needs are not fulfilled by present product-service areas.

Establishing Target Markets

Once the market segments are determined and the segmentation criteria are satisfied, the firm is ready to direct its effort toward one or more market segments. A target market is a segment that is the object of a firm's marketing mix. It is the opposite of mass marketing which does not attempt to differentiate between the market segments but instead, designs and aims its marketing mix at all segments.

A single target market approach means the selection of one primary market segment as the firm's target market. This concentrated marketing is a cost-effective way to market because there are no expensive variations of the marketing mix. Marketers narrow their sales potential by concentrating on a single market segment, but are exposed to more financial risk by not diversifying efforts into multiple target markets. A multiple target market approach means selecting two or more market segments—each will be treated as a separate target market and each will require a unique market mix. A combined target market approach means aggregating two or more similar market segments into one larger target market.

Most successful FBOs utilize the multiple and combined target market approaches. Mass marketing is not appropriate for the highly specialized product-service areas of the average FBO.

Establishing a Marketing Mix

Once the firm has determined its objectives and selected its target market(s), it is ready to begin planning the details of the marketing mix. The marketing mix was previously defined as the set of controllable marketing variables that the firm blends to produce the desired response in the target market. The marketing mix consists of everything the firm can do to influence the demand for its product. The many possibilities can be collected into four marketing mix variables: product, price, place, and promotion (with passion an always present member of the marketing mix).

The Product

A product is a combination of benefits, physical features, and services, designed to satisfy the needs/wants of identified target markets. This definition includes both tangible products and intangible services. The ability of a firm's product to satisfy wants is the key to developing exchange relationships. Purchasers of aircraft are vitally concerned with parts and service availability, warranties, image of the brand name, and other intangible benefits that contribute to the total satisfaction of owning an aircraft. Flight students purchase an intangible service but are also concerned with other benefits such as quality, reputation of the school, and professionalism of the instructors.

There are four unique characteristics of services that offer marketers challenges different from marketing tangible products such as aircraft. These four elements are referred to as the four I's of services. Services are intangible. The buyer must purchase on faith because it is often only after the sale that quality, benefits, and dimensions can be evaluated. Service marketers should stress the benefits of the service instead of the service itself. Many aviation firms today are successful because they have differentiated their product by including key benefits that are sought out by their market. For example, an FBO builds line service business by including a complimentary aircraft wash with the purchase of 100 gallons of aviation fuel. The second characteristic is inconsistency. Since services depend on the people who provide them, their quality varies with each person's training, capabilities, and attitudes. A third characteristic of services, and related to the problems of consistency, is inseparability. In most cases the provider of the service cannot be separated from the service itself (A&P mechanic repairing an aircraft). The fourth characteristic identifies the inventory problems of services because many items are perishable and cannot be stored. Marketers must implement strategies that will assist in managing the level of demand for a service in line with the firm's ability to provide the service. FBOs have a continuing challenge in providing quality and timely maintenance while keeping overhead at profitable levels.

The Price

Price represents the exchange value of a good or service. Since customers perceive price as the sacrifice or cost they must pay, marketers must maintain the price level equal to or less than utility (satisfaction level). This cost-benefit relationship plays a major role in pricing strategies.

Price planning is systematic decision making by a firm regarding all aspects of pricing. A price contains all the terms of purchase: monetary and nonmonetary costs, discounts, handling and shipping fees, credit charges and other forms of interest, and late-payment penalties.

With price competition, sellers influence demand for their products primarily through changes in price levels. Non-price competition minimizes price as a factor in customer demand. This is accomplished by creating a distinctive product or service as expressed through promotion, customer service, availability, and other marketing factors. The more specialized a product or service offering is perceived to be by customers, the greater is the freedom of the firm to set prices above competitors.

Price competition is a flexible marketing tool because prices can be adjusted quickly and easily to reflect demand, cost, or competitive factors. However, of all the controllable marketing variables, pricing strategy is the easiest for a competitor to duplicate. If an FBO lowers the price for AvGas to $4.75 per gallon, for instance, the competing FBO across the field can do the same.

Before a firm develops a pricing strategy, it must analyze the outside factors affecting price decisions. Price decisions depend heavily on elements external to the firm. This contrasts with product and promotion decisions, which are more directly controlled by the firm. The major factors affecting price decisions are customers, competition, costs, and products.

1. **Customers**. A firm must understand the relationship between price and customer purchases and perceptions. This relationship is explained by two economic principles: law of demand states that customers usually purchase more units at a low price than at a high price. The price elasticity of demand defines the responsiveness of buyers to price changes in terms of the quantities they will purchase.

   Price elasticity is computed by dividing the percentage change in quantity demanded by the percentage change in price charged:

$$\text{Elasticity of Demand} = \frac{\text{Percentage change in quantity demanded}}{\text{Percentage change in price}}$$

   Elastic demand occurs if relatively small changes in price result in large changes in quantity demanded. Numerically, price elasticity is greater than one. With elastic demand, total revenue increases when prices are lowered and decreases when prices rise. For example, if flight instruction rates decreased by 10 percent and the number of students increased by 15 percent, then demand was elastic and total revenue would increase. Inelastic demand takes place if price changes have little impact on quantity demanded. With inelastic demand, price elasticity is less than one. With inelastic demand, total revenue increases when prices are raised and decreases when prices decline. If fuel prices increased by five percent and the quantity demanded decreased by two percent, demand is inelastic. Total revenue would increase in such a case. Unitary demand exists if changes in price are exactly offset by changes in quantity demanded, so that total revenue remains relatively constant. Price elasticity is one.

   Elasticity of demand depends primarily upon three criteria: the price, availability of substitutes, and urgency of need. In general, customers tend to be more responsive to price changes of high-ticket items, such as aircraft, than they are to low-priced items, such as approach plates or FBO t-shirts sold over the counter. The more substitute products are available, the more responsive customers tend to be. Lack of substitutes is generally associated with inelastic demand. The more time customers have to shop around, the more elastic their demand. If a customer has an urgent need for a product, such as an aircraft part and cannot afford several days' delay, this customer will tend to be inelastic with regard to price.

2. **Competition**. Another element contributing to the degree of control a firm has over prices is the competitive environment within which it operates. An oligopolistic market has only a few firms that offer homogeneous products and have limited control over market pricing. Firms attempting to charge more than the current competitive price would attract few customers, because demand for any particular firm's product is not strong enough to prevent customers from switching to competitors when prices are increased. Similarly, a firm would actually lose revenue by selling for less than the market price because competitors would immediately match any price reduction, thus establishing a lower market price.

   A monopolistic competitive market contains many sellers and is characterized by moderate level of competition, well-differentiated product-service areas, and strong control over price by individual firms. In this environment, firms may succeed with higher prices because customers view their products as unique. Differentiation among FBOs may be based on reputation, professionalism of personnel, newness of aircraft, attractiveness of facilities, services offered, or other factors. Marketers desiring to sell below market price can carve out a niche in this environment by attracting customers interested in the lowest price. The choice of price level depends on the firm's strategy, target market, and competitive environment.

3. **Cost-oriented pricing**. This method is most commonly used because it has the advantage of simplicity. The price of a product must cover costs of manufacturing, promotion, and distribution, plus a reasonable profit. There are at least three variations of this approach: mark-up pricing, cost-plus pricing, and rate of return pricing. Markup pricing is appropriate when the seller is not the manufacturer. A reseller will add a percentage of the invoice cost to determine the selling price. The size of the percentage markup will depend on such factors as inventory turnover rate, competition, and degree of elasticity.

   Manufacturers of tangible products use cost-plus and rate of return pricing methods. Total unit costs are determined, and then a profit dollar amount or a desired rate of return percentage is added to arrive at the selling price. Cost-oriented approaches have a major disadvantage in that they give little or no consideration to customer demand. The price determined using this method only looks at internal factors (costs) rather than the market forces of supply and demand and the willingness of target markets to pay the asking price.

4. **Products.** There are numerous product characteristics which influence pricing. Three important ones are perishability, distinctiveness, and stage in the product life cycle.
   - Perishability. Products that are perishable in a physical sense must be priced attractively to promote sales without costly delays. Intangible products, which cannot be stored, are also very sensitive to the right price level to assure a match between supply and demand. Perishability is also a concern as it applies to the consumption rate. Products that have a long life, like airplanes, tend to have an initial high cost because large amounts of services are purchased at one time. Second, owners of these types of products have a great deal of time to make replacement pur chase decisions that reduces the persuasiveness of price.
   - Distinctiveness. One of the major challenges facing marketing managers is to make their products different from their competitors. If unsuccessful, pricing becomes a matter of meeting the market price. Distinctiveness can be achieved in many products through design changes, packaging, services provided, warranties, etc. Being able to charge higher prices for these differentiated products rewards the seller.
   - Life cycle. The four stages of the product life cycle—introduction, growth, maturity, and decline—have an important impact on pricing decisions. During the introductory stage, a skimming policy or a penetrating policy is followed. Skimming is particularly useful when introducing a unique product for which the initial price is very high and it appeals to the innovators. As competitors enter the market, price is reduced. Penetrating is setting a below-competition price in order to capture an immediate share of the market. Prices will be raised as some brand loyalty has been attained. Growth and maturity stage pricing is driven by the aggressiveness of competitors and a firm's ability to remain distinctive in product lines. Decline stage pricing is usually geared to harvest the most revenue prior to the elimination of the product.

The Place

Place is concerned with delivering the product and services to customers in a timely manner. In addition to a convenient location on the airport, the appropriate products and services must be available for each target market in the correct amount when customers need them. For example, aircraft used for flight instruction must be available when members of a target market need them—not off on a charter flight or down for maintenance. Place decisions are directly related to a firm's desired customer service level. Customer service level is a measure of how rapidly and dependably a firm can deliver what customers want. For the FBO, it might mean having the appropriate parts in inventory. If a firm decides to lower overhead costs, it may also be settling for a lower customer service level by handicapping employee's ability to efficiently handle customer requests. On the other hand, obtaining a higher service level might increase sales that would in turn offset the increased costs. Clearly, a marketing manager has a decision to make about what service level to offer. Minimizing cost is not always the right answer.

The Promotion

Promotional planning is systematic decision making relating to all aspects of the development and management of a firm's promotional effort. Promotion is any form of communication used by a firm to inform, persuade, or remind people about its products, services, image, ideas, or community involvement.

The promotional mix consists of the following four major tools.

1. **Advertising**. Any paid form of nonpersonal presentation and promotion of ideas, products, or services by an identified sponsor.
2. **Sales promotion**. Short-term incentives to encourage the purchase or sale of a product or service.
3. **Personal selling**. Oral presentation with one or more prospective purchasers for the purpose of making sales.
4. **Publicity**. Nonpersonal stimulation of demand for a product or service by placing commercially significant news about the firm in a publication like *Business and Commercial Aviation* or obtaining favorable presentation on radio or television that is not paid by the sponsor.

Within the advertising and sales promotion categories there are specific communication tools, such as mass media advertising, displays, print and specialty advertising, trade shows, brochures, literature, posters, contests, and flight training coupons. Many products, like aircraft, require the use of personal sales to first initiate contact and then use of sales skills to turn the prospect into a satisfied customer. Promotional activities such as these are often thought to be the major, if not the total, thrust of marketing at any FBO. Promotion is important, but no more important than the other three marketing mix variables. The firm's products and services, its prices and distribution strategies all communicate important information to buyers. The whole marketing mix, not just promotion, must be coordinated for the maximum communication impact.

Implementation of Plan

Marketing implementation is the process that turns the marketing plan into action assignments and ensures that such assignments are executed in a manner that accomplishes the plan's stated objectives. No matter how well the marketing program has been planned, nothing happens until a product has been sold or a service performed. All department managers must not only have input into the marketing plan, they also must enthusiastically endorse the plan and play an important role in its implementation. Specific skill areas required for successful marketing implementation include organization and execution.

Organizing for Implementation

An organization is a group of people with a common purpose or mission. This mission can best be achieved if each person has a specific responsibility, and all are joined in such a way as to facilitate and reinforce each other. All members of the organization must be guided by the marketing concept. This customer orientation requires a thorough understanding of customer needs, wants, and behaviors. The focal point, then, is the customer. Ideally, all members of the organization should attempt to learn more about customers' needs and work to develop products and services to satisfy those needs.

Another important element is coordination. First, there should be coordination within the marketing mix variables. Second, marketing efforts must be coordinated within each department and among departments. Unless all departments see themselves working toward a common goal of satisfying customers, they will not be able to assist in adhering to the marketing concept.

Executing Marketing Plans

Another ingredient to successful implementation of the marketing plan is management of the execution phase by all members of the firm. Implementation responsibilities fall into three areas: delegation, communication, and motivation.

1. **Delegation**. It is necessary in organizations to delegate responsibilities to various people. Delegation is done both formally through organizational structure and informally. In addition to determining appropriate duties, delegation also means matching people's capabilities and preferences to those duties. In other words, delegation will not result in successful implementation unless the duties to be performed have been clearly specified and appropriate personnel have been assigned to perform those duties.
2. **Communication**. After responsibilities have been delegated, they must be coordinated to achieve the firm's objectives, and the information must be communicated. Communication involves shared understanding among individuals. Ideally, information should flow throughout the firm, not just down the organizational hierarchy, but across the organizational hierarchy (among departments). Marketing plans are best implemented in a work environment that fosters complete and open information flow. Here are examples of several ways to improve communi cations:
    a. Information Dissemination: Up-to-date organizational charts, telephone directories, a company newsletter, an in-house library of industry material, and a policy for releasing information as quickly as possible to avoid rumor.
    b. Instruction: Training programs, formal performance appraisals, sessions with supervisors, and financial assistance for educational pursuits.
    c. Interaction: Informal company gatherings and interdepartmental committees.
3. **Motivation**. Delegation and communication will be to no avail unless someone in a leadership position takes the responsibility to motivate people to perform the tasks expected of them. Perhaps the most succinct method of motivating people is to reward them for a job well done. An aircraft salesperson can be rewarded with a bonus or week of vacation once a certain number of aircraft are sold each quarter/year. The salesperson on commission, for example, will devote more time to making new sales than to handling old complaints. A flight instructor can be rewarded for a good student retention rate by giving the instructor the next charter flight. Prizes can be given to the line person of the month. All of these are motivating factors designed to reward exemplary performance in carrying out the marketing objectives of the firm.

Control

Marketing control is the process of translating organizational objectives into quantifiable standards, periodically analyzing marketing results, and taking actions that will correct the deficiencies affecting the FBO's ability to reach stated marketing objectives. It starts after the marketing program has been implemented and is monitored on a continuous basis. Generally speaking, control is the process that attempts to reconcile performance of the marketing plan with marketing objectives. The types of activities and standards differ across the four marketing mix variables. Thus, control is intertwined with planning. Some marketing authorities refuse to draw a precise distinction between planning and control, preferring instead to see them as two sides of the same coin.

Setting Standards and Measuring Results

The first step in marketing control is to translate organizational objectives into standards against which performance can be measured. In general, there are three bases for performance standards: industry norms, past performance, and managerial expectations.

Industry norms can be obtained from manufacturers, trade publications, and industry organizations. They can be quite useful as guidelines for marketing performance standards. Industry sales, pricing policies, and advertising strategies are examples of the types of information included. The underlying assumption of this kind of standard is that if the firm's performance is comparable to others in the industry, things "can't be too bad." This is not necessarily true. For example, an organization's market share may hold steady while the total market declines as in the case of single-engine aircraft sales in the 1980s and 1990s. On the other hand, the firm's market share may fall while the total market is expanding. In essence, industry norms provide comparisons with average performance.

A second basis for performance standards is past performance—how do this month's or year-to-date sales compare to those of last month or last year? This information should be available from departments within the company. Past performance measures provide a minimum standard, a benchmark by which to measure subsequent efforts. Also, trends of performance over a period of time can be analyzed. However, the use of past performance assumes that historical patterns have relevance for future decisions. It may be misleading to measure current performance on the basis of these results.

The third basis for performance standards is managerial expectations. Forecasts, budgets, schedules, and policy decisions become standards against which actual performance is measured. These standards may involve both industry norms and past performance, but they also take estimates of future conditions into account. To the extent that managerial expectations are realistic, they probably provide the most useful standards for measuring performance. Assessments of future conditions based on the manager's intuition, experience, and information provide perhaps the most feasible standards for the situation. Of course, compared with industry norms or past performance, managerial expectations are more subjective and uncertain. Consequently, they are more open to criticism.

Corrective Action

Efforts at marketing control will meet with little success if the actions necessary to bring actual performance into line with standards are not taken. The first problem facing a manager contemplating corrective action is identification of specific causes for the deviation from the standard. This is sometimes easier said than done. Another difficulty is one of time lags associated with the desired corrective action. Sometimes, a manager finds that because of the time lag between recognition of a problem and a decision about corrective action, the problem has changed before it has been addressed. Perhaps a salesperson's poor performance in a given period, for example, was the result of a personal problem that has now been resolved. There are no easy answers to guide corrective action. Perhaps performance is not faulty. It may be that the objectives set by the plan were inappropriate due to unexpected competitive, economic, or governmental actions. If this is the case, the proper corrective action involves adjusting the plans rather than performance.

Summary of Marketing Management

It is clear that the marketing management process is one of planning marketing activities, directing the implementation of the marketing plan, and controlling the plan (see Figure 7-1).

In Figure 7-1, all the steps are connected to show that the marketing management process is continuous. The planning job sets guidelines for implementation and specifies expected results that are compared in the control function to see if everything has worked out as projected. This feedback is especially important and can lead to changes. A manager should not only be concerned with the present plan, but must also be proactive by always looking for attractive new opportunities and creating new strategies.

Uncontrollable Variables

The uncontrollable variables are those factors affecting a firm's performance that cannot be directed by marketing efforts. It must be recognized that any marketing plan, no matter how well conceived, might fail if adversely influenced by uncontrollable factors. Therefore, the external environment must be continually monitored and its effects incorporated into any marketing plan. The process of continually acquiring information about the trends occurring externally to the firm in order to be more efficient in planning, as well as to be proactive, is called environmental scanning. Uncontrollable variables that must be monitored and their trends analyzed are consumer demographics, competition, government regula-

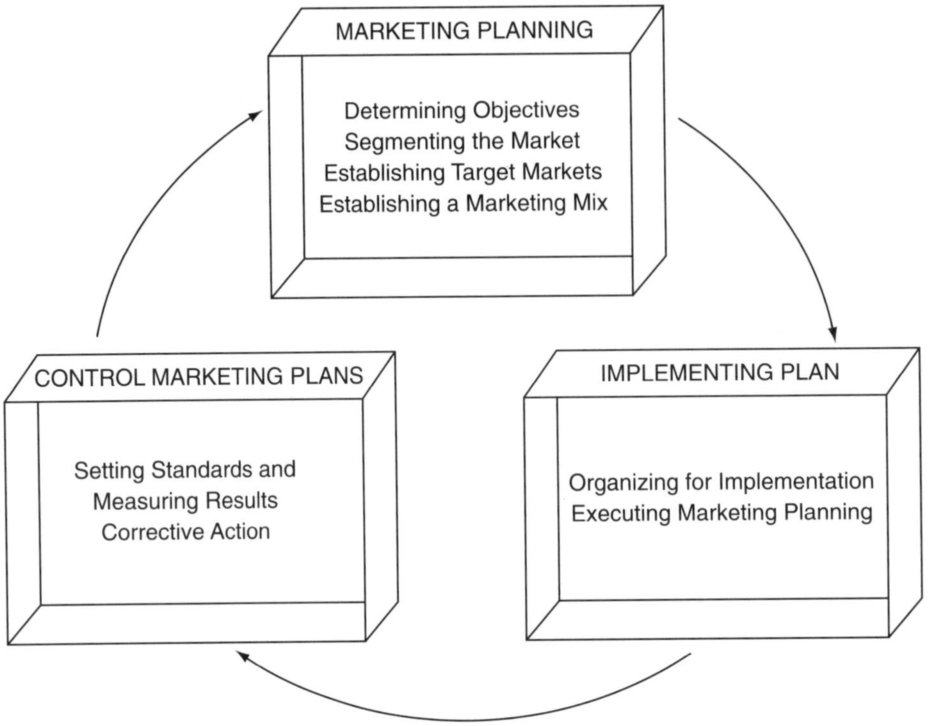

Figure 7-1 The Marketing Management Process

tions, the economy, technology, media, and public interest groups.

Consumer Demographics

Although a firm has control over the selection of a target market, it cannot control the characteristics of the population. Firms can react to, but not control, these consumer demographics: age, income levels, marital status, occupation, race, education, and place and type of residence. The U.S. population will continue to grow and there will be major changes in the country. On April 1, 2000, the population of the United States was 281,421,906 people, representing an increase of 13.1 percent over 1990. Because the U.S. population is growing slowly, the average age is rising. In 1970, the average age of the population was 28, but the 2000 census shows that the average age jumped to 37. Since most marketers use age groups as one of the criteria in selecting homogeneous target markets, the change in the percentage of the population in different age groups will affect marketing strategies. For example, in the 18-24 age group, between 1980 and 1990, there was a 17.7 percent decrease, between 1990 and 2000, a 1.4 increase, and it is estimated that between 2000 and 2010 there will be a 14.8 increase. The major reason for the changing age distribution in different age groups is the U.S. birthrate. Expressed as the number of babies born per 1,000 people, the last 50 years indicates a major rise from 1935's 18.7 to a high point of 25.0 in 1955. From this point forward the birth rate has declined to the current 2000 level of 14.0. The post-World War II baby boom (1947 to 1957) produced about 43 million babies. This is about one-sixth of the present U.S. population. This large group crowded into the schools in the 1950s and 1960s and then entered the job market in the 1970s. Many of this group started to have children in the late 1970s and early 1980s that caused another ground swell at the elementary school level. In the 1980s and 1990s, the baby boomers were middle-aged. By the early twenty-first century, this group will reach retirement age. Because the baby boomers account for a large percentage of the population, they have been extremely important to marketers. This generation has a distinct profile compared with that of other age groups. Baby boomers have the highest education level, with one-fourth of those between the ages of 25 and 35 having college degrees; they have high incomes, and during the 1990s they were responsible for about half of all consumer expenditures. Many companies are designing products and developing marketing strategies to target this very important group.

Birth rates were very low during the 1960s and early 1970s, causing a significant drop in the number of individuals entering college in the mid1980s. This factor might be one of the major causes of the decline in student pilot starts in the early 1990s.

Another significant trend is the increasing number of women in the workforce and the types of jobs they are performing. In 1950, only 24 percent of wives worked outside the home. Now that figures is over 65 percent. Women are entering many nontraditional career paths and income levels for this target group are rising, which gives them independence and purchasing power. In 1992, only 10 percent of the total number of pilots in the country were women, and by 2006, only 6 percent of U.S. pilots were women. However, it is anticipated that these percentages will grow in the years ahead as more and more females become interested in flying.

Competition

A firm's competitors frequently affect its market planning and its success in attracting those in the target market. There are three types of competition. The first is direct competition between companies offering similar products and services. Two charter companies on the same airport compete directly for that area's charter business. The second type of competition occurs between companies that offer products or services that can be substituted for one another. Automobiles are competitors for general aviation aircraft, as are commuter airlines because they both can be used to transport company personnel. The third type of competition occurs because customers have limited financial resources. Marketers of dissimilar products and services are in competition with each other. The salesperson must help customers prioritize their "wish" lists to accomplish immediate sales. A business aircraft salesperson, for example, may have to persuade the prospect to defer using credit to make a large company purchase so that credit resources will be available to secure an aircraft loan.

A firm must evaluate the marketing strategies of its competitors. Specifically, the firm must determine which markets are saturated and which are unfulfilled. The marketing plans and target markets of competitors, the images of competitors and their products, the strengths and weaknesses of competitors, and the extent to which consumers are satisfied with the level of service provided by the competition must also be considered.

Government Regulations

A third uncontrollable variable affecting market planning is governmental regulation. In addition to the federal laws involving antitrust, discriminatory pricing, unfair trade practice, and occupational health and safety, the aviation industry is faced with numerous regulations promulgated by the Federal Aviation Administration (FAA). The FAA is charged with the safe operation of aircraft in the national airspace system. In carrying out this responsibility, it develops many regulations which can have an impact on a firm's marketing plans.

In addition to federal legislation and agencies, each state and local government has its own legal environment for firms operating within its boundaries.

The political climate also affects legislation. Consumerism, nationalism, foreign trade, zoning, wage rates, and other items are discussed and debated through the political process before legislation is enacted.

The Economy

Markets require purchasing power as well as people. Total purchasing power is related to current income, profits, prices, savings, and credit availability. An economic recession, high unemployment, and the rising cost of credit all affect purchasing power. A high rate of growth means the economy in the region or country is usually good and the marketing potential large.

Of prime importance to firms are the perceptions of consumers regarding the economy. If consumers believe the economy will be favorable, they will increase spending. If they believe the economy will be poor, they will cut back on spending.

Some costs of doing business are often beyond the control of the firm. These include aircraft, parts and equipment, insurance, and interest rates. If costs rise substantially, marketing inflexibility is limited and lower profit margins may be necessary. When costs are stable, firms have greater opportunities to differentiate their strategies and expand sales.

When widespread cost increases, such as premiums for product liability insurance, drive the price of aircraft up, the result is a high rate of inflation. Thus, the prices of some products and services may go beyond the reach of many consumers, or consumers may be forced to alter their spending habits.

Of importance is what happens to consumers' real income (income adjusted for inflation) over time. The level of corporate profits after taxes can also affect the number and type of aircraft purchased by corporations. A high rate of unemployment adversely affects firms because people cut back on discretionary spending.

Technology

Our society is characterized as being in the age of technological change. Technology refers to the inventions or innovations from applied science or engineering research. The aviation industry has always been on the leading edge of technological change. Many technological advances are beyond the control of individual firms, especially smaller ones. However, unless they keep pace with improved technology, they will no longer remain competitive.

Media

The firm does not control the media, yet they can influence the perceptions of the government, consumers, and the public about an industry or a company's products and overall image. The media can provide positive or negative coverage of a company or an industry. Whenever an aircraft crashes or a drug smuggler using an aircraft is captured, the industry receives bad press. Realizing the media's job is to distribute news, companies should willingly produce positive news releases.

Public Interest Groups

The number and power of public interest groups have increased during the past two decades and represent another uncontrollable variable. The most successful is Ralph Nader's Public Citizen group, which guards consumer interests. Hundreds of other consumer interest groups, private and governmental, operate at the national, state, and local levels. Other groups to be considered are those seeking to protect the environment or advance the rights of minority groups.

Conclusion

An organization's level of success or failure in reaching its objectives depends on how well it directs and implements its controllable factors (marketing mix) and observes the impact of uncontrollable factors on the marketing plan. In order to improve the marketing effort and ensure long-run attainment of objectives, the firm needs feedback regarding the uncontrollable environment, the firm's performance, and how well the marketing plan is received. Feedback is obtained by measuring consumer satisfaction, looking at competitive trends, evaluating the relationship with government agencies, monitoring the economy, reading and reviewing the media, responding to public interest groups, analyzing sales and profit trends, talking with industry analysts, and employing other methods of gathering and assessing information.

After evaluating feedback, the firm needs to adapt its strategy to the business environment, while continuing to utilize its distinct advantages. To ensure long-term success, the firm must continually look for new opportunities that are attainable and fit into its overall corporate objectives, while responding to potential threats by revising marketing strategies.

KEY TERMS

Production era
Seller's market
Buyer's market
Sales era
Marketing concept era
Marketing concept
Utility
Marketing
Marketing plan
Marketing planning
Marketing mix
Market segmentation
Target market
Mass marketing
Single target market approach
Multiple target market approach
Combined target market approach
Product
Four I's of services
Price
Price planning
Law of demand
Price elasticity of demand
Elastic demand
Inelastic demand
Unitary demand
Oligopolistic market
Monopolistic competitive market
Markup pricing
Cost-plus pricing
Rate of return pricing
Skimming
Penetrating
Place
Customer service level
Promotion
Promotion mix
Advertising
Sales promotion
Personal selling
Publicity
Marketing implementation
Marketing control
Uncontrollable variables
Environmental scanning

REVIEW QUESTIONS

1. Define marketing and explain the three periods in the evolution of marketing.
2. Why is the ability to create utility the economic justification for a firm to be in business?
3. What is meant by segmenting the market? Why would it be helpful for a firm to compare its strengths and weaknesses against its immediate competitors? Do different target markets have different needs? Why is it preferable to express objectives in quantifiable terms?

4. A product may include more than a physical item. Explain.
5. Name and explain the four I's of services.
6. What are the major factors affecting price? Define elastic and inelastic demand. Differentiate between an oligolopolistic market and a monopolistic competitive market. How do these competitive markets affect pricing strategies? Discuss the three types of cost-oriented pricing. What is meant by customer service level?
7. Define the four major tools in the promotional mix.
8. Implementing marketing plans involves delegation, communication, and motivation. Describe the importance of these functions. How can workers be motivated? How does control differ from implementation? Describe several ways in which a firm can set standards.
9. What are the so-called uncontrollable variables that can affect a firm's marketing efforts? Why should a firm be aware of consumer demographics? Discuss several social trends that affect the marketing process. Explain the three types of competition faced by an FBO.

REFERENCES

Berkowitz, Eric N., and Roger A. Kerin, Steven W. Hartley, William Rudelius. *Marketing,* 6th Ed. Burr Ridge, IL. Irwin/McGraw-Hill, 2000.

Perreault, William D., Jr. and E. Jerome McCarthy. *Basic Marketing,* 13th Ed. Burr Ridge, IL. Irwin/McGraw-Hill, 1999.

Sandhusen, Richard L. *Marketing,* 32nd Ed. Hauppauge, New York. Barron's Educational Series, Inc., 2000.

SCENARIOS

1. As Marketing Manager for an up-start FBO, you have been tasked with establishing a marketing mix for flight instruction. Considering the "4 Ps," how would you do that?
2. As the Marketing Manager of a new FBO, the FBO Manager has asked for your help in establishing target markets for the flight school, aircraft sales, and maintenance. Target markets will be important in your marketing plan, so what are some potential target markets for these three FBO services?
3. As marketing manager for a busy FBO, you were recently asked to consider the services offered by the FBO. The FBO manager feels that the services offered by the FBO need to be more fully developed. Specifically, you need to consider the "four I's" of services. Fully develop and explain these "four I's" for each of the following services: washing aircraft, fueling aircraft, towing aircraft.
4. The FBO which you manage has decided to begin offering aircraft maintenance. What type of promotional mix can you develop to promote this new activity?
5. As the new manager of an existing FBO, you decided six months ago that a new marketing plan was necessary. Once developed, the plan was implemented. One goal was to increase new student pilot starts by five percent during the quarter. During the past month, your FBO has advertised for flight instruction via radio ads and billboards. How will you set standards and measure results of this effort?
6. As marketing manager of a full-service FBO, you have been asked by the FBO manager to evaluate competition faced by the FBO. Clearly, there is a competing FBO across the field, but is this the only competition for the FBO? The FBO currently offers flight instruction, aircraft rental, charter services, aircraft sales, and aircraft maintenance.

Notes

Chapter 8
Promotion and Sales

OUTLINE

OBJECTIVES

At the end of this chapter, you should be able to:

- Name and describe the four components in the promotion mix.
- Discuss the objectives of advertising.
- Distinguish between the following types of advertising: product, institutional, pioneering, competitive, comparative, and reminder.
- Explain the importance of an advertising budget and message.
- Summarize the advantages and disadvantages of the leading advertising media.
- Describe several methods of measuring advertising effectiveness.
- Give four examples and describe the purpose of sales promotion.
- Describe several publicity techniques that may be used by an FBO.
- Explain prospecting.
- List five aircraft prospecting sources and describe the type of information given.
- Highlight some of the basic business information needed by an aircraft salesperson to qualify a prospect.
- Discuss the approach, presentation, handling objections, close, and follow-up steps in the selling process.

The Promotional Mix

In order to communicate the availability of its products, a firm can use one or more of four promotional activities: advertising, sales promotions, publicity, and personal selling. The promotional mix is the combination of one or more of these four activities.

Advertising is any paid form of nonpersonal communication about an organization, product, or service by an identified sponsor. The paid aspect of this definition is important because advertising normally must be purchased. The nonpersonal component of advertising is also important. Advertising involves mass media that are many and varied, including magazine and newspaper space, outdoor posters, signs, banner towing, direct mail, radio, television, catalogs, directories, and circulars.

Although advertising lacks the immediate feedback of personal selling, it can reach large numbers of potential customers at relatively low cost. By using advertising in a promotional mix, a company can control what it wants to say and, to some extent, to whom the message is sent. If an FBO wants college students to receive its message on flight training, advertising space can be purchased in a college campus newspaper.

Sales Promotion involves marketing activities other than advertising, publicity, or personal selling that stimulates customer purchases and company effectiveness. Sales promotion activities include trade shows, coupons, contests, premiums, and free samples that are basically aimed at increasing sales. A $50 coupon appearing under an FBO's advertisement in a local newspaper to be used for an introductory flight is an example.

Publicity is an unpaid form of nonpersonal communication about any organization, product, or service by an identified sponsor, which can take the form of a news story, editorial, or product announcement. An announcement in the local activities section of the newspaper informing the public that the local aircraft model builders club meets in the conference room of Ace Flying Service at 7:00 p.m. on the last Thursday of the month is a form of publicity. Publicity is generally thought of as favorable and is planted by the firm or its advertising agency to promote the company by informing or reminding the public about its products and/or services. Negative publicity can occur, however, such as when an airplane crashes, or local citizens complain about noise created by airplanes taking off and landing at the local airport. Publicity can occur without the urging of a firm, simply for its news value.

Personal selling is a two-way flow of communication between a representative of the firm and a customer for the purpose of making a sale. The two-way flow of communication distinguishes personal selling from other forms of promotion.

Costs associated with personal selling are high, but there are distinct advantages. A representative can control to whom the presentation is made and can also see or hear the potential buyer's reaction to the message. If the reaction is unfavorable or not completely understood, the salesperson can modify the message. The flexibility of personal selling also can be a disadvantage because different salespeople can change the message regarding the product or service so that no consistent communication is given to all customers.

In putting together the promotional mix, a firm must consider the balance of elements to use. There is no one right promotion blend. Each must be developed as part of a unique marketing mix (four Ps) for each target market.

Advertising

Advertising can play an important role in the promotional mix. In contrast to personal selling, advertising is a form of mass selling that attempts to make potential buyers aware of and interested in a firm's products and services. In other words, it takes a "shotgun" approach, whereas personal selling zeroes in on individuals with a "riflelike" approach. While the level of advertising as a percentage of sales varies among industries, U.S. corporations average about three percent of their sales dollar on advertising. Unfortunately, many smaller firms such as FBOs pay very little attention to this important ingredient in the marketing mix.

Few companies, big or small, have the in-house expertise to develop their own advertising programs. Consequently, they turn to advertising agencies who are specialists in planning and handling mass selling details. Some agencies are one-person operations. At the other extreme, an agency may have as many as 8,000 employees. Some agencies specialize in business advertising and others in retail advertising.

Basically, an advertising agency carries out the following functions:

1. Plans advertising.
2. Selects media and contracts for space and time.
3. Prepares the advertising, including copy, layouts, and other creative work.
4. Produces finished advertisements in the physical form required by different media.
5. Creates and produces direct-mail pieces and other collateral material.
6. Checks invoices and evidence that advertising has appeared as scheduled (such as tear sheets from publications and affidavits from broadcasting stations). The bills from vendors who supplied materials and services for preparing the advertising are reviewed by the agency.

An advertising agency begins by becoming familiar with the company and what it sells. Perhaps the agency's members already have a background of experience with similar businesses. If so, they concentrate on learning about the specific operation. They study promotional objectives and determine the role advertising can play in helping accomplish the objectives. Then the agency recommends what approach the advertising message should take and the specific media to use. Perhaps the question is whether to use newspapers or radio or a combination of the two, or how much of the advertising should be in trade publications and how much in the form of direct mail and other sales literature.

Agencies are paid in four ways: commissions allowed by media; fees paid by the firm; service charges on materials and services purchased for preparation of advertising; and charges for advertising not involving commissions, such as direct mail.

Commissions allowed by media to advertising agencies are usually 15 percent of the cost of advertising space or time purchased. Most media have two rate schedules, national and local. National rates are higher and include agency commissions. When the lower local rates apply, with a few exceptions, agencies are not allowed to deduct commissions. The commissions included in the national rates are allowed only to agencies. Commissions received from media are the major source of income for most agencies.

When an advertising agency is used, an individual from the firm, working along with the agency account executive, is responsible for coordinating the agency's activities with related company activities. This individual participates in the agency's planning and conduct of advertising campaigns; thus ensuring that they are consistent with the firm's overall marketing strategy.

Advertising Objectives

Every advertising campaign should have clearly defined objectives that must flow from prior decisions on the market to be targeted and the marketing mix. Accurate measurement of stated objectives such as sales, market share, and profits should be taken before and after the campaign. Firms who fail to do this will only have an intuitive feeling about the effectiveness of their campaigns.

Advertising objectives should specify:

1. What is to be accomplished and the target market. Some examples are:
   - To increase line service business/NBAA members
   - To increase the number of flight students/College students
   - To develop charter business/Local businesses with over 100 employees
   - To increase maintenance business/Local, single-engine aircraft owners
2. The time period for accomplishing the objectives.

The objectives listed above are not as specific as they could be. A firm may want to sharpen them for its own purposes. For example, the general objective "To increase the number of flight students," could be rephrased more specifically: "To increase the number of student pilots by 20 percent during the next three months."

Setting reasonable advertising objectives is part of the art of marketing. The first time a manager sets objectives, they will probably be based on an educated guess, despite the logical analysis that may have gone into the choice. In time, however, experience in setting objectives and observing the actual results of particular advertising campaigns will allow the manager to select more realistic objectives.

The advertising objectives largely determine which of two basic types of advertising to use: product or institutional. Product advertising takes three forms: pioneering, competitive or comparative, and reminder. Product advertising tries to sell a product or service to final users or middlemen. Institutional advertising attempts to develop good will for the company and enhance its image, instead of promoting a specific product or service. In practice, a firm may employ both of these two basic types of advertising simultaneously.

Pioneering advertising tries to develop demand for a product or service category rather than for a specific company. It informs the target market what the product or service is, what it can do, and where it can be found. FBOs placing a print advertisement describing charter services in the local chamber of commerce newsletter is an example.

Advertising that promotes a specific company's products or service is competitive advertising. The objective of this advertising is to persuade the target market to select the firm's offerings rather than those of a competitor. An increasingly common form of competitive advertising used by the airlines and other segments of the aviation industry is comparative advertising. This form of advertising shows one firm's strengths relative to competitors.

Reminder advertising is used to reinforce prior knowledge about the product or service such as a brochure sent to a business aircraft owner who recently had aircraft serviced at the local FBO: "The next time you are in Fort Lauderdale, drop by and see us. It was a pleasure serving you."

Establishing an Advertising Budget

Once the advertising objectives have been determined, a budget must be established for each product or service. Deciding on the ideal amount is a difficult task because there is no precise method to measure the results of advertising spending. There are five traditional approaches to deciding how much to spend for advertising: (1) spending all the firm can afford, (2) allotting a certain percentage of net sales, (3) matching the advertising expenditures of competitors, (4) investing for future profits, and (5) the objective-and-task method.
The all-we-can-afford approach treats advertising as a luxury. This is a financial rather than a marketing approach. It does not consider what advertising can or should accomplish.

A percentage of sales approach is popular because it provides a formula—for instance, a certain percent of past sales—and it is simple and easy to use. Using the previous year's sales as the base seems to assume that advertising is the result of sales rather than sales the resulting of advertising. Furthermore, it makes no provision for increasing business and may not even allow enough money to maintain the current level of advertising. A variation of the percentage approach is the unit-of-sales method. This method establishes the amount of advertising on the basis of unit quantities of goods instead of dollar sales. This method is suitable for a firm with a narrow product line.

Trying to match the advertising of competitors is a defensive rather than an aggressive approach. It tends to produce advertising programs that are not tied to stated objectives and result in inefficient expenditures. This is reactive, rather than proactive advertising.

Advertising is considered an investment for future profit. It is primarily for introducing new products or services where extensive advertising dollars are required to get the product adopted. Any possible profits are plowed back into advertising and other promotional and sales activities.

The last of the five methods for creating advertising budgets is regarded by many as the best. The objective-and-task method builds a budget by first deciding what type of advertising is needed to accomplish the stated objectives. The principal problem with this method is the danger of being too ambitious. When the budget is totaled, the cost of the campaign may be more than the firm can possibly afford. The solution is usually to revise the objectives and/or modify the time for reaching them.

Recent research conducted by the Strategic Planning Institute for Cahners Publishing Co. identified the following decision rules that can be used to determine the size and focus of a firm's ad budget.

- Market share. A company that has a higher market share must generally spend more on advertising to maintain its share.
- Sales from new products. If a company has a high percentage of its sales resulting from new products, it must spend more on advertising compared to companies that have well-established products.
- Market growth. Companies competing in fast-growing markets should spend comparatively more on advertising.
- Unit price (per sales transaction). The lower the unit price of a company's products, the more it should spend on advertising because of the greater likelihood of brand switching.
- Product price. Both very high-priced (or premium) products and very low-priced (or discount) products require higher advertising expenditures because, in both cases, price is an important factor in the buying decision and the buyer must be convinced (through advertising) that the product is a good value.
- Product quality. Higher-quality products require a greater advertising effort because of the need to convince the customer that the product is unique.
- Degree of standardization. Standardized products produced in large quantities should be backed by higher advertising outlays because they are likely to have more competition in the market.

Most FBOs are small and have limited resources for advertising. Repeating advertisements can stretch advertising dollars. Savings occur through reduced preparation costs, both creative and mechanical. A number of studies have shown that advertisements repeated as many as four times do not lose their effectiveness. A later insertion attracts about the same number of readers as the first one.

Another way to get extra mileage from the advertising budget is to convert newspaper and magazine advertisements to direct mail. This is especially helpful when expensive color plates have been produced. The FBO already has an investment in copy, layout, art, and mechanical preparation. With little revision, a direct mail piece can be created. Another suggestion is to use a reprint of the advertisement as an attachment to a letter or as a self-mailer.

Advertising Message

Next, the firm develops its advertising message, the overall appeal for its campaign. The message in an advertisement is called the copy. Copy results from a combination of analytical thinking based upon a clear understanding of the firm's products and services with a liberal use of imagination. The advertisements are produced by creative individuals at the advertising agency (the copywriters and artists), but the overall evaluation and approval of copy is the responsibility of marketing management.

The copy must fit company and advertising objectives; it must be consistent with the target audience and the product or service itself. Generally, an early step is to develop a keynote idea or unique selling proposition, or a campaign theme as some marketing people refer to it. This keynote idea should provide continuity and have significant impact upon target market segments. For example, business aircraft have frequently been referred to as time machines, the theme being saving time and increasing productivity.

Language or visual messages projecting the central theme must be created; most advertisements use both. An effective message attracts the market's attention, is understandable, and is believable.

Media Selection

The firm's next step is choosing the advertising media to carry the message. There is a wide variety of media from which to choose and this decision is primarily related to the target audience, the product or service, available budget, and campaign objectives.

Table 8-1 summarizes the advantages and disadvantages of the leading media. Newspapers are an important local medium with an excellent potential for reaching a large audience. They also allow great flexibility in the size of ads; they may be a few lines or a complete page. Very little lead-time is needed to place or change an ad and it can be tailored to current developments. The short life of a newspaper ad is a drawback, along with the inability to tailor the message to a specific target market.

Magazines and trade journals are certainly some of the fastest growing media. Color is used most effectively in magazines, and the big advantage of this medium is the great number of special interest publications that appeal to target markets. The long lead-time required for magazine ads results in more general and less timely information. The cost of magazine and trade journal advertisements compared with other media is another disadvantage.

Table 8-1 Advertising Media

Medium	Advantages	Disadvantages
Newspapers	Short lead time needed, flexible, good local market coverage, inexpensive	Short life, poor reproduction quality, general audience, limited creativity, heavy ad competition
Magazines and Trade Journals	High geographic selectivity, long life, high quality reproduction, good pass-along readership	Long lead time, poor frequency, ad clutter, expensive
Direct Mail	Audience selectivity, no ad competition, personal approach, inexpensive	High throwaway rate, receipt by wrong person, low credibility
Radio	Selective market, high frequency, low cost	No visual contact, customer distractions
Television	Combines sight, sound and motion, high attention, persuasive	General audience, relatively expensive, lead-time, short message
Billboard	High repeat exposure, low cost, low competition, color creative options	General audience, legal restrictions, inflexible
Telephone/Business Directory	Low cost, coverage of market, specialized listings	Clutter of ads, limited creativity, long lead-time
Internet	High degree of seletivity, interactive	Large competition

Direct mail advertisements can reach a very homogeneous market and convey a great deal of information. Mailing lists can be obtained for specific aircraft owners in a particular geographic area. Direct mail advertising is a relatively inexpensive form of advertising, although many people view direct mail as junk. The challenge is to get the recipient to open the letter or brochure. In an effort to increase readership, some companies sending direct mail structure the envelope to appear official, as if it is from the IRS. This tactic, however, misleads the recipient and is not recommended.

Radio advertisements are fairly inexpensive and are particularly effective for local messages. Radio stations can be valuable in target marketing because of the different listening audiences. Lead-time for developing radio ads is short. The main disadvantage of radio is the inability of the prospective customer to review the message. Another problem is the ease with which customers can switch stations and tune out a commercial. Radio also competes with people's attention as they do other activities, such as driving or working. If used, however, a decision will need to be made whether AM or FM is more appropriate, considering cost and the target market.

Television has a major advantage over all of the other media in that it combines sight and sound. Its primary disadvantage is cost. The combination of a general audience and cost are sufficient detriments to eliminate this medium from most FBOs' promotion mix.

An effective medium for reaching a general audience in a specific locale is billboard advertising. The drawback in billboards is the inability to present lengthy advertising copy. Also, in many areas, laws have been passed to restrict the use of this medium.

Advertising in telephone and business directories is used by all firms and can be very effective because prospective customers seek out the firm. The cost is rather inexpensive but its weakness is that directory ads compete with so many other similar ads. This medium is often called directional advertising. The prospect has already established the need and is looking for the best alternative to satisfy the need.

An emerging medium, Internet advertising is booming.

The overall Web population is reaching critical mass. Recent surveys show there are 25 to 40 million adult Web users in the United States—between one-eighth and one-fifth of the population. Twenty-five million Americans use the Web at least one a week, and 8.4 million are daily users. Internet advertising offers a variety of advantages. It offers an exceptional ability to target specific customers, has the ability to be interactive, and can be customized to unique target markets. Rates on the Internet are typically $10 to $40 per 1,000 viewers, which is in line with the cost of national magazine rates.

Measuring Effectiveness

The final element in the advertising campaign is measuring its effectiveness, which should be measured in terms of criteria derived from the firm's overall advertising and marketing objectives.

If advertising objectives are sales-related (e.g., to increase sales or improve market share) then it is possible to determine whether the advertising has been effective in reaching customers. However, advertising is only one cause of sales. Other aspects of marketing, including improved product or service and other forms of promotion such as personal selling and pricing, all contribute to sales performance.

Some firms pre-test advertising effectiveness before starting the campaign. Focus groups (composed of a panel of customers or knowledgeable individuals) might be asked to rate which ad would most influence them. Customers might be asked to evaluate several ads and then recall the source and as much of the content of the message as they can. The uniqueness of an ad can be best measured by this method. Post-testing an advertisement can also be used. For example, results can be measured by orders mailed back, coupons brought in, or number of customers who respond to an ad for a sale. Recall tests can be used in which customers are asked to recall everything about an ad in a trade magazine or newspaper to which they subscribe. This test measures an ad's ability to be noticed and remembered.

Sales Promotion

Sales promotion activities supplement advertising and personal selling. It is usually not directed at as large an audience as advertising, but is directed at much larger groups than a typical personal selling effort. Included are such activities as trade shows, exhibits, coupons, trade allowances, demonstrations, and dealer incentives.

Given the diversity of sales promotion activities, it is apparent that they are designed to reach many target markets and to achieve a variety of objectives, such as the following:

1. Identifying sales leads (trade shows)
2. Inducing prospective customers to try a new service (flight instruction coupons)
3. Increasing the share of an established market (price breaks on a block of charter hours)
4. Improving name recognition (calendars, matchbooks, t-shirts, pens, and posters with the firm's name)

Sales promotion has several distinct advantages. First, it involves the prospective customer. Customers must return the flight coupons to receive instruction, or they must use free samples or discard them. Additionally, sales promotion activities can offer true value to the user; money can actually be saved. Finally, sales promotions can be directed to narrowly defined market segments. For example, flight coupons can be mailed to prospective users in high-income areas, or a brochure announcing a specially priced maintenance package can be directed to particular aircraft owners.

The following sales promotion activities are typically used by FBOs:

1. **Coupons.** Coupons are certificates entitling the bearer to a stated savings on the purchase of a specific product or service. Coupons can be mailed, enclosed with other products, or inserted in ads. They can be effective in stimulating sales and getting a customer to try a new product or service.
2. **Price incentives or deals.** Short-term price reductions are commonly used to increase trial among potential customers or to retaliate against a competitor's actions. These special deals generally work best when they are used infrequently or when the product or service being offered is relatively new.
3. **Promotional contests and sweepstakes.** Promotional activities that involve customers in games of skill are called contests, while those involving customers in games of chance are called sweepstakes. For example, in the case of a contest, customers (present or prospective) may be required to complete a puzzle, identify a vintage aircraft, or complete a sentence for a prize. Sweepstakes are often used to increase fuel sales or to sell aircraft. The aircraft manufacturers and organizations such as AOPA and Sporty's Pilot Shop have sponsored a number of sweepstakes over the years with the winner receiving a new or restored aircraft.
4. **Premiums.** Premiums are the offerings of merchandise at a low cost or free as an incentive to purchase those products or services, or suggestions to visit the locations where the products or services can be obtained. Premiums serve as reminders and include such items as calendars, miniature flashlights, key chains, business card holders, t-shirts, pens, posters, and a host of other promotional items with the firm's name displayed.
5. **Demonstrations.** Demonstrations are sometimes used by FBOs selling aircraft or charter services. A price break may be given to a prospective customer on a demonstra-

tion flight or an actual trip. Demonstrations involve a personal presentation of how the service works. It is often effective, but is an expensive technique and has limited application.

6. **Point-of-purchase promotions.** Point-of-purchase promotions are special displays, signs, banners, and exhibits that are set up in locations such as schools, stores, or mall entrances to promote a product or service. These promotions serve to remind customers that a product or service is available at a given location (a sign at the local flight shop next to the cash register advertising an FBO).
7. **Trade shows.** Many firms use trade shows such as the annual NBAA convention to advertise their products and services. Participating companies expect several benefits, including generating new sales leads, maintaining customer contacts, introducing new products and services, meeting new customers, and selling more to present customers.

Another form of sales promotion is cooperative advertising. This is an agreement in which a manufacturer, such as Cessna, pays a portion of an FBO's local advertising costs. These costs are shared on a fifty-fifty basis up to a specified limit. Sales promotion efforts can also be directed at a firm's employees. Awards or gifts might be given to employees for exemplary service. Many firms pick up the cost of uniforms and jackets with the company logo. Line personnel, pilots, instructors, mechanics, salespeople, and office personnel all could be considered for appropriate apparel. These items not only add to the professional image the company hopes to project, but also create a feeling among employees that they are part of a team.

Publicity

Publicity is the last component of the promotional mix and is another means firms can use to promote their products and services to mass audiences. It involves free promotion about the product, service, or organization in the media. Publicity is generally considered to be a part of a larger concept, that of public relations. Company public relations has several objectives, including obtaining favorable publicity for the firm, building a good image in the community, and handling adverse rumors and stories that circulate.

FBOs generally have many topics available to them with potential for publicity. Some of them are listed below:

1. New products or services
2. Product donations
3. Special events such as air shows, open houses, construction, and expansion plans
4. Airport planning activities
5. Athletic sponsorships
6. Charitable activities such as providing an aircraft for emergency purposes
7. Personnel news such as promotions, service anniversaries, retirements, new student solos and pilot certificates, contest winners, and management participation in local service clubs

Several publicity techniques are available. These include the following:

1. **News releases.** News releases are short statements about the firm's products, services, or organization released to the news media.
2. **Feature articles.** Feature articles, usually containing up to 3,000 words, are prepared for a specific publication such as a trade journal.
3. **Press conferences.** Press conferences involve inviting news people to hear a specific announcement and ask questions.
4. **DVDs and interactive CDs.** Canned speeches, DVDs and interactive CDs are available from organizations such as GAMA and NBAA for radio and television stations, to be shown in schools, or to social or civic groups.

Publicity needs to be managed carefully to be effective; it must be integrated into the total promotional campaign. In this way, the full force of advertising, sales promotion, publicity, and personal selling can complement one another.

The Personal Selling Process

Unlike the other promotional activities, personal selling is a distinctive communication form because it is two-way rather than one-way communication. Personal selling involves social interaction with the prospect and salesperson influencing each other by what they say and do. The outcome of each sales situation depends upon the success of both parties in communicating with each other and reaching a common understanding of goals and objectives. A salesperson should tailor the communication to fit the prospect's needs.

Many position titles are used to identify people in the field of sales. The titles indicate the amount of selling done and the amount of creativity required to perform the sales task. Three types of personal selling exist: inside sales, executive sales, and sales support activities. Typically, inside salespersons process routine orders, engage in telemarketing, and facilitate the exchange of products with face-to-face customers. Executive salespersons operate outside in assigned territories when appropriate and identify prospective customers, provide these prospects information, influence prospects to purchase products, close sales, and follow up after the sale to build lasting customer relationships. Sales support salespersons assist executive salespersons by performing promotional activities and providing technical expertise.

As products and services become more complex and expensive, personal selling becomes more important in the promotional mix. Highly technical products such as aircraft require greater emphasis on personal selling than other less sophisticated products. The task of an aircraft salesperson best fits the executive sales category, and the seven-step selling process will illustrate the format used to create sales by these salespersons.

Personal selling can be represented as a seven-step sequence that must be accomplished for success.

1. **Prospecting.** Searching for and identifying potential customers. Identifying primary and secondary sources.
2. **Preapproach.** Qualifying the prospects.
3. Approach. Securing an interview to perform a travel analysis.
4. **Presentation.** Developing additional information. Performing a value analysis. Making a formal presentation to the prospective firm's decision makers.
5. **Handling objectives.** Anticipating buyer resistance and developing effective responses.
6. **Closing.** Finalizing the details of the transaction and asking for the order.
7. **Follow-up.** Establishing a good relationship, reassuring the customer, and handling questions. Setting the stage for repeat sales.

Prospecting

Just as firms analyze markets seeking opportunities for their products and services, salespeople seek potential customers. Prospecting is the first step in the selling process, and it involves the continuing search for potential buyers. This search for prospects is generally the sole responsibility of the salesperson. Firms may assist by engaging in direct mail or print advertising, which invites readers to inquire about the firm's products and services. These leads are then turned over to the sales force for follow-up. Qualified prospects are the raw material for future sales. Salespersons must develop skills in this area to assure that presentations are only made to those prospects that have an unfilled need and the financial ability to satisfy that need. The process begins with an in-depth macro view of the total potential markets and then refined to organizations that fit the following profile:

- The company's operations require frequent trips beyond a 300-mile radius to destinations not well served by commercial aviation.
- These frequent trips require two or more persons to travel together.
- The financial health of the company would allow the purchase or lease of an aircraft.
- Their business operations presently require the use of air transportation to accomplish sales and marketing objectives.

Size and Scope of Markets

Most of the resources and reasons to buy general aviation airplanes lie within the business and government sectors of the economy. The best prospects for aircraft and associated services are organizations that can use them to make their own business efforts more productive and more profitable.

Businesses and governmental units include all the buyers in the nation except the final consumers. These buyers purchase and lease tremendous volumes of capital equipment, raw materials, manufactured parts, supplies, and business services. The aggregate purchases of business and government buyers in a year are far greater than those by final consumers. There are more than 23 million businesses in the United States (see Table 8-2). The first four categories of businesses (agricultural, forestry and fishing, mining, construction and manufacturing) sell tangible products and represent 20 percent of the firms. Transportation, communications, and public businesses represent 4 percent of the total businesses. Resellers (wholesalers and retailers) account for 19 percent of the firms, and the service industry (finance, insurance, real estate, and services) complete the types of businesses and represent 57 percent. Governmental units are the federal, state, and local agencies that buy goods and services for the constituents they serve. About 88,000 of these government units exist in the United States.

Measuring Business and Government Markets

Measuring the business and government markets is an important first step for an aircraft salesperson interested in gauging the size of these markets. Fortunately, information is readily available from the federal government to do this. The federal government regularly collects, tabulates, and publishes data on these markets using its Standard Industrial Classification (SIC) System. The SIC system groups organizations on the basis of major activity or the major product or service provided, which enables the federal government to list the number of establishments, number of employees, and sales volumes for each group, designated by a numerical code. Geographic breakdowns are also provided where possible.

The SIC system begins with broad, two-digit categories such as food (SIC code 20), tobacco (SIC code 21), and apparel (SIC code 23). Often each of these two-digit categories is further divided into three- and four-digit categories, which represent subindustries within the broader two-digit category. The SIC system permits a firm to find the SIC codes of its

Table 8-2 Business and Government Markets

Industry	Number of Private Businesses	
	Thousands	Percent
Agricultural, forestry, and fisheries	855	4
Mining	185	1
Construction	2,443	11
Manufacturing	845	4
Transportation, communications, and public utilities	993	4
Wholesale and retail trade	4,455	19
Finance, insurance, and real estate	3,033	13
Services	10,312	44
	23,121	100
Government market		
Government units	88	
Total	23,209	

Source: Statistical Abstract of the United States, 2000, page 299 and 535.

present customers and then obtain SIC-coded lists for similar firms that may want the same type of products and services. Also, SIC categories can be monitored to determine the growth in the number of firms, number of employees, and sales volumes to identify promising market opportunities.

Prospecting Sources

The total prospective business aircraft market can be thought of as an iceberg. Above the waterline are the highly visible corporations appearing in Fortune's top 500 or top 1,000 lists. These include such companies as General Motors, ExxonMobil, IBM, Procter and Gamble, and General Electric. Over one-half of the Fortune top 1,000 firms own or operate aircraft for business purposes. Each year *Business and Commercial Aviation* magazine, using data supplied by Aviation Data Service, Inc. breaks down the Fortune top 1,000 firms by SIC code and compares the number of aircraft operators and nonoperators for each category. There is no problem compiling information on these publicly owned firms or for that matter, on the next 25,000 leading U.S. corporations. Detailed information concerning these firms can be found in business directories such as *Dun & Bradstreet*, and *Standard & Poor's*, which are in most public libraries (see Table 8-3).

There is another layer of businesses, not listed in any national business directory, representing the balance of the 23 million companies. It is the upper one million companies of this business stratum that represents about 80 percent of the owners of general aviation aircraft. These businesses form part of the iceberg market profile that is immediately below the waterline. These are the companies listed in the telephone book, chamber of commerce directories, civil club rosters, state chamber of commerce directory, individual industry directories, medical society directories, and professional society rosters. They are companies, associations, and partnerships run by successful businesspeople in any city or area. Some major categories include the following:

- Automobile dealers
- Banks
- Food product manufacturers and distributors
- General contractors
- Insurance agents, brokers, and companies
- Machinery manufacturers
- Petroleum and natural gas companies
- Pharmaceutical companies
- Printers and lithographers
- Retailers
- Transportation equipment manufacturers
- Utility companies
- Wholesalers

Under each business type, there are hundreds of subcategories and many companies listed. The objective is to prepare the most thorough list of business prospects that could use private air transportation to accomplish one or more of the following objectives:

1. Expand sales territory
2. Make faster on-the-spot management decisions at remote branches
3. Expedite service to customers
4. Use a faster mode of travel without being subject to airline routes and schedules

Table 8-3 Resources Used for Identifying and Qualifying Prospects

Publication	Type of Information
STANDARD & POOR'S Stock Reports	Companies with stock listed on the New York Stock Exchange, the American Stock Exchange, over the counter and regional stock exchanges. Provides company history with recent financial developments and prospects for the future.
STANDARD & POOR'S Corporation Records	Corporation history, financial status and personnel of major corporations.
STANDARD & POOR'S Register of Corporations, Directors & Executives	Provides information on moderate to large size corporations. List company officers, type of business, sales volume, number of employees, etc. Also contains cross reference of directors and executives.
STANDARD & POOR'S Industry Survey	Provides history and status of basic industry.
MOODY'S Industrial Manual	Provides information on company history, financial data, subsidiaries, officers and directors, and corporate financial information.
MOODY'S Public Utility Manual	Information similar to above.
MOODY'S Bank & Finance Manual	Information similar to above.
MOODY'S Handbook of Common Stocks	Provides information on company history, recent developments, and future prospects for the company. Large U.S. corporations.
THOMAS REGISTER	Product information and profiles on more than 123,000 U.S. companies. Includes asset ratings, company executives, location of sales offices, distributors, plants, service/engineering offices.
DUN & BRADSTREET'S Million Dollar Directory	Provides sales volume, names of officers and key people of major corporations to include telephone numbers, number of employees, type of business (minimum net worth $1,000,000).
DUN & BRADSTREET'S Middle Market Directory	Provides sales volume, names of officers and key people of major corporations to include telephone numbers, number of employees, type of business (net worth $500,000 to $999,999).
BEST'S Insurance Reports	Provides information on company history, management personnel, operations and financial structure of all major U.S. life and casualty insurance companies.
WHO'S WHO	There are many *Who's Whos such as Who's Who in America*, *Who's Who in Commerce and Industry*, *Who's Who in Science*, *Who's Who in Insurance*, *Who's Who in American Women*. An ideal source for personal information on prominent persons.
NEWSFRONT'S 25,000 Leading U.S. Corporations	25,000 leading corporations grouped by state and city. Provides names of chief executive officers and financial size.
STATE INDUSTRIAL DIRECTORIES	Published by each state. Provides basic information on state's major industries, type and size of company, chief executive officer, and sales volume is typical of the information listed.
ANNUAL REPORTS	Many libraries contain recent annual reports of companies listed on the New York and American Stock Exchanges. Local brokerage houses will usually have annual reports for local industries.
TRADE DIRECTORIES	These directories contain information on many industries such as grocery, lumber, food stuffs, manufacturing, etc. Ideal for vertical prospecting within industries already favorable to aircraft utilization.

5. Utilize a quicker way to get raw materials
6. Expedite shipments of parts
7. Expand medical service to outlying areas
8. Bring customers/clients to the manufacturing plant
9. Go to buying markets
10. Develop far-reaching real estate prospects
11. Manage big farms and ranches
12. Put new marketing plans into action

With this understanding of the various types and sizes of business prospects and the answers to the above specific operational needs that air transportation can efficiently satisfy, the sales person can employ the traditional prospecting tools to build an inventory of company names. These "suspects" would then be qualified prior to attempting to make an appointment. Traditional sources of prospects would include the following:

1. **Existing customers.** A salesperson's customer base is an excellent source of leads. Frequent contacts with customers will not only provide new sales, but if the customer is pleased with the product and service, referrals will be gladly given.
2. **Interview replacement.** This technique is often referred to as the "Endless Chain Method" because if applied correctly, it becomes the primary source of leads. Prior to leaving the closing interview, successful or unsuccessful, the salesperson attempts to secure the names of three or four individuals or businesses that could benefit from the use of their own aircraft. Experience shows that out of these leads, one interview will be secured. The interview to leads ratio will be greatly enhanced if the salesperson obtains permission to use the name of the person who gave them the lead.
3. **Acquaintances and friends.** Salespersons usually enjoy being with others socially and in church and community activities. These contacts often result in good leads.
4. **Direct mail.** This technique is used to supplement the methods identified above. Lists of names, which meet predetermined criteria, are purchased and processed either internally or by a company specializing in direct marketing. Leads are generated whenever a prospect requests additional information as a result of a direct marketing communication. A study by Posner and Walcek indicates that for every 100 responses
   - Three people or companies will purchase the advertised product within three months.
   - Twenty have a legitimate need, authority, and intention to buy within 12 months.
   - Thirty-seven are gathering information to support a future purchase decision.
   - Forty are collecting information or are simply curious.

Pre-approach

The qualifying stage of prospecting, known as the pre-approach in the selling process, is extremely important. The pre-approach step involves the selection of prospects who warrant further attention. It is this smaller group that becomes the "prospect" group because the salesperson determines that each company needs the product or service, can finance the purchase, and has the authority to buy. In qualifying prospects, a sales representative will attempt to develop information regarding the following questions:

1. Who are the decision makers and what are their hobbies?
2. Are these individuals involved in the ownership or management of any other businesses? Are they located in one area or decentralized?
3. If they are involved in other businesses, what are they and what is their size?
4. What has the company's sales performance been in recent years? Growing? Diminishing? Same?
5. What is the company's competitive position (number one, trying to be number one, smallest, newest, oldest)?
6. Do other firms in the industry use business aircraft? Get examples.
7. What is the company's financial position and what is the outlook for growth in its business?
8. Describe the marketing, distribution, and field sales organizations.
9. Who are some of the company's major customers?
10. Do customers have branch offices that need to be contacted regularly? Where are they and how many?
11. Does the company ever use scheduled airlines for executive and sales travel? Shipping goods and equipment? Receiving raw materials? Moving parts and service personnel?
12. Does it ever use air charter service?
13. Which department or division of the company utilizes scheduled air transportation the most?
14. Do any employees in the company fly themselves? How many? What kind of aircraft do they fly?
15. Have they ever rented aircraft? For what purpose?
16. In the operation of the business, do they travel primarily to large metropolitan areas or to rural or outlying areas? Get examples of some of these places.
17. Do they transport major customers to their plants and offices? Would an aircraft do this job better?
18. What length trip does the company make?
19. What is the average number of people who travel together?
20. If the prospect is a manufacturing company, what raw materials does it use? Where do they come from?

From this information, the sales representative attempts to

determine the following:

1. Any possible direct relationship between an airplane and increased sales territory or sales volume. Could the prospect quickly and efficiently reach otherwise inaccessible customers with a private airplane?
2. How will the use of aircraft relate to overall expansion and growth for the prospect?
3. How will the aircraft increase the performance of the sales staff? Management personnel? Outline some examples.
4. Considering the company's financial strength and profitability, how important are tax and depreciation considerations to the prospect in the purchase of an aircraft?
5. Would a finance or lease plan be of benefit to the prospect?
6. Would the "prestige" factor of aircraft ownership be of any value to the business?
7. What additional use might there be for aircraft in the prospect's business?
8. Is there a flying group or association this company could belong to that might help it decide to fly its own aircraft? Flying Physicians, National Real Estate Fliers Association, Flying Adjusters, Lawyer-Pilots, Flying Funeral Directors, or Flying Veterinarians are some of the specialized groups.

Qualifying information is necessary before detailed plans for visiting the prospect can be formulated. Such knowledge permits the customization of selling strategy. The sources of qualifying information are, for the most part, the same as the sources already mentioned for identifying prospects and developing basic information. Qualifying, however, involves deeper research and indicates more detailed questioning of sources who know more than just basic information. Chambers of commerce personnel may have particular knowledge about operations of important area businesses. Trade association secretaries often keep clippings with details about successes and problems of industry firms. Certainly, employees of the prospective firm may be in a position to give information about who makes buying decisions and how they are made. Secretaries of prospective companies may be in a position to reveal strategic facts. They are also in an excellent position to know about a buyer's problems and competitive activity. Analysis of credit ratings and annual reports show financial strength, company plans, and buying-power information.

Sometimes it is necessary to call on prospects to gain qualifying information before setting up a formal interview. Prospects themselves are usually the best sources of information about their companies. In these cases, the salesperson must first sell the need for qualifying information or fact-finding interview because asking for management time is like asking for money. Some prospects resist preliminary surveys, feeling that they may disrupt normal activities, constitute a threat to the firm's right to privacy, or create an obligation for a detailed survey or even a purchase. Most potential aircraft users, however, realize that a sales representative selling major capital goods is unable to analyze their problems and serve their needs without detailed operational information.

Approach

The strategies used by the salesperson to secure an interview and establish rapport with the prospect is called the approach. The use of the Travel Analysis in aircraft sales necessitates that the first interview be a fact-finding one where data is gathered in order to perform an analysis of the prospect's air transportation needs. One of the following three approach strategies are used to secure this first fact-finding interview:

1. Direct personal contact. In making a personal visit, the salesperson has the opportunity to evaluate the business premises, talk to company personnel, and to become better prepared for the prospect. The advantage of this strategy is that if the prospect is available, the interview can take place immediately. The major disadvantage is the inefficient use of time caused by either having to wait to see the prospect, or finding that the prospect is out or too busy to be seen that day.
2. Telephone call. Using the telephone has many advantages over the direct personal contact. By calling ahead, the prospect will be available at the appointed time, thus resulting in more efficient use of the salesperson's time. This method allows the salesperson to efficiently schedule appointments so that daily and weekly activity quotas can be met. The major disadvantage of telephoning is that it is easy to be turned down over the telephone. Success with this approach requires skillful telephone techniques to be able to navigate through the "screeners" or "gatekeepers" and to persuade the prospect to grant an interview.
3. Personal letter. Personal letters, individually signed by the salesperson, may be the best and most professional method to use to secure an interview. Letters introduce the salesperson and the selling company, the product, or service being offered, and specifically state that a telephone call will be made in a few days to arrange a convenient time for an interview. Colorful brochures may be included that describe the product or service in more detail. During this promised telephone call, the salesperson suggests alternative times for the interview. In doing so, the prospect's attention is focused on the issue of when to meet, rather than whether to meet at all.

Presentation

Prior to the first face-to-face meeting with the prospect, the salesperson should understand that the success of that interview will depend upon understanding the following assumptions concerning the prospect and his or her environment:

1. The salesperson is interrupting the prospect. The salesperson must redirect the prospect's attention from what that person was doing immediately prior to the interview to the salesperson's objective of the meeting.
2. The salesperson must use the prospect's time wisely. The interview format must be carefully organized and well prepared.
3. If the salesperson is talking to the right person in the company, that person's perception of the worth or value of the interview will probably determine future success or failure.
4. Generally, since the salesperson initiated the interview, the prospect is satisfied with the company's current usage of air transportation.
5. The prospect wants to purchase profitability.

The type of presentation used by the salesperson depends upon the nature of the product or service. If the needs of the prospect are obvious, the product offered is standardized, and the salespersons are new and not well-trained, then the organized approach is recommended. With this method, the salesperson follows a company prepared outline—a canned sales presentation. This approach has the weakness that all potential customers are treated alike so whether successful or not, the salesperson probably won't know why or learn from the experience. The organized approach may be suitable for simple selling tasks, but for complicated situations such as selling business aircraft, it is not a satisfactory strategy.

The unstructured approach is a problem-solving one in which the salesperson and the prospect define needs and problems and then collect supporting data. The exploration of needs using the fact-finding interview technique is the first of a two-interview system used by aircraft salespersons. After the data has been analyzed to determine the best fit between prospect's requirements and selling company's product, a second interview is requested to make a presentation of recommendations.

The format for the organized approach and the second interview of the unstructured approach is centered around the following five steps:

1. **Gaining the prospect's attention.** Talk to prospects about something that interests them.
2. **Arousing the prospect's interest.** Tell the prospects what the product will do to benefit or serve them.
3. **Convincing the prospect that it is an intelligent action to purchase the product.** Give the prospect sufficient information about the product to prove that purchasing the product is justifiable.
4. **Arousing the prospect's desire to purchase.** Determine the prospect's primary buying motive and then explain how the product will satisfy the unfilled need. Finally, paint a word picture of the satisfaction to be derived from the purchase.
5. **Closing the sale successfully.** Get a positive decision by weighing the advantages against the disadvantages.

Sales presentations can be enhanced with various aids such as booklets (business aircraft feasibility studies), flip charts, slides and films, computer software demonstrations, and product brochures. Often a demonstration trip is arranged so that the prospect can learn firsthand how the use of a business aircraft can fulfill the company's transportation needs. These types of demonstrations are particularly effective in showing what the aircraft will do for the prospect and proving that the business aircraft is truly a business tool that will help solve problems and open many opportunities not presently available to the prospective company.

Handling Objections

Objections by the prospect are a natural occurrence during any sales presentation and should be welcomed as a chance to get the prospect involved and to expand the discussion into areas of concern. An objection does not mean that the prospect does not want the product. In the majority of cases, prospects object because they lack information.

The best way to handle objections is to minimize them by covering the common questions adequately in the sales presentation. The answers to the most common objections, complaints, and criticisms should be in the form of positive selling points. When objections are anticipated and minimized, it is more difficult for the prospect to form negative opinions about the proposal that might result in a fixed position or issue.

Experienced salespersons realize that selling is made easier when objections surface because it is much easier to deal with a prospect who talks than with one who doesn't. Objections shed light on the prospect's thinking and tell the salesperson what subjects need amplification before attempting to close the sale.

Successful salespersons use the basic principles of handling objections skillfully during the sales presentation. Many prospects offer excuses that are not real obstacles to buying. When the objection is identified as an excuse, the actual reason why the prospect is unwilling to buy must be established. Tactful questions can penetrate the excuse "smoke screen" and probe for valid objections which the prospect may have concealed. Another technique to deal with objections is called the boomerang. This technique turns an objection into a reason for buying. A prospect states: "Your organization is entirely too small to provide the service we will require." The response by the salesperson might be, "Our small size is one of our assets. It permits us to give personalized service." The skillful use of these techniques will keep the presentation positive and moving toward a successful conclusion.

Closing

The closing step is the logical conclusion to a well-organized sales presentation and involves obtaining a purchase commitment from the prospect. This step is the most important, as well as the most difficult, because it is often unclear when the prospect is ready to buy. Closing clues are signals that indicate that a close should be attempted. Closing clues can be either physical or verbal. Physical signals are actions by the prospect such as nodding or smiling in agreement to the proposal. Verbal closing clues may be questions or comments such as: "What kinds of financing are available?" or "That aircraft is certainly modern looking." A number of different closing techniques can be employed. Salespersons can simply ask for the order or go over the points of agreement and offer to clarify any questions the buyer may have. Another closing approach assumes that the prospect is ready to buy and the salesperson asks, "Did you decide on the special avionics package or do you prefer the standard equipment?" This technique is called the alternative choice method.

By asking the prospect, "Which paint scheme did you decide upon?" the salesperson is using the decision on minor points method. This technique is used when the prospect is reluctant to make the big decision, which is to buy or not buy, but is comfortable in making a series of minor ones. Offering the prospect specific inducements, such as attractive interest rates, a special price on a particular item of equipment, or a one-year extension on the new warranty can be effective in getting immediate positive results.

Follow-up

The last and very important step in the selling process is the follow-up after the sale. Salespersons depend upon repeat sales that are enhanced by post-sales activities. These activities include making sure that promises made at the time of the sale concerning delivery, equipment packages, training for employees, and others, are met to the customer's satisfaction. Continuing to stay in contact with the customer will usually pay dividends in the form of referrals and additional sales.

KEY TERMS

Promotional mix
Advertising
Sales promotion
Publicity
Personal selling
Product advertising
Institutional advertising
Pioneering advertising
Competitive advertising
Comparative advertising
Reminder advertising
Advertising message
Directional advertising
Cooperative advertising
Public relations
Publicity techniques
Inside salespersons
Executive salespersons
Sales support salespersons
Seven-step selling process
Prospecting
Standard Industrial Classification (SIC) system
Preapproach
Approach
Organized approach
Unstructured approach
Objectives
Closing step
Follow-up

REVIEW QUESTIONS

1. What is the promotional mix? Distinguish between advertising and sales promotion. Why do firms use advertising agencies? Give some examples of advertising objectives. Distinguish between product and institutional advertising.
2. Explain several methods of establishing an advertising budget. What is the advertising message and how is it developed? Summarize the advantages and disadvantages of the following media: newspapers, magazines and trade journals, direct mail, and radio. Give several examples of how the effectiveness of advertising can be measured.
3. What is the purpose of a firm's sales promotion activities? Identify and briefly describe five sales promotion activities used by FBOs. What is cooperative advertising?
4. How does publicity differ from public relations? Identify

some of the topics available to an FBO that have potential for publicity. Describe several publicity techniques.
5. Name and describe the three types of sales positions.
6. Define prospecting. What is the Standard Industrial Classification (SIC) system? Name seven aircraft prospecting sources.
7. What is the objective of qualifying the prospect? What is the objective of the approach stage? Discuss some of the techniques used by sales representatives in presenting a product or service to a prospective buyer. Describe several closing techniques. What is the importance of the follow-up stage?

REFERENCES

Berkowitz, Eric N., and Roger A. Kerin, Steven W. Hartley, William Rudelius. *Marketing,* 6th Ed. Burr Ridge, IL. Irwin/McGraw-Hill, 2000.

Jain, Sub hash c. *Marketing Planning & Strategy* (6th ed.) Cincinnati, Ohio: South Western College Publishing, 2000.

Kotler, Philip, and Gary Armstrong. *Marketing, An Introduction* (3rd ed.). Englewood Cliffs, NJ.: Prentice Hall, 1992.

Perreault, William D. and E. Jerome McCarthy. *Basic Marketing* (13th ed.). Burr Ridge, IL: Irwin/McGraw-Hill, 1999.

SCENARIOS

1. As the newly promoted marketing manager at a full-service FBO, you have been asked by the FBO manager to develop a new advertising campaign for the FBO. To begin, he asks you to present all of the advertising media that may be used and to create a table with the advantages and disadvantages of each type. Next, he wants you to recommend a specific advertising plan for the FBO. How would you do that?
2. You have been asked to create some specific advertising objectives for the following departments: aircraft rental, flight instruction, aircraft sales, fuel sales, aircraft maintenance. What are some specific objectives you could create that would lead to increased numbers in these areas?
3. Previously, Easy Aviation had no formal marketing/promotional plan. Additionally, this FBO did not even have a budget for these activities. However, the new owners plan to change this. As the newly hired marketing manager, you have been asked to establish an advertising budget. Explain the five approaches to advertising budgeting and recommend one to the new management.
4. As a marketing assistant intern at a full-service FBO in your hometown, you have been asked to assist with the advertising campaign for the FBO. Specifically, the FBO is embarking on an advertising campaign for flight instruction, aircraft sales, and aircraft maintenance. You have been asked to develop the advertising message for each of these three campaigns. What do you propose?
5. Executive FBO has been trying to increase their aircraft sales revenue. They mainly deal with high-end business jets. For the past three months, they have advertised on a Sunday afternoon AM radio show entitled, "Your House, Your Money." This advertising is not paying off. In fact, aircraft sales have actually declined slightly. Based on your knowledge and experience with FBO marketing, the FBO manager has contracted with you to provide some guidance on their advertising campaign. Specifically, the FBO Manager has asked you to recommend a proper advertising media for their aircraft sales campaign. What do you recommend and why?
6. The FBO you manage is planning an Air Show and LSA fly-in next September. The key for a successful event will be getting the word out. You want to attract not only the general public, but also LSA owner/operators, and other pilots. Develop a publicity campaign for this event.
7. As an intern in the Aircraft Sales division at Myers FBO, you have been shadowing the more experienced aircraft salespersons and learning as much as possible during the past month. The Manager of Aircraft Sales has asked you to study the seven steps of the personal selling process and be prepared to engage in personal selling with the Executive Director of the local Chamber of Commerce. How do you prepare for this? For each of the seven steps of the personal selling process, what will you plan to do?

Notes

Chapter 9
Marketing Research

OUTLINE

Marketing Research Defined
Scope of Marketing Research
- Market Measurement Studies
- Marketing Mix Studies
- Studies of the Competitive Situation
- Studies of Influences of Uncontrollables

Marketing Research Process
- Defining the Problem and Research Objectives
- Secondary Data
- Primary Data

Designing the Research
- Research Designs
- Types of Research Instruments
- Sampling Procedures

Methods of Collecting Data
Analyzing the Findings
Presenting the Findings

OBJECTIVES

At the end of this chapter, you should be able to:

- Define marketing research and explain its purpose within an organization.
- Give examples of different types of marketing research studies falling under market measurement, marketing mix, competitive situations, and the uncontrollable variables.
- Describe the steps involved in the marketing research process.
- Distinguish between primary and secondary data.
- Identify five major sources of secondary data.
- Describe research approaches, types of research instruments, sampling procedures, and methods of collecting data in a plan for collecting primary data.

Marketing Reseach Defined

Marketing decisions are often complex ones that have major impact upon the firm's ability to reach its market share and profitability goals. There are many variable factors in the external environment such as increasing competition, technology, governmental regulations, changes in the macro economy, and the constantly changing opinions, attitudes, and values of customers. The ultimate objective for engaging in marketing research is to assist managers in decision making, which is the essence of management. Managers at all levels spend more time defining, making, and implementing decisions than in any other activity. It is essential, therefore, that systematic information gathering and analytical procedures contribute to effective and efficient decision making. Through research, management can reduce uncertainty in decision making.

Marketing research is also a vital business activity, providing a foundation for the planning, implementation, and control of marketing programs. It is an integral part of any management information system that provides a flow of inputs useful in marketing decision making.

Marketing research is the systematic process of gathering, recording, analyzing, and utilizing relevant information to aid in marketing decision making. Marketing managers today should understand that marketing research is an aid to decision making, not a substitute for it. Having the right kind of information available can greatly increase the probability that the best decision will be made.

Scope of Marketing Research

Marketing research has a broad scope including various types of studies (see Table 9-1). These studies can be grouped into four major categories: (1) market measurement studies, (2) marketing mix studies, (3) studies of the competitive situation, and (4) studies of the uncontrollables.

Market Measurement Studies

Market measurement studies are designed to obtain quantitative data on potential demand —how much of a particular product or service can be sold to various target markets over a future period, assuming the application of appropriate marketing methods.

This data relates to market potential, sales potential, or both. Market potential is the maximum possible sales oppor-

Table 9-1 Types of Marketing Research Studies

1. Market Measurement
   a. Demand research
      (1). Determination of market characteristics
      (2). Measurement of market potential
      (3). Short-range forecasting (up to one year)
      (4). Long-range forecasting (over one year)
      (5). Buyer motivation
   b. Performance research
      (1). Market share analysis
      (2). Sales analysis
      (3). Establishment of sales quotas
      (4). Evaluation of test markets
      (5). Customer surveys
2. Marketing Mix Research-Controllable influences
   a. Product or service research
      (1). New product or service acceptance and potential
      (2). Existing products or service in new markets
      (3). Diversification of products
   b. Place research
      (1). Methods of delivering product or service to customers
      (2). Facility location
   c. Price research
   d. Promotion research
      (1). Studies of advertising effectiveness
      (2). Sales compensation studies
      (3). Media research
      (4). Studies of sales promotion effectiveness
3. Competition research
   a. Competitive product or service studies
4. Uncontrollable Influences
   a. Studies of business trends
   b. Studies of legal constraints-rules and regulations
   c. Environmental impact studies
   d. Demographic studies

tunity open to all sellers of a product or service during a stated future period to a target market. Sales potential is the maximum possible sales opportunity open to a particular company selling a product or service during a stated future period for a target market. For example, consider the business jet market. The market potential, macroperspective, for business jets over the next three years is around 2,000 units. Considering the VLJ market, industry estimates as many as 5,000-10,000 by 2015. This represents total units all aircraft manufacturers participating in these market segments could sell over this time period. Using the business jet example, Cessna's sales potential, microperspective, would be approximately 775 units based upon their market share of 42.9 percent over the same stated three-year period.

Market measurement data is especially helpful in planning overall marketing strategy. In evaluating a proposed new twin-engine charter service, for example, management must estimate its probable marketing success. Analysis of market measurement data provides insights as to whether a potential market exists and, if so, its size. If management decides to add a new product, such as flight simulators, market measurement data is again helpful in determining target markets. In addition, breakdowns of potential sales by types of customers make it possible to ascertain which groups should be the targets for promotional efforts of varying amounts, and in what order they should be pursued. Management make similar use of market measurement data in resolving questions of whether to drop certain services, closing the avionics shop, for instance, or de-emphasizing promotion to particular market segments.

Buyer motivation research studies probe the psychological, sociological, and economic variables affecting buyer behavior. These studies require trained psychologists, sociologists, and economists to undertake them and interpret the resulting data. Few companies employ such people, and most motivation research is handled by outside consultants.

Marketing Mix Studies

Most marketing research studies focus on the elements of the marketing mix: product, place, price, and promotion. Management uses studies of these controllable variables to appraise the effectiveness of current product, service, pricing, and promotion policies, and to plan future policies and practices. Many firms make frequent studies of the effectiveness of advertising and other promotional devices, individual salespeople, existing sales methods, and sales compensation plans. Management can change the controllable variables with any formal study, but change is more effective with the added insight gained from research.

Studies of the Competitive Situation

More firms emphasize studies of the competitive position of their own products and services than they do studies of the nature and impact of their competitors' activities. Specifically, a study measuring the market share of a firm's products and services is more common than one which appraises the strengths and weaknesses of a competitor's products and services, evaluates the effects of a competitor's service improvement, measures the impact of a competitor's price change, or checks the effects of a competitor's revised advertising approach. Most companies could benefit by delving into competitors' marketing practices and policies. Management needs this information to understand how competitors' actions affect marketing strategy.

Studies of Influences of Uncontrollables

The studies of business trends, economic data, and industry statistics through the process of environmental scanning are the most widely used type of study in this category. Published information is available on such uncontrollables as interest rates, level of consumer credit, corporate profits, business expansion plans, and age and income distribution trends. Federal government publications such as the Statistical Abstract of the United States, the County and City Data Book, and Survey of Current Business, and the Federal Reserve Bulletin contain a great deal of information on the uncontrollables. The U. S. Census of Manufacturers, published about every five years, lists the number and size of manufacturing firms by industry group (Standard Industrial Classifications-SIC Codes). The U. S. Census of Retail Trade, also published about every five years, provides comparable detailed information on retailers. The U.S. Department of Commerce Office of Business Economics gathers and publishes data on the national economic outlook. The Department of Commerce also maintains field offices to help firms looking for specific types of information. The FAA Statistical Handbook, and Aerospace Facts and Figures, an Aerospace Industries Association (AIA) databook, both provide statistical data on an annual basis. In addition, aviation trade associations such as General Aviation Manufacturers Association (GAMA) and National Business Aviation Association (NBAA), universities, and aviation and business periodicals provide detailed data of value to firms doing marketing research. *Business and Commercial Aviation*, *Air Transport World*, *Commuter Air*, *Business Week*, *The Wall Street Journal*, and *Sales and Marketing Management* are sources with considerable information on uncontrollables.

Marketing Research Process

The marketing research process consists of a series of activities: defining the problem and research objectives, designing the research, collecting the data, preparing and analyzing the data, and presenting the findings.

Defining the Problem and Research Objectives

The first step in research requires management to carefully define the problem and clearly state the research objectives. If the president of an FBO asks the flight department manager to "Go and develop data on the charter market or flight training market," the results will be disappointing. Hundreds of subjects can be researched about those two markets. If the research findings are to be useful, they must relate to a specific problem or opportunity facing the firm. The president and the researcher, in this case the flight department manager, must agree on the problem. "How can we attract more charter business or how can we improve the student pilot retention rate?" Collecting information is too costly to allow the problem to be defined vaguely or incorrectly.

At this point, management needs to set the research objectives. A well-defined problem statement gives direction to the research and assists in the formulation of research objectives. Some form of exploratory research is often needed to both refine and clearly state the problem and set research objectives. This informal investigation will attempt to uncover as much relevant information as possible. Sources for the investigation include knowledgeable employees who are directly involved in the situation, customers and current flight students who are directly affected by the problem, and internal sales and financial reports that pertain to the situation. Questions to be answered are: What is the frequency of use of our existing charter customers? What percentage of target businesses in the area is even aware of aircraft charter services? What is their perception regarding the cost of this service? At what stage in the flight-training program are students dropping out? What are their reasons? At the end of this first step, the researcher should know (1) the current situation; (2) the nature of the problem; and (3) the specific question or questions the research will be designed to answer.

Secondary Data

Secondary data consists of information that already exists, having been collected for another purpose. Researchers usually start their investigation by collecting secondary data that can be obtained from internal or external sources. Internal secondary data is available within the company. External secondary data must be extracted from sources outside the firm. Table 9-2 shows many sources of secondary data.

Primary Data

Primary data is data collected from original sources for a particular study. Some researchers, unfortunately, collect primary data by developing a few questions and finding some businesses to interview. Data gathered this way might be useless or, even worse misleading. Instead, a plan should be created for collecting credible (valid and reliable) primary data. Table 9-3 shows a plan that requires decisions on research

Table 9-2 Sources of Secondary Data

1. Internal Sources
   Profit and loss statements, balance sheets, sales analysis, sales-call reports, inventory records, maintenance job orders, pilot training records, customer complaints, and previous research reports.
2. External Sources
   a. Government publications
      (1). *U.S. Industrial Outlook* provides information on industry segments including the costs of production, sales, and employment.
      (2). *Statistical Abstract of the U.S.* provides summary data on demographic, economic, and social data in the United States.
      (3). *County and City Data Book* presents statistical information on cities and counties on education, employment, income, housing, bank deposits, and retail sales.
      (4). Other government publications—*Census of Population, Census of Retail Trade, Wholesale Trade and Selected Services, Census of Transportation, Federal Reserve Bulletin, Monthly Labor Review, Survey of Current Business, Vital Statistics Report, FAA Statistical Handbook,* and the *FAA Forecasts of Aviation Activity.*
   b. Associations
      There are a wide variety of associations of manufacturers, distributors, and end users. The Encyclopedia of Associations lists every major trade and professional association. These associations often collect and distribute statistics and studies on their industry. Aviation associations such as ATA, RAA, NBAA, AOPA, GAMA, ADMA, NASAO and many others listed in the World Aviation Directory provide a wealth of information.
   c. Periodicals and books
      (1). General business—*Business Week, Forbes, Fortune,* and *Duns*. Business Periodicals Index lists business articles appearing in a wide variety of business publications. Standard and Poor's *Industry Surveys* provide updated statisitics and analyses of industries. *Moody's Manuals* provide financial data and names of executives in major companies.
      (2). Marketing—*Journal of Marketing, Journal of Marketing Research, Journal of Personal Selling, and Sales Management, Industrial Marketing Management, Business Marketing,* and *Sales and Marketing Management.*
      (3). Aviation trade magazines—A wide variety of trade magazines exist which collect valuable statistics as well as provide surveys and reports. Some of these are *Business and Commercial Aviation, Air Transport World, Commuter Air, Aviation Week,* and *Space Technology, AOPA Magazine, Professional Pilot,* and *Aviation Equipment Maintenance.*
   d. The Internet
      Internet browsers like Netscape Navigator and Microsoft Internet Explorer have user-friendly menus to activate and Internet search. Popular search engines like Yahoo (*www.yahoo.com*) and Google (*www.google.com*) are especially effective tools to use in researching the internet. Many computerized databases and index services are now available on the Intenet by governmental agencies, libraries and public firms. For example, hundreds of publications, including newspapers from around the world are available for a small user fee from Dow Jones's interactive news retrieval system (*www.djnr.com*) Using the Internet to search for relevant secondary data does offer the researcher many advantages that result in reduced research time and costs. Areas that increase productivity include research staff who can work from their own desks rather than physically going to libraries and other research locations; Web-based information is already in digital form that allows convenient downloading into electronic spreadsheets. Most reports are either free or require a small user fee, and the information desired over the Internet is often more current and more focused because search engines allow time frames to be inserted and key words that provide very specialized information.
   e. Consultants
      There are a number of aviation and marketing consulting firms that have data on projects of a similar nature, broad experience in the area, and/or contacts that can provide useful information.
   f. Nonprofit agencies
      Educational institutions including those with aviation programs. Foundations like Ford and Carnegie, the Conference Board, and the Marketing Science Institute. Local chambers of commerce and the research section of the local library.
   g. Commercial sources
      A.C. Nielson provides data on tetevision audiences and magazine circulation data. Simmons Market Research Bureau provides annual reports covering television markets for a wide variety of products, including demographic data be sex, income, age and brand preferences. Stock brokerage firms can provide annual reports on businesses. Local marketing research firms can provide surveys.

Table 9-3 Plans for Primary Data Collection

Research Designs
- Survey method
- Observation method
- Experiment method

Types of Research Instruments
- Questionnaire
- Mechanical Instruments

Sampling Procedure
- Sampling unit
- Sample size
- Sample group

Method of Collecting Data
- Personal interview
- Telephone interview
- Mail questionnaire
- Electronic questionnaire
- Focus group interview

design, typs of research instruments, sampling procedures, and methods of data collection.

Designing the Research

Once the research problem has been defined and objectives stated, the next step is to select a research design. A research design is a master plan that specifies the methods and procedures for collecting and analyzing the required information. It is a blueprint of the research plan of action. The stated objectives of the research are included in the design to ensure that information collected is germane to solving the problem. There are three basic design techniques for descriptive and causal research: survey, observation, and experiment. The most common is the survey. In the survey method, information is obtained directly from individual respondents through personal interviews, telephone interviews, mail questionnaires, electronic questionnaires, and focus groups. Questionnaires are used for specific responses to direct questions or for general responses to open-ended questions.

The survey method has two main uses: (1) to gather facts from respondents, and (2) to report their opinions. The survey method's accuracy and reliability varies in each application. Generally, it is most accurate and reliable when gathering facts and less so when recording opinion.

In the factual survey, respondents are asked to report actual facts such as, "Have you ever used a charter flight service? During an average month, how many times do three or more employees travel to a meeting location within 300 miles of your office? How often does your present travel mode or modes cause you to remain overnight or travel long hours?" Even the answers to factual questions are subject to error because some respondents have faulty memories, are unable to generalize about personal experiences, or may give answers they believe interviewers want.

The opinion survey is designed to gather expressions of personal opinion and record evaluations of air travel matters. "How do you feel about the quality of flight instruction received?" "What were your instructors strengths? weaknesses?" "What was the most difficult problem you encountered in using the self-paced learning materials?" Opinion surveys share the potential errors of factual surveys and, by forcing immediate answers to questions on subjects that the respondents have not thought about lately, may produce answers not accurately reflecting real opinions. In addition to response errors, survey results can be biased by excluding people who were not contacted (they were not at home) or who refused to cooperate. The statistical differences between a survey that includes only those people who responded and a survey that also includes those who failed to respond are referred to as nonresponse error. This problem is especially important in mail and telephone surveys because of the normally low response rate. To be able to use the survey results, the researcher must be sure that those who did respond were representative of those who did not. By selecting a group of nonrespondents and then contacting them, a researcher can determine the extent of the nonresponse error.

FBOs that rely on self-administered questionnaires must be aware of the self-selection bias that makes the survey results less useful. Surveys left for charter customers to fill out at the end of the trip fall into this category. A man who suffered minor injury due to turbulence or had coffee spilled on his suit is more likely to fill out the questionnaire than those passengers who were indifferent about the trip. Self-selection biases the survey because it tends to be overweighted by passengers with extreme positions and underweighted by those who were indifferent about the charter experience.

The second basic design technique is the observation method, where marketing research data is gathered not through direct questioning of respondents, but by observing and recording consumers' actions in a marketing situation. For example, line personnel are observed while they greet and service customers' aircraft. Students' questions and reactions are observed during preflight and postflight discussions with instructors.

The experiment method is the third technique and calls for selecting matched groups of subjects, giving them different treatments, and checking on whether observed differences are significant. An FBO, for example, may run two versions of a proposed advertisement (ad A and ad B) in a city newspaper, with half the circulation-carrying ad A and the other half carrying ad B. This experiment might be used to determine the more effective advertisement in different markets, which might then be placed in all newspapers and other direct mailings in the area.

Types of Research Instruments

Marketing researchers have a choice of two main research instruments in collecting primary data questionnaires and mechanical devices.

The questionnaire is by far the most common instrument used in collecting primary data. It consists of a set of questions presented to respondents for their answers. The questionnaire is very flexible in that there are many ways to ask questions. Questionnaires need to be carefully developed, tested, and debugged before they can be used on a large scale.

Prior to the actual start of constructing a questionnaire, the researcher must identify the questionnaire objectives, type, and method of collecting the data. Since the purpose of a questionnaire is to formulate questions to carry out the research objectives, it is imperative that these objectives be clearly understood. Questionnaires can be either highly structured or unstructured. Unstructured questions allow the interviewer to probe respondents and guide the interview according to answers received. Most questionnaires are highly structured so that responses can be summarized in numbers, such as percentages, averages, or other statistics. The structured format provides fixed responses to questions that elicit uncomplicated answers that the respondent is both willing and able to provide. Five methods are used to collect data: personal interview, telephone, mail, Internet and focus groups. The method selected will have a major impact on the format of the questionnaire.

In constructing a questionnaire, the marketing researcher carefully chooses the questions to be asked, the form of the questions, the wording of the questions, and the sequencing of the questions. Common errors occur in questions by including those that cannot be answered, would not be answered, or need not be answered, and by omitting questions that should be answered. Each question should be checked to determine whether it contributes to the research objectives. Questions that are merely interesting should be dropped because they lengthen the time required and try the patience of respondents.

The form of the question can influence the response and there are four types of question formats available for communicating question content: open-ended, multiple choice, dichotomous, and attitude rating scale questions.

Open-ended questions allow respondents to answer in their own words. Open-ended questions tend to reveal more because respondents are not limited in their answers. This form of question is especially useful in the exploratory stage of research where the researcher is trying to determine how people think, rather than measuring how many people think in a certain way. A major disadvantage of open-ended questions is that the responses are difficult to record and tabulate, which makes them very expensive and time-consuming to process. Content analysis is typically used with open-ended responses. This allows the researcher to look for common themes among respondents.

Multiple-choice questions offer respondents a number of alternatives. Multiple-choice questions require less interviewer skill, take less time, and are easier for the respondent to answer. Four alternatives is the standard number of choices offered, and the respondent should be informed if more than one alternative can be selected. Researchers should rotate question sequence to help alleviate position bias, the tendency of respondents to select the first alternative in this type of question format.

Dichotomous questions require the respondents to choose one of two alternatives. The answer can be a simple "yes" or "no," and this is the most widely used of all question formats. Like multiple-choice questions, they eliminate interviewer bias and are easy and inexpensive to tabulate.

When the objective of the survey is to measure subjective variables like attitudes, motives, and perceptions, researchers use attitude-rating scales. The two most common rating scales are the Likert scale and the semantic differential scale. The Likert scale allows the respondents to indicate their attitude by checking how strongly they agree or disagree with statements about products or services that range from very positive to very negative.

An FBO might use the following statement in a survey concerning the quality of their maintenance department: *The use of internet maintenance scheduling greatly speeds up the process.*

- Strongly Disagree (1)
- Disagree (2)
- Neutral (3)
- Agree (4)
- Strongly Agree (5)

Researchers assign weights to the alternative responses to be able to quantify the measurement of the attitude. A weight of 5 is assigned to the very positive attitude, strongly agree. The weightings typically do not appear on the questionnaire itself.

The semantic differential is a popular attitude measuring scale and consists of a product or service question that allows the respondent to select on a seven-point scale one of two bipolar words that best represents the direction and intensity of their feelings. Bipolar adjectives such as inexpensive and expensive, good and bad, or clean and dirty are examples of words that are at opposite ends of the scale.

An FBO attempting to measure prospective students' attitude about the price of a proposed new flight option might ask:

Check the box below that describes how you feel about the cost of the new "Simulator-based" flight training program.

Inexpensive 1 2 3 4 5 6 7 Expensive

Care must be given to the wording of questions. The respondent alone fills out most surveys (self-administered) so there is no opportunity to ask for clarification. The semantics problem in communication is always an area that needs attention. Words mean different things to different people depending on culture and geographical location. Words to avoid include often, frequently, many, some, rush, good, fair, and poor. The researcher should use simple, specific, unbiased wording, and the questions should be tested before they are widely used. Attention should also be given to sequencing. When lead questions are simple to comprehend, interesting, and easy to answer, respondents' cooperation can be maintained throughout the questionnaire. Respondents whose curiosity is not piqued early will get discouraged, and not complete the survey. Difficult or personal questions should be asked toward the end of the interview, and they should be presented in logical order.

Mechanical instruments include eye cameras, tachistoscopes, and galvanometers. An eye camera measures how long the eye lingers on a particular item in an advertisement. The tachistoscope flashes an advertisement to a subject with a predetermined interval; then the respondent describes what he or she remembers. A galvanometer measures a respondent's interest in or emotional reaction to a particular advertisement or picture based on body response. The use of these instruments us typically more time consuming and expensive, and often lack the quality data the researcher is interested in.

Sampling Procedure

A sample is a portion or subset of the population from which it is drawn. A population or universe is any complete group of people or businesses that share some set of characteristics. Since only a small number of people in the population are surveyed, sampling cuts costs, reduces labor requirements, and gathers vital information quickly. Marketing researchers must develop a procedure that will help them find the appropriate sample for their research. First, who is to be surveyed? This is not always obvious. In the case of the charter services survey, should the sample be made up of businesses in any industry or businesses in selected industries with over 100 employees? In rating flight instructors, should only students who have dropped out of the program be surveyed? Should all students be surveyed at a certain stage in the flight program or only after completion? The researcher must decide what information is needed and what population or subset should be targeted.

Second, how many people or firms should be polled? Large samples are more reliable than small samples, but, depending on the population size, a researcher typically does not have to survey more than 5 percent of the actual or estimated population to get accurate answers.

Third, how should the people or firms in the sample be chosen? Sampling techniques fall into two categories: probability samples and nonprobability samples. The choice of sampling technique depends on the accuracy needed, cost, available information, research objectives, and other factors.

All samples observed or surveyed during marketing research studies are either probability or nonprobability samples. A probability sample is one in which every person or firm in the identified population being surveyed has a known chance of being sampled. An example of a probability sample is a simple random sample in which all members in the population have an equal probability of being chosen to participate in the sample. If you know, for example, that there are 500 Bonanza aircraft owners in your state, and you use a simple random sample, each owner is assigned a number from 1 to 500. Then you select, using a table of random numbers, the actual owners to be questioned. When the selected population contains disproportionate demographics like gender, researchers may choose to use a stratified random sample to eliminate the bias. The population is divided into strata, such as two subgroups (males and females), and then a random sample is selected from each group. This method is an efficient procedure where subgroups hold divergent opinions. Probability sampling prevents the researcher's bias from influencing who is sampled, because the makeup of the sample is determined not by the researcher, but by chance. The use of this technique allows the researcher to assign a statistical level of confidence. A 95 percent level of confidence means that the estimate will include the true value of what is being estimated 95 percent of the time.

Researchers using nonprobability sampling techniques arbitrarily select the sample according to their own convenience or judgment. Examples of nonprobability sampling include (1) convenience samples—any population member who is available; (2) judgment samples - individuals who are known to have a common interest in a type of product or service; and (3) quota samples—population is divided into subgroups and include a certain number of individuals from each subgroup. Savings in time and money are the major advantages of using this type of sampling. It is, however, inappropriate to apply standard statistical testing to nonprobability samples.

Methods of Collecting Data

Sampling is one of the most important aspects of marketing research because it involves identifying the respondents upon which conclusions will be based. Once the population to be surveyed has been identified, a researcher will select a representative (sample) group.

Personal interviewing is the most versatile of the five methods. The interviewer can ask more questions and can supplement the interview with personal observations. Generally, the interviewer follows a questionnaire and accurately records the responses. Personal interviewing is the most expensive method and requires a great deal of planning, training of interviewers, and supervision. The face-to-face interview can be plagued with inaccurate responses because the respondent desires to please or impress the interviewer, or the respondent feels obligated to give an immediate estimate rather than a carefully thought out reply.

The telephone interview consists of an interviewer asking questions of a respondent over the telephone. After self-administered surveys, telephone interviewing is the most widely used method of collecting data. Its popularity derives from its low cost and rapid response. The telephone is less versatile than is face-to-face interviewing. The interviewer is less likely to be able to ask detailed open-ended questions on the telephone than in a face-to-face interview, but at the same time its anonymity allows the interviewer to ask questions that could not be asked face-to-face. A telephone interview is also limited because members of the sample may not have telephones, may have unlisted numbers, may not be available, or simply may not care to be interviewed.

The mail questionnaire may be the best method for reaching persons who will not give personal interviews or who may be biased by interviewers. It consists of a questionnaire sent to the respondent that is completed and returned by mail to the researcher. The primary problem with mail questionnaires is the low percentage of returns that result in a possibility of nonrespondent error. Nonrespondent error is the possibility that the people who did respond are different from the people who did not respond; therefore, the data would not represent the population. Low response rates can be enhanced with a successive number of contacts.

With the growing number of available e-mail addresses, the electronic questionnaire is becoming more popular. Researchers can purchase a list of e-mail addresses of persons or businesses that fit the intended survey population and send them a questionnaire. Follow-up is inexpensive, but researchers have found that many people do not have the technical skill to put the e-mail questionnaire into a "reply and edit" mode to type their answers in the appropriate places. Many companies and survey research firms (such as Survey Monkey) utilize the Web to post questionnaires. Respondents can select their answers from drop-down menus or easily type responses to open-ended questions. Additionally, an email can be sent to intended respondents containing a link to the online questionnaire.

Focus group interviewing consists of inviting from six to ten persons to gather for a few hours with a trained interviewer to discuss a product, service, organization, or other marketing topic. The qualified interviewer has objectivity, knowledge of the subject matter and general aviation industry, as well as understanding of group dynamics and consumer behavior. An unqualified interviewer's results can be worthless or misleading. The interviewer encourages free and easy discussion among the participants, hoping that the spontaneous discussion will disclose attitudes and opinions about a situation that would not be revealed by direct questioning. The comments are recorded through note taking or tape recording and are subsequently studied.

Analyzing the Information

After the information has been gathered, it must be analyzed. The purpose of this step is to extract the important information and findings from the data. A variety of analytical software programs are available ranging from simple descriptive statistics (means, medians, modes) to complex multivariate analyses. Microsoft Excel can accomplish simple statistics, while programs such as SPSS are capable of a full range of statistical analyses. Coverage of these topics is beyond the scope of this discussion. The researcher computes such statistics as frequency distribution and averages in preparing the findings. Tables, figures, and charts are often used to illustrate the findings.

Presenting the Findings

The last step in the marketing research process is presenting results, which are usually in the form of a written report, to management. It is recommended that the researcher not overwhelm management with numbers and sophisticated statistical techniques. The researcher should present relevant findings that are useful in major marketing decisions facing management. Often, this presentation will greatly affect decision making and impact large financial decisions. Therefore, in preparing the presentation, emphasis must be placed on presenting data that is both reliable and valid in a professional manner.

KEY TERMS

Marketing research
Market measurement studies
Market potential
Sales potential
Marketing research process
Secondary data
Internal secondary data
External secondary data
Primary data
Research design
Survey method
Factual survey
Opinion survey
Self-selection bias
Observation method
Experiment method
Questionnaire
Open-ended questions
Multiple-choice questions
Dichotomous questions
Likert scale
Semantic differential scale
Mechanical instruments
Sample
Population
Probability sample
Simple random sample
Stratified random sample
Nonprobability sample
Convenience samples
Judgment samples
Quota samples
Personal interviewing
Telephone interview
Mail questionnaire
Electronic questionnaire
Focus group interviewing

REVIEW QUESTIONS

1. What is the purpose of marketing research? Give several examples of market measurement studies. Distinguish between market potential and sales potential. Give an example of a market research study involving a competitive situation.
2. Why are defining the problem and determining the research objectives so critical for effective market research? Distinguish between primary and secondary data. Give four examples of external secondary data sources. Which is the most commonly used research design? Distinguish between a factual and an opinion survey. How does the observation method differ from the experiment method?
3. What is the most common instrument used in collecting primary data? In questionnaires, distinguish between open-ended, multiple, and dichotomous questions. Give examples of a Likert and a semantic differential scale used to measure attitudes. What is a sample? What questions must be determined in developing an appropriate sample? Differentiate a simple random sample and a stratified random sample. Describe three methods of collecting primary data. Differentiate probability samples and nonprobability samples and give an example of each.

REFERENCES

Alreck, P. L. & Settle, R. B. *The Survey research handbook: Guidelines and strategies for conducting a survey*. Chicago: Irwin Professional Publishing, 1995.

Evans, Joel R., and Barry Berman. *Marketing* (6th ed.). New York: Macmillan, 1994.

Dillman, D. A. *Mail and internet surveys: The tailored design method,* 2nd ed.. New York: John Wiley & Sons, 2000.

Perreault, William D., Jr. and E. Jerome McCarthy. *Basic Marketing*, 13th ed.. Burr Ridge, IL, Irwin/McGraw-Hill, 1999.

Posner, Gerald, and Emil J. Walcek. "Implement Lead Follow-up System for More Business Marketing Sales," *Marketing News,* October 1985, p. 22.

Sandhusen, Richard L. *Marketing*, 3rd ed. Hauppauge, New York, Barron's Educational Series, Inc., 2000.

Strauss, Judy and Raymond Frost. *E-Marketing*, 2nd ed. Upper Saddle River, NJ. Prentice Hall, 2001.

Zikmund, William G. *Business Research Methods*, 6th ed. Orlando, FL. Harcourt, 2000.

SCENARIOS

1. As the new marketing manager of a full-service FBO, you have been asked to conduct some market research. First, however, you must get a handle on the uncontrollable variables influencing the rate of student pilot starts at your FBO. What are they?
2. As a summer intern at Exceptional FBO, you have been asked to gather some primary and secondary data regard-

ing the used aircraft sales market. Specifically, you must gather data about industry trends affecting used aircraft sales and the interest in used aircraft among potential buyers. What are some sources of primary and secondary data you could search?

3. As marketing manager at Joe's FBO, you feel that some marketing research is needed to enable your FBO to be successful in the challenging times ahead. Specifically, you are interested in discovering the perceptions of based pilots about your FBO's fuel prices, rates for T-hangars, and line service. As you begin your market research process, you must decide on whether to utilize survey, observation, or experiment methods. Which one do you choose and why?
4. Based on your response to scenario number three, how will you conduct research to determine perceptions on each of the three areas of interest? What type of research instrument(s) will you utilize? What questions/items/experiments will guide your research effort? Who will you include in your sample/population? How will you collect data?
5. You have collected a great deal of data regarding the perceptions of based pilots regarding your FBO's fuel prices, rates for T-hangars, and line service. In general terms, these pilots are quite pleased with your low fuel prices, feel that rates for T-hangars could be lower, and would like to see more experienced and knowledgeable line service personnel. How would you prepare a presentation of these findings to senior management? What would the presentation look like? They have asked you not to whitewash the findings, rather, present the good and bad of your findings. Additionally, what can you recommend to senior management to improve in these areas?

Chapter 10
Transportation Needs Assessment

OUTLINE

OBJECTIVES

At the end of this chapter, you should be able to:

- Explain the business-to-business market and give several examples.
- Describe the following demand patterns in the organizational market: direct channels, derived demand, and inelastic demand.
- Name and explain the three types of organizational purchase decisions.
- Describe the buying center concept and identify and explain the traditional five roles of the members.
- Describe the four major areas of investigation in a business aircraft travel analysis.
- Distinguish between geographic, volume, and time dispersion.
- Identify the three levels of airline service and how each relates to business aircraft use.
- Describe five types of business aircraft use.
- Highlight the five principal factors to consider in the equipment selection process.
- Summarize the major considerations in the cost of owning an aircraft.
- List the principal expenses under fixed and direct operating (variable) costs of use.
- Explain the significance of a cash flow analysis.
- Determine principal and interests payments using a loan amortization schedule.
- Describe the use of present value in aircraft purchase decisions.
- Explain break-even analysis as a sales tool for business aircraft.

Business-to-Business Marketing

The focus of this chapter is the travel analysis, which serves as a powerful marketing tool used to assist non-users of business aircraft in working through an in-depth transportation needs assessment. The prospect for this study is Champions Stores, Inc., a large sporting goods retailer, with its home office located in Montgomery, Alabama. To be effective in selling business aircraft, marketers must understand the nature of organizational markets, their unique demand, and purchasing characteristics.

Nature of Organizational Customers

Business-to-business marketing is a term that pertains to buying and selling goods and services between businesses. The products purchased are either for resale or for use by the purchasers in their day-to-day business operations. This type of marketing is far different from marketing products to household consumers. The term customer is used to describe business purchasers, whereas consumer commonly refers to purchases by individuals for personal needs. Business-to-business marketing is occurring when Cessna sells an aircraft to one of its dealers, and it also occurs when the dealer in turn sells the airplane to Southern Equipment & Supply Corporation for executive travel. When Office Depot sells office supplies to the local FBO, it is engaging in business-to-business marketing.

Unique Characteristics of Organizational Markets

When formulating strategies and developing marketing mixes, marketers will find that characteristics and demand patterns of the organizational market are different from the consumer market. Organizational markets tend to be more geographically concentrated than consumer markets. Many industries are located in specific areas of the country. Most aircraft manufacturers are located in Wichita, Kansas, and California's Silicon Valley is the home of the computer chip industry. This concentration of customers does offer efficiency opportunities for marketers, especially in promotion and distribution.

The potential number of customers in the organizational market is considerably less than in most consumer markets. Gulfstream Aerospace Corporation, a wholly owned subsidiary of General Dynamics, can sell its Gulfstream GV-SP to fewer than 1,500 organizations throughout the world. When segmenting this market, marketers must evaluate carefully whether there is a sufficient number of homogeneous businesses to make the target market a legitimate business opportunity. The small number of potential customers also stresses the need to develop strong customer relationships to ensure repeat business.

Demand patterns in the consumer market differ from demand patterns in the organizational market in the following areas:

1. **Direct channels** - Business buyers traditionally purchase directly from the manufacturer, rather than from a middleman as consumers do. This is especially true for products that are complex and expensive. Manufacturers will often use industrial distributors to sell and distribute products that are inexpensive and frequently purchased as accessories and supplies.
2. **Derived demand** - Manufacturers buy products to be used in the production of business-to-business goods and consumer goods. Thus, as the demand for these finished goods increases, the demand for components will also increase. For example, the need to purchase passenger seats by Hawker Beechcraft is driven by the demand for their airplanes.
3. **Inelastic demand** - The demand for business goods tends to be inelastic, which means that the demand for a good or service is not sensitive to changes in price. This is opposite to elastic demand, where there are significant changes in quantity demanded as a result of a meaningful change in price. This inelastic demand characteristic occurs because the organizational product is often only a fraction of the total price of the final product of which it is part and will have little effect on the product's total price. Demand will not change with a change in price in the short run because it is difficult for manufacturers to modify production equipment that has been designed to handle specific component parts. The demand for corporate aircraft tends to be inelastic because the importance of purchase price is mitigated by the potential purchaser's need for speed, cabin configurations, capacity, avionics, and cost of use.

Buying Process

As businesses today strive for increasing productivity, the buying function in organizations has taken on added importance as a profit center. It is now viewed that investment in goods and services can be strategically managed and controlled to improve profitability and help maintain a competitive advantage. This changed perception of accountability of the purchasing function can spell opportunity for aircraft marketers who understand the change and are able to develop presentations to fit this new emphasis.

Organizational buying decisions are highly variable, ranging from routine decisions, which require little time and effort, to complex decisions entailing in-depth negotiations between the salesperson and the company. Organizational purchase decisions can be categorized into three types: straight rebuy, modified rebuy, and new buys. Straight rebuys are simply reorders. The products ordered are usually standard products that are routinely used and maintained in inventory. Straight rebuys would be similar to your purchasing bread and milk at the convenience store on your way home from school or work. Modified rebuy situations are essentially straight rebuy situations that require some additional information due to a change in price or specifications, or dissatisfaction with the present supplier. New buys involve products or services never considered before by the company. There is a high degree of risk and cost associated with this category of purchase decision. The investigation into the purchase of a business aircraft by Champions Stores fits into this category.

The increasing accountability and complexity of the purchasing function has led to the development of the buying center concept that pulls together key individuals who provide different expertise needed to make quality major purchases. The size of the group will vary from company to company and the membership will also change depending upon the product being purchased. In the business aircraft purchase decision, one of the members will certainly be the chief pilot. Different members in the buying center have different roles in the decision. The five traditional roles in the buying center are *users*, *gatekeepers*, *influencers*, *deciders*, and *buyers*. *Users* initiate the process by identifying the need, and generally will be users of the product or service. *Gatekeepers* have the responsibility and authority to control information, and the role is often played by the purchasing manager. Gatekeepers can determine which suppliers have access to the organization and its decision makers. *Influencers* are usually technical employees who have defined the criteria the purchase must meet. Sometimes the influencer is an outside consultant with expertise in the specific area under investigation. The *decider* is the executive who has the authority to select which product to purchase. Sometimes, the decision to purchase is not made by one individual, but by a group of individuals selected to participate as an executive committee. The *buyer* is the employee who actually has the authority to place the order with the selected vendor. It is usually an executive in the purchasing department. To be successful in selling to businesses, salespersons must be able to identify the various members of the buying center and understand their roles. This is oftentimes a challenge. The buying center concept emphasizes the importance of comprehending the corporate culture in marketing to organizational buyers.

Clearly, business-to-business marketing is unique. However, armed with the knowledge of this important aspect of marketing, the aircraft salesperson approaching a business such as Champions Stores will understand and appreciate the uniqueness of the market and the marketing strategies required to be successful.

Travel Analysis

The potential use of a business aircraft is based on its ability to make travel more efficient by either reducing travel time or increasing productivity for a given amount of time. Travel analysis is an evaluation of a firm's current travel modes and the amount and nature of travel presently undertaken. There are four major areas of investigation that guide an aircraft sales representative in attempting to determine if a business could use a company airplane. They are (1) amount and nature of travel; (2) travel dispersion; (3) type and frequency of airline service; and (4) potential aircraft utilization.

Knowing the amount and nature of travel is needed to determine whether there is enough travel to make a business aircraft feasible and if it is the kind of travel for which a private aircraft is suited. Travel dispersion categorizes the trips in terms of distance, frequency, and volume of passengers. This information is useful in further defining a firm's travel patterns and determining whether these patterns are suitable for business aircraft use. The type and frequency of airline service is studied to determine the amount of time being spent traveling and whether a business airplane could reduce that time. The culmination of this study is to estimate the total annual utilization of a business aircraft for the firm.

Amount and Nature of Travel

Evaluating the possible uses of a business aircraft begins with estimates about the overall amount of travel within the organization and the potential growth of such travel. However, this kind of evaluation can be more of a limiting factor than a justifying one. In other words, just proving the existence of a large quantity of travel is not necessarily sufficient evidence that the company could use an aircraft economically, as some trips may not be suited to business aircraft use.

The amount and nature of travel are determined by reviewing a prospective customer's past travel records. Depending upon the size of the firm and amount of travel, an average month or quarter is generally selected for analysis.

In analyzing Champions Stores, Inc. based in Montgomery, Alabama, one would look at the firm's travel record for one month. Assume that the month selected is representative of travel throughout the year and therefore, will be used to make annual projections.

An analysis of the travel within this sample period by a sales representative indicated that 19 individual round trips were made to 13 separate destinations (see Table 10-1). The trips were made by 16 employees including 4 executive officers, 3 department managers, 6 buyers, and 3 other administrative personnel. The information covers travel primarily by employees based at the company's home office in Montgomery.

Records indicate that the company's primary modes of travel are by automobile and scheduled airline. Costs of transportation were not provided. In addition, charter service has been utilized in the past. Poor airline service to company destinations and the emergency need to travel were listed as reasons for using charter service. The number of passengers on these charter flights was two to three people.

Approximately 50 percent of the Champions Stores' travel is scheduled (20 percent scheduled one to two weeks in advance and 30 percent scheduled two to five days in advance). Scheduled trips lend themselves to business aircraft usage

Table 10-1 Potential Aircraft Utilization—Champions Stores, Inc.

	Average No. of Passengers	Total Round Trips (1 Mo)	Total Annual Round Trips	Number One-Way Miles	Total Miles
From Montgomery, AL to:					
1. Atlanta, GA	2	2	24	160	7,680
2. New Orleans, LA	2	2	24	275	13,200
3. Greenville, SC	2	1	12	280	6,720
4. Charlotte, NC	4	1	12	330	7,920
5. Greensboro, NC	3	1	12	480	11,520
6. Mexia, TX	3	1	12	610	14,640
7. Fitzgerald, GA	3	1	12	180	4,320
8. Dallas, TX	2	1	12	600	14,400
9. London, KY	1	1	12	400	9,600
10. El Paso, TX	2	1	12	1200	28,800
11. Jacksonville, FL	2	2	24	325	15,600
12. Blount, TN	2	1	12	275	6,600
From New Orleans, LA to:					
Sherman, TX	2	1	12	475	11,400
13. Jackson, MS	2	2	24	180	8,640
Dallas, TX	2	1	12	450	10,800
TOTAL		19	228*		171,840*

*Since the potential total annual miles is likely to exceed any one aircraft's capabilities, this amount has been reduced by 25 percent to reflect trips which will probably be made by other travel modes due to scheduling conflicts, maintenance requirements, and so forth. This reduction results in a potential 171 round trips and 128,880 miles or 475 to 700 hours of flying time, depending on the aircraft selected.

due to the flexibility of scheduling thereby accommodating many more trips on the aircraft. The remaining 50 percent of travel, however, was listed as on-demand. For on-demand or emergency-type trips the availability of an immediate, fast transportation mode is an obvious necessity.

Travel Dispersion

An analysis of an organization's geographic time and volume dispersions of business travel is very important to a salesperson in determining the need for a corporate aircraft. The object of this analysis is to examine the environment within which a company aircraft would operate and includes the cities served, distances, and schedules to be maintained. Such an examination reveals valuable information regarding the efficiency of past travel and the probability of improving the efficiency.

Geographic dispersion of business destinations partially indicates whether or not a company aircraft can be effectively substituted for present travel (i.e., if present travel is primarily between large metropolitan cities with frequent and direct airline service, chances for substantial savings in employee time may be minimized). Volume dispersion is the number of people traveling and indicates the relative importance of each destination. Time dispersion is the interval between trips taken by various individuals to the same destinations or destinations having proximity. This information helps determine the potential for combining company trips with the aircraft, which enables the aircraft to be used more efficiently. From this investigation of travel dispersion comes a clear picture of existing travel patterns, how a business aircraft could fit into these patterns, and how a company would benefit from using a company plane.

Champions Stores' travel destinations are located, for the most part, in the southeastern part of the United States, within the states of Texas, Georgia, Florida, Louisiana, Kentucky, North Carolina, Tennessee, Alabama, and Mississippi. The most distant destination within the company's primary marketing area is about 610 miles. Airline trip data shows the longest trip undertaken to be approximately 1,200 miles to El Paso, Texas.

Trips during only certain times of the year may reduce the need for a business aircraft. Fortunately, an examination of the company's past business travel indicates that it is not seasonal. Assume, for the example, that travel will occur with equal frequency throughout the year. Checking the trips made by Champions Stores shows that the most frequently visited cities were Atlanta, GA, New Orleans, LA, Jacksonville, FL, and Jackson, MS. The frequency of air travel to other destinations will undoubtedly increase with the availability of a company aircraft. Most companies find that passenger load factors tend to grow as executives learn how to use the aircraft to their advantage.

Type and Frequency of Airline Service

Airline services provide a valuable business tool. However, these services have undergone considerable changes since deregulation in 1978. The trend has been for certified carriers to concentrate more on service to large hub cities and less to smaller cities. Conversely, business continues to expand from large metropolitan areas to smaller cities. When the present mode of travel is primarily scheduled airlines, the kind of airline service available to destinations determines the practicality of a business aircraft.

Three distinct classes of airline service exist: direct, indirect via connections, or none. The frequency of service will further modify the direct and indirect levels. If there are both frequent and direct airline flights to a company destination, a business aircraft's only measurable advantage may be its ability to transport company travelers at a savings in total direct costs. If service is infrequent and/or indirect, a company plane can significantly reduce travel time, airport layovers, and overnight stays, as well as take advantage of direct cost savings through group travel. If no airline service is available to a company destination, the alternative is usually either automobile travel or a combination of airline and rental car. An aircraft can generate substantial savings depending upon the proximity of the destination to one of 6,000 public airports not served by scheduled airlines.

An examination of Champions Stores' travel indicates that the majority of the travel is to cities with airline service. A significant portion of these cities, however, (50 percent) requires making connections due to lack of direct flights. Airline service is divided into the following classes:

1. Frequent Direct 6 percent
2. Frequent Indirect 25 percent
3. Infrequent Direct 13 percent
4. Infrequent Indirect 25 percent
5. No Airline Service 31 percent

Potential Aircraft Utilization

The projected use of a company airplane is an integrated function of all the elements discussed so far. It is relevant to address both the amount of use the aircraft would receive and the ways in which it would be employed.

Measuring the potential for a company-owned aircraft requires some subjective analysis since the dates of individual trips are not known and the potential grouping of such trips involves an approximation of an average passenger load. Based on the data in the example, this average passenger load is estimated to be two to three people. In all probability, the passenger load will increase as the company finds new ways of using the aircraft to its advantage. Table 10-1 outlines the potential utilization of a company aircraft over a one-year period. As shown in this table, a conservative estimate indicates potential for 228 round trips covering approximately 171,840 miles. Although the aircraft will be based at the company headquarters in Montgomery, it would be used for several trips originating from the company's distribution warehouse in New Orleans. These figures have been included in the potential.

The amount of utilization indicated above is likely to be in excess of any single aircraft's capabilities. This is because of the large number of potential flying hours and round trips. With this type of utilization, conflicts are likely to occur regarding the availability of the aircraft for other business trips and necessary maintenance. For these reasons, Champions Stores may wish to consider a second aircraft at some time after initial acquisition.

For this analysis, the annual potential has been reduced by 25 percent to more accurately reflect realistic figures for one aircraft. This reduction allows for such issues as occasional maintenance and scheduling conflicts. The 25 percent reduction results in a more conservative potential for 171 round trips covering approximately 128,880 miles annually. Annual hours of utilization are determined by the following formula:

$$\frac{\text{Annual statute miles traveled}}{\text{Cruise speed in miles per hour}}$$

For a used twin-engine turboprop aircraft being considered by the management of Champions Stores, the annual hours of utilization would be 128,880/283 = 455 hours over approximately 200 flight days.

Types of Business Use Aircraft

Let the model fit the mission is the rule in selecting a business airplane. Recognizing this, manufacturers offer numerous models, including fixed-wing or rotary-wing (helicopter), single engine or multiengine, piston or pure jet, and each can be tailored to meet the specific requirements of a firm. *Tailored* is an appropriate word for the business airplane. Just as there are wardrobes for different occasions, there are airplanes for different uses. Like a wardrobe, once the proper airplane is selected, it can be "altered" to fit specific uses with the selection of avionics equipment, seating arrangements, wheels or floats (or both), and in cargo or passenger configuration (or both).

The purpose of this section is briefly to review the categories of aircraft that a firm may consider. The next section will focus on the equipment selection process and how it relates to the hypothetical example of Champions Stores, Inc.

The Single-Engine Airplane

Most small businesses start with a single engine airplane. Many times this beginning is because an employee may use an airplane the way other employees use their automobiles. From this use comes recognition of the benefits that are translated to other employees in similar situations.

The small business owner, the professional, or one of the key employees of a relatively small business usually flies an aircraft in this category personally. A single-engine airplane's range is utilized best in frequent trips in the 1,000 to 1,200 mile limit although it is capable of extended flight. A long flight requiring frequent business stops en route also can be handled well by the single-engine model. It has the capability to fly into and out of most airports, including grass strips. Since the traveler usually flies it, the cost of a professional pilot is saved.

Despite their relatively small size and low price tag, single engine models are capable of carrying the most sophisticated instruments and communications equipment available, such as satellite-based Global Positioning Systems (GPS) and a variety of all-weather flight control and guidance equipment. Since most of the flights are usually over short-stage lengths, the speed of one model over another frequently is not the most important consideration. Over a 300-mile distance, for instance, an airplane traveling at 150 miles an hour will take two hours to complete the trip, while one having a speed of 180 miles an hour will do it just 20 minutes faster.

Turbocharging in engines raises both speed of the airplane and its ability to operate at higher altitudes. This makes possible some "over-the-weather" flying and permits taking advantage of more favorable winds. These factors make longer distance travel more practical and begin to place a premium on speed when greater distances are a consideration. Convertibility of most single-engine models to cargo configuration enables carrying displays, samples, and similar equipment.

There are many modern piston-engine aircraft available to serve this entry level business market. Cessna, Cirrus, New Piper, Raytheon, Mooney, and Commander all offer a number of different and well-proven single engine aircraft for business use. Cessna offers the updated version of the 172 Skyhawk and the 182 Skylane. Cirrus offers the SR-22 in several variations. Piper's single engine offerings include the Warrior III, Archer III, Arrow, and the high performance pressurized Malibu Mirage. Raytheon, which markets its aircraft under the Beech trade name, continues to offer the very popular Bonanza line.

Although the single engine aircraft allows the most economical entry into business aviation, businesses will still have to consider whether the benefits justify the costs. A new single engine piston aircraft will have a price tag of $160,000 to $850,000, depending on engine and avionics selected. Used aircraft may be more economical and can be acquired for less (in some cases, a great deal less) than the price of new models.

The Light Twin

More than an additional power plant is added on the twins. Utility increases many times over. In the twin field, night and weather travel takes on added meaning. While seating capacity and payload of the light twin does not vary much from the high performance single engine models, the added power plant expands the use during darkness and adverse weather. Deicing equipment may be added for convenience and safety.

Seating capacity ranges from four to six. The light twin sometimes is flown by a professional pilot and sometimes by the individual businessperson who is making the trip. Since a flight over long distance is more likely to encounter varying weather conditions, the twin increases mobility for the company whose travel profile includes trips to different parts of the country.

Light twin engine piston aircraft can range from about $450,000 to more than $850,000, depending on equipment installed. Piper's Seminole and Seneca V models and the popular Beech Baron 58 are excellent choices for economical acquisition and operating costs as compared to turbine aircraft.

The Medium Twin-Piston

When the company has a number of people traveling over the same routes, when inflight conferences are required, or when all-weather operations are a routine matter, a medium twin is appropriate.

Customizing interiors to fit the specific needs and desires of the company begins in this range. High density seating in some models provides airline comfort for up to 10 or 12 passengers. Foldout tables, side facing seats or swivel seats make a mobile conference room. Divans offer seating for several, or bedroom comfort allows an executive to arrive at his destination thoroughly refreshed. A professional crew usually flies the medium twins. Their all-weather capability, range, and speed give great flexibility for short and long-distance flights.

The Turboprop

The turboprop provides the best of two worlds—the lower costs of propeller-driven aircraft with some advantages of the jet. Falling into the medium twin category, the turboprop usually is professionally flown. Its jet power and pressurization makes it well suited for medium and long trips at average speeds over 300 mph, yet it operates efficiently on short runs. This versatility is demonstrated by the Pilatus PC-12. With a 330 cubic foot pressurized cabin volume, the PC-12 can carry nine passengers over 1,600 nautical miles with VFR reserves and 1,400 nautical miles with IFR reserves.

Turboprops have higher operating costs than piston aircraft, partially because they consume more fuel per hour of flying. At that same time, the range is greater allowing greater distances to be covered. Initial purchase price is higher than for piston powered twins, but is still under the cost of most pure jets (some VLJs being the exception). The turboprop can fly into and out of smaller airports than the pure jet can. As U.S. industry moves away from larger cities, the need to use smaller airports can be an important consideration. This is a major consideration for a company like Champions Stores.

A number of foreign and domestic manufacturers offer turboprops designed for the business market. The leading twin-engine turboprop aircraft is Raytheon's Beech King Air Series with five different versions and the King Air's larger cousin, the 1900 Airliner.

The Pure Jet

At the top of the business fleet is the pure jet. With speeds well over 500 mph, it rivals the best of the airliners, and in flexibility, the best of the piston powered aircraft. The mission of the business jet is to compress great distances into short expanses of time. Almost invariably professionally flown, the pure jet moves corporate executives to widely scattered points and returns them in a matter of hours. The environment of the jet is high altitude. For this reason it is most efficient for medium and long distance travel. Because of its speed, the jet, probably more than any other business airplane is used most frequently to drop off and pick up individuals over wide distances.

Business jets have been designed in a variety of sizes and capabilities to meet the needs of various target markets. The smallest, known as a Very Light Jet (VLJ), are able to carry from four to eight passengers and are certificated for single-pilot operation. These smaller jets can be purchased from $1-$4.0 million, again depending on the avionics and other equipment selected. The new HondaJet, Eclipse 500, and Cessna Mustang are examples of relatively new choices available in this entry jet market. The majority of business jets in operation today, however, seat eight to ten passengers in a typical business configuration and operate efficiently over transcontinental or transatlantic distances. The largest market share in this niche is Cessna's Citation family. Other manufacturers offering models for this market segment include Raytheon's Beechjet 400A, Learjet's models 31, 60, and 45. Israel Aircraft Industries (IAI) produces the six to nine passenger Astra SPX and the Galaxy can be configured as a corporate shuttle and carry up to 18 passengers.

As more and more larger corporations turn to business aviation as a tool to increase productivity, a new class of business jet, the super midsize aircraft, is beginning to emerge. These aircraft are larger, but not as large as the so-called large class of jet. Their attractiveness is that they allow large teams of employees to be transported economically over longer ranges than standard midsize jets.

The IAI Galaxy, Raytheon Hawker Horizon, Cessna Citation X and the Dassault Falcon 2000 and Falcon 50EX are examples of this new class of jets. The Galaxy, for example, has a cabin that is 6 ft. 3 in. high and 7 ft. 2 in. wide. Powered by two Pratt & Whitney Canada PW306A engines, it has a range of 3,602 nautical miles at a Mach 0.82 cruise speed. The Falcon 2000 is powered by two CFM International CFE738-1-1B turbofans that produce 5,918 lb. thrust each. The cabin is 26 ft. 3 in. long, 6 ft. 2 in. high and 7 ft. 8 in. wide.

Large business jets are gaining popularity with global corporations that need intercontinental travel. Nonstop flights such as Chicago-Tokyo, New York-Abu Dhabi, and London Honolulu are now well within the capability of such aircraft as the Boeing Business Jet (BBJ), the Gulfstream V and GIV-SP, and the Bombardier Global Express.

The Boeing Business Jet is based on the popular 737-700 airliner fuselage joined to the 737-800 wings and landing gear. The BBJ cabin has 807 square feet of space and can accommodate about 20 people in a business setting.

The Gulfstream V has a modified and lengthened Gulfstream IV fuselage with a new and more efficient wing and larger tail surfaces. The 90,500-pound aircraft features a 50 ft. 1 in. cabin that is 6 ft. 2 in. in height and 7 ft. 4 in. in width. The aircraft can maintain a 6,000 ft. cabin altitude up to an operating altitude of 51,000 ft.

The Bombardier Global Express carries up to 19 passengers and has a range in excess of 6,500 nautical miles. This range will give a company the ability to fly from New York to Tokyo nonstop. This range is due to Global Express' third-generation supercritical airfoil that gives it a Mach 0.88 cruise speed.

The Helicopter

Corporate use of helicopters is not new. The first civil helicopters were placed into use right after World War II. Corporate reliance on helicopters has expanded dramatically, growing with the machine itself. Today, Robinson, Bell, Sikorsky, Schweizer, Agusta, Eurocopter, and MD Helicopters produce highly efficient business helicopters.

The business applications of helicopters are almost endless, including herding livestock, moving bank papers and checks, harvesting seed cones from the tops of coniferous trees for propagation of the best species without damage to the trees, timely movement of work crews and material for construction projects, and aerial survey/photography, to name just a few.

However, the most visible business application of helicopters is for the reliable, rapid transport of corporate executives. Many CEOs who regularly fly in helicopters refer to them as "time machines," because of the great savings in executive time made possible by the helicopters. The concept of "portal-to-portal" travel really pays off in convenience and time when one is able to eliminate ground travel by limo or taxi to and from the airport. Many firms have corporate helipads adjacent to their headquarters. The passengers walk to the helicopter and, ideally, fly directly to a heliport within walking distance of their destination.

When it is not practical to make the entire trip by helicopter, there is still a considerable advantage in using a corporate helicopter to shuttle passengers between the airport and their destination. There really aren't any typical business helicopters. They range from the compact but practical Robinson R-22, which is the world's smallest commercial helicopter, to the 44-passenger Boeing "Chinook." Some of the purely corporate machines are especially outfitted with plush upholstery, swivel chairs, and environmental control systems, and they are flown by a two-pilot crew. Others are much more austere, and some are flown by the CEO. However, the helicopters in use today are "third generation" helicopters which incorporate design features that have been proven safe, reliable, and practical during many millions of hours of helicopter flight.

Equipment Selection Process

The choice of a business aircraft must follow a detailed and comprehensive evaluation of a company's travel requirements, its current financial position, and intangible benefits which accrue through aircraft ownership. An aircraft's capability compared to the company's need must also be evaluated. The rule of thumb most commonly used is that the aircraft should be no more than is needed to satisfy most of the company's requirements. An aircraft with substantially greater capabilities than the company needs may have an adverse impact on long-term ownership.

As with any management decision, selecting suitable equipment is a matter of determining the relative importance of each of several factors, and then making a choice which best fits the resulting profile. There are normally five principal rational factors upon which to base an aircraft and equipment selection analysis. While all of these factors are important, the degree of importance of each factor rests with specific travel requirements.

1. **Trip Distances and Number of Passengers.** This information will help decide the size, range, and payload requirements that must be met. This factor is also important in selecting necessary or desirable equipment.
2. **Use and Users of the Aircraft.** Expected users of the aircraft will affect the type of aircraft, seating arrangements, performance requirements, and interior appointments. Special uses, such as cargo needs, will also affect the selection.
3. **Environmental Aspects of Route and Destinations.** The need for special systems, such as pressurization and turbo charging, runway performance requirements, and navigational package, is often predicted by these factors.
4. **Frequency of Trips.** This information helps qualify the relative importance of other factors. In addition, trip frequency requirements aid in equipment decisions, such as avionics and convenience options.
5. **Financial and Performance Considerations.** In any equipment selection decision, this information provides a rationale by properly balancing needs against costs.

The selection process is still subjective to a certain degree. Equipment such as cabin stereo systems, interior appointments, and convenience accessories remain largely a matter of personal taste.

Trip Distances and Number of Passengers

An examination of all potential trips likely to be undertaken by Champions Stores' aircraft indicates that the one-way distances range from approximately 160 to 1,200 miles. Table 10-2 is a frequency distribution of these one-way distances. As shown by this distribution, an aircraft capable of traveling 1,200 miles nonstop could meet 100 percent of the trip legs. However, 94.7 percent of all trip legs fell within the 101 to 700 mile range. Therefore, it would appear more realistic to give primary consideration to those trips falling within the 101 to 700 mile range. The company aircraft should have a nonstop range of at least 700 miles. Based on examination of travel data, an average passenger load is two to three passengers.

However, is still necessary to establish what the maximum passenger density might be for Champion Stores. For example, assume that the salesperson in the interview with company personnel learned that the maximum number of people who have traveled together on past business trips was six. The company does not anticipate the maximum passenger requirement to increase with use of a business airplane. In aircraft selection, primary consideration should be given to aircraft with a maximum of eight seats (six passengers plus two pilots).

Table 10-2 Frequency Distribution of Trip Distances

Distances	Number of Trips Legs* 100%	75%	Percent	Cumulative Percent
0–100	0	0	0	0
101–200	120	90	26	26
201–300	96	72	21	47
301–400	96	72	21	68
401–500	72	54	16	84
501–600	24	18	5.3	89.3
601–700	24	18	5.3	94.7
701–800	0	0	0	94.7
801–900	0	0	0	94.7
901–1000	0	0	0	94.7
1001–1100	0	0	0	94.7
1101–1200	24	18	5.3	100
	456**	342**	100	

*Leg = Point A to Point B.
**The 342 annuailzed trip legs were determined by reducing the original 456 annualized total by 25 percent. (228 round trips × 2 = 456 trips legs × 75% = 342 trip legs). The 342 legs would translate into 171 round trips.

Use and Users

Champions Stores' aircraft will be used primarily for transporting company executives and other personnel to various business destinations including company-owned stores and warehouses as well as to major cities such as Jacksonville, Dallas, New Orleans, and Atlanta where buyers make substantial purchases. The possibility of flying in manufacturers' representatives for meetings with company personnel also exists. Based on the number of potential hours of utilization and safety of corporate executives, the services of a qualified, full-time pilot and copilot will be used in this case.

Environmental Aspects of Routes and Destinations

A review of the flight routes which will be flown by the company indicates the en route terrain, for the most part, is not mountainous. A flight altitude of 5,000 feet above mean sea level would be adequate to meet the minimum en route IFR (Instrument Flight Rules) requirements for this area of the country.

Other types of terrain that will be encountered involve rough, densely wooded areas (North and South Carolina) and swampy areas (Florida and Louisiana). Additional flights over water may occur in the Gulf coast area. With the amount of travel that Champion Stores will be doing, low ceilings and fog, as well as icing conditions may be encountered occasionally by the aircraft. The information obtained indicated that a significant portion the company's travel (50 percent) is on an "on-demand" or emergency nature. This type of travel would probably require some night flying. In addition, speed in reaching the destination may be important.

Since an analysis of environmental conditions and seating requirements indicate the need for a twin-engine aircraft, for this example, only a twin-engine aircraft will be recommended. High altitudes en route on longer legs are anticipated, so a pressurized aircraft will be needed. Similarly, if high altitudes en route or landing at high elevation airports were anticipated, the airplane will have to have the additional power to operate in the rarefied air at high altitudes.

While our examination of the environmental aspects of routes and destinations does not necessarily indicate the need for pressurization or extra engine power, the company might prefer aircraft with these features because of concern for the comfort of its passengers.

Frequency of Trips

For this example, a potential for 171 round trips was demonstrated, accounting for approximately 455 hours of utilization annually. Since this indicates an above average utilization rate, it will be recommended that the aircraft selected have IFR capability, full deicing equipment for all-weather capability, dual communications, navigational equipment, (including co-pilot instrument panel) and autopilot. The prevailing weather experienced in this part of the country would add validity to this recommendation.

Performance and Financial Considerations

To complete the equipment selection process, the performance characteristics of various aircraft under consideration must be

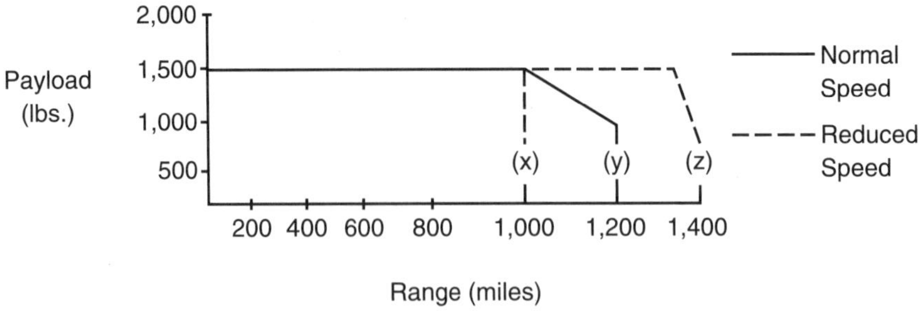

Figure 10-1 Payload Range Chart

examined in relation to costs. Within the criteria thus far established, a salesperson might now select three or four models that appear to meet the company's needs.

Performance Analysis

The technical performance capabilities of the aircraft under consideration must be fully evaluated. These include such factors as short runway performance, high temperature operating characteristics, payload-range capability, speed, and operational reliability.

Every aircraft has a given ability to land and take off on runways of varying lengths. This capability is certificated by the FAA and is shown in the flight manual for the aircraft. Normally, the shorter the runway, the smaller the load the aircraft can carry—either passengers or fuel. On extremely short runways, the load restriction may be so great as not to permit landing or takeoff at all. For example, small twin-engine propeller aircraft can operate on runways of 2,000 to 3,000 feet, whereas bigger and faster turbine (turboprop and jet) aircraft may require 5,000 to 7,000 feet, especially at higher temperatures. VLJs, although at the small end of the jet market, are able to operate with 2,500 to 3,500 feet available for takeoff and landing.

An aircraft performance analysis must therefore take into consideration the length of runways offered at all airports that the company might wish to use. Those lengths must then be compared to the performance capabilities of the aircraft under consideration. This comparison would indicate what restrictions, if any, might affect the company's operations at particular airports.

Air temperature and airport altitude can also affect an aircraft's performance. The higher the temperature and the higher the altitude, the greater the runway length that is needed under specific payload (fuel and passenger) conditions. Conversely, with a constant runway length, higher temperatures or altitudes will tend to restrict the load the aircraft can carry. When an aircraft carries more fuel to travel longer distances, it invariably needs more runway length in which to take off.

Another performance consideration is the payload range capability of the aircraft. Each aircraft has, according to its particular weight, fuel capacity, engine type, and performance characteristics, a capability to carry a certain payload over a certain distance. A typical payload range chart is shown in Figure 10-1. This figure indicates that the aircraft can carry a maximum payload for a certain number of miles (point x). If additional range is desired, payload must be reduced to carry the necessary fuel load. The maximum range with a reduced payload would be represented by the point y. Some variation to this performance data would result from differing cruise speeds; an aircraft is normally able to fly farther if it travels at slower speeds, as indicated by the dashed line to point z.

When the payload-range capabilities of the different aircraft under consideration are known, the company is in a position to determine which aircraft will meet its earlier requirements, namely, the amount of fuel and the number of passengers to be carried.

The payload-range capabilities must also be compared to the runway lengths the company plans to use to determine what actual limitations may exist, either runway length restrictions or payload-range restrictions.

Financial Analysis

The final factor in the equipment selection process is the cost of the various aircraft under consideration. Normally, the costs arising from ownership of the aircraft are considered separately from those costs associated with its operation.

Cost of Ownership

Three principal items determine the purchase price of an aircraft: the base price, the price of the customized interior desired, and the avionics equipment (radios, navigational instruments, radar, and similar items) chosen. The costs associated with avionics equipment and customized interiors can add 30 percent or more to the base price of an aircraft. The prospective company may consider an outright purchase, a financed purchase, or lease arrangement. These various options will be considered further in chapter 11.

Used aircraft may also be considered, often at prices sub-

Table 10-3 Corporate Federal Income Tax Rates

Taxable income over	But not over	The tax is:			Of the amount over
$0	$50,000			15%	$0
$50,000	$75,000	$7,500	+	25%	$50,000
$75,000	$100,000	$13,750	+	34%	$75,000
$100,000	$335,000	$22,250	+	39%	$100,000
$335,000	$10,000,000	$113,900	+	34%	$335,000
$10,000,000	$15,000,000	$3,400,000	+	35%	$10,000,000
$15,000,000	$18,333,333	$5,150,000	+	38%	$15,000,000
$18,333,333				35%	0

stantially below a new aircraft cost. Of course, with a used aircraft, it is important to analyze the maintenance records of the aircraft and its engines. Total hours on the engines is also a major consideration if the number is high. However, a good used aircraft may be bought at a considerable price reduction over a new model without a substantial difference in performance or passenger convenience.

The status of production must be examined relative to cost. Each aircraft undergoes a significant evolutionary development after its initial design has been adopted. Thus, improvements to most operating criteria are made through increased engine power, increased weights, longer cabins, and increased speed and range. Prior improvements and the potential for additional improvements must be considered, recognizing that some of the future improvements may or may not be readily incorporated in an earlier model.

A forecast of the future disposal or trade-in value of the aircraft must be made to determine the net aircraft cost to the company (purchase price less disposal value). According to *Aircraft Value Reference* 2001, Volume 2, published by VREF Publishing, Inc. in Shawnee Mission, Kansas, a five-year-old high performance single engine aircraft had a disposal value of 90 percent, a five-year-old light twin, 86 percent, and a turboprop 73 percent.

Reliability and maintainability must be investigated with regard to cost. The broad spectrum of business aircraft includes a wide variety of technical and mechanical complexity in engines, avionics, and aircraft systems. Each step in overall complexity causes incremental changes in the amount of spare parts required, the technical proficiency of maintenance personnel, the cost of maintenance, the sophistication of test and maintenance equipment, and the overall thoroughness of the maintenance program.

Thus, maintainability is tied directly to the cost of ownership—what the company can support. A more sophisticated aircraft may require more attention for equal reliability. The local resources (either within the company or available at the airport) must be surveyed to determine if reliability might be compromised because of local inadequacies.

For smaller aircraft operation, maintenance can be accomplished almost entirely by a qualified maintenance repair station, where there would be little or no requirement for the company to keep facilities for its own mechanics. The larger and more sophisticated flight operation usually requires substantial maintenance manpower, many spare parts with room to store them, machine shop, testing facilities and perhaps an avionics shop. Also, there should normally be major hangar facilities, often an exclusively used hangar.

The cost of owning an aircraft affects the amount of income taxes paid. Aircraft are sold to individuals, sole proprietors, partnerships, and corporations. Tax considerations exist for all of these kinds of business enterprises even though the rate of taxation might differ. A business organized as a sole proprietorship or as a partnership does not pay taxes as such, but the individual proprietors or partners reflect their share of the profits or losses on personal income tax returns. Rates vary according to the individual's taxable income. A corporation is a legal entity that pays its own income taxes.

As Table 10-3 indicates, corporations today pay federal income taxes on a marginal rate basis starting at a minimum of 15 percent and with a maximum of 39 percent. Corporations are also liable for state income taxes and in Alabama, the rate is a flat 5 percent. To reflect these combined rates, all financial calculations and analysis involved with the proposal for the purchase of a business aircraft by Champions Stores, a combined federal and state income tax of 39 percent will be used. Tax rates are an incentive for companies to purchase and operate aircraft. For example each dollar of deductible expense by Champions Stores will actually cost the corporation about 61 cents.

One of the more important features of the Tax Reform Act of 1986 was the improved depreciation allowance. Aircraft used by corporations and individuals for their own business

Table 10-4 Depreciation and Book Value—$2,363,800 Business Aircraft—Six Years

End of Year	Depreciation Tax Basis***	Depreciation %	Depreciation Expense	Tax Savings (39%)	Book Value**
0					$2,363,800
1	$2,363,800	20%	$ 472,760	$184,376	1,891,040
2	1,891,040	40%	756,416	295,002	1,134,624
3	1,134,624	40%	453,850	177,002	680,774
4	680,774	40%	272,310	106,201	408,464
5	680,774	40%	272,310	106,201	136,154
6	680,774	20%	136,154	53,100	0
Totals			$2,363,800	$921,882	

*First and last mid-year averaging conventions apply
**Book Value equals cost of aircraft minus accumulated depreciation
***Depreciation tax basis equals aircraft cost plus State Sales tax

transportation are in the five-year class for determining the depreciation expense.

The allowable deductions will be computed using a 200 percent declining balance method. For five-year class property, this accelerated method doubles the straight-line rate (20 percent) thus providing additional tax savings during the early years. The depreciation schedule automatically switches from double declining to straight-line at the end of the third year. The depreciation calculations still include a half-year convention, which in effect treats the aircraft as if it were placed in service at midyear. The new system extends the half-year convention to all dispositions of property. In other words, half a year of depreciation will be allowed for the year in which the aircraft is sold. The effect of this is to spread the deduction for aircraft one year beyond the name of its class-six tax years for five-year property. Table 10-4 illustrates book value and depreciation for the proposed twin-engine turboprop aircraft for Champions Stores.

At the time of resale, the gain realized between the aircraft sales price and the current book value (called depreciation recapture) is treated as ordinary income.

The tax benefits of ownership directly reduce the actual cost of the aircraft. Table 10-5 Capital Recovery Guide illustrates how much capital Champions Stores will recover through tax savings and disposition of the aircraft after six years. The monthly net cost of ownership is only $6,613 over the 72-month period.

Cost of Use

The cost of use includes two types of expenses: fixed costs and direct operating expenses (variable costs). Fixed costs include those expense items which are incurred regardless of the amount of flying performed. Examples include crew salaries, recurrent training, insurance, and hangar rental or tie-down expense. Direct operating expenses or variable costs are the actual expenses of fuel, maintenance, and miscellaneous expenses that occur as a direct result of hours flown. Some aircraft components have predetermined or expected normal service lives that can be used to calculate an hourly cost of operation figure. For example, aircraft engines must be completely overhauled after say 2,100 to 3,600 hours depending on the engine. Other components like airframe, propeller and avionics are accounted for by conservative estimates of their maintenance requirements.

Tables 10-6 and 10-7 show the major items included under fixed and direct operating expenses for a twin-engine turboprop aircraft under consideration by Champions Stores. The figures are only illustrative. The actual costs would vary due to differences in accounting methods as well as differences in the cost of such items as fuel, labor services, engine overhaul, remanufactured engines, and avionics. In addition, the manner in which the aircraft is flown and used will have a direct effect on the actual hourly cost of use (number of hours flown annually, power settings used, type of airports encountered, environmental conditions, experience of the pilot).

Cash Flow Analysis

One the most frequently misunderstood and misused business terms is cash flow. It is often mistaken for operating income, revenue, or profit. A profitable FBO will need substantial inflows of cash from outside sources to keep it generating profit objectives. You can't spend profit; you only spend cash. Accurate cash management is as critical to a successful long-term business venture as accurate fuel management is for a long distance flight. Performing a cash-flow analysis by aircraft salespersons is essential for not only selling aircraft to corporations with in-house flight departments, but for all types of business aircraft acquisition. This includes company-owned with operations contracted to another company, wet or dry lease, and fractional ownership. These variations will be discussed in detail in chapter 11. Every prospect must under-

Table 10-5 Capital Recovery Guide

Twin Engine Turboprop Aircraft—Six Year Analysis		
Aircraft Acquisition Cost		
Purchase Price		$2,230,000
State Sales Tax @ 6%		$133,800
Toral		$2,363,800
Depreciation Expense		$2,363,800
Resale Value @ 71%		$1,583,300
Six Year Capital Recovery		
Tax savings (39% corporate tax rate)		
Depreciation	$921,882	
Total Tax Savings		$921,882
Disposal of Aircraft*		
Resale value	$1,583,300	
Less Taxes on Sale	$617,487	
Net Proceeds From Sale		$965,813
Total Capital Recovered		$1,887,695
Total Acquisition Cost		$2,363,800
Total Capital Recovered		$1,887,695
Net Cost of Ownership—Six years		$476,105
Per Year		$79,351
Per Month		$6,613

*If the aircraft is traded in, rather than sold outright, the taxes due on sale will be deferred. The depreciation basis on the new airraft will be decreased by the trade-in value since the book value is zero.

Table 10-6 Fixed Cost for a Twin-Engine Turboprop Business Aircraft

Expense Category		Estimated Cost Per Year
Crew Salaries		
	Captain	$60,000
	Co-Pilot	$39,840
	Benefits	$29,952
Hanger Rental		$24,147
Insurance (1)		
	Hull (Physical Damage Coverage)	$8,920
	Single Limit Liability—25 Million Per Occurence	$5,500
	Guest Voluntary Settlement Coverage	$1,000
Recurrent Training		$12,600
Computerized Maintenance Program		$1,850
Aircraft Modernization		$8,920
Refurbishing		$8,280
Weather Service		$2,235
	Total Annual Fixed Costs	$203,244

(1) Hull coverage rate 40 cents per $100 of value
$500,000 GVS covereage
$5,000 medical payments coverage at no charge

stand thoroughly the impact the airplane will have on cash flows each year it is used.

When a company such as Champions Stores is considering the purchase of a business aircraft, it is concerned with more than the initial purchase price and the amount of down payment. The net, after tax cost of operating the aircraft projected on a year-to-year basis for the entire period of ownership is of vital importance. This may turn out to be the key factor in the buy/not buy decision. The cash flow analysis example in Table 10-8 demonstrates this net after tax cost for

Table 10-7 Direct Operating Expenses (Variable Costs) for a Twin-Engine Turboprop Business Aircraft

Expense Category		Estimated Cost Per Hour
Fuel (1)		$259.00
Maintenance Labor (2)		$104.00
Parts—Airframe/Engine/Avionics (3)		$115.00
Engine Restoration (4)		$127.00
Propeller Overall		$3.00
Miscellaneous Expenses		
	Crew Expenses	$135.00
	Landing/Parking Fees	$6.00
	Supplies/Catering	$32.00
	Total Direct Operating Costs Per Hour	$781.00

(1) Fuel costs .... $2.29 per gallon
Gallons per hour 113
(2) Maintenance labor costs per hour $69
Maintenance hours per flight hour 1.5
(3) Engine Model PT6A-42
(4) 3600 hours

Table 10-8 Twin-Engine Business Aircraft Purchase Cash Flow Analysis

Input Data:

Aircraft Cost	$2,230,000	Federal Income Tax Rate: 39%		Monthly Payment: $29,697
State Sales Tax @ 6%	133,800	Finance Rate: 9.25% APR	8 Years	Inflation Rate: 3%
Total Acquisition Cost	$2,363,800	Money Value: 18%		Annual Hrs of Utilization: 455

Expenditures	Year 0	Year 1	Year 2	Year 3	Year 4	Year 5	Year 6
Fixed Cost		$203,244	$209,341	$215,622	$222,090	$228,753	$235,615
Down Payment (15%)	$354,570						
Balance of Purchase	$2,009,230						
Principal Payment		$177,926	$195,101	$213,933	$234,582	$257,225	$282,053
Interest Payment		$178,436	$161,262	$142,430	$121,780	$99,137	$74,309
Loan Balance Payoff							$648,410
Taxes Due on Sale							$617,487
Operating Expenses		$355,355	$366,016	$376,996	$388,306	$399,955	$411,954
TOTAL EXPENDITURES	$2,363,800	$914,961	$931,720	$948,981	$966,758	$985,070	$2,269,828
CASH SOURCE							
Aircraft Loan	$2,009,230						
Disposal of Aircraft (71%)							$1,583,300
TOTAL SOURCES	$2,009.230						$1,583,300
TOTAL CHANGE (before taxes)	$(354,570)	$(914,961)	$(931,720)	$(948,981)	$(966,758)	$(985,070	$(686,528)
TAX REDUCTIONS							
Fixed Cost		$79,265	$81,653	$84,093	$86,615	$89,214	$91,890
Depreciation		$184,376	$295,002	$177,002	$106,201	$106,201	$53,100
Interest		$69,590	$62,892	$55,548	$47,494	$38,663	$28,981
Operating Expenses		$138,588	$142,746	$147,029	$151,439	$155,982	$160,662
TOTAL TAX REDUCTION		$471,819	$582,283	$463,672	$391,749	$390,060	$334,633
CHANGE IN CASH FLOW	$(354,570)	$(443,142)	$(349,437)	$(485,309)	$(575,009)	$(595,010)	$(351,895)

TOTAL CASH FLOW	$(3,154,372)	Cost Per Mile (Average Annual Cost) / (Cruise Speed × Annual Hrs)	$525,729 / 283 × 455	$4.08
Cost per Hour	$1,155			
Net Present Value Cost	($1,963,285)	Cost /Seat Mile (Cost Per Mile) / (Passenger seats)	$4.08 / 6	$0.88

Champions Stores.

Experience has demonstrated that the cash flow statement can accomplish the following benefits for the salesperson:

1. Adds a professional touch to the sales presentation.
2. Assists the salesperson in dealing with the company's financial concern.
3. Satisfies the prospect's need for detailed cost information and net present value Analysis.
4. Helps move the sales process toward a favorable conclusion.

The significance of a cash flow analysis is that it shows the potential user an accurate estimate of the total after-tax cost of owning a business aircraft and projects the changes in the company's cash flow year by year. The following definitions are relevant:

1. Fixed Cost (Table 10-6). Annual fixed costs have been increased by an inflation factor of three percent.
2. Loan Balance Payoff = $648,410 because there are two years remaining on the loan contract.
3. Taxes Due at Sale are $617,487. This represents a corporate tax rate of 39 percent multiplied by the selling price in excess of book value.
4. Depreciation Method is a double-declining balance.
5. Operating Expenses (Table 10-7). Annual direct operating costs have been increased by an inflation factor of three percent.
6. Disposal of Aircraft is based on the present resale value of a similar six-year-old
aircraft in relation to its original retail price (71 percent).
7. Total Cash Flow indicates the total after tax cost of ownership over the six-year period.
8. Cost Per Hour is the average annual after-tax cost per hour of owning and operating the twin-engine turboprop aircraft. ($3,154,372)/2,730 hours.
9. Net Present Value Cost is derived from the money value rate of 18 percent. It represents the actual amount the aircraft will cost, based on borrowing money and keeping the company's funds free for reinvestment in the company at its average return on investment rate (Table 10-9).

Financing Aircraft

Attractive low-rate, long-term financing on up to 100 percent of an aircraft purchase price is essential in marketing aircraft. Some lending institutions have eliminated the down payment requirement, offer variable interest rates based on one or two percentage points over prime, and with terms of 12 years or more. A major general aviation manufacturer recently unveiled the following finance plan for several of its aircraft: Interest free for the first six months, 4.9 percent interest for the following year, interest at the prime rate for the succeeding year, and on the balance of the loan term, floating prime rate plus 2 percent. This type of creative financing illustrates that aircraft manufacturers generally play down lending activities and use incentive finance programs to stimulate sales.

Table 10-9 Present Value Factor

Period	8%	10%	12%	14%	15%	16%	18%	20%
1	.926	.909	.893	.877	.870	.862	.847	.833
2	.857	.826	.797	.769	.756	.743	.718	.694
3	.794	.751	.712	.675	.658	.641	.609	.579
4	.735	.683	.636	.592	.572	.552	.516	.482
5	.681	.621	.567	.519	.497	.476	.437	.402
6	.630	.564	.507	.456	.432	.410	.370	.335
7	.583	.513	.452	.400	.376	.354	.314	.279
8	.540	.467	.404	.351	.327	.305	.266	.233
9	.500	.424	.361	.308	.284	.263	.226	.194
10	.463	.386	.322	.270	.247	.227	.191	.162

Note: These present value factors are rounded to a greater degree than is done by a computer; consequently, a calculation done manually may vary somewhat from the computer's result.

The twin-engine turboprop aircraft being proposed to the management of Champions Stores is being financed over an eight-year period at 9.25 percent annual percentage rate (APR). After making a 15 percent down payment of $354,570, a fixed-rate loan for 8 years of $2,009,230 was arranged using Table 10-10, the following finance data for the cash flow analysis can be determined:

Monthly Payment	1.478022 × $20,092.30 = $29,697
1st Year Annual Interest	8.880811 × $20,092.30 = $178,436
1st Year Principal	8.855453 × $20,092.30 = $177,926
Loan Balance Payoff	32.271553 × $20,092.30 = $648,410

Present Value

The concept of present value is widely used by companies as they approach investment decisions. Financial comparisons among types of aircraft cannot be made accurately without it because this technique will tell the purchaser how much the aircraft will really cost over a predetermined period. Money that will be received in the future is presently worth considerably less than its stated value. The promise of $10,000 twenty-five years from now sounds good, but if 10 percent per annum could be earned on the investment, then this promise is now worth less than $1,000. The present value of future payments is the reciprocal of compound interest.

This reciprocity of compound interest and present value is illustrated by the following example:

Today	**5 years later**
$1,000 Compounded @ 9%	= $1,538,62

$1,538.62 is the present value of $1,000 in five years

The present value of money due in the future will differ

Table 10-10 Sample Loan AmortizationSchedule 9.25% Monthly-Fixed Rate

Years 8 Monthly Payment 1.478022

Year	Annual Interest	Annual Principal	Year Ending Balance
1	8.880811	8.855453	91.144547
2	8.026046	9.710218	81.434329
3	7.088775	10.647489	70.786840
4	6.061036	11.675229	59.111611
5	4.934094	12.802170	46.309441
6	3.698376	14.037889	32.271553
7	2.343380	15.392884	16.878669
8	0.857595	16.878669	0

This Table shows how a $100 loan at 9.25 percent is paid off over an eight-year period by a level monthly payment. The Table also shows the total annual interest and principal payments and the year-end balance each year of the loan.

Table 10-11 Net Present Value of Cash Flow Twin-Engine Turboprop Aircraft Money Value Rate 18%

Year	Actual Cash Flow		Factor	Present Value
0	$(354,570)	×	$1.000	$(354,570)
1	$(443,142)	×	$0.847	$(375,341)
2	$(349,437)	×	$0.718	$(250,896)
3	$(485,309)	×	$0.609	$(295,553)
4	$(575,009)	×	$0.516	$(296,705)
5	$(595,010)	×	$0.437	$(260,019)
6	$(351,894)	×	$9.370	$(130,201)
Total Cash Flow	$(3,154,372)			$(1,963,285)

from company to company. It depends upon the rate of return (money value or discount rate) that is either available to the company or that the company has the ability to earn internally. This explains why a company can borrow for use in its business and still make money. The loan from the financial institution requires a lower rate of interest than can be achieved by the borrower.

Present value is used as the final step in the cash flow statement. This statement illustrates the net cash flow for each year Champions Stores owns and operates its aircraft. The present value of each of these net cash flows is determined and summarized; the resulting figure is the net present value (Table 10-11). This dollar figure tells the company how much money must be invested now at the company's stated money value to earn enough cash to meet all of the aircraft expenses as they come due each year. The net present value figure also brings six years of expenses to a single figure. Prospective aircraft purchasers can use net present value during the evaluation stage to compare the total expense of owning and operating comparable aircraft.

Sales Application/Break-even Analysis

The travel analysis is a powerful means of assisting a firm in analyzing the feasibility of purchasing an airplane for employee travel. In situations where the prospective firm is going to use the airplane to generate revenue, the break-even analysis is more appropriate. The aircraft salesperson will find it useful to calculate the prospective buyer's breakeven point, that point at which the cost of operating the aircraft exactly matches the revenues generated through such activities as light instruction or charter. Since business firms must do better than just break even, this analysis will help determine revenue levels sufficient to generate a predetermined profit objective.

To apply break-even analysis, two types of costs must be determined. Fixed costs are those whose level remains unchanged when hourly usage changes (monthly interest on aircraft loans, insurance, crew salaries, general overhead allocation). Direct operating expenses are those that do change in proportion to changes in aircraft use, and include gas, maintenance, and hourly charges for maintenance reserves. To illustrate break-even analysis, a sales proposal based on a twin-engine aircraft used for charter purposes by a hypothetical company, Seacoast Charter, Inc., would be based on the following data:

Annual total fixed cost = $203,244

Charter revenue per hour = $2,200

Direct operating expense per hour = $781

Mathematically, Seacoast Charter's total evenue hours required to break-even can be determined by using the following Formula:

$$\text{BE (hrs)} = \frac{\text{Total Fixed Costs}}{\underset{\text{Hr.}}{\text{Charter Revenue}} - \underset{\text{Per Hr.}}{\text{Direct Operating Expense}}}$$

$$= \frac{\$203{,}244}{\$1{,}200 - \$781}$$

$$= 485 \text{ hours}$$

Break-even point in hours is the point where total fixed and direct operating expenses equal total charter sales revenue. Either raising or lowering the hourly charter rate can change the break-even hours. If the competitive environment would allow an increase of $50.00 per hour to $1,250, the new break-even hours would be reduced by 52 hours to 433 hours.

The president of Seacoast Charter would also like to know how many charter hours the firm must sell to make $24,998 in

$$\text{Hours required} = \frac{\text{Total Fixed Costs} + \text{Profit}}{\text{Charter Revenue Hr.} - \text{Direct Operating Expense Per Hr.}}$$

$$= \frac{\$203{,}244 + 24{,}998}{\$1{,}200 - \$781}$$

$$= 545 \text{ hours}$$

the next 12 months. Using the following formula, the aircraft salesperson would be able to provide him with the answer.

To further assist Seacoast Charter in planning, the break-even concept can be used to determine the number of charter customers required over the next 12 months to meet the $24,998 profit objective. A review of past sales records indicates that the typical charter flight lasted 7.5 hours. Since 545 total hours were required, and the average hourly usage per charter flight was 7.5, then about 73 customers (545 hrs/7.5 hrs) must be sold during the next year.

In spite of some limitations, break-even analysis can be a powerful tool for aircraft salespersons to use in marketing business aircraft to corporations that will use the aircraft commercially to generate profits.

KEY TERMS

Business-to-business marketing
Direct channels
Derived demand
Inelastic demand
Straight rebuys
Modified rebuy
New buys
Buying center concept
Users
Gatekeepers
Influencers
Decider
Buyer
Travel analysis
Amount and nature of travel
Travel dispersion
Type and frequency of airline service
Geographic dispersion
Time dispersion
Trip distances and number of passengers
Use and users of the aircraft
Environmental aspects of routes and destinations
Frequency of trips
Financial and performance considerations
Payload-range capability
Cost of ownership
Purchase price
Status of production
Trade-in value
Reliability and maintainability
Tax considerations
Depreciation
Capital Recovery Guide
Cost of use
Fixed costs
Direct operating costs
Compound interest
Present value
Break-even
Cost per mile
Cost per seat mile

REVIEW QUESTIONS

1. Describe business-to-business marketing.
2. Identify and explain three business market characteristics and demand patterns that are different from the consumer market.
3. Differentiate the three types of buying decisions made by organizations and explain the buying center concept.
4. What is the purpose of a travel analysis? How can the amount and nature of a firm's travel be determined? What is the object of the travel dispersion analysis? Distinguish between geographic, volume, and time dispersion. Describe the general trend of airline services since deregulation. What are the three levels of airline service and how do they relate to business aircraft use?
5. What is meant by the statement "let the model fit the mission"? Distinguish between the single engine and light twin-engine aircraft in terms of performance. What are the major criteria for stepping up to a medium twin? When would the use of a corporate helicopter be prudent?
6. Trip distances and number of passengers help determine aircraft requirements. What is the significance of determining the use and users of the aircraft? Describe what is meant by the environmental aspects of routes and destinations. Why is it important to determine the frequency of trips?
7. What are the major factors to consider in a performance analysis? What is a pay-load range chart? Discuss the importance of status of production, trade-in value, and reliability and maintainability in selecting an aircraft. Describe the significance of depreciation expense to a corporation.
8. Distinguish between cost of ownership and cost of use.

Travel Analysis of Jeff's Airport Consulting
(See 2 under SCENARIOS)

	Avg. No. of Pax	Total RT (1 mo.)	Total Annual RT	Number One-Way Miles	Total Miles
From Tampa, FL to:	3	2	24		
Lakeland, FL	3	2	24		
Tallahassee, FL	3	3	36		
Miami, FL	3	3	36		
Orlando, FL	2	1	12		
Atlanta, GA	2	1	12		
Nashville, TN	4	1	12		

Give some examples of fixed costs of use and direct operating costs. Determine the cost per mile for an aircraft whose annual cost is estimated to be $50,000; cruise speed 200 mph; and estimated 500 annual flying hours. If this aircraft has five passenger seats, what is the cost per seat mile?

9. Identify three benefits of a cash flow analysis to the sales process.
10. Use the Sample Loan Amortization Schedule to determine the monthly interest on an eight-year, 9.25 percent loan for $450,000.
11. Compound interest is the reciprocal of present value. Explain how prospective aircraft purchasers use net present value analysis in their decision making process?
12. Describe how break-even analysis can be used as a sales tool.

REFERENCE

Aircraft Value Reference 2001. (Vol 2). Shawnee, MO: VREF Publishing

SCENARIOS

1. As an intern in the Aircraft Sales division of Executive Flight Management, you have been tasked with studying the buying center concept and determining the key individuals in each of the five roles in the buying center at Wayne's Widgets, Inc. What are these roles and how would you figure out the individual in each of these roles within that company?
2. As a new aircraft sales associate with Executive Aircraft Sales, you have been asked to perform a Travel Analysis of Jeff's Airport Consulting. The only information given you appears in the table at the top of this page. Complete the Table (similar to Table 10-1) and conduct a full travel analysis for this company.
3. In the beginning phases of conducting a travel analysis for a corporate executive, you realize he is very interested in aviation and asks you for an explanation of the different types of aircraft that are available and the preferred uses of each type. What do you tell this executive?
4. Using the information gathered in scenario number two, perform an equipment selection process to arrive at three or four aircraft that would appear to meet the needs of Jeff's Airport Consulting.
5. Your manager has asked you to conduct a break-even analysis for a company, East Coast Charter. Determine the total revenue hours required to break even by using the following data.
   Annual total fixed cost = $189,307
   Charter revenue per hour = 1,150
   Direct operating expenses per hour = $708

Chapter 11
Methods of Acquiring a Business Aircraft

OUTLINE

OBJECTIVES

At the end of this chapter, you should be able to:

- Compare and contrast the purchase of new versus used aircraft.
- Give several reasons for the company owned/management company operated method of acquiring a business aircraft.
- List the primary factors on which finance charges on an aircraft loan are based.
- Describe the four methods available to owners desiring to sell their aircraft.
- Discuss some of the factors to consider in purchasing a used aircraft.
- List several of the major points included in an aircraft sales contract.
- Distinguish between simple interest and add-on interest.
- Describe floor planning as a financial technique.
- Determine the retail price of an aircraft using the markup formula.
- Discuss the advantages and disadvantages of leasing.
- Compare the capital lease with the operating lease.
- Discuss the major elements in fractional ownership programs.
- Identify some of the advantages of fractional ownership.
- Explain how a firm might use charter aircraft for business purposes.
- Distinguish between chartering and contract flight service.
- Summarize the four major methods of acquiring business aircraft.

Introduction

The decision to acquire a business aircraft is a major step for any business. A company that has never owned or operated an aircraft must first determine that an airplane is a worthwhile acquisition. Companies that already operate planes and want to expand or upgrade their fleets possess the aviation experience to guide them in evaluating new equipment.

Once there is agreement that an airplane is desirable, management can select a particular make and model, properly equipped, from the great variety available.

Need and cost, as previously discussed, are the basic considerations, but potential users of business aircraft also must weigh many other factors to determine whether an airplane has a valid place in their organizations. Many companies seek outside advice in making their business aviation decisions. Sales representatives from the aircraft dealers and distributors as well as specialized aviation consulting firms offer advice and counsel. Assistance from other companies, including members of NBAA who operate aircraft, is often available.

Chapter 10 demonstrated that weighing potential need for an aircraft usually involves detailed examination of company travel records covering a representative time period, to measure total volume and to identify travel patterns. This examination should reveal how many employees travel regularly, which ones do the most traveling, where they go, at what times of the day or week, typical length of trips, extent of group travel, and the proximity of frequently visited destinations to airports. Total annual cost of travel and the value per man-hour (VMH) of those traveling are usually considered in making comparisons between airline and automobile with a business aircraft.

Because of the wide range of aircraft available, it is important to identify company travel characteristics and requirements as clearly as possible in order to match them with aircraft capabilities. Some companies that have experience with business aircraft have developed internal checklists to help management evaluate and select aircraft.

A great majority of planes operated by business firms are owned or leased by the companies that use them, but a growing number of users are choosing fractional ownership. The point is that a company seeking private air transportation can obtain it in a variety of different ways. Although there are many variations and combinations among the methods of acquiring use of a business aircraft, they can be reduced to four basic methods:

1. Company-owned, new or used
    a. Company-owned aircraft, in-house flight department
    b. Company-owned aircraft, management company
    c. Joint ownership, in-house flight department
    d. Co-ownership, management company
2. Leasing, wet or dry
    a. Capital lease
    b. Operating lease
3. Fractional ownership
4. Charter, individual or contract

What might be an appropriate method for one company may be completely inappropriate for another. Like a suit of clothes, the method has to fit the company's needs to wear well. This chapter will discuss the four basic methods, along with slight variations.

Company-Owned Aircraft

The principal advantages of ownership are optimum utility, convenience, and safety. Consequently, corporate aviation departments get maximum use from their aircraft. All business owners carry on their flight operations in accordance with FAA regulations.

Many also have developed additional corporate procedures that have resulted in safety records comparable to those of the scheduled airlines.

Usually, one company-owned airplane, efficiently used, can satisfy 75 percent of the air transportation needs of the people it is intended to serve. Anything over 75 percent will usually necessitate special charter or lease arrangements. Many companies have different types of aircraft in their fleets to meet various needs.

An aircraft in-house flight department affords the highest possible levels of control, service, and security/confidentiality. If there are no intercompany scheduling conflicts or maintenance downtime, the aircraft will always be available. If the aircraft is not available, the owner can use charter, airlines, timeshare, or interchange to meet flight demands.

A time-sharing agreement involves the lease of an airplane with flight crew to another party, and no charge is made for the flights conducted under that arrangement other than the following:

1. Fuel, oil, lubricants, and other additives.
2. Travel expenses of the crew, including food, lodging, and ground transportation.
3. Hangar and tie-down costs away from the aircraft's base of operations.
4. Insurance obtained for the specific flight.
5. Landing fees, airport taxes, and similar assessments.
6. Customs, foreign permits, and similar fees directly related to the flight.
7. In-flight food and beverages.
8. Passenger ground transportation.
9. Flight planning and weather contract services.
10. An additional charge equal to 100 percent of the expenses listed under number one.

Under an interchange agreement, one company leases its airplane to another company in exchange for equal time, when needed, on the other company's airplane, and no charge, assessment, or fee is made, except that a charge may be made not to exceed the difference between the cost of owning, operating, and maintaining the two airplanes.

A company-owned aircraft is the most flexible method of business flying. As owner, the company is not subject to restrictions imposed by charterers or lessors with regard to insurance requirements, operating restrictions, and other contractual provisions. On the other hand, having an owned aircraft can be inflexible if the company is not getting the hourly utilization expected, or if it has purchased the wrong aircraft and must dispose of it.

The owner maintains total control over and manages aircraft operations. As such, the owner is completely liable for all operations. All flight department personnel are on the owner's payroll, and the owner must deal with in-house personnel issues. Crew quality is consistent and owner-controlled, and the owner is directly in charge of training crew and maintenance personnel.

Cost per hour flown is the lowest of any of the methods of operation as long as the annual hourly utilization is achieved. Ideally, a company should use its own aircraft as extensively as possible to derive the greatest productivity from business flying.

Operating costs vary depending on aircraft use, and the lowest cost of operations is realized at reasonable utilization levels (above 400 flight hours per year), although deadheading or positioning costs can play a factor. To help offset costs, a flight department can opt to charter out its aircraft, but only after receiving Part 135 approval to do so.

Since the department operates under Part 91, the federal excise tax (FET) does not apply; instead, the noncommercial fuel tax is applied. The aircraft may be fully depreciated over a six-year period, realizing the maximum tax benefit for the company. However, state sales tax must be paid on the acquisition cost. This option requires a higher capital investment of the negotiated acquisition cost, but the owner has the freedom to purchase any aircraft at any price. The owner also has complete control over how the aircraft is outfitted. In addition, the aircraft can be sold, upgraded, or downgraded at any time.

Company Owned – Management Company Operated

Operation of a company-owned aircraft by a management company is attractive to firms not wanting to take on the responsibility of operating their own aircraft. Under contract, the management company provides crew, maintenance, and all administrative responsibilities. Because of this arrangement, the owner shares liability with the management company. Flight department personnel are not on the owner's payroll.

This method can provide excellent, customized service. Like a company-owned, in-house flight department, the aircraft is nearly always available. If the aircraft is not available due to maintenance or scheduling conflicts, the owner can use charter, airlines, timeshare, or interchange to meet flight demands.

The level of safety can vary widely, depending on the competence and operating philosophy of the particular management company. Nearly all management companies that offer this type of service operate under Part 135 of the Federal Aviation Regulations (FARs), which is designed for commercial operators and requires higher minimum safety standards than Part 91 (which is the FAR most company-owned and operated aircraft are operated under). However, these are minimum regulations and not closely scrutinized by the FAA. As a result, there is considerable variance in the safety standards adhered to by individual management companies.

As a rule, the company-owned, management company-operated method is expensive simply because the company has to pay for the services provided. One of the major selling points for using management company services is that the company owning the aircraft will be able to save some fixed costs by selling time on the aircraft when the owning company is not using it. In some cases, selling time is valid and workable.

Operating costs vary depending on aircraft use, and the lowest cost of operation is realized at reasonable utilization levels, but deadheading or positioning costs can increase these costs.

Simply stated, aircraft management firms offer the one- and two-aircraft operator the economies of scale generally available only to large fleet operators. The scope of services differs widely among the many aircraft management firms. Most of the larger firms provide flight planning, 24-hour central dispatch and flight following, storage, insurance, training, backup pilots, and most maintenance. Some firms have set up agreements with their customers whereby each customer has an entire fleet of aircraft at its call, if necessary. For example, if a company owns one aircraft but needs four others for some special purpose one day, it can borrow time, in effect, on these other aircraft, with the stipulation that it will repay this borrowed time by permitting other companies to use its aircraft.

In addition to timesharing agreements, virtually all aircraft management firms can charter a customer's aircraft under a commercial certificate, which also improves utilization while helping to offset some of the client's operating costs.

The owners pay the noncommercial fuel tax as long as they maintain possession of and control over the aircraft. The aircraft may be fully depreciated over a six-year period, realizing the maximum tax benefit for the company. However, state sales tax must be paid on the acquisition cost.

This option requires higher capital investment of the negotiated acquisition cost, but the owner has the freedom to purchase any aircraft at any price. The owner has complete say in how the aircraft is outfitted. The aircraft can be sold, upgraded, or downgraded at any time.

In summary, there are five distinct advantages of a management operation:

- It maintains an "arm's-length" arrangement with the owner in which all the aircraft-related administrative functions are performed outside the owner's company, thus relieving the need to commit internal resources.

- It can deliver Part 135 charter revenues back to the owner to help defray costs.
- It removes from the company any political or employee-sensitive aircraft-related cost accounting.
- It provides anonymity and security because an owner's aircraft becomes part of a fleet of many owners, and those who might be trying to use Internet tracking programs or the FAA Web site to identify a particular aircraft user find it extremely difficult.
- It maintains a pragmatic perspective toward the owner's aircraft. The aircraft is looked upon as a business asset detached from personal involvement, perhaps unlike a flight department.

Joint Ownership – In-House Flight Department

Joint ownership is an arrangement whereby one of the registered joint owners of an airplane employs and furnishes the flight crew for that airplane and each of the registered joint owners pays a share of the charges specified in the agreement.

A joint-ownership in-house flight department can also provide excellent and customized service. However, aircraft availability requires coordination with the joint owners and advance planning. If the aircraft is not available, either owner can use charter, airlines, timeshare, or interchange to meet flight demands.

Owners maintain control over and manage aircraft operations, and the liability for these operations is shared by both owners. Flight department personnel are on the owners' payroll, and the owners must jointly address any in-house personnel issues. Crew quality is consistent and controlled by the owners, who are responsible for crew and maintenance personnel training.

Operating costs vary, depending on aircraft use (again, the lowest cost of operations is realized at reasonable utilization levels), and deadheading or positioning costs increase these costs. To help offset operating costs, the owners can opt to charter out their aircraft, but this may put more of a squeeze on aircraft availability.

Owners pay the noncommercial fuel tax since they operate the aircraft under Part 91. However, FET charges could apply if an owner's aircraft share does not closely match the percentage of use. For example, Company A owns 90 percent of the aircraft, while Company B owns 10 percent, but each uses the aircraft equally. Because Company B's share is not proportional to its aircraft use, the IRS deems this to be a commercial operation (FET applies), even though operations are conducted under Part 91. Aircraft depreciation is shared by the owners and they must pay state sales tax on their share of the aircraft acquisition fee.

This option requires a higher capital investment for the negotiated acquisition cost on the part of the owners. They must also agree on what aircraft to purchase and how to outfit it. Either owner can sell its share in the aircraft at any time, and the aircraft can be sold, upgraded, or downgraded as needed.

Co-Ownership – Management Company

A co-ownership management company also provides customizable service, but aircraft availability requires coordination and planning. If the aircraft is not available, either owner can use charter, airlines, timeshare, or interchange to meet flight demands.

Owners maintain control over, but delegate the management of, aircraft operations. Liability for these operations is shared by the owners and the management company. Flight department personnel are not on the owners' payroll, and crew quality is consistent. The owners also delegate control of crew and maintenance personnel training to the management company.

Operating costs are inversely proportional to aircraft use, and deadheading or positioning costs will increase these costs. Annual operating costs may be higher than joint ownership due to management fees. To help offset operating costs, the owners can opt to charter out the aircraft, but this could adversely affect availability.

Owners pay the noncommercial fuel tax as long as they maintain possession of and control over the aircraft. However, the aforementioned share/use percentage rule applies, as well. Aircraft depreciation is shared by the owners, and they must pay state sales tax on their share of the aircraft acquisition price.

This option requires the owners to ante up a high capital investment of the negotiated acquisition cost. They must also agree on what aircraft to purchase and how to outfit it. Either owner can sell its share in the aircraft at any time, and the aircraft can be sold, upgraded, or downgraded as needed.

New versus Used Aircraft

The demand for new and used business aircraft has been strong since the mid1990s. Although many companies have considered fractional ownership or charter, others have realized that a company-owned plane is an excellent choice. It will remain the prime source of large and small business aircraft. Used aircraft are generally less expensive to purchase; however, prices have drifted upward in recent years reflecting scarcity of certain models, particularly trainers. However, an intelligent decision about buying new or used should draw on all aspects of expense, not simply the purchase price.

Many new aircraft dealers and distributors are active in

the used aircraft market because they frequently take older planes in trade against the sale of new aircraft. Also, some firms specialize in handling used planes. These firms, operating similarly to used automobile wholesalers, usually sell in large numbers, often to dealers and distributors overseas; they are also active in the reconditioning of individual aircraft for sale at retail. Then, too, there are brokers for the sale of used aircraft.

Although the used aircraft market can be compared to the used automobile market in some respects, it is very different in at least one critical aspect. While the buyer of a used automobile may buy a "lemon," this is definitely not the case with used airplanes. Aircraft must be licensed by the FAA when put into service initially, then must be relicensed annually thereafter. The licensing procedure requires the plane to be subjected to periodic inspections to ensure that it is being maintained in airworthy condition. Records of inspection, along with records of maintenance and repair activities, are a permanent part of each airplane's records and are passed along from one owner to another. Thus, it is possible to get a good picture of a used airplane's current condition by studying the records of its usage, maintenance, and repair. This requirement for regular inspections of airplanes and written records of repairs and overhauls may also partially explain why an active used aircraft market exists today and why there is ready acceptance on the part of buyers of well-maintained used aircraft. In addition, many used aircraft have enjoyed stable market values at a high percentage of their original purchase prices. The AOPA puts out an excellent booklet entitled "How to Buy a Used Aircraft" which includes a checklist of special precautions for prospective used aircraft purchasers.

Good pre-owned airplanes represent substantial value. Over 80 percent of all corporate aircraft sold in the United States are pre-owned. A company can buy a five-year-old aircraft, reconfigure the interior to its specific requirements, upgrade the avionics with the latest safety enhancements, and have the equivalent of a brand-new airplane at a fraction of the cost. The company's financial exposure is minimal because, historically, used airplanes hold their values over time. They are very liquid assets. A five-year-old airplane can retain 80 to 90 percent of its original value, and many aircraft, such as King Airs, have actually appreciated beyond their original cost.

Despite the active sales in used aircraft in recent years, new airplanes still offer some sound advantages.

Financing is apt to be more liberal on a new airplane, with lower interest rates and longer repayment terms. Lending institutions tend to feel that their investments are better secured with new rather than used equipment and will make some financial concessions to encourage new purchases.

Similarly, insurance companies are generally more eager to insure new rather than used airplanes, and their rates reflect that attitude. A new aircraft has no wear on the components, so there is a greater statistical probability that everything will function normally for a longer period of time than on a used airplane.

A new aircraft warranty can also be an advantage particularly if a firm is considering buying a sophisticated single or twin-engine aircraft with complex systems. Though most modern airplanes are reasonably trouble-free, there is definitely a correlation between maintenance cost and systems complexity; the more complex an airplane, the more it will cost to maintain.

Another consideration is the fact that a new airplane has no maintenance or operation history. The first buyer has the opportunity to control the break-in and day-to-day flight record of the aircraft. A firm can strictly regulate operating practices and make certain the aircraft is properly treated to maximize utility and efficiency. Though logbooks can give some indications of how well or poorly a used airplane was treated, there is no way to know for sure.

High among the benefits of buying a new aircraft are the advantages that go with better performance, greater comfort, improved efficiency, and personalized appearance. Innovations in aerodynamics and powerplants often allow new aircraft to realize better speed and efficiency than older models. State-of-the-art avionics are part of the newer equipment. While it is true that new communication radios and navigation equipment may be fitted to older airplanes, avionics installations typically will be simpler and cleaner if done at the factory when the aircraft is built. Also, a buyer may realize a lower price purchasing new radios with the aircraft, because the manufacturer can benefit from volume discounts not always available to outside vendors.

Cabin comfort is a subjective judgment, but there is little doubt that interior appointments and even cabin size improve with newer models. Today's aircraft often offer more luxurious and durable fabrics and leathers than older models. Buying new also offers a firm the option of personalizing the paint and interior to its individual taste. How important these latter items are to a firm in evaluating a new versus used aircraft is really a management decision.

Maintenance

Whether purchasing a new or used airplane, maintenance is a major factor that prospective owners need to study carefully. Aircraft must be maintained according to strict FAA rules and regulations. Good maintenance can be costly, but it is infinitely less expensive than having an engine quit somewhere between airports. Also, a well-maintained aircraft will bring a higher price when it is time to trade it in.

There are hundreds of FBOs located on virtually every sizable airport in the country, as well as around the world, that provide maintenance. These businesses must meet stringent FAA requirements. Many FBOs are also the authorized service centers for the major airframe and engine manufacturers. Larger corporate operators of business aircraft have their own in-house maintenance organizations, or possibly they share a maintenance operation with two or three partners. This concept is generally only viable with companies operating a fleet of aircraft.

Financing the Aircraft Purchase

Most companies have lines of credit available through their banks. However, it is often preferable to keep this credit available for other needs such as short-term borrowings, working capital requirements, or capital improvements. There are a number of aircraft financing specialists, including banks, finance companies, and the manufacturer's finance organizations. The majority of these institutions finance nationwide and are able to handle most transactions by telephone, e-mail, fax, or mail. Once a call is received from an aircraft dealer or purchaser, preliminary financial information is taken over the phone along with a complete description of the aircraft. Financial statements are usually forwarded by mail. Credit investigation is often handled by phone. In many instances, a decision is made on the loan within hours of receipt of the financial statements.

Most finance charges on aircraft loans are based primarily on four factors:

1. **Amount of the loan.** A larger loan may warrant a lower rate than a small loan.
2. **Amount of the down payment.** Greater equity in the aircraft results in less risk, thus a lower rate.
3. **Terms of the loan.** Lenders tend to look for a higher rate over a long term as a hedge against inflation.
4. **Credit strength of the borrower.** The most credit-worthy customers will enjoy the best rates.

Most financial institutions will require a down payment of 20 percent on used aircraft and 25 percent on a new aircraft. The additional amount for new aircraft is because of increased depreciation which occurs during the first year. Lenders experienced in aircraft finance keep abreast of the total aircraft market and consider this in setting down payment rules on specific aircraft. If a company can purchase an aircraft at an exceptionally good price, a smaller down payment would be requested. Once again, terms of the loan and credit of the borrower are factors in determining the necessary amount of cash required on the purchase.

The majority of aircraft loans are repaid in monthly installments. Aircraft loan specialists know that some borrowers have specific needs. Repayment plans have been set up quarterly, semiannually, or on annual schedules. Occasionally, fixed-principal payments plus interest are arranged. Under this plan, each payment is smaller than the one before it since interest is less as the principal balance declines. Once in a while a company may desire smaller monthly payments than would normally be necessary to repay the loan. The lender may be able to arrange such a loan with a balloon payment at the end which would be paid in a lump sum or would be refinanced. These basic plans vary among aircraft lending institutions.

Lending institutions specializing in aircraft financing are equipped to handle the paperwork involved with aircraft purchase and financing in an orderly and rapid manner. They have direct connections with the FAA in Oklahoma City and can obtain a title search on an aircraft in a matter of hours. There are often documents pertaining to the aircraft which may cloud the title, such as forms unrecorded for some reason or old liens which have not been released. The lender can usually clear up these problems in a short time. The registration of an aircraft is also handled by the lender. This is an area where the financial institution can be of considerable assistance to the borrower.

Strong economic growth in recent years and unprecedented demand for business aircraft have created a favorable climate for financing aircraft. First, banks and financial institutions that have not previously been willing to fund business aircraft purchases have overcome their preconceptions about the market in a bid to share in this period of strong demand. Second, relatively low interest rates and abundant capital markets have combined to make borrowing an attractive and feasible proposition.

The late 1990s have brought in a number of new capital sources looking for a piece of the business aviation loan market. The residual values of business aircraft have proven themselves to be stronger than those of commercial aircraft. To aircraft finance consumers, more financial sources mean more choices and more competitive deals.

For customers with good credit histories, the range tends to be lower and narrower. Specialist business finance sources generally focus on expertise and flexibility as ways to set themselves apart from opportunistic rate cutters in the marketplace.

The options available to business aircraft purchasers are set to be further expanded by the emerging Internet-based finance tools. Following the trend in retail banking, these sources will likely make their way into the market with highly competitive interest rates made possible by pared administrative costs. However, the newcomers' lack of specialist knowledge could further obfuscate an already complex choice for would-be loan and lease customers.

Manufacturers play a vital role in securing funding for sales of both new and used aircraft in their broad portfolio of products. However, manufacturers tend to push their own finance facilities first.

Buying and Selling Used Aircraft

The Market

Used aircraft come from many sources. Aircraft manufacturers estimate that one out of every four new airplanes go to first-time owners, while three out of four new airplanes go to individuals and businesses trading in an older aircraft. This chain reaction provides a constant supply of pre-owned aircraft, and puts the fixed based operator actively in the used aircraft business. Often the profit on the transaction is not fully realized until the trade-in is successfully sold. Other major sources for used aircraft are businesses in distressed industries; individual owners; repossessions from banks, leasing companies, and finance companies; foreign sellers; and corporate owners who desire to replace their aircraft.

Owners desiring to sell their aircraft can approach the disposal in one of four ways. The best approach will depend upon the owners' desire to receive "top" dollar for their airplanes, the owners' know-how in handling the details of the transfers, and their ability to expose the airplanes to a sufficient number of qualified prospects. The advantages and disadvantages of the four approaches are as follows:

1. **Sale by owner.** If a buyer can be found quickly, this approach has the potential to generate the highest profit. The owner must have tracked the market well enough to know precisely what the aircraft is worth. Owners have difficulty in getting adequate exposure for their aircraft, and they lack the expertise to handle the many details required to complete the exchange.
2. **Sale by a broker.** A broker acts as an agent to bring a buyer and a seller together. This method involves listing the aircraft with an established broker who will then represent the owner in the sale of the aircraft. When the sale has been consummated, the broker will typically deduct five percent from the selling price for the commission. For their five percent commission, brokers bring exposure, know-how, and prompt action. The broker will handle all details in the transfer, saving the owner considerable time.
3. **Sale to a dealer.** From an economic standpoint, selling or trading an aircraft to a dealer is like selling it wholesale. The dealer must buy the airplane at a price which allows a markup sufficient to cover expenses on the transaction and make an appropriate profit. A dealer takes physical possession of the aircraft for resale, often upgrading the interior or avionics before it goes on the market. This method is the quickest and simplest of the approaches, but with an obvious cost.
4. **Sale to an original equipment manufacturer (OEM).** An OEM's resale group normally offers good after-sales support, pilot training, and referrals to insurance agencies, FBOs, and maintenance shops that have experience with the particular aircraft. At the same time, OEMs usually carry out an extensive inspection of any trade-in or resale aircraft in their own shops before it goes on the market. This can mitigate a substantial amount of risk to the preowned aircraft customer, but also adds to the cost.

Currently, about 80 percent of used business aircraft transactions worldwide are completed through independent dealers and brokers. The choice between a dealer, broker, or OEM is often not clear cut, since each sector has its advantages. OEMs are a particularly good source for higher valued business aircraft because of their quality business practices. By the same token, there are many ethical brokers and dealers. Although many late-model aircraft changing hands are normally still under a manufacturer's warranty, which will transfer to the new owner, most dealers and brokers sell older aircraft on an as-is basis without warranties. For this reason, buying an aircraft from a dealer with an extensive maintenance capability is often advisable, especially if that dealer is situated near where the individual or company plans to base the aircraft. However, that is often not possible.

While most independent dealers do not offer warranties on used aircraft, those with in-house maintenance capability are more receptive to negotiating special after-sale customer-support programs. But even without on-site maintenance, independent dealers offer some advantages not always available from the manufacturers that sell the aircraft they have taken in trade for new equipment. The dealers tend to be smaller and more streamlined and, for this reason, decisions as to what will be included in the price of an aircraft can be made more rapidly because there is no large bureaucracy to deal with. Arrangements include upgrades, modifications, and maintenance that need be done on the aircraft before it is delivered to the buyer. The important thing is that a reputable dealer is always trying to build a special relationship with customers so that they will want to come back to buy their next airplane.

It is important in dealing with dealers or OEMs that the company or individual stick to aircraft that they have determined will meet their needs. Often dealers or OEMs are more concerned with selling what they have in inventory to make their commission, rather than selling an aircraft that will really meet the customer's needs.

Prices for a quality used aircraft depend on recent market trends for the specific model being considered. The best benchmark for appraisal is what the prices have been for the past six months. This information can be obtained from dealers or brokers, who can research this through the four recognized database sources: the Aircraft Blue Book, Vref, Jetnet, and Amstat.

Although prices of late-model used aircraft tend to be high, some buyers are willing to spend the money, since the wait for delivery of new aircraft can average one to two years from the time they are ordered. Although a used aircraft may cost less, many older aircraft require significant upgrades or refurbishment that can be time consuming, particularly in a tight market.

Purchasing Used Aircraft

It is important to examine the history of the aircraft, regardless of its age, by making a comprehensive inspection of all records pertaining to the aircraft's operation and maintenance. Buyers are encouraged to have the aircraft inspected by a qualified mechanic and a pilot in the case of higher valued business aircraft. In the case of incomplete maintenance logbooks, the buyer should initiate an in-depth research effort to fill in any gaps in the aircraft's maintenance history.

Some manufacturers who accept trade-in aircraft actually interview past owners and talk with the managers of facilities that have maintained the aircraft. The company will also contact the FAA to find out if any Form 337s have been filed for the aircraft. An FAA Form 337 must be filled out in the event of a major alteration or repair of the aircraft. The forms are available at the FAA's Oklahoma City facility. Form 337s are examined because the information they provide may have a bearing on any work that the buyer might want to have done on the aircraft. If the buyer is considering a significant upgrade of the avionics or a completely new interior, the Form 337 will indicate what weight-and-balance changes have been made as a result of the alterations.

In addition to the maintenance log, the prospective buyer should review the airframe log, which deals with hours flown and cycles, as well as incidents and accidents. A complete airframe log should also indicate compliance with past airworthiness directives, as well as the manufacturer's recommended inspection schedules. Airworthiness directives are used to notify aircraft owners of unsafe conditions about their aircraft and to prescribe the conditions under which the airplane may continue to be flown. "The Airworthiness Directives Summary," published by the Superintendent of Documents, should be consulted by the prospective purchaser to verify which Ads have applied to the aircraft in question.

Airworthiness certificates are issued by a representative of the FAA after the aircraft has been inspected, is found to meet the requirements of the Federal Aviation Regulation (FAR), and is in a condition for safe operation. This certificate is displayed in the aircraft and is transferred when the aircraft is sold. It is important to note that the Standard Airworthiness Certificate remains in effect as long as the aircraft receives the required maintenance and is properly registered in the United States. It does not assure that the aircraft is currently in a safe operating condition. A general guideline when looking at logbooks is to note the ratio of flight hours to cycles. Fewer cycles (takeoffs and landings) normally mean that less stress has been put on the airframe. As a rule of thumb, buyers should not consider an aircraft that has less than two flight hours per cycle, because the aircraft will probably require some near-term heavy maintenance.

Once the logbooks have been inspected, a demonstration flight that allows the buyer to make a trial run may be in order. Most OEMs and dealers will permit this. However, unlike a short flight in the vicinity of the airport in a small aircraft in which the seller usually bears the cost, the buyer will have to pay the seller for any expenses incurred on a long demonstration flight.

For most heavy turboprop and jet equipment, a demonstration flight over a planned route is very desirable. If there is going to be a problem with the pressurization system, it is going to occur when the aircraft reaches flight altitude. For those companies that do not want to make a demonstration flight in the form of an actual point-to-point trip, a test flight of at least one hour at different altitudes is recommended.

In addition, any squawks revealed in the demonstration or short test flight allow the buyer to go into the all-important pre-purchase inspection with at least some knowledge of what should be looked at more closely. The former owner's maintenance facility is likely to be aware of something that perhaps was not entered into the logbook by a previous owner, since the authorized service center or OEM may have done the repairs. This is especially true if the airplane has been maintained under some type of factory maintenance plan, which is always a good reference when considering a pre-owned aircraft.

The buyer should ask if the engines are on a recognized engine management program, because those that are will have a complete set of maintenance records.

Pre-Purchase Inspection

The aircraft buyer should approach a pre-purchase inspection in a proactive fashion. The first thing to look for is any sign of corrosion and cracking. Corrosion is irreversible in its deteriorating effects on the airframe, and it is important to know whether damage has been done to the aircraft. It is also important to know if maintenance squawks have been addressed to assure that there are absolutely no hidden problems waiting to appear.

Technicians should perform a thorough engine inspection. They should check compression, examine the insides with a borescope, and do an oil analysis. If there is a problem with the engine, that should be factored into the purchase price. Technicians should check the mechanical components, the pulleys, linkages, and other mechanical parts. These are readily replaced, if necessary, but needed repairs are identified before purchase, not after. It is important for the buyer to look for functional avionics. If the airframe and engine are acceptable but avionics equipment needs upgrading, it should be installed at the time of purchase so that it can be included in the financing package, and possible dealer discounts on avionics at time of purchase can be used. This is also the time to upgrade the interior if it needs work.

A complete pre-purchase inspection can take from several hours for a light single engine aircraft to seven or eight days for a typical business jet. With the advice of the person who has reviewed the logbooks, the buyer should go to the shop with a complete written description of the specific items the pre-purchase inspection is to cover. This is important because the OEMs and most service centers will offer a prepackaged type of pre-purchase inspection. It is important to make sure that the inspection covers anything not included in the package that the adviser recommends.

If the aircraft under consideration is about due for a major inspection, the buyer may want to use that event as the basis for any pre-purchase inspection. The major inspection that would have to be done anyway could be the foundation for the inspection.

Pre-purchase inspections are not free. Sellers are not obligated to cover the pre-purchase inspection costs. An inspection on a light single-engine aircraft can cost several hundred dollars and from $8,000-$30,000 dollars for a corporate aircraft, depending on its size and complexity.

Although the buyer normally pays for the inspection, the buyer can negotiate with the seller to pay for repairs that might be needed as a result of what turns up. Most reputable sellers will agree to do that, even though the buyer might not always get dollar for dollar.

The bottom line for every pre-purchase inspection is to find what needs to be fixed so that the airplane will be ready to fly upon acceptance. The buyer may have decided beforehand that he or she wanted to have the aircraft repainted, the avionics suite upgraded, or a new interior installed; but these items would have been something the buyer would have done after accepting the aircraft. The important thing is that the aircraft is flyable with no problems upon acceptance.

The following list includes the major items to be considered in evaluating a used aircraft:

1. **General:**
   a. Total hours airframe?
   b. Hours flown while seller had it?
   c. Date of latest annual inspection?
   d. Latest 100-hour inspection?
   e. Number of hours since latest annual or 100-hour inspection?
   f. Have you checked carefully for metal corrosion inside wings and tail?
   g. Any sign of touch-up painting? Aircraft in any accidents?
   h. Are all parts readily available?
   i. How many gallons of fuel used per hour?
   j. How many quarts of oil?
   k. Does the plane look clean and well-cared for?
2. **Engine:**
   a. Total time? Engine ever been overhauled?
   b. Top or major? When?
   c. Total time since overhaul?
   d. Engine clean? Free of rust, corrosion?
   e. Evidence of oil leaks? Checking on hose?
   f. Clamps cutting? Copper lines cutting?
   g. Chafing? Sharp bends?
   h. Metal particles in the oil screen?
   i. Does the engine turn up maximum rated rpm on the ground?
   j. Have you checked the cylinders for compression?
   k. How much will a new or exchange engine cost?
3. **Propeller:**
   a. Finish in good condition?
   b. Any looseness in prop? Free travel?
   c. Have all propeller bulletins been complied with?
   d. Any evidence of oil leaks?
   e. Spinner in good condition and secure?
4. **Wings:**
   a. Cuts in leading edge?
   b. Dents?
5. **Controls:**
   a. Do all surfaces move freely and evenly?
   b. Hinges in good shape?
   c. Control cables have proper tension? Securely attached?
   d. Are cables rusty or worn looking?
   e. Everything properly secured?
6. **Landing gear:**
   a. Tires worn or cracked?
7. Doors and windows:
   a. Open easily?
   b. Loose or twisted hinges?
8. **Cabin interior:**
   a. Upholstery clean?
   b. Condition of windshield?
   c. Seats move easily, lock securely?
   d. Heater works?
9. **Radios and instruments:**
   a. Have you checked all radios and instruments?

b. Are all installations neat?
c. VOR equipment meets accuracy tolerances?
d. Record of VOR equipment checks for IFR operation?
e. Are transmitters FCC type-accepted?
f. Are they listed on FCC license?
g. All instruments properly calibrated?
h. Do gyros precess excessively?
i. Altimeter/static system inspection for IFR within last 24 months?

Negotiating the Purchase

When all inspections and evaluations are satisfactory, it is time to make the owner an offer. The offer should allow for an adequate markup. This format will allow the dealer to put money into the aircraft to make it attractive to a prospective buyer. A dealer attempting to build a sound aircraft sales business will not follow the principal "Buy the airplane for as little as possible, put as little money as possible in the clean-up phase, and then sell the airplane at the highest price possible."

When the offer has been accepted, a binder is given along with the signing of a simple sales agreement. The sales agreement identifies the parties, the specific airplane by "N" number, price, date of closing, and any other terms or conditions of the sale.

This is the definitive purchase agreement spelling out all of the criteria that must be met before the aircraft is accepted. As examples, sales contracts generally state that the aircraft will be delivered to the buyer in airworthy condition as a baseline, but they can also include all of the conditions agreed to. They could include repairs, refurbishment, the completion of a successful test flight, and/or the delivery time and date. If a certain component the buyer wants installed is not available by the time the airplane is scheduled for delivery, it is important that the buyer and seller have an understanding that the component will be installed by a specific date.

With all the points to be covered in buying a used aircraft, the final responsibility for what is ultimately delivered comes down to the buyer. The buyer must beware.

The following sample sales contract covers many points aimed at protecting the interests of the buyer and seller. Obviously, the particular points in an agreement of this type are open to negotiations originating from either side.

(Buyer's name) hereby formally offers to Purchase one (manufacturer) (model) bearing
(manufacturer's Serial No. and FAA Registration No.) from (Seller's name) for an agreed-upon price of $ USD subject to the following terms and conditions:

1. Receipt by (Seller) within (x) hours of a deposit in the amount of $ USD from (Buyer), which shall be refundable to (Buyer) in whole or in part as specified herein.
2. (Seller) has made representations to (Buyer) that the subject aircraft, with the specifications as presented to (Buyer) on (date), is in good working order and properly maintained, that the paint and interior as (representative condition), and that it will be delivered to (Buyer) in an airworthy condition with no fuel, oil, or hydraulic leaks, and with all integral components and systems in normal operating order.
3. (Seller) represents that it is the legal owner of the aircraft, holding good and beneficial title thereof, and at the time of delivery will be able to transfer free and clear title to the aircraft to (Buyer) on or before (date).
4. (Seller) shall make the aircraft available to (Buyer) at (location) no later than (date) to allow (Buyer) to perform a pre-purchase inspection, which inspection shall be completed no later than (date), for purposes of verification of specifications and representations as to appearance and condition. The cost of performing this inspection shall be borne by (Buyer); the cost of positioning the Aircraft shall be borne by (Seller).
5. Upon completion of the above inspection, (Buyer) may, at it's sole and absolute discretion, elect not to proceed with the purchase, such decision to be made within (x) hours of completion of the inspection. In that event, (Seller) shall immediately refund to (Buyer) the deposit monies previously tendered, less (Seller's) direct expenses for moving the aircraft to and from (location of inspection). However, if the inspection reveals the representations of the condition of the aircraft were knowingly or significantly inaccurate, and (Buyer's) election not to purchase is based on these revelations, then the deposit monies held by (Seller) shall be immediately returned to (Buyer) in full, and (Buyer) shall not be liable or responsible to (Seller) for any costs incurred by (Seller) whatsoever.
6. If, after completion of the inspection, (Buyer) wishes to proceed with the purchase, (Buyer) will notify (Seller) within (x) hours of such intent, and (Seller) hereby agrees to rectify, at (Seller's) expense, any discrepancies revealed by the inspection.
7. Upon such notification to proceed, (Buyer's) deposit shall become binding and nonrefundable pending structure and execution of a contract of sale to be finalized Within (x) days, and delivery of the Aircraft on or before (date). Both parties agree to exercise their respective best efforts to formulate and finalize this contract.
8. (Seller), upon receipt of this offer to purchase, will immediately notify (Buyer) in writing by letter, e-mail, or fax of (Seller's) understanding, acceptance, and agreement with the terms and conditions herein.

Before the closing date, the buyer should make, or have made, a search of the records and encumbrances affecting ownership at the Aircraft Registration Branch, FAA Aviation Records Building, Aeronautical Center, 6400 South MacArthur Boulevard, Oklahoma City, Oklahoma 73125. A list of title search companies will be furnished upon request. When the title search is received, it will show the present owner, the lien-holder if any, and the dollar amount of the lien.

Aircraft Registration

After purchasing the used aircraft, a Certificate of Aircraft Registration must be secured from the FAA Aircraft Registry. An aircraft is eligible for registration only if it is owned by a citizen of the United States or a governmental unit and is not registered under the laws of any foreign country. An Aircraft Registration Application, AC Form 8050-1, consisting of an original (white) and two copies (green and pink) can be obtained from any FAA General Aviation District Office.

When applying for a Certificate of Aircraft Registration, an Aircraft Bill of Sale, AC Form 8050-2 must also be submitted. Until the permanent Certificate of Aircraft Registration is received, the pink copy of the application serves as a temporary certificate for 90 days and must be carried in the aircraft.

Financing

An aircraft dealer has three basic financing alternatives: cash, installment loans, and floor planning contracts.

Paying cash for expensive inventory, like aircraft, is generally considered unwise. Most managers of FBOs need capital for operating expenses and therefore must look to outside sources for funds to purchase used aircraft. Paying cash is the simplest of the three methods, but usually not practical.

To build adequate levels of inventory, newer aircraft dealers will turn to installment loans for their source of funds. These types of loans are available from banks and finance companies like Cessna Finance Corporation and CIT Corporation. Financing aircraft inventory by this method requires equal monthly payments over a period of six months or more. The payments include an interest charge and a partial principal payment. Financial institutions offer loans on either a simple interest basis or on an add-on interest basis.

Simple interest is charged only on the outstanding balance of the loan. The required monthly payment can be determined from financial tables or by multiplying the stated interest rate by the outstanding balance at the end of each month. A $50,000.00 one-year loan at 12 percent APR (annual percentage rate) would require monthly payments of $4,442.50. Since the interest is charged only on the outstanding balance of the loan, the annual percentage rate under this method of financing equals the stated rate.

The add-on interest method of determining monthly payments is commonly used in aircraft financing and results in a much higher APR than does the simple interest method. The one-year $50,000 loan with a stated interest rate of 12 percent used in the above example would require monthly payments of $4,666.50 with the add-on method. Aircraft dealers need to understand the difference between simple and add-on interest methods of computing finance changes to efficiently finance their aircraft inventory.

Established aircraft dealers will employ the use of floor planning to assist them in maintaining a good selection of aircraft. Floor planning is a financial arrangement whereby the bank, or other financial institution, will provide the dealer with short-term financing at moderate interest rates.

Floor plan programs vary depending on competition, economic conditions, and geographical location. A typical program will charge the dealer one percent per month on the wholesale value of the aircraft. The bank will either take title to the aircraft or place a lien on the title as its protection in the event of default by the dealer. The dealer will have from four to six months to sell the aircraft. If the aircraft is still in inventory at the end of this time, the aircraft will be placed on an installment loan basis, and the dealer will be required to make monthly principal and interest payments.

Floor planning is the preferred method of financing inventory. It allows the dealer to carry an adequate inventory of used aircraft while conserving capital. Since only interest is being paid on the wholesale value of inventory, the monthly cost is much less than the installment loan method where both principal and interest must be paid. The major disadvantage of floor planning is the tendency to carry too many or too expensive aircraft in inventory because of the minimum cost associated with this method.

Retailing Aircraft

Since the objective of pricing is both sales and profit, the dealer must be very careful to select the right price. In pricing, a number of issues must be considered. Some of the more important ones are the following:

1. **Price competition from competitors.**
2. **Effects on exchange.** Price is simply value expressed in terms of dollars. Potential buyers will equate the price of the aircraft with the perceived quality.
3. **Influence on profits.** The selling price must generate sufficient revenue to cover expenses and to provide an acceptable profit.

The pricing technique traditionally used in aircraft sales is markup pricing. Markup is the dollar amount added to the cost of the aircraft to determine the selling price. The size of the markup is the result of two factors:

1. Expenses to prepare the aircraft for resale, marketing, financing, general overhead allocation, and a target profit.
2. Inventory turnover rate. Usually, the greater the turnover rate, the smaller the markup required to accomplish the FBO's objective.

Markup is expressed as a percentage of selling price, and the formula used to determine the retail selling price of the aircraft is:

$$\text{Selling Price} = \frac{\text{Cost}}{100\% - \text{Markup}\%}$$

The following example illustrates how Ace Aviation, Inc., determined the retail price for used aircraft which cost $90,000 and the profit on the completed transaction which took three months to close.

Price Determination – Used Aircraft

Retail price ($90,000/100% – 38%)		$145,161
Purchase price		90,000
Gross margin or gross profit (38%)*		55,161
Expenses		
Floor plan (1%) ($90,000 × .01 × 3 months)	$2,700	
Insurance		
Hull coverage – $1.00 per $100 of aircraft value. ($900 × $1.00/4)	225	
Liability – $1,000,000 single limit. $800 per year. ($800/4)	200	
Minor repairs and detailing the aircraft	1,450	
Selling costs		
Advertising – newspaper, handbills, etc.	1,350	
Sales commission – 10% of gross profit (.10 × $55,161)	5,516	
General overhead	2,500	
Total expenses		13,941
Net profit before taxes		$41,220

*The 38 percent markup was determined from past sales experience to be adequate for target profit objectives.

Leasing

Leasing is another way of acquiring the use of a business aircraft. Business aircraft can be leased from professional leasing companies; some banks; aircraft manufacturers, either directly or through their finance subsidiaries; and even through some larger aircraft dealers, distributors and fixed base operators.

Leasing is typically done for a first aircraft or if the company has been downsizing, because then it will only show up on the books as an operating expense. Leasing is not as common today in corporate aviation as it was a decade ago. People often leased at that time because they were afraid that the aircraft would become obsolete, but in fact, several used aircraft types have since become more valuable than they were new. With interest rates having been relatively low, it has been easier to offset the expense through finance rather than a lease.

Other financiers take the view that leases are still in vogue in the right circumstances, such as for customers who want lower debt loads and a higher return on the asset base of the company. Apart from keeping the aircraft off the balance sheet, other features include a lower annual cash outflow and a slower amortization of the cost, which is more evenly spread and never taken down to zero. In these days of long production backlogs for new business jets, for example, leases also allow companies to take advantage of an interim aircraft while waiting for their new model to be delivered.

Essentially, the lease versus loan equation comes down to an individual customer's propensity for risk: his experience as an aircraft operator and level of confidence about reselling the asset. With a lease, a customer is taking no risk on how the aircraft will hold its value since the asset is entirely owned by the lessor. The client basically forfeits the tax benefits associated with aircraft ownership in favor of a reduced rental rate, with the lessor taking the fiscal breaks.

Similar to automobile leases, aircraft leases will routinely specify detailed maintenance requirements for the aircraft and specifications for the condition in which it must be returned at the end of the lease term. The assumption is generally made that all parts will be in their mid-time-between-overhaul condition, and it will normally be a requirement that the next major checks have been completed. Insurance also has to be maintained, with specified coverage. Some manufacturers of large corporate aircraft are willing to tie guaranteed maintenance costs per flight hour programs to a lease.

A lease may be either short-term, a few months or a few years, or long-term, as many as 15 or 20 years. The maximum length of the lease is determined mostly by the type of aircraft. Average lease terms are 8 to 10 years, but it is common for these to be terminated early as the customer's needs change. It is not uncommon in the United States for operators to break their original lease before the 5-year mark. This trend has underscored the importance of ensuring that sufficiently flexible cancellation terms are written into a lease.

There are two basic methods of leasing an aircraft: wet or dry. A wet lease is a contract whereby the owner of the aircraft (the lessor) makes an aircraft available for the user (the lessee), and also provides everything needed to operate the airplane: fuel and oil, maintenance, insurance, and storage. A flight crew may also be provided. The lessee's rental payment includes a fee that usually covers the cost of ownership, fixed and variable operating costs, and reserves, plus a profit to the lessor. In many ways the wet lease is similar to a charter except that the wet lease is usually made for a longer period of time. Depending on whether the lessor can provide these services more efficiently than the lessee, the rental payment for a wet lease may or may not be less expensive for a company. A dry lease or net lease is the more common type of lease arrangement. Here the lessor supplies only the airplane for a fee and the lessee is obligated for all fixed and variable operating expenses.

Advantages and Disadvantages of Leasing

Some of the advantages of leasing are summarized below:

1. **Conservation of capital.** One of the major advantages of leasing is that it conserves working capital. Generally, firms engaged in leasing do not require a substantial down payment at the beginning of the lease. Depending on the credit worthiness of the lessee, only one or two months' advance payment may be required, whereas the down payment required on the purchase of an aircraft using loan financing can be 15 percent of the purchase price or more. This saving can be substantial, assuming the lessee earns more on its working capital than the effective interest rate of the lease.
2. **Tax savings.** There are two ways a company can benefit from the tax savings of leasing. First, the full amount of each monthly lease payment of a properly structured lease is a deductible business expense for federal income tax purposes. Under the purchase scenario, a company is entitled to depreciation deductions, but only the interest portion of its loan payment is deductible. Second, if a company cannot take full advantage of its depreciation deductions, a leasing company can generally take full advantage of the tax benefits of depreciation and pass the benefit of these deduction to the lessee in the form of a lower monthly lease payment.
3. **Preservation of credit lines.** A lease is generally not considered debt and, in most instances, does not restrict a company's borrowing capacity or reduce the amount of funds available under existing credit lines.
4. **Flexibility.** No assets are required to refinance or to liquidate before upgrading equipment. Leasing makes it easier to upgrade and time acquisitions with changing market conditions and company growth.
5. **Extends length of financing.** This is an important subcategory of the preceding benefit. In contrast to typical loans, leases may be obtained for nearly the entire length of the economic life of the aircraft.
6. **Reduces the risk of technological and physical obsolescence.** The risk associated with the expected value of an aircraft at the end of the lease term is placed on the lessor. If the company purchased the aircraft, and the expected value of the aircraft declines, the overall cost of ownership to the company would increase.

There are several disadvantages in leasing. During the lease term, the lessee usually cannot own the airplane or have an equity interest in it. Should the airplane have a residual value higher than the amount used to determine the lease rental payments, the lessor would receive this gain as owner, not the lessee. An improperly structured lease could be determined to be a purchase agreement or fail to meet the Internal Revenue Service (IRS) guidelines for a lease and the lessee would lose the tax and accounting benefits of leasing. Depending on the specific terms and conditions, a lease may cost the lessee more than a purchase. For instance, if the lessor requires additional insurance coverage or maintenance to be performed by the lessee, this can result in higher costs than if the aircraft had been purchased.

Types of Leases

Leasing companies offer many different types of leases with different term lengths and various options. Within the leasing industry, the accounting profession, and under the Internal Revenue Code there are numerous names or titles for leases. As a consequence, sometimes there is a great deal of overlap and confusion, since the same type of lease may be known to the lessee, lessor, tax accountant, and financial analyst by a different name. However, from a lessee perspective, there are two basic types of leases: a capital lease, and an operating lease.

A capital lease resembles the acquisition of a business aircraft with the use of debt financing, and for income tax and financial accounting it is treated exactly like a loan. The aircraft is included as an asset and the lease obligation (payments) is recorded as a liability on the lessee's balance sheet. The lessee is allowed to include only the imputed interest portion of the lease payment and the applicable depreciation amounts for the period as expenses and as a tax deduction. Under this form of lease, the company's monthly rental payment will amortize the entire cost of the aircraft plus a fair return (interest) for the lessor. At the termination of the lease term, the lessee has the option to purchase the aircraft for $1.00 or some other nominal amount.

The lessor may offer various options, such as an early termination based on a formula similar to paying off a loan early. For example, assume that a company has a seven-year capital lease for a $100,000.00 aircraft with the option to terminate the lease and purchase the aircraft at the end of five years. The lease contract calls for monthly payments of $1,634.40 for a total of $37,289.60 plus a $1.00 purchase option. At the conclusion of the 84-month period, the lessee would have paid the entire cost of the aircraft plus an effective rate of interest of 9.5 percent per year over the term and can acquire the aircraft for $1.00. If the lessee wishes to terminate the lease early, the payoff or purchase price to the lessee would be $33,660.46 plus the $1.00 purchase option. This amount is equal to the amount necessary to payoff a 9.5 percent $100,000.00 loan at the end of five years.

In recent years, increased tolerance of so-called synthetic leases on the part of the IRS has offered a way for U.S. corporate operators to have their cake and eat it, too. These leases allow customers to keep the aircraft on their books for tax purposes, while allowing them to keep the asset out of the company's annual report. This sounds-too-good-to-be-true proposition will work only for firms and individuals with the right tax and accounting profiles.

The more traditional operating lease, which has become a standard feature of the commercial airline finance market, is suitable for those who cannot enjoy further tax benefits and who want to get their aircraft completely off the books. An operating lease, which is known as a "true lease" according to IRS regulations, provides the lessee with the use of the aircraft for a fixed period of time in exchange for rental payments. At the conclusion of the lease term, the lessee returns the airplane to the lessor. Alternatively, the lessor may offer a purchase option, but the amount of this purchase option must be for the fair market value of the aircraft. Usually, this type of lease is recognized by the accounting profession in accordance with Generally Accepted Accounting Principles (GAAP) and by the IRS as a lease and not a purchase, and the company receives the accounting and tax benefits of leasing. Neither the aircraft nor the lease obligation is recorded on the company's balance sheet, and the rental payments are fully deductible for federal income tax purposes. The guidelines established by the IRS and GAAP specify the accounting and tax treatment of leases based on the specifics of the lease agreement. These guidelines should be consulted to be sure the lease agreement being proposed will be treated as a lease.

The structuring of operating lease payments is one of the more complicated aspects of leasing. Payments can be structured using either pre-tax, after-tax, return on investment (ROI), or return on equity (ROE) structuring methodologies. Ordinarily, a lessor estimates the residual value of the aircraft at the termination of the lease contract. They then calculate the rental amount required to achieve its required rate of return, taking into consideration the tax benefits (e.g., depreciation deductions) available to it as the owner of the aircraft.

Fractional Ownership

The concept of fractional ownership was started by Executive Jets' NetJets program with four fractional jet owners in 1986. It evolved from a program that began in 1964 when the Pennsylvania Railroad provided the start-up capital for Executive Jet Airways. The new company ordered ten of the then-brand new Learjet 23s, and the mission was to provide a service where people would buy blocks of usage and jets would be dispatched with efficiency to take customers wherever they wanted to go. The company went international in 1965 and changed its name to Executive Jet Aviation. By 1974 Executive Jet, or EJA as it was widely known, had expanded its fleet to include airplanes other than Learjets, up to and including a Boeing 707, until it was bought in 1986 by RTS Capital Services, a New York firm engaged in equipment financing through leveraged leasing. This gave EJA additional capital and airplanes for its charter fleet and provided RTS with operational and technical support for its fleet of leased aircraft.

The name was changed to Executive Jet, Incorporated, which became the parent company of the NetJets' fractional ownership program. The basis of the fractional ownership concept was to combine the flexibility of chartering with the advantages of ownership. This concept is not new, however. The genius of fractional ownership came in the form of a "core fleet" of aircraft. The core fleet is a group of airplanes owned by the fractional ownership provided directly and not resold to users. This fleet is used to supply transportation to shareowners when the inevitable scheduling conflicts occur. The application of the core fleet concept has proven to be the basis of fractional ownership success.

Fractional Ownership Programs

Fractional ownership programs are multi-year programs covering a pool of aircraft, each of which is owned by more than one party and all of which are placed in a dry lease exchange pool to be available to any program participant when the aircraft in which such participant owns an interest is not available. As an integral part of these multi-year programs, a single company provides the management services to support the operation of the aircraft by the owners and administers the aircraft exchange program on behalf of all participants. By purchasing an interest in an aircraft that is part of the program, an owner gains round-the-clock access to a private jet at a fraction of the cost. In addition to access to the aircraft in which it owns an interest, it also has access to all other aircraft in the program, as well as the support of a management company that will handle all arrangements relating to maintenance, crew, hiring, and all administrative details relating to the operation of a private aircraft.

Table 11-1 Typical Cost of Fractional Ownership

Model	Quarter Share Purchase Cost	Fixed Annual Management Fee	Hourly Operating Cost
Eclipse 500 VLJ	$521,244	$47,988	$1,059
Hawker 800XP	$3,090,000	$244,698	$1,807
Citation Ultra	$1,670,000	$182,580	$1,341
Beechjet 400A	$1,607,000	$179,880	$1,355
Gulfstream IV SP	$7,400,000	$468,000	$3,051

Share size determines the amount of the down payment, the monthly management fee, and the annual flight hour allocation. For example, a one-quarter share will require a down payment equal to one-quarter of the manufacturer's suggested retail price. The down payment secures the one-quarter share access to the aircraft, or through the interchange agreement, another aircraft in the program, 24 hours a day, 7 days a week, for up to 200 hours of occupied flight time per year. The monthly management fee is also related to the share size and covers all operational costs of the aircraft. This fee takes care of pilots, maintenance, catering, and all other operational aspects of owning a private jet. Therefore in total, fractional owners pay a proportionate part of the list price for an aircraft, typically one quarter share, and then pay the fractional ownership company a fee for each occupied flight hour and an overall fixed management fee which covers deadhead, maintenance, and administration of the program.

Share sizes are typically available incrementally from one-sixteenth or 50 flight hours per year; one-eighth or 100 flight hours per year; one-quarter or 200 flight hours per year, to one-half, 400 flight hours per year. Share owners may "upgrade" to a larger aircraft, or "downgrade" to a smaller aircraft, trading flight hours based upon a predetermined exchange rate. Share size also determines simultaneous availability of multiple aircraft; the larger the share, the more likely multiple aircraft are available. There is also a fee charged for occupied hours flown. Owners share tax liabilities and benefits as a percentage of the share owned. See Table 11-1 for a quick look at the quarter share cost, fixed annual management fee, and hourly operating costs of four typical models.

Effective February 2005, fractional aircraft operations were required to either fly under FAR Part 91-Subpart K or FAR Part 135. The new Subpart K addresses the issues of safety of flight; regulatory compliance; pilot qualifications; aircraft maintenance and technician training requirements; aircraft weight, size, and runway landing requirements; and the installation of advanced safety equipment on aircraft. Under Subpart K, passengers would see little difference, except the requirement for the lead passenger to show a photo ID to the flight crew and provide verbal acknowledgement for all other passengers. FAR Part 135 Part 135 flights are subject to Transportation Security Administration (TSA) regulations which require each and every passenger to present a valid, government issued photo ID to the flight crew for positive identification.

A lower capital outlay equal to the share bought must be paid up front, and this acquisition cost may or may not be negotiable depending on the provider. Owners can lease or purchase their shares, but they are limited to selecting an aircraft available via the provider. Fractional aircraft of a given program generally have standard interiors and exteriors, and the share owners usually have no say in how the aircraft are outfitted.

Owners can upgrade or downgrade their aircraft at any time (hourly rates for upgrades/ downgrades are charged via a predetermined sliding scale). In addition, owners may liquidate their shares after meeting a minimum time requirement or paying an early withdrawal penalty. In any case, share sellers must pay a "remarketing fee" to the fractional provider, which ranges anywhere from four to ten percent of the aircraft's "selling price." Furthermore, the airplane's residual value may be lower due to higher cycles and airframe hours (fractional aircraft each average more than 1,100 flight hours per year). In 1986, when NetJets began, there were four fractional jet owners; by 1993, there were 89 and the number was growing fast. Annually, NetJets flies over 370,000 flights, covering 220,000,000 miles, visiting 150 countries, and serving 40,000 unique city-pairs.

In July 1998, Berkshire Hathaway, Inc., acquired Executive Jet, adding strong confirmation to the considerable value in fractional ownership. The Berkshire Hathaway acquisition also added financial resources and strength, ensuring Executive Jet's continued growth around the world.

NetJets aircraft range from light jets like the Cessna Citation SII, Citation V-Ultra, and Citation Excel to the midsize Citation VII, Hawker 800XP, and Hawker 1000. The newest additions are the super-midsize Dassault Falcon 2000, the Citation X, which is the world's fastest business jet, and the Boeing Business jet.

Bombardier entered the fractional ownership market in

May 1995 with its Dallas-based Flexjet program. The Flexjet program began with 22 owners and grew to 683 by 2000. At a portion of the full-ownership cost, a company can purchase shares in a Bombardier Learjet 40XR, Learjet 45XR, Learjet 60 XR, and Challenger 300. Flexjet owners can also gain global flight capability with shares in a wide-body Challenger 605.

Raytheon launched its Travel Air fractional ownership company in August 1997 with one customer, and by 2000 it had 683 shareholders. In 2002, Travel Air merged with Flight Options to create a fractional aircraft ownership company with 200 aircraft. Today, the combined company gives owners access to the Hawker 400XP, Hawker 850 XP, Cessna Citation X, and the Embraer Legacy 600. Flight Options has a unique leasing option for those not wishing to purchase a fractional share. With Flight Options' lease program, not only are clients able to choose a jet, but also to select the lease timeframe and aircraft model that suits them best. Unique financing options also contribute to the ease in leasing an aircraft.

Additional fractional ownership companies include Citation Shares, Avantair, HeliSolutions, JetSolutions, PlaneSense, PlaneSmart, and Our Plane. Both PlaneSmart and OurPlane offer single-engine aircraft. The Cirrus SR22-G3 is offered by PlaneSmart and the Pilatus PC-12 is offered by OurPlane.

Today, the four major fractional providers are NetJets, Flight Options, Flexjet, and CitationShares. According to AvData, in 2007 the fleets of these four companies totaled a combined 809 aircraft and the number of shareowners totaled 5,219. The number of aircraft sold into service (representing the cumulative number of fractional shares sold) among the top four during a six month period in 2008 was 524.34 aircraft. Lastly, as shown in Figure 11-1, NetJets currently has 52.4 percent of the market, Flight Options has 19.7 percent, Flexjet has 10.6 percent, CitationShares has 9 percent, Avantair has 3.1 percent, PlaneSense has 2.4 percent, and the remaining 22 local/regional providers have 2.8 percent of the market.

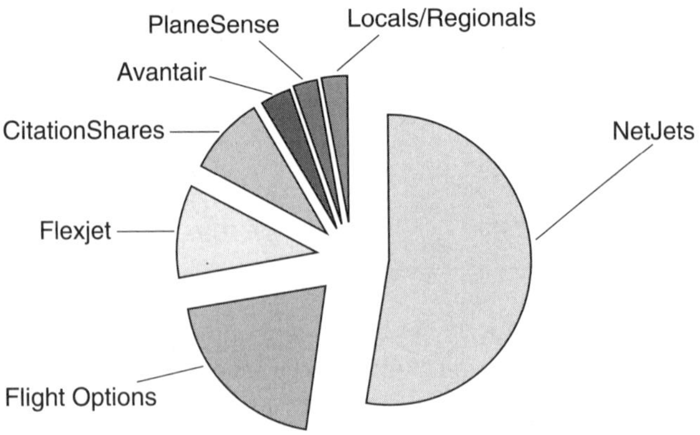

Figure 11-1

Advantages of Fractional Ownership

Fractional ownership offers many unique advantages over full ownership. Aircraft availability is guaranteed at any time with as little as four hours' notice, and all aspects of the aircraft's operation are managed by a provider. All of the leading providers, and most of the new entrants, do not charge for "deadhead" flight segments. A deadhead leg is one in which the aircraft is positioned without passengers for subsequent use. In a fractional ownership, deadhead legs are required to position aircraft for a shareowner's use, position the aircraft for one of the other aircraft shareowner's use, or return the aircraft to its base of operations. If a fractional owner operates to and from the same point of origin, the benefits of a fractional share can be substantially diminished. However, positioning flights are common, and more frequent deadhead legs further justify fractional ownership.

It has been estimated that roughly 80 percent of fractional owners are new to business aviation, and many of the other 20 percent use fractional participation to supplement their own in-house business flight capability. The advantages of fractional ownership regarding the deadhead segments and the availability of multiple aircraft have enabled the traditional flight department to become more efficient through the use of "supplemented lift." The term supplemented lift describes the use of a fractional share to supplement an existing corporate fleet. Supplemental lift is used to reduce the costs of deadheading, to facilitate maintenance schedules, and as a fleet multiplier when the demand for aircraft exceeds the flight department's existing fleet. This provides a flight department additional aircraft types. For example, a Challenger 604 or Global Express may be a perfect fleet complement for an intercontinental flight with 10 passengers aboard, while an economical Eclipse 500 may be just right when two passengers are flying a short distance.

Aircraft availability is essential to the success of a fractional ownership program. Aircraft availability is enabled by the core fleet by limiting the number of shares sold per aircraft, and by drawing upon charter aircraft. The core fleet, as previously mentioned, is a number of aircraft that are held in reserve and in which shares are not sold.

Fractional ownership offers all the usual financial advantages of owning capital equipment, plus the unique advantage in that the terms of the fractional agreement typically guarantee the liquidity of the investment. A fractional share offers an effective means of air transportation, with costs directly proportionate to utilization.

Even with these many advantages, it pays to consider the

following four general categories of aircraft ownership and operating costs and make an informed decision of the benefits of fractional ownership versus purchasing: Acquisition and Capital Costs; Direct Operating Costs, which includes items such as fuel and maintenance; Indirect Operating Costs, which include insurance, hangar rent, pilot salaries and benefits, and recurrent training; and Other Deductible Expenses, such as interest expense and aircraft depreciation for tax purposes, which can be deducted from a company's income tax burden and hence help to offset the cost of ownership of the aircraft. Experts explain that fractional ownership may not make economic sense for the typical corporate flight operation. However, it is a good option for users with extremely low flight time requirements. The break-even point between the costs of full ownership and fractional ownership occurs somewhere between 100 and 200 hours per year. If flying more than this, full aircraft ownership is less expensive. Additionally, charter offers a viable alternative to fractional ownership in these hour ranges and any company considering buying a fractional ownership aircraft for flight times less than 200 hours per year should investigate the charter option as well

Charter

Charter service companies provide aircraft and crew to the general public for hire. It offers the ultimate in air-travel flexibility. Chartering an airplane is similar to hiring a taxi for a single trip. The charter company provides the aircraft, flight crew, fuel, and all other services for each trip. The client pays a fee, usually based on mileage or time, plus extras such as waiting time and crew expenses. Chartering aircraft is particularly attractive for a firm that does not frequently require an airplane or does not often need a supplement to its aircraft.

Chartering can also be cost effective for a group of executives traveling together or for an emergency. When the individual businessman is traveling alone, the airlines, including regional carriers, would be more cost efficient, especially if the trip were between two cities well served by scheduled carriers.

In the past, chartering involved Learjets and Gulfstreams bound for Las Vegas because of the image that evoked. Today, chartering is a working tool for business. Indeed, although charter travel is expensive, it provides greater value due to on-demand scheduling flexibility, closer proximity to business sectors, increased productivity, greater security, and overall time savings

Charter costs can range from as little as a couple hundred dollars per hour for a four-place single-engine piston aircraft to as much as five or six thousand dollars per hour for a corporate jet (see Table 11-2). In addition, there may be extra fees for position, waiting, catering, airport use, crew overnights, and so forth. Charges vary from region to region, with the highest rates being levied in the northeastern United States and southern California.

Table 11-2 Average Hourly Charter Rates

Model	2006	2005	Percent Change
Bell 206	$755	$703	7.4%
King Air B200	$1,156	$1,101	5%
Learjet 35	$1,889	$1,858	1.7%
Hawker 800	$2,872	$2,798	2.6%
Falcon 50	$3,607	$3,522	2.4%
Gulfstream III	$4,317	$4,220	2.3%

Source: Aviation International News. Alcock & Saini (2006). The Charter Market.

One of the most comprehensive resources available for charter customers is The Air Charter Guide, a compendium of more than 3,000 charter operators worldwide, including 1,800 in the United States. It is available in print or on CD-ROM, or accessible from the Web site www.Aircharterguide.com.

Most of the revenue gained from the charter flight goes to the aircraft owner (charter companies seldom own more than a couple of aircraft; most of their fleets are on leaseback or other agreements with the actual owners or lessors) with the charter operator receiving a commission, usually between 10 and 15 percent of the cost of the entire trip. The charter rate can be wet, meaning the costs for fuel, on-board catering, landing and positioning fees, crew expenses, and other charges are included in the cost. A dry rate means that these and other charges are added onto the hourly rate. Most charter firms also charge a two-hour-per-day minimum rate on their jet-powered aircraft and a one-hour minimum on their turboprops.

The weak economy during the early 1990s, along with a rash of company acquisitions forced a number of companies to reduce the size of their fleets or eliminate them entirely. Many of these companies turned to chartering aircraft as an alternative. Some corporations opted for the least costly havens of aircraft management firms, while others simply appended their planes onto a convenient FAR 135 charter certificate to defray the costs of ownership.

Since the mid 1990s and the growth of fractional ownership, many of the better charter operators are busy supporting the fractional companies. Backup lift provided to fractional ownership companies provides the nation's charter services with substantial revenue. Backup lift support is not the only form of flight services that charter operators offer to fractional providers. When faced with the inevitable grounded aircraft, a fractional provider must respond quickly. Response to a grounded aircraft is frequently more readily facilitated by a charter organization. Getting flight crews, technicians, tools, and parts to the disabled aircraft as quickly as possible is essential to the fractional provider. Consequently, fractional ownership has stimulated significant air charter business in recent years.

Many corporate aircraft operators charter aircraft for the following reasons:

1. **To keep flying when its own aircraft are down.** When company airplanes are in for maintenance, repair, outfitting, or refurbishment, chartering allows employees to continue to fly as usual.
2. **Supplement its airlift capability.** A flight department can offer broader services by chartering aircraft of similar capacity to their own, or those with different mission capabilities (helicopters or corporate aircraft, for example).
3. **Avoid over-equipping.** Generally, it is more cost efficient to charter occasionally than it is to underutilize a larger aircraft.
4. **Have a less expensive alternative to airline travel.** If a company needs to transport a large number of people to a single location at one time, it may be less expensive and more convenient to charter a large aircraft that it would be to send the group on the airlines.
5. **Test the business aviation waters.** Chartering may be the safe method for a company to become involved with business aviation. The classic way in which companies get their own aircraft is through an evolutionary process that begins with spot chartering and leads to contract chartering, leasing, participation in an aircraft management program and, finally, establishment of a corporate flight department.
6. **Reenter the field of business aviation.** Many companies gave up their aircraft during the last recession and have now found chartering a good way to enjoy once again the benefits of business aviation without making a capital commitment.
7. **Fly before buying.** For those companies that are contemplating upgrading to a new class of aircraft or adding equipment, chartering is a good way to conduct an in--depth operational evaluation of additional capability.

As commercial operators, charter firms must conform to more stringent operating and maintenance requirements called for in Federal Aviation Regulations. In addition, each charter operator, regardless of the types of airplanes used, must have an air taxi certificate on file with the FAA. This certificate is issued by the FAA after proper application and local inspection. It also evidences minimum insurance coverages and limits.

A review of any local listing in the yellow pages of the telephone directory will reveal no lack of charter operators. Local FBOs chartering single engine aircraft to large operations chartering jumbo jets can be found.

The following checklist includes the major factors to be considered in evaluating a charter operator's performance. Many companies also use the services of a consultant to perform an impartial safety audit of charter operators or contract flight departments that have used specific operators in the past.

1. **Operations:**
   a. Pilot qualifications and records: total hours, time in type, and ratings.
   b. Pilot training: source, flight training, ground school, and continuing proficiency training.
   c. Pilot turnover: average length of employment.
   d. Flight crew knowledge of the operations manual.
   e. Schedule, average weekly flight time, and working conditions.
2. **Maintenance:**
   a. Number of personnel, regular and temporary.
   b. Staff qualifications: records and experience, school training, and average number of years' experience.
   c. Staff turnover: average length of employment.
   d. Supervision and sign-off authority.
   e. List of factory approvals for service work, including rebuilding.
   f. Equipment and shop facilities: airframe, powerplant, and avionics.
   g. Record keeping: computer, staff, and facilities.
   h. Company maintenance manual evaluation.
   i. Program for timed removal of key aircraft components.
   j. Airworthiness Directives compliance.
   k. Ground safety, including fueling, servicing, and fire and crash facilities, if any.
   1. FAA repair station approval?
   m. Engine overhaul in house? If not, where?
   n. Premature failures of engines and major components.
   o. Spare parts stock.
3. **Fleet Equipment:**
   a. Type and number of aircraft, including year of manufacture.
   b. General condition of aircraft.
   c. Survival equipment, including over-water flights.
   d. Weight and balance records, including staff responsibility.
   e. Instruments: avionics for IFR flights, and international flights over water.
   f. Cabin equipment: catering service, phones, seating, lighting, and air conditioning.

4. **Fitness:**
   a. Financial condition and credit rating.
   b. Insurance coverage, including copy of certificate.
   c. Owner and length of time in business.
5. **Safety:**
   a. Total hours flown during the past five years.
   b. Number and type of incidents.
   c. Accidents: minor, major, and fatal.
   d. Ratio of hours flown to accidents.
6. **Morale:**
   a. Responsiveness of staff.
   b. Flight crew professionalism, general appearance, and courtesy.
   c. Evaluation of management.

Service can vary widely among charter companies, ranging anywhere from poor to excellent. Aircraft availability depends on market demand, and there is no guarantee of aircraft availability from any one charter operator. If a particular charter aircraft is not available, another vendor or the airlines must be used to meet travel demands.

Crew and mechanics are employed by the charter provider, which also controls personnel training. Crew changes are likely as they rotate from a pool. The charter firm is fully liable for the flight.

This option typically provides the lowest cost at lower usage levels, and reduced hourly charges may be negotiated at higher utilization rates (commonly referred to as block charter). Charter customers must pay for all ancillary charges, including deadheading and positioning costs, catering bills, landing fees, taxes (FET applies), and so on. No depreciation tax benefits are available to charter customers, but they may write off charter costs as a business expense.

Contract Flight Service

Contract Flight Service is the same as chartering an aircraft except that the customer buys a block of airplane time, mileage, or trips, usually over a certain period. Contract flight service is particularly suited to a company that has frequent and predictable need for business aircraft which is not enough to justify owning or leasing an airplane. This method also is used by companies who operate aircraft but need to supplement their own service.

Contract flight service can be very effective for a company which requires frequent travel that can be planned well in advance, and for companies scheduling many simultaneous trips in different directions.

Almost all charter operators will negotiate flight service contracts over a specified time period based on aircraft miles, hours, or trips. In terms of cost, this arrangement can be more attractive than individual charter flights. However, similar to charter flights, beyond 200 hours of annual use the company will probably find it less costly to consider leasing or owning.

Comparison of Methods

As a general guideline, charter service is best when annual utilization is less than 100 hours. Fractional ownership is the preferred approach when utilization is between 100 and 400 hours, and total ownership is best when annual utilization is above 400 hours.

Any one of these estimates is not a precise indictor of which type of service is best in all cases. The choice is not based solely upon annual utilization rates. The best method is affected by a number of factors. Included are:

1. Route structure
2. Daily round trips
3. Extended-stay, one-way trips
4. Fixed or variable passenger capacity
5. Demand for multiple aircraft
6. New or used aircraft
7. Positioning or deadhead legs
8. Owner status (no flight department or an existing flight department)
9. Service quality
10. Cost
11. Liability
12. Capital commitment
13. Tax consequences

Another underlying factor is level of control. A business must consider who they want to control such factors as aircraft availability, type, and quality, as well as liability and crew qualifications and training.

The dilemma is that in business aviation one size does not fit all. What may work for one company is not necessarily the right move for another, and a choice made today may not meet next year's travel needs. The stakes are quite high. Business aviation is a complex field where the wrong choice can cost a lot of money.

To justify establishing a new flight department to support a corporate aircraft, the annual utilization rate should be forecast between 350 and 400 hours at a minimum. An existing flight department, one with operational and support resources already established, should have a forecast annual utilization rate around 250 hours. In either case, however, purchase of a used aircraft instead of a new aircraft can reduce the annual utilization rate estimate by as much as 100 hours.

The used aircraft purchase evaluation must also take into consideration the costs associated with maintaining aging airframes, powerplants, associated systems, and noise abatement.

One reason for the interest in fractional ownership in recent years is the increased residual value of business aircraft, particularly business jets.

Leasing aircraft reached its peak during the mid 1990s. It kept the aircraft off the company's balance sheet. This changed during the late 1990s when a company could buy an aircraft, operate it for two or three years, and sell it at well above what it cost. Consequently, leasing has lost its popularity.

Whether buying, leasing, fractional ownership, or charter, the same rule still applies. The company must know what its travel requirements are before utilizing business aviation. Its needs must be determined, not its wants.

Tables 11-3, 11-4, and 11-5 provide a summary of the methods discussed in this chapter.

Conclusion

Although many companies have acquired the use of business aircraft through various methods, few suddenly have purchased or leased their own airplanes without having had some previous experience that helped identify their needs. The normal introduction into business aviation is through a process that allows adjustment to one level before ascending further. Sales representatives use their own aircraft or rent them for business purposes or may begin by chartering. If the demand is great enough, contracting for a block of time is the next logical step. If the amount of chartering indicates that a firm would be better off with an airplane of its own, wet leasing might be considered. While wet leasing, the company has the opportunity to evaluate whether or not it should progress up the ladder to dry leasing. Here a company might want to enter first into a short-term dry lease as trial. After this, the company should have enough experience in business aviation and sufficient knowledge of its needs to determine whether or not to enter a fractional ownership program or to purchase an airplane outright, enter into a long-term dry lease or to step back to one of the previous rungs on the ladder more appropriate to its requirements.

KEY TERMS

Timesharing agreement
Interchange agreement
Management company
Joint ownership
Co-ownership management company
FAA Form 337
Airworthiness directives
Airworthiness certificates
Pre-purchase inspection
Certificate of aircraft registration
Simple interest
Add-on interest
Floor planning
Markup
Wet lease
Dry lease
Capital lease
Synthetic leases
Operating lease
Core fleet
Fractional ownership
FAR Part 91, Subpart K
Remarketing fee
Deadhead leg
Positioning flights
Supplemental lift
Charter services
The Air Charter Guide
Contract flight service

REVIEW QUESTIONS

1. Why is a company-owned aircraft the most flexible method of business aviation? What are timesharing and interchange agreements? List some of the advantages of company-owned aircraft operated by a management company. What are some of the pros and cons of joint ownership?
2. Finance charges on aircraft loans are primarily based on four factors. What are they? What is the reason for the strong competition in the field of aircraft finance in recent years? Describe four methods owners may use in selling their aircraft. What are some of the areas to be considered in evaluating the purchase of a used aircraft? Define: FAA Form 337; airworthiness directives, and airworthiness certificates.
3. What are the major points covered in an aircraft sales contract? Distinguish between simple and add-on interest. What is floor planning? Give an example of the retail price of an aircraft including all of the items in the markup formula.
4. Why is leasing an aircraft not as popular as it was in the early 1990s? Distinguish between a dry and a wet lease. List four distinct advantages in leasing an aircraft. What is the primary disadvantage of leasing? What is a capital lease? How does this differ from an operating lease? What are synthetic leases?
5. How was the concept of fractional ownership started? What are fractional ownership programs? Who are the major fractional providers? What is the function of FAR Part 91, Subpart K? Discuss some of the reasons for the

Table 11-3 Company-Owned or Leased Aircraft—New or Used. Adapted from NBAA material

	In-House Flight Department	Management Company
Definition	• An entity is the only registered owner of an aircraft and uses an in-house department.	• An entity is the only registered owner of an aircraft and a management company operates the aircraft.
Service Quality	• Highest level of control/service possible • Immediate availability likely • If aircraft not available, must use charter, airlines, timeshare, or interchange • Best possible confidentiality/security	• Potentially excellent; customizable • Immediate availability likely • If aircraft not available, must use charter, airlines, timeshare, or interchange • Pax can leave personal items on aircraft
Aircraft Administration	• Owner/lessee maintains total control over and manages aircraft operations • Personnel on owner's payroll; must deal with in-house personnel issues	• Owner/lessee maintains control over, but delegates management of aircraft operations to management company • Personnel not on owner's payroll
Crew Quality	• Consistent; owner-controlled • Owner controls training of crew and mechanics	• Consistent, owner input, crews possibly assignable • Owner delegates control of pilot and mechanic training
Operating Costs	• Variable; utilization-dependent, lowest cost of operation at reasonable utilization levels • Subject to deadhead/positioning expense	• Variable; utilization-dependent • Annual costs may be higher than an in-house flight department (because of management fee) • Subject to deadhead/positioning expense
Cost Offset	• There may be a charter option to help offset costs	• There may be a charter option to help offset costs • Possible availability of fleet discounts for fuel, Insurance, and crew training
Liability Tax Consequences	• Completely liable • No commercial federal excise tax applicable • Noncommercial fuel tax applies • Maximum depreciation benefit	• Shares liability with management company • No commercial federal excise tax (owners pay noncommercial fuel tax instead) as long as owner maintains possession, command, and control of the aircraft • Maximum depreciation benefit
Capital Commitment	• Higher capital investment of negotiated acquisition cost	• Higher capital investment of negotiated acquisition cost
Aircraft Acquisition and Disposition	• Can lease or purchase any aircraft at any price • Can select aircraft make/model, interior and exterior • Can choose when to upgrade, downgrade, or sell	• Can lease or purchase any aircraft at any price • Can select aircraft make/model, interior and exterior • Can choose when to upgrade, downgrade, or sell

Table 11-4 Joint Ownership/Co-Ownership. Adapted from NBAA material

	In-House Flight Department	Management Company
Definition	• Two or more entities are registered owners of an aircraft, and one of the owners operates the aircraft for both owners	• Two or more entities are registered owners of an aircraft and use a management company to manage the aircraft for both
Service Quality	• Potentially excellent; customizable • Availability requires coordination and planning • If aircraft is not available, must use charter, airlines, timeshare, or interchange	• Potentially excellent; customizable • Availability requires coordination and planning • If aircraft not available, must use charter or airlines
Aircraft Administration	• Owners/lessees maintains total control over and manage aircraft operations • Personnel on owner's payroll, owner must deal with in-house personnel issues	• Owners/lessees maintain control over, but delegate management of aircraft operations to management company • Personnel not on owner's payroll
Crew Quality	• Consistent; owner-controlled • Owner controls training of crew and maintenance personnel	• Consistent, owner input, crew possibly assignable • Owners delegate control of pilot and mechanic training
Operating Costs	• Variable; utilization-dependent • Subject to deadhead/positioning expense	• Variable; utilization-dependent • Annual costs may be higher than joint ownership (because of management fee) • Subject to deadhead/positioning expense
Cost Offset	• There may be a charter option to help offset costs	• There may be a charter option to help offset costs • Possible availability of fleet discounts for fuel, Insurance, and crew training
Liability Tax Consequences	• Completely liable • Owners share tax liabilities and benefits • No commercial federal excise tax applicable • Noncommercial fuel tax applies • Owners share depreciation benefit	• Shares liability with management company • Owners share liabilities and benefits • No commercial federal excise tax (owners pay noncommercial fuel tax instead) as long as owners maintain possession, command, and control of the aircraft • Owners share depreciation benefit to the share owned
Capital Commitment	• Owners share higher capital investment of negotiated acquisition cost	• Owners share higher capital investment of negotiated acquisition cost
Aircraft Acquisition and Disposition	• Can lease or purchase any aircraft at any price • Can jointly select aircraft make/model, interior and exterior • Can jointly choose when to upgrade, downgrade, or sell	• Can lease or ourchase any aircraft at any price • Can jointly select aircraft make/model, interior and exterior • Can jointly choose when to upgrade, downgrade, or sell

Table 11-5 Fractional Ownership and Charter. Adapted from NBAA material

	Fractional Ownership	Charter
Definition	• Several entities are registered owners of an aircraft and hire a management company to manage the aircraft and allow the management company to exchange this aircraft among their fleet of aircraft.	A company that provides aircraft and crew to the general public for compensation or hire (profit)
Service Quality	• Potentially excellent; more generic • Aircraft availability guaranteed at all times, sourced via owned, fleet or charter aircraft • Advance notice required (4–8 hours) • More than one aircraft may be available at the same time, depending on contract trems and/or subject to availability • Charter aircraft may be substituted for program aircraft • Unable to leave equipment and/or personal belongings on board aircraft	• Potentially excellent; more generic • Possible inconsistent service from vendor to vendor • Availability depends on market demand; no guarantee of aircraft availability from any one vendor • If aircraft not available, must use other charter vendor or airlines
Aircraft Administration	• Owners maintain control over but delegate management of aircraft operations to fractional provider (management company) • Personnel not on owner's payroll	• None, not applicable • Personnel not on owner's payroll
Crew Quality	• Crew changes likely, rotating from pool • May not be able to request specific crew or use own crew • Owners deligate control of pilot and mechanic training	• Crew changes likely, rotating from pool • No control of pilot or mechanic training
Operating Costs	• Fixed on a per-hour basis, based upon flight time, plus set ground time per operation used to calculate billed usage charges • All fees (including deadhead and positioning changes), except international handling and custorms changes included in overall fee structure • Higher costs when compared to other forms of ownership at higher utilization levels, or charter at lower utilization levels	• Lowest overall cost at minimun usage levels • Consistent charges at low utilization rates, subject to negotiated reductions at higher usage levels • Subject to ancillary changes such as catering, landing • Subject to deadhead/positioning expense
Cost Offset	• Not applicable	• Not applicable
Liability Tax Consequences	• Shared liability with fractional provider • Owners share tax liabilities and benefits • Federal excise tax imposed on direct operating costs • Owners share depreciation benefits to the share owned	• Not necessarily immune from liabaility • Federal excise tax imposed on charter rate • No depreciation benefit available as no aircraft are owned
Capital Commitment	• Lower capital outlay equal to a percentage of an aircraft share which may or may not be negotiated	• None
Aircraft Acquisition and Disposition	• Can lease or purchase • Limited to aircraft available via provider • No aircraft customization • Can choose to upgrade at any time; can choose to downgrade or sell after meeting minimum time requirement or pay penalty • A remarketing fee is charged for aircraft disposition • There may be penalties for early withdrawal from the program • Lower residual value because of higher hours/cycles; known at purchase	• None; no ownership

tremendous growth in fractional owners during the late 1990s. What is meant by the term "supplemental lift"?

6. When might chartering an aircraft be considered the most effective method of acquiring the use of a business aircraft? List some of the reasons why corporate aircraft operators may charter aircraft. What are the major factors to be considered in evaluating a charter operator's performance? How does a straight charter differ from contract flight service?
7. What are the general guidelines, in terms of annual hourly utilization, when considering charter, fractional ownership, company ownership, or leasing? What are some other factors that may be considered? Compare and contrast fractional ownership with a company-owned aircraft in terms of service quality, aircraft administration, crew quality, operating costs, liability, tax consequences, capital commitment, and aircraft acquisition and disposition.

REFERENCES

Aviation International News. The Charter Market.
AvData Fractional Data.

SCENARIOS

1. You were recently able to convince a company, Media Consultants International, of their need for a corporate aircraft. They have decided on an Eclipse 500 VLJ. They would like to own the aircraft, but they do not want the hassle associated with an in-house corporate flight department. So, you suggest a company owned, management company operated option. They have asked you to fully explain this option, including the pros and cons. What do you say?
2. You work in the Aircraft Sales division of Corporate Jet Transport. A client has decided to purchase an aircraft, but does not have the $850,000 necessary to complete the sale. Rather than lose the sale, you need to assist this client with financing. What are this client's options?
3. In preparing a used, but very clean, Cessna 172 for sale, you need to determine the selling price. The aircraft was purchased by your FBO for $92,000, but has since had a new paint job, new avionics installed, etc. These, and other, expenses, plus profit, total 35 percent markup. Based on the formula in this chapter, what would the selling price need to be to allow recovery of the cost plus markup?
4. A prospective client was considering purchasing an aircraft from you. However, this person is now leaning toward fractional ownership. As a matter of fact, many of your prospective clients are leaning toward fractional ownership. The FBO for which you work currently only sells used aircraft. Should your FBO consider getting involved in the fractional ownership market? If so, how would your FBO do that?
5. As a new sales associate with Executive Aircraft, you have been tasked with fully researching methods that may be used by a company to acquire a business aircraft. This presentation will be part of every sales presentation, allowing clients to see all available options for acquiring a business aircraft. What do you include in this presentation? Can you explain?

PART FOUR: MANAGING AN FBO

Chapter 12
Management Functions and Organization

OUTLINE

OBJECTIVES

At the end of this chapter, you should be able to:

- Summarize the characteristics of well-managed FBOs.
- Discuss the importance of planning.
- Describe the step-by-step approach to planning.
- Distinguish between line and staff personnel.
- Define unity of command and span of control.
- Explain the purpose of the Operations Manual.
- Discuss the role of leadership in directing a business plan.
- Define personality and motives as they relate to understanding employees.
- Compare and contrast Maslow's theory of human wants and needs with Herzberg's motivators and hygiene factors.
- Describe the decision-making process.
- Discuss the purpose of the controlling process.

MANAGING A FIXED BASED OPERATION

In his book *Thriving on Chaos,* Tom Peters argues that our national economy is in a volatile state. Rapid change is the order of the day. Those businesses that intend to survive must learn to love change. In turn, they must "thrive on chaos." Firms can only expect to successfully compete in the economy of the new century if they are willing to quickly adapt to changing customer preferences, pursue fast-paced innovation, and achieve flexibility by empowering people to reach their full potential. What better an environment to thrive on chaos than the FBO industry? The important point here is not to just cope with chaos but to thrive on it. Chaos implies change and it is only through change—rapid change—that an FBO can stay ahead of competitive forces.

Owners and top managers will have tremendous opportunities during this dynamic new millennium to influence (and even control) the future profit performance of their businesses. However, in order to do so, they need to objectively assess where the business is now and where the management team needs to be in terms of management expertise.

Characteristics of Well-Managed FBOs

Well-managed and successful FBOs have been good in developing strong organizational cultures that reflect the values and practices of their owners and managers. In fact, one of the primary roles of management is to shape and manage the values of the company. The outstanding FBOs have certain core values that are considered almost sacred throughout the organization. There is an esprit-de-corps among all employees. Firms with distinctive cultures tend to have higher morale and productivity. In short, a strong culture is the binding agent that holds everything together.

Change is a given in the FBO business. When change occurs, it is generally fast with little notice or lead time. Hence, the well-managed FBO must be creative in structuring the organization to minimize reaction time.

Well-managed FBOs get quick action because they maintain organizational fluidity. They have developed successful techniques for informal communication. They use special methods and unorthodox approaches to attack difficult problems or affect sudden change. In short, they do not organize to promote bureaucracy and inflexibility. They have been successful in promoting the spirit of entrepreneurship and capitalism throughout the organization. In fact, it is part of their culture. All employees should understand the concept of risk and return and the link between productivity and profitability. FBOs that encourage the entrepreneurial concept the furthest in today's market are likely to be the most profitable in the future.

Certainly getting the job done on schedule and at a reasonable price is an FBO's continuing challenge. However, companies cannot become so production-oriented that employees are treated like things. This approach can work in the short term, provided the company has enough supervisors to watch employees every minute of the day. Obviously this approach is not conducive to long-term productivity. Well-managed FBOs successfully balance the concern for people and production. They understand and practice the philosophy that people are their most important assets. There is genuine respect for the individual and an abiding faith that the source of productivity gain is through people.

Well-managed FBOs use positive reinforcement. It is specific and immediate. There are generally programs designed to enhance the employee's self-image. People are encouraged to achieve their full potential. Well-managed FBOs do not expect people to be motivated in a vacuum. They promote an environment of achievement. It is part of their culture. They expect extraordinary results from ordinary people and get it through positive reinforcement.

Quality conscientiousness is another important trait of well-managed FBOs. With some it is almost an obsession. They understand the only cost of quality is the expense of doing things wrong. Therefore, they encourage the attitude and reward the behavior of making quality certain. The result is more competitive pricing, a satisfied customer, and higher profits.

Well-managed FBOs strive to maintain an awareness of the industry's technological advancements, trends, and concepts. They are not timid about applying new technology, such as the integration of simulators into flight training and computerized management information systems in record keeping, financial planning, and management. They attend trade shows and seminars to discover new approaches and methodology. They understand that such expenditures are an investment for the future. The end result is greater efficiency which leads to a competitive advantage and/or higher long-term profits.

Well-managed FBOs are marketing-oriented. They have a complete understanding of their markets and know their niche in those markets. They know their strengths and weaknesses and those of the competition. They have been successful in differentiating themselves from their competitors. Well-managed FBOs stress their technological and/or service orientation, focusing on quick turnaround time, quality, and reliability. In short, they compete as much as possible on anything other than price.

The well-managed FBOs have paid their dues in the community, to trade associations, and to customers. They listen and learn and use that valuable knowledge to prepare strategic and tactical plans. The bottom line is they are proactive rather than reactive in their marketing efforts.

An important corollary to the marketing orientation is honesty in dealing with people. Customers, suppliers, and even employees have respect for an FBO's integrity. One's word is one's contract, and relationships are built on trust rather than suspicion. This philosophy builds long-term relationships that are beneficial, particularly during tough times.

Finally, well-managed FBOs can literally manage by report. Their management information system provides timely and accurate reporting by profit and cost centers. Administration is viewed as a support function, not an end unto itself. Administrative people understand their service role and cooperate with operations people in solving problems. Reports are formatted in a manner that operations people can easily understand and use to better manage the business.

In short, whether it is job or equipment costing, purchasing and inventory control, or financial management, the system works and people know how to use the information provided. Moreover, direct costs and overhead expenses are budgeted, compared to actuals, and corrective strategies are taken when appropriate. Well-managed FBOs know how to evaluate their cost and capital structures, yielding information that results in better pricing strategies. This provides valuable information on how to be competitive yet profitable.

Although these concepts are simple, they are not necessarily easy to achieve; however, taken as a whole, they do provide a framework for a well-managed FBO. Excellence is, in fact, achievable, but only in degrees. Few FBOs have completely mastered all of the attributes, which should not be surprising. These principles imply degrees of achievement and the need for constant striving to reach for higher levels of success.

Planning

Effective management begins with planning, which in turn implies setting goals. Planning is the most important function of all in establishing and maintaining a business. In essence, planning is problem solving and decision making: speculating on the future (both near and far), setting objectives (short and long term), considering alternatives, and making choices.

Planning for the future necessitates flexibility to cope with the unexpected, setting timetables, establishing priorities, and deciding on the methods to be used and the people who will be involved. A manager must analyze the existing situation, formulate targets, and apply both logic and creativity to all the details in between.

Owners and managers of small FBOs typically are so busy running their operations that they often put off planning. Yet, its importance cannot be overemphasized. As the owner or manager of a small FBO, planning takes on added significance because, unlike larger organizations with ample financial resources, poor or no planning can put a smaller firm out of business. Small FBOs have an aversion to business planning. Possibly the reason for this tendency lies in the fact that most owners and managers would prefer to be doing something physical like flying or overhauling an engine.

Some people are a bit suspicious about planning because they realize it has to do with the future, not the present, and the future is really unpredictable. Furthermore, many people have never been taught how to plan and do not have any idea how to proceed.

Maybe they resist the need for imposing self-discipline or do not have enough confidence in themselves. Perhaps they are reluctant to think on a conceptual level. Perhaps they have never mastered the art of establishing priorities.

Whatever the reasons, planning is often deferred to the future. Yet, planning gives purpose and direction to daily business activities. Without it, such activities are aimless and uncoordinated.

Types of Plans

Long-term plans are set up by top management to give overall direction to company efforts. Strategic in nature, long-term plans are needed to cope with an ever-changing environment. Operational plans design day-to-day work details. Single-use plans are formulated for specific situations. Standing plans, on the other hand, are set up for repeated use over a longer period of time.

Company policies are examples of standing plans. They serve as guidelines for management and employees, imparting solidarity and dependability to company operations. These policies exist in all areas of a well-managed business: in service, pricing, distribution, personnel, finance, and the like. To illustrate, consider these few examples of service policies:

- We shall inventory only those aircraft parts with a high turnover rate.
- We intend to add to the product line of our counter sale of up to three new items each year.
- We shall always have one single-engine aircraft available for short-notice charter flights.

Budgets are plans that have been translated into dollars-and-cents projections and that are the culmination of a great deal of careful analysis. In effect, they are both guides to follow and targets to shoot for. Materials budgets, sales budgets, labor budgets, and budgets for capital expenditures all become standards for management action. Good budgeting is needed to direct internal activity and to assign responsibility.

Step-by-Step Approach to Planning

The following outline will help to internalize the process of planning. Practice makes perfect, and it is often helpful to plan for something concrete the first time around, such as an open house in conjunction with the annual air show.

1. Assess the present state of affairs, external (the economy, competition, etc.) as well as internal.
2. Set target date for the activation of the plan.
3. Make a forecast of the future state of affairs (at the target date and, thereafter, for the duration of the proposed plan).
4. List specific objectives that are both reasonable and attainable.
5. Develop methods for reaching the objectives.
6. Work out the details by using the "Five Ws" (Who? What? Where? When? Why?) and How? Determine the resources available and structure of the plan with a time schedule.
7. Commit the details to paper.
8. Set up a control system to monitor the plan's operation and to make adjustments for deviations from planned outcomes.
9. As the plan unfolds, make the necessary changes to compensate for such deviations.

Planning is disciplined thinking, which is based on the present and oriented to the future. Plans begin with an analysis of the way things are and with a forecast of the way things will (or should) be. Of course, predicting future events based on an extrapolation of current and incomplete information can never by entirely accurate.

Organization

As a business grows and sales increase, additional duties and responsibilities follow. Additional personnel are required and the need for specialization and division of work becomes apparent. Each new employee must be placed in an appropriate niche and assigned specific duties. It is up to management to define those niches and then locate the right people to fill them.

Figure 12-1 depicts the organizational structure of a small FBO.

Over time, a company's management is increasingly challenged by the task of coordinating the activities of daily operations. Each business depends on the people who, interlocked and strategically deployed in some structural arrangement, perform all the functions necessary for the total system to accomplish its objectives. This framework or struc-

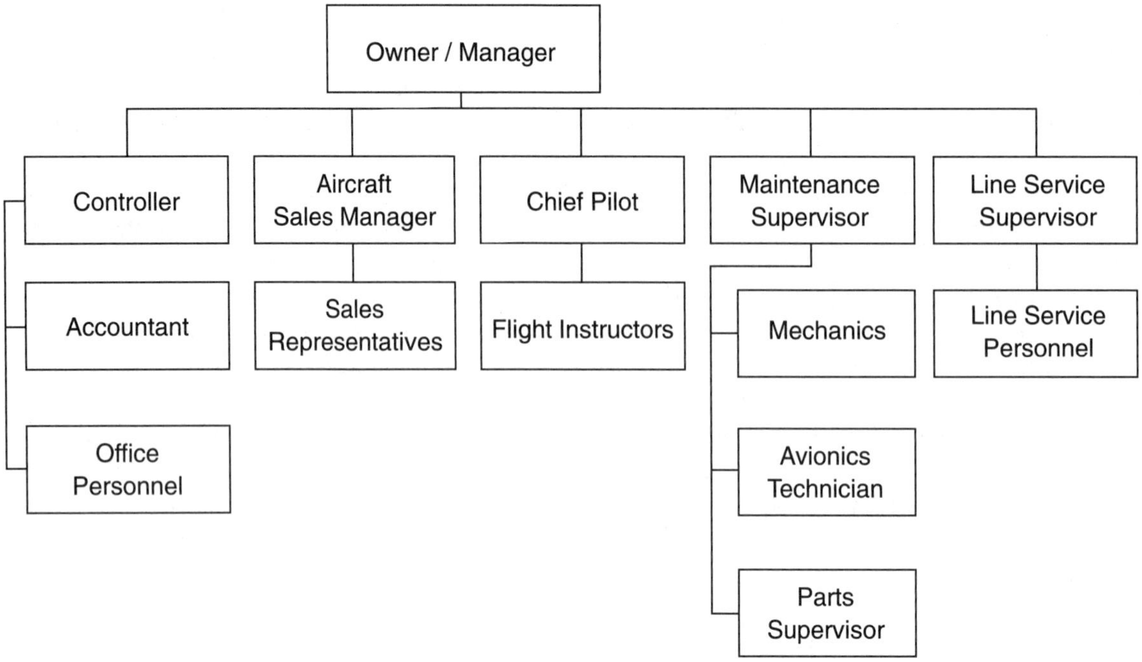

Figure 12-1 Organization Chart for Small FBO

ture, called organization, represents the overall strategic design for operating the business.

Organization Theory

Organization is not and cannot be an exact science; theories of organization cannot specify wholly "right" answers. Nevertheless, the small FBO manager ought to be familiar with the dimensions that are most frequently discussed by organizational theorists. Some examples are conflicts between individual and organizational goals, departmentalization, line and staff positions, flat versus tall organizations, and unity of command.

Employee Goals Can Be at Odds with Company Goals. It should be recognized that people working in an organization are there primarily to satisfy their own needs. Perhaps they want security and income or the feeling that they have a place within a group, or they need to be recognized as somebody important, and so on. Although they will work willingly toward the firm's objectives, this will happen only if their personal aims remain attainable through employment with the company. Their goals and the goals of the company are not identical; at times, differences between individual and group goals will result in conflict. For the sake of internal harmony, a manager must concentrate on reconciling any differences that arise.

The Need for Departmentalization. As anyone in business knows, a wealth of activities must be performed by employees. Handling these myriad tasks is made easier by classifying the many work details into departments. Departments are segments of the business whose work functions are interrelated and so can be grouped together under the supervision of a single specialist. In addition to the line service, flight instruction, and maintenance departments, other departments commonly found at FBOs include aircraft sales, charter and rental, and corporate flight service.

Line and Staff Personnel. Most organizations have been arranged according to the line-and-staff concept. Line people both give and receive orders along the chain of command from the head of the company down to the lowest level worker. People in staff positions, on the other hand, are outside this chain of command. They are present to aid and support the line personnel. Examples of these staffers include administrative assistants, legal advisors, accountants, HR specialists, and other supportive service workers. These people possess a much more limited kind of authority. Within their own specialized areas of responsibility, of course, they direct their own department personnel.

Should the Organization Be Flat or Tall? As a business grows, the organizational structure shows layers of authority: top, middle, and lower (supervisory) management. Communication barriers tend to form between the layers. People at the top of the hierarchy usually have little contact with people at the bottom. In the traditional "tall" structure, people become relatively confined within their own specialized positions, and dissatisfaction begins to emerge from persons in middle and lower positions. Broadly interpreted, their feeling is that they are not really making a significant contribution to the business. This attitude spreads or deepens, and decisions are more and more likely to be made at the top and filtered down to the bottom levels.

Furthermore, management positions multiply. The organization gradually becomes laden with many chiefs and high salaries. A kind of rigidity sets in that mitigates against creative problem solving and results in an overabundance of red tape.

In the "flat" type of organization, on the other hand, there are only one or two levels of management. The supervisory leadership exercised by the executives is of a more personal nature, with more face-to-face contact. People in lower management niches take on more responsibility for their efforts and make more decisions. The fact that these individuals are closer to the action than higher management and are permitted to make decisions on the spot makes for increased initiative and higher morale.

One Manager or More? The unity of command principle is one policy that should seldom be violated. Most workers would agree that no employee, indeed no executive, should have to answer to more than one superior. Having more than one supervisor can cause confusion, as, for example, when an employee working within a partnership arrangement is given two opposing directives by the partners.

How Many Subordinates Can Be Supervised? The principle here is referred to as span of management (or span of control). The average manager finds it relatively easy to oversee one to several workers on the job: to watch over them, train them, direct them, and guide them. As the number of subordinates increases, it becomes more and more difficult for the supervisor to devote enough attention to each person. How many people a supervisor can oversee depends on several factors: the supervisor's capabilities, the abilities and characteristics of the subordinates, and the nature of the work being performed. The greater the span of management (that is, the number of individuals under one superior), the fewer the number of supervisors and departments necessary. A narrow span, however, enables supervisors to work more closely with their people.

The average small FBO owner can often manage up to six or eight subordinates before things become too unwieldy. This often results in several shift supervisors, who oversee six or eight employees on a given shift with a Department Director/Manager who then oversees the shift supervisors.

Decentralization. As a business grows, the mass of work details increases. Yet it is hard for the entrepreneurial personality to delegate, to let go of the responsibilities so far handled alone, and to assign them to people who he or she fears are less capable and less motivated!

Some managers keep a firm grasp on everything. They maintain control where power, authority, and tight supervisory controls are centralized. Others decentralize to the point where a capable group, to a large degree autonomous, manages each major division of the business. This concept of decentralization, organizing a firm around self-governing "profit centers" banded together in a loosely controlled federation, maximizes individual initiative, ensures localized decision making, and facilitates pinpointing responsibility.

Developing an Operations Manual

Operating a company without a formal set of rules and regulations would be similar to taking a cross-country flight without navigational charts. Rarely can objectives be reached without an operations manual. There are at least eight ways an operations manual can benefit a company. An operations manual

1. establishes a comprehensive source of company policies and procedures;
2. facilitates even-handed, consistent administration of personnel policies;
3. promotes continuity in management style throughout the organization;
4. helps identify problems before they arise, minimizing "crisis management";
5. reduces the number of emotional decisions, encouraging a businesslike climate of objectivity;
6. defines authority clearly and distributes responsibility;
7. becomes a training tool for employees; and
8. offers examples of standard forms, reducing the number and variety of forms used.

In any small FBO, generally no one has the time for an extra project such as creating an operations manual. Top management must personally endorse the project and provide leadership to keep it moving, establish deadlines, and designate a "doer" in the company to get the job done.

The manager must gather all existing procedures, systems, and forms. Ideas from all levels of management and staff must be put into the process. The manual must be discussed with all operations personnel to ensure that all actual day-to-day working needs will be covered. Input from former personnel can be helpful too. Concurrently, a checklist of points covered in the company's operations manual should be prepared. These 10 basic sections should be included:

1. **Introduction:** Purpose of the manual; how the company started; business objectives and philosophy; description of products and services; economics of the business.
2. **Organization chart:** Who reports to whom; job descriptions; addresses of company's facilities; importance of each department and division.

3. **General employee information:** Attitude toward customers, suppliers, and other employees; statement on how to handle telephone callers and visitors; housekeeping policies.
4. **Personnel administration:** Hiring practices; employment forms; when and how workers are paid; outside employment; reprimands; hours of operation; coffee breaks and lunch hours; dress code; personal behavior; frequency of salary reviews; advancement opportunities; benefits paid by the company; contributory benefits; explanation of payroll deductions; labor laws; use of time cards; scheduling; overtime; vacation entitlement and holidays.
5. **Products and services:** Customer relations; supplier relations; sales procedures; taking pride in what the company does.
6. **Paperwork:** Administrative procedures; ensuring accountability; billings; sample of each form; purpose of each document; routing flow chart for paperwork; summary of deadlines and due dates.
7. **Safety and security:** Protection of physical premises; personal security; statement about protection of company assets; importance of safety to the employee and the company; handling of confidential information.
8. **Emergencies:** How to handle accidents; what to do in case of fire; emergency telephone numbers; power failures; robberies and thefts.
9. **Maintenance and repair:** Telephones; service people; repairs; who should authorize; trash removal; key control; handling of equipment; property damage or loss.
10. **Legal:** Compliance with local, state, and federal laws; handling of regulatory agencies; inspections; record keeping requirements; maintaining ethical standards.

The instructions should be presented in a logical order and be specific. Exceptions should be stated if those exceptions have occurred frequently in the past. Language and examples should be common to the company's employees. Finally, a qualified outsider (preferably an educator or a professional editor) should do the editing.

A loose-leaf, three-ring notebook format permits great flexibility in using, reviewing, and updating material. "Sections" should correspond to chapters of a book. Within each section, the material should be in outline form. There should be no "Miscellaneous" section because that would become a catchall, revealing less-than-thorough categorization.

Each page should contain the section title, the date the page was issued, and a page number. This simplifies both the task of keeping the manual updated and the distribution of new or revised material. To complete the manual, a thoroughly cross-referenced index to topics covered should be prepared.

A chain of command should be established to make revisions, with one person in top management approving all proposals for change. Otherwise, duplication and overlap will create confusion. Finally, the operations manual should be reviewed at least once a year because a growing company is always changing.

Directing

Once the plan has been prepared and the firm has been organized and staffed to carry out its objectives, the next step is putting the plan into action and directing it. Up to this point, most of the activity has been in the mind of the planner(s). Now the game really starts. People in the organization must be motivated, persuaded, led, coordinated, encouraged, and so on. Involved here are concepts such as teamwork, supervision, and productivity.

Leadership

Leadership involves interaction. It is a way of behaving, of persuading and inducing, of guiding and motivating. A totally rounded leadership form calls for a mastery of certain skill areas, the creation of the right climate within which the work group can function properly, and the direction and control of group activities.

Leadership style is often a reflection of personality; however, a single, consistent type of behavior may not always be applicable or desired. What works well with one person (or group) may not necessarily work at all with the next. Individuals, as well as groups, are extremely varied. Consequently, effective leadership requires an eclectic approach, taking into account the three-way match among leader, group members, and the situation at hand. Most people, over the long term, tend to rely on the style that yields the best results. Many of us are guilty of holding stereotypical notions about leaders. We tend to believe that a good leader is one who commands respect; who electrifies the atmosphere when entering a room; who is, without a doubt, aggressive, domineering, capable of manipulation, a skilled communicator, an extrovert. Our concepts even go beyond personality to physical attributes; we think that a good leader is usually taller and heavier (and more attractive) than the rest of us.

Oddly enough, some of the greatest leaders in world history, and many capable managers of major corporations, have been quiet, unassuming, introspective, short, and thin people. Management experts have often theorized about the kinds of personal traits necessary for effective performance in the role of leader. Studies have compared the qualities of top executives with the qualities of unsuccessful leaders in order to uncover the characteristics that differentiate them. Several distinguishing attributes keep showing up; however, it must be kept in mind that leadership has three dimensions: the leader, those who are led, and the individual situation. Consequently, whether one rates high or low in these attributes does not necessarily make a person a good or bad leader.

A review of the following list of personal traits can be valuable in dealing with others:

adaptability
alertness
communication skills
confidence
creativity
curiosity
dependability
drive
enthusiasm
evaluation skills
flexibility
human relations skills
maturity
open-mindedness
optimism
patience
persuasive powers
poise
resourcefulness
sensitivity to others
supportiveness
teaching ability
tolerance
warmth
willingness to listen
willingness to take chances

In as much as leadership activity also has a task-oriented, impersonal dimension, certain additional skills need to be developed. Among these are

1. the ability to establish priorities
2. a capacity for giving credit when due
3. skill at planning and scheduling
4. proficiency in problem solving
5. a willingness to delegate responsibility to others

Understanding Employees

Each individual within an organization is a complex, multifaceted person. Among his or her many sides are the intellectual, the physical, and the emotional, along with economic, social, political, and moral. So it is not surprising that people's behavior can be as complex and as difficult to interpret as people are themselves.

Personality is an amalgam of values, attitudes, and interpersonal response traits:

1. **People hold values.** Values are concepts we come to accept over the years as we interact with others and with our environment.
2. **People form attitudes.** Attitudes serve as vehicles for organizing knowledge, for adjusting to the world around us, for shielding us from confusion and pain, and for orienting us toward things that are pleasurable.
3. **People develop response traits.** We have habitual ways of responding to and dealing with others.

A review of any basic psychology text can provide many insights into human behavior. In turn, psychological understanding can enhance a manager's capability in motivating and directing employees.

Motives are the energizing forces that drive all of us and are behind most behavior. Many of our actions result from the interplay of several motives. Some motives are largely rational and based on logic; for example, filing an IFR flight plan under marginal weather conditions. In this instance, the motives are quite clear and logical: (1) an accident could occur endangering life and property; and (2) violation of FAA regulations. On the other hand, many motives are of an emotional (or nonrational) nature.

The line of demarcation between rational and emotional motives is rather hazy. Not filing an IFR flight plan may be based on the emotional motive: fear of being cited by the FAA.

Furthermore, what motivates one person does not necessarily motivate the next. The same motive can lead to varied behaviors in different people. The same behavior in different people can result from different motives.

All of us are driven by many motives: economic, safety, social, or physiological ones like hunger, thirst, the need for sleep, and sex. The majority of our motives, however, are learned— those that we develop as we interact with our environment. One way to understand better the subject of human needs and wants is to review a notable theory proposed many years ago by the eminent psychologist Abraham Maslow. He suggested a hierarchy of human needs that can be arranged on different levels according to their "potency" for influencing behavior. He postulated that all of us are constantly struggling upwards to attain higher steps on this "pyramid of needs" until we reach its pinnacle. From time to time, most people are restrained from proceeding up the hierarchy or may be knocked down to lower levels by outside conditions (or, perhaps, by inner forces).

Translating Maslow's concepts into modern human resources thinking, we can expect employees to seek such things as the following:

1. **Level 1 (Physiological Needs):** a salary competitive with other firms with similar positions, adequate to provide the necessities of life.
2. **Level 2 (Safety Needs):** job security and safe working

conditions. This need may lead to health and life-insurance coverage for spouse and children and a 401K program.

3. **Level 3 (Love and Belongingness Needs):** the feeling of being part of an organization and having a place in the group; acceptance by co-workers and employer; a friendly environment.
4. **Level 4 (Esteem Needs):** ego satisfaction, recognition (an occasional pat on the back), authority, and status within the group; the belief that the person's work is both responsible and respected.
5. **Level 5 (Need for Self-Actualization):** a chance for growth and the opportunity to demonstrate initiative; encouragement for the individual to participate and contribute to the fullest.

Several other well-known management concepts are worth mentioning because of their relationship to businesses of all sizes.

Theories X and Y. More than 50 years ago, management theorist Douglas McGregor investigated the attitudes of supervisors toward their employees. His studies led him to conclude that most supervisors could be classified as belonging to one of two camps. Those who subscribe to what McGregor termed the Theory X approach are convinced that the average person doesn't like to work, has little if any ambition, and tries to avoid responsibility. Consequently, these supervisors feel that they need to watch workers closely (micromanagement) and depend on the strategic application of both rewards and punishment in order to obtain satisfactory performance.

Other supervisors follow a different philosophy, the more positive Theory Y approach. They believe employees consider work to be as natural as play and rest, and that once committed to specific objectives, they will not only put out effort willingly but will also seek responsibility.

Theory Z. In recent years, much favorable publicity has appeared in the press with regard to Japanese management techniques. One popular book outlined the more salient attributes of the Japanese approach, dubbing the overall concept Theory Z, an obvious reference to McGregor's assessment of supervisory types. Substantial delegation of responsibility, trust in each individual, and decision by group consensus are characteristically seen in Japanese companies. Of course, some of their attributes (such as lifetime employment) cannot be incorporated easily into our own economy. Still, owners of small FBOs might well profit by modifying and applying other attributes to their own enterprises; for example, the participative approach to decision making and a genuine concern for one's employees.

Job Motivators and Hygiene Factors. In the 1960s, management theorist Frederick Herzberg researched the workplace to uncover those factors that appeared to exert some influence on the job satisfaction of employees or on worker motivation. He found two distinct sets of such factors: motivators (or satisfiers) and hygiene factors (dissatisfiers). Herzberg maintained that motivators appeal to higher level human needs and, therefore, not only motivate employees but can also increase the level of job satisfaction. Examples include recognition, responsibility, advancement, growth, and the work itself. On the other hand, some factors in the workplace that cater to people's lower needs (hygiene factors) apparently do little to encourage worker motivation. Nevertheless, they can, of course, contribute to employee dissatisfaction. Salary, working conditions, company policies, and relations with one's supervisor are hygiene factors.

Obviously then, owners and managers of FBOs might do well to review Herzberg's findings. Morc highly motivated and satisfied employees might be developed through effective management policies that lead to (among other results):

1. top-quality working conditions
2. catering to the worker's need for security
3. delegating more responsibility
4. encouraging group goal setting and decision making
5. flexible scheduling
6. job enhancement and/or redesign
7. offering a promotional ladder with the company
8. recognizing and rewarding the exceptional contribution

Clearly, the focus by management should be on the need to motivate employees; even so, discipline is occasionally called for. The purpose in discipline is to change negative behaviors. If these behaviors can be changed using positive reinforcement, that should be attempted first. When necessary, discipline (or negative reinforcement) should be conducted in private. The goal is not to humiliate the employee. Rather, the goal is to get the employee's attention and correct negative behavior.

Empowering Employees

Employees are responsible for making themselves perform well, but managers are responsible for creating an environment where that seems possible. As discussed in chapter six, *empowerment* means releasing an individual's power to succeed by removing the barriers that prevent it, such as lack of skills, not enough direction, or too little responsibility and authority. In order to empower employees, managers must create small successes and recognize the employee for the success. For these small successes to happen, managers must establish an environment where employees feel that they can succeed. This means encouraging creativity, setting goals, giving feedback, and recognizing performance.

Effective feedback needs to be timely, specific, and should focus on the behavior, not the individual. Positive feedback should be offered, and alternatives should be provided so employees can set measureable performance goals. Negative feedback should be depersonalized, while managers should personalize the positive.

Coaching is one method managers can use to give feedback. But it can also be used to teach, motivate, or challenge employees. There are seven basic steps in the coaching process:

1. Observing performance and recording observations.
2. Analyzing performance so it can be linked to behaviors.
3. Providing feedback that is timely and specific.
4. Interviewing by asking open- and closed-ended questions.
5. Setting goals and action plans for higher performance.
6. Following up on action plans to fine tune performance.
7. Reinforcing effective behaviors by complimenting efforts and results.

Although informal feedback is important, the need for a formal performance appraisal is necessary. It is important that managers and supervisors clearly outline expectations, observations, and evaluations in writing. Frequent and comprehensive work sampling and written open-ended appraisals are necessary. If employees are surprised by information in their annual appraisals, they are not receiving enough informal feedback.

Decision Making

In business, most management decisions are made by intuition. Owners of small FBOs especially appear to fly by the seats of their pants in much the same way that Charles Lindbergh flew over the Atlantic many decades ago without the benefit of the vast array of intricate instruments that decorate the cockpit of today's jet aircraft.

Intuitive decision making stems partially from a lack of familiarity with problem-solving techniques and partially from the realization that extensive resources—time, energy, and funds— should only be diverted to the most serious and complex problems. Happily, these major problems do not occur very often. When they do (for example, when one is contemplating a major building expansion or marketing campaign), the owner is often better off relying on the assistance of an experienced consultant.

Fortunately, most problems in business repeat themselves, so once a satisfactory solution has been worked out (or accidentally hit upon), the entrepreneur knows how to solve the problem the next time it pops up. Only the new, infrequent, unique problems present a strong challenge.

Decision making is but one step in the problem-solving process. It is the last step in which the manager chooses the one alternative that seems best. The whole process is as follows:

1. **Diagnosing the problem.** On a sheet of paper, the manager writes a clear statement of the problem's "essence"; this will help pinpoint the problem clearly as the manager works towards its solution. Many problems are quite complex; often there is a need to go further and break down the original problem statement into its major parts. Each part should then be summarized and written down as a "subproblem" statement. Another useful trick is to draw a simple diagram of the problem situation, making certain to put in all the elements involved.
2. **Gathering information.** Hunt for pertinent information to help solve the problem. (Facts are not only available from internal records, external sources of data, and primary research, they are also readily obtained from people.)
3. **Generate alternative solutions.** Develop a number of alternative solutions to the problem. (Creative thinking can help here.)
4. **Evaluate the alternatives.** Rate the alternatives according to each of several criteria; for example, cost, time, judged effectiveness or payoff, effect on management, and so on. Use a simple numerical rating scale, such as 0 = Poor, 1 = Fair, 2 = Good, 3 = Very Good, and 4 = Excellent. If some criteria are more important to the firm than others, then accord more weight to those in the analysis.
5. **Select the best alternative(s).** At this juncture, the manager makes his or her decision.
6. **Translate the decision into action.**

Of course, many more sophisticated techniques are currently in vogue for solving business problems. For the most part, these approaches are used by the larger companies and not by the small firm. There are methods that take into account chance or probability, those that use mathematics and statistics, those that require computer programming, and so on. These include game theory, decision theory, queuing theory, decision matrices, simulation, and linear programming. All of these methods (and others, too) lie well outside the scope of this chapter. A number of good books are available on the topic of decision making in business and industry.

Controlling

There is a need to measure the results of the organizational plan while it is unfolding, as well as the necessity to make adjustments where and when needed. Logically, the control function cannot be separated from the planning function; they are interdependent, much like the two sides of the same coin.

Controlling is a process that includes analysis, setting standards, monitoring, securing feedback, and taking corrective action.

1. **Analysis:** Study and compare, for quantity and quality, the output of people and machines, the services provided, the systems employed, and so forth. Examine everything with a careful eye to standards and decision making.
2. **Setting Standards:** As a result of analysis, establish acceptable standards of performance in all areas. In turn, these standards become control valves, quantitative and qualitative measurements for future performance, guidelines for projecting cost, time, and sales.
3. **Monitoring:** The need for regular inspection and performance checks to note exceptions to the standards that have been set and possible reasons for the deviations.
4. **Securing Feedback:** A foolproof system for reporting deviations from standards must be established so that the proper people are notified regularly and promptly.
5. **Corrective Action:** Finally, all exceptions to the established standards must be acted on. Adjustments need to be made promptly so that contingent outcomes are brought back on target.

All areas of the business must be subject to this control function. Generally, managers think quite readily of inventory control, order processing, quality control, and production control. Yet controls are just as necessary in the personnel area (for example, in performance evaluation); in the financial end of things (where ratios can be used to investigate a variety of problems); in the long-term planning of projects; and so forth. For control is, in essence, self-discipline.

Communication

Service organizations such as FBOs run on communication. Prospective customers are located, contacted, and persuaded to buy products and services through communication. Similarly, employees are found, hired, trained, and directed; departments are managed; machines are manned and operated. Communication is the oil that lubricates the various gears and cogs in the free-enterprise system.

In the process of communication in business, there are a number of components involved. Indeed, communication in business appears to be a closed system with all parts interacting in synergistic fashion. The major elements which simplify a company's external communications with its customers are:

1. **Source:** the sender or originator of the messages.
2. **Messages:** information emitted by the source and directed to the receivers.
3. **Media:** the various carriers or transmitters of the messages (such as radio, newspapers, billboards, and so on).
4. **Receivers:** those for whom the messages are intended.
5. **Feedback:** customer reactions, demographic information, and other facts returned by or drawn from customers to assist management in its decision making.

Improvements within any of these areas, for example, in the quality of messages sent or the refinement or elaboration of the feedback process, improve the productivity of the entire communication system.

Applied to a firm's internal organization, communication starts with verbal or written messages (orders, instructions, and the like) passed down from the top to lower levels. Feedback moves upward, completing the system. Of course, the effectiveness of this internal system also depends on unimpeded horizontal communication on each individual level. Unfortunately, poor communication is commonly observed within organizations, perhaps due to the pressures of day-to-day details, which often make communicating face-to-face nearly impossible.

All messages to employees should be transmitted in terms that can be clearly understood and that convey the manager's exact meaning. To accomplish this objective, employers must understand the employees' point of view. Moreover, good listening skills constitute an important asset in communication; half-hearted listening interferes considerably with effective management. Encourage employees to listen, too. Employees should understand instructions and be encouraged to ask questions. As a final point, all supervisory personnel should be effective in communications.

KEY TERMS

Planning
Long-term plans
Operational plans
Single-use plans
Standing plans
Budgets
Organization Departments
Line and staff
Unity of command
Span of control
Operations manual
Directing
Leadership
Personality
Motives
Theory X
Theory Y
Theory Z
Motivators
Hygiene factors
Controlling

REVIEW QUESTIONS

1. Identify and briefly describe the characteristics of well-managed FBOs. Why is planning considered to be the most important management function? What types of plans are there? Give several examples of each. List the step-by-step approach to planning.
2. Define organization. How can employee goals be at odds with company goals? What is the purpose of departmentalization? Describe the line-and-staff concept. What are some problems associated with flat and tall organizational structures? Explain the organizational principles of unity of command and span of control. What is the purpose of an operations manual? Briefly describe the sections normally included in an operations manual.
3. Why is it said that the game really begins with directing? Why is effective leadership so important in directing a company? Identify 10 personal traits that can be helpful in dealing with others. List five additional skills found in successful leaders. Define personality and motives. Discuss Maslow's levels of human needs and wants. Compare McGregor's Theory X and Theory Y approaches to supervision. What are the motivators and hygiene factors described by Herzberg? What is meant by empowering employees?
4. Describe the six steps in the decision-making process. Discuss the process of controlling. Give several examples of the control function in such areas as marketing, line service, and parts inventory. Why is communication the "oil that lubricates the various gears and cogs in the free--enterprise system"? Describe how communication is applied to a firm's internal organization.

REFERENCES

Boyd, Bradford B. *Management-Minded Supervision,* 2nd ed. New York: McGraw-Hill, 1984.

Brown, Deaver. *The Entrepreneur's Guide.* New York: Ballantine, 1980.

Burstiner, Irving. *The Small Business Handbook* (Rev. ed.). Englewood Cliffs, NJ: Prentice-Hall, 1989.

Donnelly, James H., Jr., James L. Gibson, and John M. Ivancevich. *Fundamentals of Management: Functions, Behaviors, Models,* 5th ed. Plano, TX: Business Publications, 1984.

Herzberg, Frederick. *Work and the Nature of Man.* New York: Thomas Y. Crowell, 1966.

Levinson, R.E. "Problems in Managing a Family-Owned Business," *Family Business Sourcebook*, ed. C. Aronoff and J. Ward, Detroit: Omnigraphics, Inc., 169-174, 1987.

SCENARIOS

1. Two months ago, you resigned your position as FBO manager at a small-hub airport to manage an FBO at a medium-hub airport. Now two months into your new position, you have learned that the current Director of Line Service has an extremely poor work ethic. He rarely attends required meetings, and seemingly offers little input into the operation of the organization. In fact, other employees have mentioned how this employee has never given 100 percent to his job since he was hired 5 years ago. As a result, the success of his department (and the FBO) is suffering. Another item worth mentioning: this individual is the son of the FBO owner, the same owner who hired you. What options do you have and which will your pursue?
2. One year into your new position as manager of an FBO with 25 employees, you are feeling as if most employees don't respect you and don't enjoy coming to work. Employees rarely participate in company meetings, and customer service seems to be nonexistent at times. Some aircraft owners have even moved their aircraft to another FBO located on the field. As you look out your office window, business seems to be booming at the FBO located across the field. You then glance at your year-in-review numbers on your desk and can't avoid seeing the declining sales and reduced net profit. Just then, your phone rings. The owner of the FBO is calling you after having looked at the year-in-review numbers and strongly urges you to "fix the problem." As you begin this new year, what approach should you take?
3. You just graduated from college this past Spring with a degree in Aerospace Administration. You searched for jobs in the aviation industry all summer and finally discovered an opening for FBO Manager at a nearby FBO with 10 employees. To your delight, you were interviewed and offered the position. You readily accepted. It is Sunday afternoon, and you anxiously await your first day on the job tomorrow. You've read a great deal in college about various leadership styles, management principles, etc. However, you've never actually had to supervise employees before. What philosophy/management style will you adopt as you manage this organization and these 10 employees?
4. As the new manager of a small FBO with 18 employees (not including yourself), you have decided a new organizational chart is needed. The FBO currently has administration (three employees), line service (eight employees), flight instruction (three employees), and a small charter operation (four employees). Each department has a Manager. Draw an organizational chart for this organization.

5. A recent employee survey conducted shows that employees are dissatisfied with the level of communication by management throughout the organization. Many employees feel as if they are "in the dark" regarding major management decisions and future plans for the FBO. How do you, as Manager of the FBO, correct this? What are your ideas to improve the flow of communication throughout the organization?

Chapter 13
Risk Management

OUTLINE

OBJECTIVES

At the end of this chapter, you should be able to:

- Discuss the role of risk mitigation in FBO management.
- Explain the different types of risks an FBO may face on a daily basis and how these risks may be mitigated.
- Discuss the various types of insurance policies an FBO would be expected to have in effect.
- Discuss the importance of safety for an FBO.
- Explain how safety can be enhanced at an FBO.
- Discuss the role of security at an FBO.
- Explain how security can be enhanced at an FBO.

Introduction

This chapter discusses three important considerations in managing an FBO: risk mitigation, safety, and security. Regardless of the skill at serving customers, the FBO that neglects any of these three areas will incur additional expenses, a poor reputation, and possibly legal action which could result in the eventual bankruptcy of the business. Thus, it is imperative for FBO managers to be proactive in these areas.

Risk Mitigation

An FBO will be exposed to a number of different risks on a daily basis. These risks, although they can be mitigated, can never be completely eliminated. Thus, FBOs purchase insurance policies, educate employees, and develop plans and procedures to mitigate these known risks. Many FBO lease agreements actually require FBOs to purchase insurance policies proving specific coverages and in certain amounts to protect both the FBO and the airport from any possible claims. Typical insurance policies for an FBO would provide coverage for:

Workers' compensation
Aircraft liability (Damage to company-owned and non-owned aircraft)
Airport liability
Hangarkeeper's liability
In-Flight Hangarkeeper's liability
Business auto liability
Environmental impairment (pollution) insurance
Property insurance

Worker's Compensation

All businesses, including FBOs, have a legal responsibility to their employees to make the workplace safe. To protect employers from lawsuits resulting from workplace accidents and to provide medical care and compensation for lost income to employees hurt in workplace accidents, businesses are required to buy worker's compensation insurance. Worker's compensation insurance covers workers injured on the job, whether they're hurt on the workplace premises or elsewhere, or in auto accidents while on business. It also covers work-related illnesses. Workers compensation provides payments to injured workers, without regard to who was at fault in the accident, for time lost from work and for medical and rehabilitation services. It also provides death benefits to surviving spouses and dependents. Typical worker's compensation limits for FBOs would be \$100,000 each accident, \$100,000 disease for each employee, and \$500,000 disease policy limit.

Aircraft Liability (Damage to company-owned and non-owned aircraft)

Aircraft liability insurance covers the FBO for liability, including liability to passengers or resulting from the ownership, operation, maintenance, or use of all owned, non-owned, leased, or hired aircraft on, or in connection with, any premises. To mitigate this risk, FBOs purchase aircraft liability insurance. Insurance alone, however, is not enough. FBOs require check-out of aircraft for new pilots, which includes some flight time with an instructor to be certain of the pilot's capabilities before renting the aircraft. The FBO also hires qualified and competent flight instructors to adequately train flight students. The typical minimum limit for a policy of this sort would be $1,000,000 each occurrence.

Airport Liability

Similar to a mortgage company requiring the homeowner to maintain property insurance naming the mortgage company an insured, airports must also protect their interests by requiring FBOs to maintain appropriate airport liability insurance. This coverage provides for the liability resulting out of, or in connection with, ongoing operations performed by, or on behalf of, the FBO under the FBO Lease Agreement or the use or occupancy of Airport premises by, or on behalf of, the FBO. Typical policy limits would be $1,000,000.

Hangar-keepers Liability

This risk is specific to storing aircraft in a hangar and the liability that results from storing assets belonging to others. If the hangar catches fire, the FBO would not only need insurance to cover the damage to the hangar, but insurance to cover the damage to aircraft and equipment stored inside the hangar. In essence, FBOs are required to maintain this insurance for aircraft in their care, custody, or control. Typical limits would be $1,000,000 each aircraft and $2,000,000 each occurrence for all aircraft.

In-Flight Hangarkeeper's Liability

In-flight hangarkeeper's liability policies are designed to cover liability resulting from the pickup and redelivery of aircraft, test flights, instruction, and charter flights. This policy differs from an aircraft liability policy in that in-flight hangarkeeper's policies cover damage to aircraft, whereas aircraft liability polices cover liability to passengers and aircraft that are not in flight, nor stored in a hangar. Typical limits would be $1,000,000 each aircraft and $1,000,000 aggregate.

Business Auto Liability

In addition to the use of aircraft, FBOs utilize automobiles to a large degree in connection with their business. Flight crews may use an FBO-owned courtesy car. Customer service personnel may park a private auto for a client. Limousine service may be provided by the FBO. Each of these occurrences simply increases risk to the FBO. Thus, business auto liability insurance becomes necessary. This policy will cover all owned, hired, and non-owned vehicles and will typically have a $1,000,000 policy limit for each occurrence (bodily injury and property damage combined).

Environmental Impairment (Pollution) Insurance

FBOs may cause environmental pollution. They maintain fuel farms, store moderate amounts of hazardous chemicals, and generate hazardous waste in the form of used oil, for example. If not stored and disposed of properly, the FBO can face serious consequences. Although proper procedures are most effective at preventing environmental problems, FBOs may be required to maintain environmental impairment (pollution) insurance. This insurance will cover the FBO from liability resulting from pollution or other environmental impairment arising out of, or in connection with, work performed under the lease agreement, or which arises out of, or in connection with, the use or occupancy of airport premises in connection with the lease agreement. The typical policy limits are $1,000,000 each claim and $2,000,000 annual aggregate.

Property Insurance

FBOs have extensive property which is at risk to fire, vandalism, and theft. The potential for fire at an FBO is very high, mainly due to the large volumes of aviation fuel being stored and moved. The wise FBO manager will practice proper fire fuel safety as detailed in chapter four. Additionally, FBOs use fire resistant materials, automatic fire sprinkler systems and fire extinguishers. Personnel should also be trained in proper housekeeping practices, fire prevention, and fire fighting. Although rare, vandalism is always a possibility. This can be prevented by proper security equipment and procedures (discussed later in this chapter). Likewise, theft is an ever-present risk at FBOs. This may include theft of pilot supplies, cash, aircraft parts, or the aircraft themselves, perpetrated by employees or external customers. In any event, security equipment and procedures, as well as having proper checks and balances and hiring only employees that have successfully completed background checks will minimize this risk.

In addition to procedures to mitigate these risks, property insurance polices will be carried to minimize any associated financial loss. This policy will have the airport as an added insured. This insurance will cover any existing or constructed building, structures, or any other improvements to real property located on the property leased by the FBO. Typical policy limits for property insurance are $1,000,000.

Safety

Safety begins on the ramp and continues throughout the hangar and into the terminal building. As discussed in chapter four, line service has inherent dangers (such as spinning propellers, jet blast, high noise levels, moving aircraft and vehicles, and fuel). Wise FBO managers begin training new line service personnel on the importance of safety on day one. The National Air Transportation Association (NATA) created a Safety First line service training program specifically to assist FBOs with educating line service personnel about the importance of safety on the ramp. This program has been used by FBOs nationwide to educate line service specialists about proper towing techniques, fire safety, proper marshalling, etc. Other FBOs have created their own form of safety training, which may include daily safety briefings, monthly safety meetings, and employee of the year award.

In addition to safety on the ramp, the Occupational Safety and Health Administration (OSHA) demands safety throughout the workplace. Specifically, FBOs must furnish for employees a workplace free from recognized hazards. FBOs must comply with all occupational safety and health standards issued under the *Occupational Safety and Health Act*. Furthermore, employees have the right to request an inspection by OSHA if they sense an unsafe work environment, requiring the employer to correct workplace hazards if a citation is issued. In any event, FBOs have a vested interest in maintaining a safe working environment for all employees and should attempt to enhance workplace safety in all areas.

The FAA, in harmony with the International Civil Aviation Organization (ICAO) has issued guidance to airports in creating Safety Management Systems (SMS). The application of a systematic, proactive, and well-defined safety program (as is inherent in a SMS) allows an organization producing a product or service to strike a realistic and efficient balance between safety and production. Principal to implementing an SMS is conducting a safety risk assessment and proactively creating a safety culture at airports. FBOs should use this information to further ensure a high level of safety awareness among all employees.

Security

September 11, 2001 was a terrible day on which aviation was used to attack the United States. The world changed and general aviation (GA) was not immune from this change. In fact, GA became the target of lawmakers and others concerned about the security of our nation. GA was seen as a weak link in the national security chain and the target of criticism. Many agree that GA aviation facilities are potentially high profile targets with large congregations of people, extensive structures, storage of large volumes of fuel or chemicals, and access to sophisticated aircraft. Today, however, GA has righted itself and is once again seen as a safe and vital link in the nation's air transportation system. However, this was not accomplished overnight and the risk to losing this trust is great. Thus, FBO managers must take active measures to maintain and enhance security at their facilities.

In response to the concern about the lack of security at GA airports, the newly created Transportation Security Administration (TSA) in May 2004 created the *TSA Security Guidelines for General Aviation Airports*, also referred to as Information Publication A-001. These guidelines provide specific guidance to GA airport managers and FBO managers in how to enhance security at their facilities. Truly, security needs to be a cooperative effort by airport management and FBO management (as well as all other businesses located on airport).

As an information publication, the aim is to provide a set of federally endorsed security enhancements and methods for determining when and where these enhancements may be appropriate. It only applies to smaller airports that are not required to comply with FAR Part 1542. In developing the guidelines TSA understood that a one-size security approach would not fit the entire spectrum of GA airports. The document provides options, ideas, and suggestions for the airport operator, tenants, and users to enhance security of the airport. The guide covers the following sections:

Airport characteristics

- Airport Location (proximity to mass population areas or sensitive sites)
- Based Aircraft (Increased risk with larger numbers of based aircraft)
- Runways (Airports with longer paved runways are higher risk)
- Operations (All operations, including infrequent ops, are potential risk)

Personnel

- Passengers and visitors
  GA passengers are generally better known than the typical airline passengers
  - Visitor escorts into movement area
  - Suspicious activities, such as cash for flights or probing and inappropriate questions
  - PIC should verify identify of passengers, baggage, and cargo
- Flight Schools and Student Pilots
  - Require flight students to use proper entrances/exits
  - Establish positive ID
  - Control aircraft ignition keys

  - Consider having student pilots check in before being allowed access to aircraft
  - No keys to students without instructor or management approval
  - Different ignition and door lock keys
- Aircraft Renters
  - Regular renters are well known, and new renters are required by insurance companies to complete a flight check
  - ID should be verified
  - First-time renter should be familiarized with local airport operations
  - Vigilant for suspicious activity
- Transient Pilots

  ID non-based pilots and aircraft using the facilities (sign-in, sign-out or assigned parking spots)

Aircraft

- Ensure door locks are used to prevent unauthorized access
- Use keyed ignitions
- Store aircraft in hangar with locked hangar doors
- Use auxiliary locks (props, throttle)
- Ensure ignition keys are not stored inside aircraft

Airports/Facilities

- Hangars
  - One of the most effective ways to secure GA aircraft
  - Hangar locks, proper lighting, alarms
- Locks
  - Simply a delaying device, not a complete bar to entry
  - Cipher lock vs. keys
- Perimeter Control
  - Walls, fencing, natural barriers, electronic barriers
  - Expending resources on unnecessary security enhancements (complete perimeter fencing) instead of more facility-specific and effective method (tiedown chains with locks) may be detrimental to airport's security posture
- Lighting
  - Prevents theft, vandalism, or other illegal activity at night
  - Connected to emergency power source if possible
  - Ensure that lighting does not interfere with aircraft operations
- Signs
  - Provide a deterrent by warning of facility boundaries and consequences of violation
  - Warnings against trespassing, unauthorized use of aircraft and tampering with aircraft, and reporting of suspicious activity
  - Should include phone number of local law enforcement, 911, or 1-866-GA-SECUR
- Identification System
  - Method of identifying airport employees
  - Range from simple laminated ID card with photo to swipe card with biometric data
- Airport Planning
  - Planning of security should be an integral part of any project undertaken.
  - Prevent unauthorized access, construction staging areas, prevent inadvertent movement area entry

Surveillance

- Airport Community Watch Program
  - AOPA Airport Watch Program
  - Post signs
  - Involve stakeholders
  - Encourage participation
- Reporting Procedures
  - Report to airport management
  - Utilize GA-SECURE hotline (TSA developed with National Response Center)
  - Contact local law enforcement or 911
- Airport Security Committee
  - Comprised of airport tenants and users to develop effective and reasonable security measures
- LEO Support
  - Important to establish and maintain a liaison with local law enforcement agencies
  - Law enforcement should be familiar with operational and security procedures at the airport
- Closed circuit television (CCTV)
  - Make it possible for fewer individuals to maintain a constant watch on all areas of the facility
  - Expensive and must be monitored to be effective
- Intrusion Detection System (IDS)
  - Typically constantly monitored by contracting company
  - If an intrusion or fire or power outage is detected, the system administrator notifies police, fire, and/or airport management

Security Procedures and Communications

- Security Procedures
  - Helpful to develop written security procedures
  - Documentation provides managers with a traceable and auditable method of adherence to security procedures
- Threat Level Increases

  - Department of Homeland Security advisory system
  - Consider additional security measures under orange or red threat levels—Perimeter inspections, limiting access points, ensuring positive ID of pilots and tenants, closing the facility, etc.
- Threat Communication System
  - Comprehensive Contact List
  - It is essential for first responders and airport management to have the capability to communicate (Incident Command Center, emergency message board)
  - Disseminate new security policies, procedures, etc., to tenants and other users

Specialty Operations

- Agricultural aircraft ops
  - Use multiple devices to secure aircraft
  - Store aircraft in hangars
  - Park heavy equipment in front of and behind agricultural aircraft when hangars are not available for storage
- Airport Tenant Facilities
  - Airport operators should coordinate with tenants to ensure that their areas are secure and don't leave gaps in the security system
- Aircraft and Vehicle Fueling Facilities
  - Security fencing, lighting, and access controls when possible
  - Trucks should be secured when not in use
- Military Facilities
  - If adjacent or on-airport military facilities, detailed coordination between airport and military facility must occur for security procedures and responses.

The two most effective aspects of the Guidelines are found in Appendix A and B of the Guidelines. Appendix A contains the Airport Characteristics Measurement Tool. This tool allows GA airport operators and FBO managers to asses risk areas by assigning points to higher risk areas. Upon completion of this task, readers can utilize Appendix B, Suggested Airport Security Enhancements, for ideas in how to enhance security at the airport based on the risks identified in Appendix A. Overall, the TSA Guidelines are an excellent reference for airport operators and FBO managers to more effectively adopt an overall security posture and strengthen the security of these important GA airports.

On of the recommendations contained in the TSA Guidelines is use of the AOPA Airport Watch Program. This program, developed by AOPA, is designed as a sort of neighborhood watch program for GA airports. As previously discussed, GA airports are typically small, resulting in a GA airport "family" where everyone knows each other. This tight-knit environment can be the best defense against security threats. Particularly, the AOPA Airport Watch Program encourages those at the airport to always be on the lookout for suspicious activity and report it if it does occur. Signs are also posted warning unauthorized individuals of the Airport Watch Program. AOPA created a companion DVD for this program to further educate GA airport operators and tenants about how to implement the Airport Watch Program on a daily basis. Only when this attitude of awareness is integrated into the daily routine at the airport will it truly be successful.

Another aspect of the daily security posture is challenge procedures. Required at all TSA Part 1542 airport (air carrier), this involves challenging individuals in the sterile area (or AOA) with no ID badge visible on their person. This is most effective on the ramp or flight line. However, it becomes difficult at GA facilities because there are typically a large number of flight crew and passengers on the ramp with no ID badge. These individuals don't work at the airport and may be transient; thus, they would not have an airport-issued ID badge. Common sense and a sense of vigilance are required to recognize suspicious behavior and effectively apply the challenge procedure at GA airports.

Finally, a security threat may be received via the telephone. This may include a bomb threat or other threat against the business or GA aircraft operations. The key is to listen closely to the caller's voice (accent, timbre, gender) and discern as much information as possible so that an assessment of the threat may be made. If possible, it is best to alert someone to the call while the caller is still on the line. Typically, threat assessment will be made after the call has ended in consultation with local law enforcement and local management (airport and FBO).

KEY TERMS

Risk mitigation
Damage to company-owned and non-owned aircraft
Bodily injury and property damage
Premises and product liability
Hangar-keeper's liability
Underground fuel-storage tanks
Hazardous wastes
Fire
Vandalism
Theft
Safety
Security
Surveillance
CCTV

IDS
DHS Threat Level

REVIEW QUESTIONS

1. What types of risks are FBOs exposed to? Why is it important to mitigate these risks?
2. Why is safety important to an FBO?
3. What areas are addressed by the *TSA Security Guidelines for GA Airports*?
4. What role does the AOPA Airport Watch Program play in FBO Security?
5. What are challenge procedures?
6. What should be remembered when answering a telephone threat?

REFERENCES

AOPA Airport Watch Program
FAA Safety Management System. AC 150/5200-37
NATA Safety 1st Program.
TSA Security Guidelines for General Aviation Airports.

SCENARIOS

1. During the past few years, insurance rates have been increasing dramatically. Specifically, you, as FBO manager, are confronting higher rates in worker's compensation, hangar keeper's liability, business auto liability, environmental pollution insurance, aircraft liability insurance, property insurance, and employee medical insurance. Obviously, it may be more expensive NOT to be insured. However, what can you do to minimize the financial impact of these increasing insurance premiums?
2. You have been recently hired as the Manager of Risk Management at a full-service FBO. The FBO Manger has asked you to conduct a comprehensive risk assessment to the FBO, including the risks associated with fire, crime/theft, aircraft, business auto, environmental, and hangar keeper's. Specifically, what are your ideas to reduce risk in these areas?
3. As Manager of an FBO at a GA facility, you have grown more concerned about security since the events of 9/11. What are some areas you should be considering when ensuring the security of your facility, as well as the GA airport? What ideas do you have to ensure a secure GA airport?
4. Safety is definitely a concern in the operation of an FBO. Just last week, you had an employee hit by a tug, another badly burned in a fueling incident, and yet another employee injured in the maintenance shop.What are some considerations for your FBO in attempting to ensure a safe working environment for your employees? Specifically, how do you prevent such incidents from occurring in the future?
5. Your goal as FBO Manager is to run a safe, secure airport operation with adequately trained staff. You realize you cannot eliminate all risk. However, your goal is to reduce your business' exposure to risk as much as possible. Obviously, insurance is one way to reduce your financial risk to aircraft accidents, fire, liability, etc. However, insurance by itself is not enough. What else is an FBO Manager to do to reduce the risks associated with operating an FBO?

Chapter 14
Financial Planning and Control

OUTLINE

OBJECTIVES

At the end of this chapter, you should be able to:

- Describe the purpose and major categories of the balance sheet and statement of income.
- Distinguish between balance sheet, income statement, and management ratio analysis and give examples of each.
- Explain the purpose and factors affecting pro forma statements.
- List the steps in preparing a pro forma statement.
- Define break-even analysis and summarize the steps in calculating the break-even point.
- Discuss the importance of cash flow budgets and give several examples of typical budget reports.
- Distinguish between equity capital, working capi tal, and growth capital and identify the major sources of loans for each.
- Discuss the importance and process of short-term and long-term financing.
- Compare and contrast EBITDA analysis and discounted cash flow analysis in determining the value of an aviation business.

Financial planning affects how and on what terms an FBO will be able to attract the funding required to establish, maintain, and expand the business. Financial planning determines the number and type aircraft an FBO can afford to buy, the services provided, and whether or not the FBO will be able to market them efficiently. It affects the human and physical resources the FBO will be able to acquire to run the business. In short, it will be a major factor in determining the profitability of the firm. This chapter provides an overview of the essential components of financial planning and management.

Financial Management

Financial management is the use of financial statements that reflect the financial condition of a business to identify its relative strengths and weaknesses. It enables the firm to plan, using projections, future financial performance for capital, asset, and personnel requirements to maximize the return on shareholders' (owners) investment.

Specifically, a financial management system enables the firm to

1. interpret past performance,
2. measure present progress,
3. anticipate and plan for the future,
4. control operations,
5. uncover significant trends,
6. compare results with similar firms within the particular industry,

7. make financial decisions, and
8. comply with government regulations.

The Balance Sheet

The balance sheet provides a picture of the financial health of a business at a given moment, usually at the close of an accounting period. It lists in detail those material and intangible items the business owns (known as its assets) and what money the business owes, either to its creditors (liabilities) or to its owners (shareholders' equity or net worth of the business).

Assets include not only cash, merchandise inventory, land, buildings, equipment, machinery, furniture, patents, and trademarks, but also money due from individuals or other businesses (known as accounts receivable or notes receivable). Liabilities are funds acquired for a business through loans or the sale of property or services to the business on credit. Creditors do not acquire business ownership, but rather promissory notes to be paid at a designated future date.

Shareholders' equity (or net worth or capital) is money put into a business by its owners for use by the business in acquiring assets.

At any given time, a business's assets equal the total contributions by the creditors and owners, as illustrated by the following formula for the balance sheet:

Assets	=	**Liabilities**	+	**Net Worth**
(total funds invested in assets of the business)		(Funds supplied to the business by its creditors)		(Funds supplied to the business by its owners)

This formula is a basic premise of accounting. If a business owes more money to creditors than it possesses in value of assets owned, the net worth or owner's equity of the business will be a negative number.

The balance sheet is designed to show how the assets, liabilities, and net worth of a business are distributed at any given time. It is usually prepared at regular intervals; for example, at each month's end, but especially at the end of each fiscal (accounting) year.

By regularly preparing this summary of what the business owns and owes (the balance sheet), the business owner/manager can identify and analyze trends in the financial strength of the business. It permits timely modifications, such as gradually decreasing the amount of money the business owes to creditors and increasing the amount the business owes its owners.

All balance sheets contain the same categories of assets, liabilities, and net worth. Assets are arranged in decreasing order of how quickly they can be turned into cash (liquidity). Liabilities are listed in order of how soon they must be repaid, followed by retained earnings (net worth or owner's equity), as illustrated in Figure 14-1, the sample balance sheet of XYZ Aviation Company.

XYZ Aviation Company
Balance Sheet
December 31, 20__

ASSETS	
Current Assets:	
Cash	$52,500
Accounts receivable	40,000
Prepaid expenses;	10,000
Including insurance premiums	
Inventory of aircraft	284,650
Parts	23,000
Total Current Assets	$410,150
Fixed Assets:	
Shop equipment	21,500
Office equipment	7,000
Parts room	5,000
Improvements to leased facilities	100,000
	$133,500
Less depreciation and obsolescence	17,500
Net fixed assets	$116,000
Total Assets	$526,150
LIABILITIES AND NET WORTH	
Liabilities:	
Trade accounts payable	$21,700
Notes payable (aircraft)	220,500
Other payables	17,000
Accruals	10,000
Total Liabilities	$269,200
Net Worth:	
Investors' contribution	$200,000
(Capital stock or capital loans)	
Add Surplus	56,950
	$256,950
Total Liabilities and Net Worth	$256,150

Figure 14-1 Balance Sheet for XYZ Aviation Company

Balance Sheet Categories

The categories and format of the balance sheet are established by a system known as Generally Accepted Accounting Principles (GAAP). The system is applied to all companies, large or small, so anyone reading the balance sheet can readily understand the story it tells.

Assets and liabilities are broken down into the following categories:

Assets: An asset is anything the business owns that has monetary value.

- Current assets include cash, government securities, marketable securities, accounts receivable, notes receivable (other than from officers or employees), inventories, prepaid expenses, and any other item that could be converted into cash within one year in the normal course of business.
- Fixed assets are those acquired for long-term use in a business such as land, facilities, equipment, machinery, leasehold improvements, furniture, fixtures, and any other items with an expected useful business life measured in years (as opposed to items that will wear out or be used up in less than one year and are usually expensed when they are purchased). These assets are typically not for resale and are recorded in the balance sheet at their net cost less accumulated depreciation.
- Other assets include intangible assets, such as patents, royalty arrangements, copyrights, exclusive-use contracts, and notes receivable from officers and employees.

Liabilities: Liabilities are the claims of creditors against the assets of the business (debts owed by the business).

- Current liabilities are accounts payable, notes payable to banks, accrued expenses (wages, salaries), taxes payable, the current portion (due within one year) of long-term debt, and other obligations to creditors due within one year.
- Long-term liabilities are mortgages, intermediate and long-term bank loans, equipment loans, and any other obligation from money due to a creditor with a maturity longer than one year.
- Net Worth is the assets of the business minus its liabilities. Net worth equals the owner's equity. This equity is the investment by the owner plus any profits or minus any losses that have accumulated in the business.

The Statement of Income

The second primary report included in a business's financial management picture is the Statement of Income (or Income Statement). The Statement of Income is a measure of a company's sales and expenses over a specific period of time. It is also prepared at regular intervals (again, each month and fiscal year end) to show the results of operating during those accounting periods. It too follows Generally Accepted Accounting Principles (GAAP) and contains specific revenue and expense categories regardless of the nature of the business. Figure 14-2 illustrates a sample Statement of Income for XYZ Aviation Company.

Statement of Income Categories

The Statement of Income categories can be summarized as follows:

- **Income** (gross sales less returns and allowances)
- Less **Cost of Goods** (costs charged directly against gross sales)
- Equals **Gross Profit** (gross income, minus direct costs before operating expenses)
- Less **Operating Expenses** (salaries, rent, heat, utilities, insurance, advertising and sales promotion, interest, office supplies, bad debt allowances, travel and entertainment, dues and subscriptions, depreciation, and miscellaneous expenses such as automobile expenses, legal fees, and so forth)
- Equals **Operating Profit** (profit before other non-operating income or expense)
- Plus **Other Income** (income from dividends on invest-ments, interest on bank accounts, customer charge accounts, and so forth)
- Less **Other Expenses** (interest expense)
- Equals **Net Income (or Loss) *Before* Taxes** (the figure on which taxes are calculated)
- Less **Income Taxes** (if any are due)
- **Equals Net Income (or Loss) *After* Taxes**

Calculation of the Cost of Goods Sold category in the Statement of Income (or Profit and-Loss Statement as it is sometimes called) varies depending on whether the business is primarily a service organization like an FBO or a manufacturer of aircraft components. The cost of goods sold during the accounting period involves beginning and ending inventories for an FBO. In manufacturing or a completion work shop (aircraft interior work), it involves not only finished-goods inventories, but also raw materials inventories, goods-in process inventories, direct labor, and direct manufacturing overhead costs. The Handbook of Small Business Finance, U.S. Small Business Administration Small Business Management Series No. 15 has excellent illustrations of the different methods of calculation for Cost of Goods Sold for the various business types.

Financial Ratio Analysis

The two major accounting statements, the balance sheet and the income statement, contain a great deal of information about the results of company operations and the current state of the firm's finances. Company management can manipulate

XYZ Aviation Company
Income Statement
December 31, 20__

Income:	
Sale of aircraft	$130,000
Gross receipts from flight training, charter, and other flights	28,800
Receipts from sale of parts and accessories	48,000
Gross receipts for maintenance and repair of customers' aircraft	30,000
Gross receipts from line service (sale of fuel, cleaning, washing, and other services to customers' aircraft)	164,000
Payments received for storage of customers' aircraft	14,000
Gross Income	$414,800
Cost of Goods:	
Cost of aircraft sold	102,000
Cost of fuel, spare parts, and other costs charged directly against receipts from flights and charters listed above (not including labor)	14,000
Cost of parts and accessories sold to customers	38,000
Cost of parts and accessories charged against receipts for maintenance and repair of customers' aircraft	10,000
Cost of line services to customers' aircraft (including cost of fuel sold, but not including labor)	89,000
Total direct costs (excluding labor)	$253.000
Gross Profit (on sales)	$161,800
Operating Expenses:	
Salaries	$70,000
Rent, heat, and utilities	15,000
Insurance (on aircraft, structures, equipment, liability, and other insurance)	20,000
Advertising and sales promotion	2,000
Interest (on money borrowed to purchase aircraft and other equipment)	5,000
Office supplies	3,000
Bad debts allowances	1,500
Travel and entertainment	500
Dues and subscriptions	200
Depreciation (on buildings, equipment, and other fixed assets which are owned)	20,000
Miscellaneous expenses	5,000
Total Operating Expenses	$142,200
Operating Profit	19,600
Other Income:	
Dividends	$700
Interest on bank accounts	400
Total Other Income	1,100
Total Income before taxes	20,700
Other Expenses:	
Interest expenses	$1,200
Net Income (or Loss) before taxes	19,500
Less provision for income taxes	1,600
Net Income (or Loss) after taxes	$17,900

Figure 14-2 Income Statement for XYZ Aviation Company

this information in ways that yield meaningful insights for decision making. One of these ways is ratio analysis. Ratio analysis enables management to spot trends in a business and to compare its performance and condition with the average performance of similar businesses in the aircraft service industry. An FBO can make comparisons of its ratios with other similar FBOs as well as its own ratios for several successive years. Unfavorable trends can be detected. Ratio analysis may provide the all important early warning indications that allow a firm to solve business problems before they ruin the firm.

Balance Sheet Ratio Analysis

Important balance sheet ratios measure liquidity and solvency (a business's ability to pay its bills as they come due) and leverage (the extent to which the business is dependent on creditors' funding). Liquidity ratios indicate the ease of turning assets into cash. They include the current ratio, quick ratio, and working capital.

Current Ratio. The current ratio is one of the best known measures of financial strength. It is figured as shown below:

$$\textbf{Current Ratio} = \frac{\text{Total Current Assets}}{\text{Total Current Liabilities}}$$

The main question this ratio addresses is "Does the business have enough current assets to meet the payment schedule of its current debts with a margin of safety for possible losses in current assets, such as inventory shrinkage or collectable accounts?" A generally acceptable current ratio is 2 to 1. The minimum acceptable current ratio is obviously 1:1, but that relationship is usually too close for comfort.
If the business's current ratio is too low, a firm may be able to raise it by the following means:

1. Paying some debts.
2. Increasing the current assets from loans or other borrowings with a maturity of more than one year.
3. Converting noncurrent assets into current assets.
4. Increasing the current assets from new equity contribu--tions.
5. Putting profits back into the business.

Quick Ratio. The Quick Ratio is sometimes called the "acid-test" ratio and is one of the best measures of liquidity. It is figured as shown below:

$$\textbf{Quick Ratio} = \frac{\text{Cash + Government Securities + Receivables}}{\text{Total Current Liabilities}}$$

The quick ratio is a much more exacting measure than the current ratio. By excluding inventories, it concentrates on the really liquid assets, with value that is fairly certain. It helps answer the question "If all sales revenues should disappear, could the business meet its current obligations with the readily convertible 'quick' funds on hand?"

An acid test of 1:1 is considered satisfactory unless the majority of the "quick assets" are in accounts receivable, and the pattern of accounts receivable collection lags behind the schedule for paying current liabilities.

Working Capital. Working capital is more a measure of cash flow than a ratio. The result of this calculation must be a positive number. It is calculated as shown below:

$$\textbf{Working Capital} = \begin{matrix}\text{Total}\\ \text{Current}\\ \text{Assets}\end{matrix} - \begin{matrix}\text{Total}\\ \text{Current}\\ \text{Liabilities}\end{matrix}$$

Bankers look at net working capital over time to determine a company's ability to weather financial crises. Loans are often tied to minimum working capital requirements.

A general observation about these three liquidity ratios is that the higher they are, the better, especially if the firm is relying to any significant extent on creditor money to finance assets.

Leverage Ratio. The debt/worth or leverage ratio indicates the extent to which the firm is reliant on debt financing (creditor money versus owner's equity):

$$\textbf{Debt/Worth Ratio} = \frac{\text{Total Liabilities}}{\text{Net Worth}}$$

Usually, the higher this ratio, the more risky a creditor will perceive its exposure in the business, making it correspondingly harder to obtain credit.

Income Statement Ratio Analysis

The following Income Statement ratios measure a firm's profitability. Profitability ratios simply measure the profitability or unprofitability of a firm. Profits may be measured against a variety of data, such as sales, net worth, assets, and so forth. Generally, profitability ratios are expressed as percentages rather than proportions or fractions.

Gross Margin Ratio. The gross margin ratio is the percentage of sales dollars left after subtracting the cost of goods sold from income. It measures the percentage of sales dollars remaining (after obtaining or manufacturing the goods sold) available to pay the overhead expenses of the company.

$$\textbf{Gross Margin Ratio} = \frac{\text{Gross Profit}}{\text{Income}}$$

(Gross Profit = Income –Cost of Goods Sold)

Net Profit Margin Ratio. The net profit margin ratio is the percentage of sales dollars (gross income) left after subtracting the cost of goods sold and all expenses, except income taxes. It provides a good opportunity to compare the company's "return on sales" with the performance of other companies in the industry. It is calculated before income tax because tax rates and tax liabilities vary from company to company for a wide variety of reasons, making comparisons after taxes much more difficult. The net profit margin ratio is calculated as follows:

$$\textbf{Net Profit Margin Ratio} = \frac{\text{Net Profit Before Tax}}{\text{Gross Income}}$$

Management Ratios

Two additional management ratios derived from the balance sheet and Statement of Income are important for small businesses like FBOs.

Return on Assets Ratio. The return on assets ratio measures how efficiently profits are being generated from the assets employed in the business when compared with the ratios of firms in a similar business. A low ratio in comparison with industry averages indicates an inefficient use of business assets. The return on assets ratio is calculated as follows:

$$\textbf{Return on Assets} = \frac{\text{Net Profit Before Tax}}{\text{Total Asets}}$$

Return on Investment (ROI) Ratio. The return on investment (ROI) is perhaps the most important ratio of all. It is the percentage of return on funds invested in the business by its owners. In short, this ratio tells the owner whether or not all the effort put into the business has been worthwhile. If the ROI is less than the rate of return on an alternative, risk-free investment such as a bank savings account or certificate of deposit, the owner may be wiser to sell the company, put the money in such a savings instrument, and avoid the daily struggles of running a small FBO. The ROI is calculated as follows:

$$\textbf{Return on Investment} = \frac{\text{Net Profit Before Tax}}{\text{Net Worth}}$$

These liquidity, leverage, profitability, and management ratios allow the business owner to identify trends in a business and to compare its progress with the performance of others through data published by various sources. The owner may thus determine the business's relative strengths and weaknesses. Sources of comparative financial information may be obtained from any public library or publishers listed under the references under this chapter.

Forcasting Profits

Forecasting, particularly on a short-term basis (one year to three years), is essential to planning for business success. This process, estimating future business performance based on the actual results from prior periods, enables the FBO owner/manager to modify the operation of the business on a timely basis. This allows the business to avoid losses or major financial problems should some future results from operations not conform with reasonable expectations. Forecasts, or Pro Forma Income Statements as they are usually called, provide the most persuasive management tools to apply for loans or attract investor money. As a business expands, there will inevitably be a need for more money than can be internally generated from profits.

Factors Affecting Pro Forma Statements

Preparation of forecasts (Pro Forma Statements) requires assembling a wide array of pertinent, verifiable facts affecting the business and its past performance. These include the following:

1. Data from prior financial statements, particularly:
   a. previous sales levels and trends;
   b. past gross percentages;
   c. average past general, administrative, and selling expenses necessary to generate former sales volumes;
   d. trends in the company's need to borrow (supplier, trade credit, and bank credit) to support various levels of inventory and trends in accounts receivable required to achieve previous sales volumes.
2. Unique company data, particularly:
   a. facility capacity,
   b. competition,
   c. financial constraints,
   d. personnel availability.
3. Industry-wide factors, including:
   a. overall state of the economy,
   b. economic status of the FBO industry within the economy,
   c. population growth,
   d. elasticity of demand (responsiveness of customers to price changes) for the products or services the business provides,
   e. availability of aircraft.

Once these factors are identified, they may be used in Pro Formas, which estimate the level of sales, expense, and profitability that seem possible in a future period of operations.

The Pro Forma Income Statement

In preparing the Pro Forma Income Statement, the estimate of total sales during a selected period is the most critical forecast. The owner/manager must employ business experience from past financial statements.

If, for example, a 10 percent increase in sales volume is a realistic and attainable goal, the first step is to multiply last year's gross income by 1.10 to get this year's estimate of total gross income. Next, this total has to be broken down by month, by looking at the historical monthly sales volume. From this it can be determined that the percentage of total annual sales fell on the average in each of those months over a minimum of the past three years. It might be determined that 75 percent of total annual sales volume was realized during the six months from July through December in each of those years and that the remaining 25 percent of sales was spread fairly evenly over the first six months of the year.

Next, an estimate of the cost of goods sold must be made by analyzing operating data to determine on a monthly basis what percentage of sales has gone into cost of goods sold in the past. This percentage can then be adjusted for expected variations in costs, price trends, and efficiency of operations. Operating expenses (sales, general and administrative expenses, depreciation, and interest), other expenses, other income, and taxes can then be estimated through detailed analysis and adjustment of what they were in the past and what they are expected to be in the future. Putting together this information month by month for a year into the future will result in the firm's Pro Forma Statement of Income.

Preparation of the information is summarized below and in Figure 14-3.

1. **Income (Sales)**. List the departments in the firm. A reasonable projection of the monthly sales for each department is entered in the "Estimate" columns. The actual sales are entered in the "Actual" columns for the month as they become available. Any revenue not strictly related to the business is excluded from the Income (Sales) column.
2. **Cost of Sales**. The cost of sales estimated for each month for each department is entered in the "Estimate" column. For product inventory, the cost of the goods sold for each department is calculated by subtracting the current inventory from beginning inventory plus purchases and transportation costs during the month. The "Actual" costs are entered each month as they accrue.
3. **Gross Profit**. Total cost of sales is subtracted from total sales.
4. **Expenses**. Total direct and indirect expenses for each department are entered in the "Estimate" columns. The "Actual" expenses are entered each month as they accrue. The advantage of departmentalizing expenses is that each segment of the business is held directly accountable. This often proves valuable when analyzing where cutbacks, expansion, or other actions might take place, and time is saved when reviewing specific numbers for segments of the operation. This system can also be useful for monitoring the performance of department managers. Direct expenses may be either fixed or variable in nature. Fixed expenses are those costs that remain fairly constant, regardless of business volume. For example, if a charter department is established as a profit center, pilot salaries and aircraft lease payments are examples of direct fixed expenses. Variable expenses, on the other hand, vary directly with business volume. If using aircraft flight hours as the volume, then fuel and maintenance costs would be examples of direct variable costs. The more flying, the higher the expenses.

   Overhead (indirect) expenses are typically allocated costs and are fixed. Generally, they cannot be attributed to one particular department. Costs which may fit this description are administrative salaries, telephone, utilities, taxes, rent, advertising/ promotion, office supplies, insurance, professional services, and interest. These indirect expenses must be allocated in an equitable, justifiable method to each department or profit center.

   One accepted method is to allocate indirect expenses on a square footage basis. If the charter department occupies 20 percent of the total square footage of the facility, then 20 percent of the rent, utilities, administrative, and other indirect costs can be allocated to that profit center.

   Another common allocation method that works in some situations is to allocate indirect costs as a percentage of sales for that profit center. If the profit center generates 15 percent of the firm's revenues, then 15 percent of the indirect costs are allocated to that profit center.
5. **Net Profit**. Total expenses are subtracted from gross profit to determine net profit. Because the individual departments have been divided into individual profit centers, management is now provided with a powerful financial decision-making tool. No longer will unprofitable or marginally profitable departments be hidden.

The Pro Forma Statement of Income, prepared on a monthly basis and culminating in an annual projection for the next business fiscal year, should be revised not less than quarterly. It must reflect the actual performance achieved in the immediately preceding three months to ensure its continuing usefulness as one of the two most valuable planning tools available to management.

Should the Pro Forma reveal that the business will likely not generate a profit from operations, plans must immediately be developed to identify what is necessary to at least break even: increase volume, decrease expenses, or put more owner capital in to pay some debts and reduce interest expenses.

XYZ Aviation Company
Pro Forma Statement of Income
December 31, 20__

Departments	Sales		Cost of Sales		Gross Profit		Expenses: Direct: Fixed		Expenses: Direct: Variable		Expenses: Overhead Indirect		Net Profit	
	Est.	Act.	Est.	Act.	Est.	Act.	Est.	Act.	Est.	Act.	Est.	Act.	Est.	Act.
Fueling														
Used Aircraft														
New Aircraft														
Charter/Air Taxi														
Rental														
Flight Training														
Hanger Mgmt.														
Aircraft Mgmt.														
Maintenance														
Parts														
Avionics Sales														
Paint Operations														
Display Case Sales														
Totals														

Figure 14-3 Pro Forma Statement of Income for XYZ Aviation Company

Break-Even Analysis

The break-even point means a level of operations at which a business neither makes a profit nor sustains a loss. At this point, revenue is just enough to cover expenses. Break-even analysis enables the firm to study the relationship of volume, costs, and revenue to determine this point.

Break-even analysis requires the FBO owner/manager to define a sales level in terms of revenue dollars to be earned within a given accounting period at which the business would earn a before-tax profit of zero. This may be done by employing one of various formula calculations to the business estimated sales volume, estimated fixed costs, and estimated variable costs.

Ordinarily, the volume and cost estimates assume the following conditions:

1. A change in sales volume will have no effect on selling prices.
2. Fixed expenses will remain the same at all volume levels.
3. Variable expenses will increase or decrease in direct proportion to any increase or decrease in sales volume.

The steps for calculating the break-even point are as follows:

1. Obtain a list of expenses incurred by the company during its past fiscal year.
2. Separate the expenses into either a variable or a fixed expense classification.
3. Express the variable expenses as a percentage of sales. For example, let's assume gross income (sales) was $1,200,000; fixed expenses, $400,000; variable expenses, $720,000; and net income, $80,000. Variable expenses are 60 percent of sales ($720,000 divided by $1,200,000). This would mean that 60 cents of every sales dollar is required to cover variable expenses. Only the remainder, 40 cents of every dollar, is available for fixed expenses and profit.
4. Substitute the information gathered in the preceding steps in the following basic break-even formula to calculate the break-even point.

$$S = F + V$$

Where: S = Sales at the break-even point
F = Fixed expenses
V = Variable expenses expressed as a percentage of sales

This formula means that when sales revenues equal the fixed expenses and variable expenses incurred in producing the sales revenues, there will be no profit or loss. At this point, revenue from sales is just sufficient to cover the fixed and the variable expenses. In this formula "S" is the break-even point.

Using the numbers in step 3, the break-even point may be calculated as follows:

$$S = F + V$$
$$S = \$400{,}000 + 0.60S$$
$$1.00s - 0.60S = \$400{,}000$$
$$0.40S = \$400{,}000$$
$$S = \$1{,}000{,}000$$

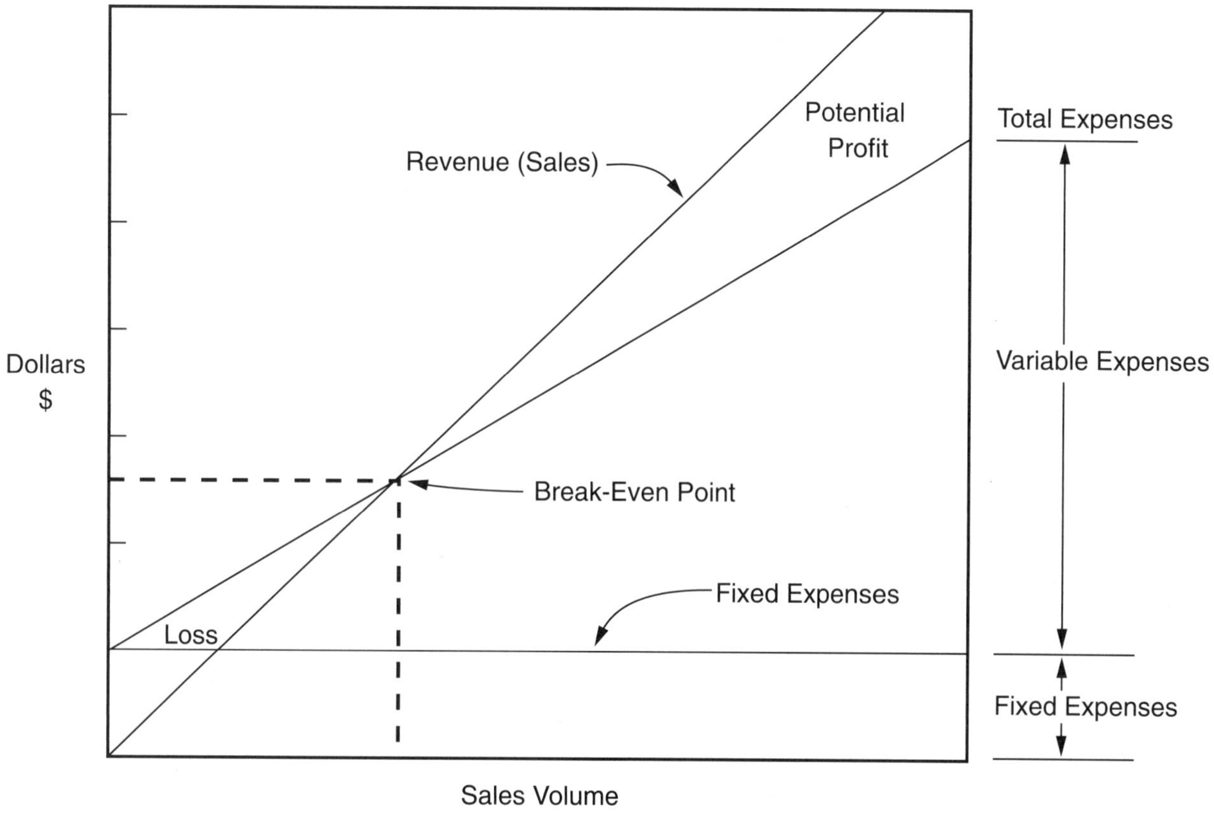

Figure 14-4 Break Even Chart

The break-even formula can be modified to show the dollar sales required to obtain a certain amount of desired net income (or loss). To do this, let S equal the sales required to obtain a certain amount of net income (or loss), say $80,000. The formula then reads:

S = F + V + Desired Net Income	S = F + V + Desired Net Loss
S = $400,000 + .60S + $80,000	S = $400,000 + .60S + $80,000
1.00S –.60S = $480,000	1.00S +.60S = $320,000
.40 = $480,000	.40 = $320,000
S = $1,200,000	S = $800,000

Break-even analysis may also be represented graphically by charting the sales dollars required to break even as shown in Figure 14-4.

Budgeting and Cost Comtrol

Budgets are detailed plans that represent set objectives against which to measure results. They are valuable management tools. In effect, they are blueprints that enable the firm to anticipate what will be, establish specific objectives, and chart the right course to assist the business in attaining those objectives.

Additionally, by monitoring what happens as the firm passes through the budget period, management will be in a position to make necessary adjustments to keep the plan on target.

Cash flow budgets identify when cash is expected to be received and when it must be spent to pay bills and debts. It shows how much cash will be needed to pay expenses and when it will be needed. It also allows the manager to identify where the necessary cash will come from. For example, will it be internally generated from sales and the collection of accounts receivable—or must it be borrowed? (The cash flow budget deals only with actual cash transactions; depreciation and amortization of goodwill or other noncash expense items are not considered.)

The cash flow budget, based on management estimates of sales and obligations, identifies when money will be flowing into and out of the business. It enables management to plan for shortfalls in cash resources so short-term working capital loans may be arranged in advance. It allows management to schedule purchases and payments in a way that enables the business to borrow as little as possible. Because all sales are not cash sales, management must be able to forecast when accounts receivable will become "cash in the bank" and when expenses, whether regular or seasonal, must be paid so cash shortfalls will not interrupt normal business operations. The cash flow budget enhances control by allowing management

Report of Actual and Budgeted Fuel Sales
for the Year Ending December 31, 20__

Actual	Fuel Sales ($) Budgeted	Quarterly	Variations From Budget (Under) Cumulative
1st Quarter	$	$	$
2nd Quarter			
3rd Quarter			
4th Quarter			

Figure 14-5 Break Even Chart

to continually compare actual receipts and disbursements against forecast amounts. This comparison helps management to identify areas for timely improvement in financial management.

By closely watching the timing of cash receipts and disbursements, cash balance on hand, and loan balances, management can readily identify such issues as deficiencies in collecting receivables, unrealistic trade credit or loan repayment schedules. Surplus cash that may be invested on a short-term basis or used to reduce debt and interest expenses temporarily can be recognized. In short, it is the most valuable tool management has at its disposal to refine the day-to-day operation of a business. Additionally, it is an important financial tool bank lenders evaluate when a business needs a loan, for it demonstrates not only how large a loan is required, but also when and how it can be repaid.

The cash flow budget can be prepared for any period of time. However, a one-year budget matching the fiscal year of the business is generally recommended. As in the preparation and use of the Pro Forma Statement of Income, the cash flow budget should be prepared on a monthly basis for the next year. It should be revised not less than quarterly to reflect actual performance in the preceding three months of operations to check its projections.

In order to make the most effective use of cash flow budgets to plan profits, reporting devices have to be established. These reports and reviews enable management to compare actual performance with budgeted projections and maintain control of the operations. They can be established for sales, cost of goods sold, selling expenses, administrative expenses, direct labor, and other areas. Two typical budget reports are shown in Figures 14-5 and 14-6.

Cash flow budgets allow the owner/manager to anticipate problems rather than react to them after they occur. It permits comparison of actual receipts and disbursements against projections to identify errors in the forecast. If cash flow is analyzed monthly, the manager can correct the cause of the error before it harms profitability.

Types, Use, and Sources of Capital

The capital to finance a business has two major forms: debt and equity. Debt (creditor money) comes from trade credit, loans made by financial institutions, leasing companies, and customers who have made prepayments on orders. Equity is money received by the company in exchange for some portion of ownership. Sources include the entrepreneur's own money; money from family, friends, or other nonprofessional

Budgeted Report on Administrative Expenses
for the Year Ending December 31, 20__

Month of__________			Year to Date			
Budget	Actual	Variation	Budget	Actual	Variation	Remarks

Figure 14-6 Administrative Expenses Budget

investors; money from venture capitalists; and money from Small Business Investment Companies (SBICs) and Minority Enterprise Small Business Investment Companies (MESBICs), both funded by the Small Business Association (SBA).

Debt capital, depending upon its sources (e.g., trade, bank, leasing company, mortgage company) comes into the business for short or intermediate periods. Owner or equity capital remains in the company for the life of the business (unless replaced by other equity) and is repaid only when and if there is surplus at liquidation of the business, after all creditors are repaid. Acquiring such funds depends entirely on the business's ability to repay with interest (debt) or appreciation (equity). Financial performance (reflected in the financial statements discussed earlier in the chapter) and realistic, thorough management planning and control (shown by Pro Forma statements and cash flow budgets), are the determining factors in whether or not a business can attract the debt and equity financing it needs to operate and expand.

Business capital can be further classified as equity capital, working capital, and growth capital. Equity capital is the cornerstone of the financial structure of any company. Equity is technically the part of the balance sheet reflecting the ownership of the company. It represents the total value of the business, all other financing being debt that must be repaid. Usually, the firm has difficulty acquiring equity capital, at least during the early stages of business growth.

Working capital is required to meet the continuing operational needs of the business, such as "carrying" accounts receivable, purchasing inventory, and meeting the payroll. In most businesses, these needs vary during the year, depending on activities (flying hours, inventory build-up, seasonal hiring or layoffs, etc.) during the business cycle.

Growth capital is not directly related to cyclical aspects of the business. Growth capital is required when the business is expanding or being altered in some significant and costly way that is expected to result in higher and increased cash flow. Lenders of growth capital frequently depend on anticipated increased profit for repayment over an extended period of time, rather than expecting to be repaid from seasonal increases in liquidity as is the case of working capital lenders.

Every growing business needs all three types of capital: equity, working, and growth. The firm should not expect a single financing program maintained for a short period of time to eliminate future needs for additional capital.

As lenders and investors analyze the requirements of the business, they will distinguish between the three types of capital in the following ways: (1) fluctuating needs (working capital); (2) needs to be repaid with profits over a period of a few years (growth capital); and (3) permanent needs (equity capital).

If a firm is asking for a working capital loan, management will be expected to show how the loan can be repaid through cash (liquidity) during the firm's next full operating cycle, usually a one-year cycle. If the firm is seeking growth capital, management will be expected to show how the capital will be used to increase the business enough to be able to repay the loan within several years (usually not more than seven). If the firm is seeking equity capital, it must be raised from investors who will take the risk for dividend returns or capital gains, or a specific share of the business.

Borrowing Working Capital

Working capital was defined earlier as the difference between current assets and current liabilities. To the extent that a business does not generate enough money to pay trade debt as it comes due, this cash must be borrowed.

Commercial banks obviously are the largest source of working capital loans, which have the following characteristics: (1) The loans are short term but renewable; (2) they may fluctuate according to seasonal needs or follow a fixed schedule of repayment (amortization); (3) they require periodic full repayment; (4) they are granted primarily only when the ratio of net current assets comfortably exceeds net current liabilities; and (5) they are sometimes unsecured but more often secured by current assets (e.g., accounts receivable and inventory). Advances can usually be obtained for as much as 70 to 80 percent of quality (likely to be paid) receivables and to 40 to 50 percent of inventory. Banks grant unsecured credit only when they feel the general liquidity and overall financial strength of a business provide assurance for repayment of the loan.

The firm may be able to predict a specific interval, say three to five months, for which it needs financing. A bank may then agree to issue credit for a specific term. Most likely, management will need working capital to finance outflow peaks in the business cycle. Working capital then supplements equity. Most working capital credits are established on a one-year basis.

Although most unsecured loans fall into the one-year line of credit category, another frequently used type, the amortizing loan, calls for a fixed program of reduction, usually on a monthly or quarterly basis. For such loans, the bank is likely to agree to terms longer than one year, as long as the firm continues to meet the principal reduction schedule.

It is important to note that while a loan from a bank for working capital can be negotiated only for a relatively short term, satisfactory performance can allow the arrangement to be continued indefinitely.

Most banks will expect the firm to pay off loans once a year (particularly if they are unsecured) in perhaps 30 or 60 days. This is known as "the annual clean up," and it should occur when the business has the greatest liquidity. This debt reduction normally follows a seasonal sales peak, such as the summer or fall when flying weather is best, and most receivables have been collected.

Sometimes a firm finds that it is progressively more difficult to repay or "clean up" within the specified time. This difficulty usually occurs because (1) the business is growing and its current activity represents a considerable increase over the corresponding period of the previous year; (2) the firm has increased its short-term capital requirement because of new promotional programs or additional operations; or (3) the firm is experiencing a temporary reduction in profitability and cash flow.

Frequently, such a condition justifies obtaining working capital and amortizing loans. For example, management might try to arrange a combination of a $15,000 open line of credit to handle peak financial requirements during the business cycle and $20,000 in amortizing loans to be repaid at, say $4,000 per quarter. In appraising such a request, a commercial bank will insist on justification based on past experience and future projections. The bank will want to know how the $15,000 line of credit will be self-liquidating during the year (with ample room for the annual clean up) and how the business will produce increased profits and resulting cash flow to meet the schedule of amortization on the $20,000 portion in spite of increasing the firm's interest expense.

Borrowing Growth Capital

Lenders expect working capital loans to be repaid through cash generated in the short-term operations of the business, such as selling goods or services and collecting receivables. Liquidity rather than overall profitability supports such borrowing programs. Growth capital loans are usually scheduled to be repaid over longer periods with profits from business activities extending several years into the future. Growth capital loans are, therefore, secured by collateral such as aircraft and other equipment, fixed assets which guarantee that lenders will recover their money should the business be unable to make repayment.

For a growth capital loan, management will need to demonstrate that the growth capital will be used to increase cash flow through increased sales, cost savings, and/or more productivity. Although the building, equipment, or aircraft will probably be used as collateral for growth capital funds, management will also be able to use them for general business purposes. Even if the firm borrows only to acquire a new aircraft, the lender is likely to insist that all aircraft and equipment be pledged.

Instead of bank financing for a particular aircraft, it may be possible to arrange a lease, as discussed in chapter 11. The firm will not actually own the aircraft, but it will have exclusive use of it over a specified period. Such an arrangement usually has tax advantages. It lets the firm use funds that would be tied up in the aircraft, if the firm had purchased it. It also affords the opportunity to make sure the aircraft meets the FBO's needs before it is purchased.

Major equipment may also be purchased on a time payment plan, sometimes called a Conditional Sales Purchase. Ownership of the property is retained by the seller until the buyer has made all the payments required by the contract. (Remember, however, that time payment purchases usually require substantial down payments, with leases even requiring cash advances for several months of lease payments.)

Long-term growth capital loans for more than five but less than fifteen years are also obtainable. Real estate financing with repayment over many years on an established schedule is the best example. The loan is secured by the land and/or buildings the money was used to buy. Most businesses are best financed by a combination of these various credit arrangements.

When an FBO goes to a bank to request a loan, it must be prepared to present the company's case persuasively. Management should bring its financial plan consisting of a cash budget for the next twelve months, Pro Forma Balance Sheets, and Income Statements for the next three to five years. Management should be able to explain and amplify these statements and the underlying assumptions on which the figures are based. Obviously, the assumptions must be convincing and the projections supportable. Finally, many banks prefer statements audited by an outside accountant with the accountant's signed opinion that the statements were prepared in accordance with generally accepted accounting principles and that they fairly present the financial condition of the business.

Borrowing Equity Capital

Equity capital sometimes comes from sources other than the business owner/manager or stockholders. Venture capital is one such source. Difficult to define, it is high risk capital offered with the principal objective of earning capital gains for the investor. While venture capitalists are usually prepared to wait longer than the average investor for a profitable return, they usually expect in excess of 15 percent return on their investment. Often they expect to take an active part in determining the objectives of the business. These investors may also assist the FBO owner/manager by providing experienced guidance in marketing, product ideas, and additional financing alternatives as the business develops. Even though turning to venture capital may create more bosses, their advice can be as valuable as the money they lend. However, venture capitalists are looking for businesses with real potential for growth and for future sales in the millions of dollars.

Financial Planning

Studies overwhelmingly identify ineffective management as the leading cause of business failure. Ineffective management typically results in poor financial planning by management. All too often, the owner/manager of an FBO is so caught up in the day-to-day tasks of managing the operation, seeing that aircraft are maintained, and struggling to collect receivables to meet the payroll that he or she does not plan. There never seems to be time to prepare Pro Formas or budgets. Often, FBO managers understand their business, but not the financial statements or the records, which they feel are for the benefit of the IRS or the bank. Such overburdened owner/managers can scarcely identify what will affect their businesses next week, let alone over the coming months and years.

Success may be ensured only by focusing on all factors affecting a business's performance. Focusing on planning is essential to survival. Short-term financial planning is generally concerned with profit planning or budgeting. Long-term financial planning is generally strategic, setting goals for sales growth and profitability over a minimum of three to five years.

The tools for short- and long-term plans have been discussed earlier in this chapter: Pro Forma Income Statements, cash flow statements or budgets, and ratio analysis. A business's short-term plan should be prepared on a monthly basis for a year into the future, employing Pro Forma Income Statement and the cash flow budget.

Long-Term Planning

The long-term or strategic plan focuses on Pro Forma Statements of Income prepared for annual periods of three to five years into the future. It is difficult imagining all the variables that will affect a business in one year, let alone the next three to five years. However, the key is control: controlling the firm's future course of expansion through the use of the financial tools discussed earlier in this chapter.

The first step is to determine a rate of growth that is desirable and reasonable. Using Pro Forma Statements and cash flow budgets, the next step is to calculate the capital required to finance the inventory, aircraft, equipment, and personnel needs necessary to attain that growth in sales volume. The FBO owner/manager must anticipate capital needs in time to make satisfactory arrangements for outside funds if internally generated funds from retained earnings are insufficient.

Growth can be funded in only two ways: with profits or by borrowing. If expansion outstrips the capital available to support higher levels of accounts receivable, inventory, fixed assets, and operating expenses, a business's development will be slowed or stopped entirely by its failure to meet debts as they become payable. Such insolvency will result in the business's assets being liquidated to meet the demands of the creditors. The only way to avoid this "outstripping of capital" is by planning to control growth. Growth must be understood to be controlled. This understanding requires knowledge of past financial performance and of the future requirements of the business.

These needs must be forecast in writing, using the Pro Forma Income Statement in particular, for three to five years in the future. After projecting reasonable sales volumes and profitability, the cash flow budget must be used to determine (on a quarterly basis for the next three to five years) how these projected sales volumes translate into the flow of cash in and out of the business during normal operations. Where additional inventory, equipment, or other physical assets are necessary to support the sales forecast, management must determine whether or not the business will generate enough profit to sustain the growth forecast.

Often, businesses simply grow too rapidly for internally generated cash to sufficiently support the growth. If profits are inadequate to carry the growth forecast, the owner/ manager must either make arrangements for working growth capital to borrow, or slow growth to allow internal cash to "catch up" and keep pace with the expansion. Because arranging financing and obtaining additional equity capital takes time, this need must be anticipated well in advance to avoid business interruption. Planning is a perpetual process. It is the key to prosperity for any company.

Determining the Value of a Aviation Business

With an increasing number of ownership changes and mergers taking place in the industry, determining the value of airport-based businesses is on the rise. The concept of value is viewed in a variety of ways. Market value is generally defined as the most probable selling price of a property, assuming a willing and informed buyer and seller.

Although this may appear to be a simple concept, "willing and informed" are not always appropriate terms in the sale of a fixed base operation or other aviation business. Frequently, the owner/operator has reached a value conclusion based on various personal issues associated with the operation (time/ money invested, years and effort devoted towards the business, loyalty to employees, retirement needs, and so forth), ignoring the actual foundations that create or diminish the business value.

The process of determining the value of a current business must be based upon a more objective and substantial financial analysis. Business valuation is always a difficult task, but appraising a fixed base operation is typically even more complex. FBOs as ongoing business enterprises are typically valued by two methods:

- Multiples of Earnings Before Interest, Taxes, Depre-

ciation, and Amortization (EBITDA); and/or a
- Discounted Cash Flow (DCF) analysis

Even though the multiple of EBITDA analysis is the most common in the aviation industry, the Discounted Cash Flow Analysis is often more appropriate in situations where an unstable market exists. An EBITDA analysis represents the conversion of one year's income into a value, while a DCF projects and evaluates an income stream over time. Both are appropriate means of valuation and use net income after the exclusion of certain noncash flow items.

EBITDA Analysis

This type of analysis is best suited for a stable operation that has experienced consistent revenue and expense trends historically, with similar trends expected over the next few years. This does not mean that the business has to have been stagnant, but that it has not shown significant fluctuations in either revenue sources or volumes in recent years.

This method analyzes one year's net income, converting it into a value estimate, using a "multiple" based upon the expected future stability of the business, overall economic climate, and financial risks associated with the business. The ability to project stabilized earnings is critical. An erratic revenue or expense history makes projecting future trends very difficult, in turn, reducing the reliability of the analysis.

Another difficult task in the EBITDA analysis is determining the appropriate multiple. Multiples represent the relationship between the selling price of an FBO or other aviation business, and its net earnings at the time of sale, or its pro forma earnings. The multiple is typically derived from sales of other FBOs or aviation businesses and, therefore, is only as good as the information that is available from either the buyer or the seller. Multiples are "all inclusive" of the buyer's perception of the stability of the business, anticipated growth trends, return on equity requirements, motivation of buyer and seller, and terms of sale. Without obtaining all of the details surrounding the transaction, multiples of EBITDA can be deceiving figures.

Discounted Cash Flow Analysis

The Discounted Cash Flow (DCF) analysis is typically more appropriate in an unstable market, which probably describes most FBOs and specialized aviation businesses. An unstable market may be a situation where an operator is experiencing significant growth trends or is acquiring a competitor on the field whereby market share and margins are expected to change dramatically, or a scenario where a market is declining as the result of outside (or even internal) influences. In any case, this method works best when changes are occurring or are anticipated, either positively or negatively.

The DCF analysis projects revenues and expenses into the future based upon historic trends and prospective market and economic conditions. This projection is typically performed on a departmental or classification basis, with each line item addressed individually. This allows for an analysis of specific revenue or expense items that may be expected to grow at a faster rate than others, as well as to account for those items that are fixed or will change as a percentage of another item.

The result is a more detailed "real world" assessment of an ongoing aviation business. As one might expect, an accurate and supportable projection of revenue and expense trends is the most significant factor in a DCF analysis.

The annual net income stream is converted into a present value by a discounting process. Each year's projected net income is "discounted" into a present value, using a rate of return consistent with the associated risk (based on the idea that revenues received in the future are worth less than the same revenues received now). Each year's discounted income is added to provide a current value estimate.

In some cases where a significant lease term remains after the selected discounting period (usually five to ten years), a reversionary value is added to reflect the fact that, if there is a continuing lease, the ability to generate income does not stop after the initial discounting period. The discount rate used in a DCF analysis is based upon investor return requirements given the risks associated with the future income stream. Depending upon the physical and economic characteristics of an FBO or aviation business, the existing lease agreement, the competitive environment, and overall stability of the business, discount rates may vary anywhere from 15 to 30 percent.

The complexity of the EBITDA or the DCF method lies in the evaluation and "recast" of financial information presented by the operator, with every operator offering his or her own method of bookkeeping. For instance, on the revenue side, many operators do not keep an accurate analysis of historical fuel volumes, types of fuel sales (retail, discounted retail, into-plane), or the historic margins associated with each. However, such information is critical to the analysis of both past and future fuel revenues, which may significantly impact the profitability (and value) of the business. Expenses are also often inappropriately or incorrectly categorized. A misinterpretation of either revenue or expense items results in a skewing of the EBITDA, as well as the corresponding value conclusion.

Interest, Taxes, Depreciation, and Amortization

Interest, income taxes, depreciation, and amortization are generally excluded from a business valuation. The result is that the firm is on a cash basis without consideration to the current owner's equity basis, financing terms, equipment basis, or competency of the accountant. All of the above items are a direct result of current owner investment and accounting procedures, not day-to-day cash flow, and differ from operator to operator, depending upon the desired taxation and yield results. By excluding these variable items, a business valuation can be done on a similar basis and a true value can be estimated.

Revenues, Cost of Sales, and Expenses

Revenues generated by an FBO or other aviation business are generally straightforward and typically reflect all income, excluding taxes. However, some forms of revenue warrant a greater risk than others, such as aircraft sales. Consequently, if significant, these revenues and corresponding expenses are typically extracted from overall revenues and analyzed separately, with alternative multiples or discount rates applied.

Cost of sales has a tendency to become a complex issue when evaluating an operating statement. In general, cost of sales represents the actual cost of the materials associated with the sale of specific items, such as fuel, catering, parts, pilot supplies, etc. In the case of fuel, both taxes and airport flowage fees are typically included, since each is part of the direct selling price, and may be reasonably calculated in the wholesale cost of the fuel.

Operating expenses generally create the greatest ambiguity during the valuation process. Every business operator handles the accounting function a little bit differently, with some creative accounting principles applied where appropriate. Although this is fine for the IRS, it is important to assess carefully all categories of expenses to ensure that they are applicable only to the day-to-day operations of the business. A frequent example relates to the owner's compensation package. In some cases, the owner's compensation is well beyond what is normally attributed to the day-to-day management of an operation.

Personal and auto expenses, special management perks, excessive travel budgets, or expenses related to the personal use of company aircraft are not typically included in a recast operating statement for the valuation process. This also goes for excessive legal or accounting expenses which may occur in a given year. Typically, more normalized expense allocations are utilized in the valuation.

Another typical error found in many operating statements involves the repair and maintenance expense category. Improvements to facilities or acquisition of equipment are often deemed operating expenses, when it is more appropriate to recognize them as one-time capital improvements. Only the routine maintenance associated with the facilities and equipment are pertinent operating expenses. A good rule of thumb is that, if it is not a consistent annual expense, then it is probably better categorized as a capital expenditure.

Summary

The most important factor in determining the value of a current business is simply the level of profitability that is currently presented and which can reasonably be expected to continue over time. Profitability is impacted by several significant components, including:

Historic operating statistics

- Type and strength of the revenue stream
- Control of material costs
- Expenses associated with the operation of the business

Other significant factors that contribute to value are location (geographic area, size of airport, services offered); length of lease term and/or operating agreements; competition; and the conditions and terms of existing contracts (air carriers, cargo handling, and so forth).

While the influence of the emotional attachment to the business cannot be understated to a seller, the ability to generate a stable, consistent cash flow is the most significant factor in the creation of value for the buyer.

KEYTERMS

Financial Management
Balance Sheet
Assets
Liabilities
Shareholders' Equity (or net worth or capital)
Statement of Income
Ratio Analysis
Liquidity Ratios
Current Ratio
Quick Ratio
Working Capital
Leverage Ratio
Profitability Ratios
Gross Margin Ratio
Net Profit Margin Ratio
Management Ratios
Return on Assets Ratio
Return on Investment (ROI)
Pro Forma Income Statements
Direct Expenses
Overhead Expenses
Break-Even Analysis
Budgets
Cash Flow Budgets
Debt
Equity
Equity Capital

Working Capital
Growth Capital
Working Capital Loans
Growth Capital Loans
Conditional Sales Purchase
Venture Capital
Short-term Financial Planning
Long-term Financial Planning
EBITDA Analysis
Discounted Cash Flow Analysis

REVIEW QUESTIONS

1. What is the purpose of financial management? Describe the major categories of the balance sheet. Why must it balance? How does it differ from the Statement of Income? Summarize the categories under the Statement of Income.
2. What is the purpose of ratio analysis? Give several examples of liquidity ratios. Define "working capital." What is the leverage ratio? How does Income Statement ratio analysis differ from balance sheet ratio analysis? Distinguish between gross margin ratio and net Profit margin ratio. Why is the ROI ratio considered one of the most important ratios?
3. What are Pro Forma Income Statements? Discuss some of the factors affecting Pro Forma Statements. Describe the steps in preparing a Pro Forma Income Statement. Distinguish between direct expenses and overhead expenses. How can overhead expenses be allocated to individual profit centers?
4. What is the purpose of break-even analysis? What are the basic assumptions in preparing a break-even chart? List the steps involved if preparing such a chart. What is the formula used?
5. Why are cash flow budgets so important? What time frame are they normally prepared for? Give several examples of typical budget reports.
6. Distinguish between equity capital, working capital, and growth capital. What is the primary source for working capital loans? What is the time frame to "clean up" such loans? Why are growth capital loans generally secured by collateral assets? What is the advantage of leasing equipment?
7. What is a conditional sales purchase? How does venture capital differ from other equity finance sources? Distinguish between short-term and long-term planning. Why is long-term planning so difficult for the small FBO? What is the difference between EBITDA analysis and Discounted Cash Flow analysis in determining the value of an aviation business? Summarize the important factors in determining the value of an aviation business.

REFERENCES

Boyd, Bradford B. *Management-Minded Supervision,* 2nd ed. New York: McGraw-Hill, 1984.
Brown, Deaver. *The Entrepreneur's Guide.* New York: Ballantine, 1980.
Burstiner, Irving. *The Small Business Handbook* (Rev. ed.). Englewood Cliffs, NJ: Prentice-Hall, 1989.
Donnelly, James H., Jr., James L. Gibson, and John M. Ivancevich. *Fundamentals of Management: Functions, Behaviors, Models* (5th ed.). Plano, TX: Business Publications, 1984.
Herzberg, Frederick. *Work and the Nature of Man.* New York: Thomas Y. Crowell, 1966. Levinson, R.E. "Problems in Managing a Family-Owned Business," *Family Business Sourcebook*, ed. C. Aronoff and J. Ward, Detroit: Omnigraphics, Inc., 169-174, 1987.

SCENARIOS

1. You were recently contacted by an old friend who is in the process of establishing an FBO at a busy GA airport. He has asked you to join his management team as Chief Financial Officer. This is an exciting opportunity and you gratefully accept. During your first meeting with your friend, now your boss, he asks you to develop a funding plan. In essence, he will need to raise an additional $3 million in start-up funding. What are your thoughts in establishing this plan? What sources of start-up funding are available and how will you recommend those to rely on?
2. Upon graduation from college with a degree in Aviation Management, you and four of your former classmates have decided to start an FBO. A nearby airport has recently issued Request for Proposals (RFP) from firms interested in operating a full-service FBO at the field. As you and your partners consider all factors, you determine you'll need additional funds for working capital, growth capital, and equity capital during your first few years of business. What sources are available for these three types of capital? Which options will you most likely pursue and why?
3. As you finish your first year as owner/manager of a small FBO, you determine your Return on Investment (ROI) to be four percent. Are you satisfied with this performance? If yes, why? If not, what options are available to you at this time?

4. Your group consists of department managers of a large, full-service FBO. The FBO manager has called a meeting of all department managers to report that revenues for all departments have been relatively flat for the past three years. The FBO manager would like to see revenues increase, but feels new ideas are needed. So, she has called each of you into this meeting to brainstorm of ways in which to explore new sources of revenue. What does your group come up with?

5. As you and three partners begin planning your new FBO, conversation turns to profit projections. You would like to realize $50,000 in net income in your first year of operation. With projected fixed expenses of $308,000 and variable expenses representing 58 percent of sales, what level of income is required in this first year to reach your desired $50,000 net?

Notes

Chapter 15
Human Resources

OUTLINE

HR Function
Employment Data and FBO Positions
Staffing
  Recruitment, Selection, and Promotion
  Training
Salary and Benefits
The Turnover Problem

OBJECTIVES

At the end of this chapter, you should be able to:

- Explain the role of Human Resources.
- Describe typical positions at an FBO.
- Describe the steps in a typical interviewing process.
- Discuss how prospective FBO employees are recruited.
- Highlight some issues surrounding the promotion of employees.
- Describe the importance of employee training.
- Discuss the importance of and solutions to the turnover problem.
- Describe the role of HR in setting salary and benefits.

HR Function

Human resources are the most important resources for FBOs. Without a sufficiently qualified and capable workforce, the FBO would not be able to provide necessary services to stay in business. Thus, the function of the Human Resources (HR) Department is extremely important.

The HR Department performs several functions. It assists in recruiting and selecting employees, training and promoting employees, arranging for salary and benefits, and coordinating separation from service. Generally, the HR Department acts in a support role to specific departments within an organization (staff function). In this way, Department Directors and supervisors are able to maintain control of their employees and decide who specifically gets hired, promoted, or fired.

Employment Data and FBO Positions

Anyone who has knowledge of the aviation industry would agree that it is cyclical. The current problem is that we're in that phase of the cycle where there is currently a shortage of various skilled laborers that make up the industry. FBOs are not immune to this shortage and are, in fact, affected to a great degree. Whereas flight instructors once stayed employed at an FBO for two years or so, it is rare today to have one employed longer than eight months on average, because airlines are hiring new pilots with as few as 500 flight hours and 100 multi-engine hours. As one pilot stated, "FBOs need to sweeten the pot for pilots. It doesn't pay much. It's not steady work. What's the draw there?" Certified Flight Instructors typically start earning \$20-\$25 per hour of flight or ground instruction at an FBO.

Mechanics are also in demand by major air carriers, regional airlines, air-taxi operators, and fractional providers. As a result, many FBOs are unable to grow their maintenance facility due to this shortage of mechanics. To compete, many FBOs have attempted to increase maintenance technician compensation steadily during the past decade to reflect the shortage of qualified personnel in the industry, as well as the growth of responsibility and advancements in aircraft technology. Over the next few years, it is estimated that there will be an annual average of 10,000 job openings for aviation maintenance technicians. Aircraft maintenance technicians typically start earning \$20-\$25 per hour at an FBO with maintenance.

In addition to flight instructors and aviation maintenance technicians, the typical full-service FBO will also need to hire and retain personnel in the following positions:

Accountant
Aircraft Pilot
Avionics Technician
Custodial Worker
Customer Service Manager
Customer Service Representative
Line Service Personnel
Maintenance Technician
Management

Office Management/Administration
Sales Personnel

Staffing

Employees are the major resource of any firm. The wise FBO manager realizes that the very basis of the human resources function involves people, and hiring the right people is important. Oftentimes, candidates for entry-level FBO positions do not have any aviation experience. Rather than being frustrated by this, the HR department can focus on those individuals with the right attitude and work ethic and then once hired, groom them into that FBO's culture and way of doing things. Hiring the right people and training them well can directly affect profitability of the business. Specific personnel policies should be included in the firm's operations manual. These become useful guides in all areas: recruitment and selection, compensation plan and employee benefits, training, promotions and terminations, and the like. All attendant systems and paperwork should be carefully designed and personnel files set up to hold application forms, testing and medical records, evaluation forms, changes in status, and so forth.

One practical activity that can be helpful in setting policy is preparation of job descriptions for all positions in the company. Each position should be analyzed and the details then set down on paper. It should include the specific job title, the duties and responsibilities assigned, the relationships with other segments of the business, and any other relevant details. This information will help in advertising job specifications for any opening that arises. In addition, special qualifications needed by the employee should be included, such as the levels of education and experience required, familiarity with special equipment, and minimum physical requirements.

The staffing process includes all activities pertinent to the recruiting, selection, promotion, and training of employees. Outlining the details and correct procedures in advance can prevent errors later on that can create trouble and unnecessary expense.

Recruitment, Selection, and Promotion

The most common recruiting sources include the following:

1. Advertising through classified and display advertisements in newspapers, radio advertising, aviation trade publications and Web sites.
2. Advertising through posted announcements, window signs, and other "point-of need" methods.
3. Recommendations (referrals) from others: friends, employees, and acquaintances.
4. Schools and universities: vocational, academic, technical, business.
5. Employment agencies: public, private.
6. Agencies that provide temporary help.
7. People who just drop by or write in for positions.

Hiring is typically a multi-step process. Among the tools available to help in hiring and rejecting applicants are the employment application, the employment interview, the reference check, tests, and the probationary period for new employees.

Standard employment application forms are available at any local office supply store. They ask for the applicant's name, address, telephone number, work experience, education, health and financial information, and personal data. This form can also be adapted to meet any FBO's particular needs.

First, the HR department conducts an initial screening of applications and resumes to develop a list of applicants qualified for the position. Those meeting minimum qualifications for an entry-level position will typically have a certain level of education and some degree of previous work experience (although not necessarily in aviation). Next, the manager of the department in which the applicant may potentially work reviews the list of qualified applicants and either makes a short list (reducing the larger list to a smaller, more manageable pool of applicants) or decides to accept the list as is. If possible, at least three candidates would be interviewed for a position.

The employment interview is usually the next step and is one of the major tools in processing job applicants. Essentially, it has two aims: (1) to elicit information to supplement the facts submitted on the application form; and (2) to gain useful insights into the appearance, behavior, and personality of the prospective employee.

Because it is comparatively easy for an interviewer to be overly influenced by an outstanding characteristic of an applicant, it is wise to develop and use an interview rating form that touches on all important areas, which will help objectify the assessment of an individual. The art of interviewing comes with experience and any library has books on human resources administration and interviewing techniques.

Interviews can be patterned and directive. This means planning the approach in advance, such as the kinds of questions to be asked, the order in which they will be asked, what in particular the FBO is looking for, etc. Interviews can also be nondirective: Here, the basic approach is to refrain from doing much talking and to encourage the interviewee to speak at length.

There are certain undesirable characteristics or symptoms that in themselves are generally sufficient cause for turning down an applicant. Among the more common factors are the following:

1. evidence of frequent job-hopping in the past,
2. excessive indebtedness,
3. poor communicative ability,
4. poor emotional control,
5. too high a standard of living, and
6. unexplained gaps in the employment record.

As a general rule, it is best for the owner/manager to personally check all references offered by job applicants. A simple form letter and questionnaire can be developed to cover the major points of concern. Contacts with former employers and other references can alternatively be made by telephone. This method is often preferable, not only for quicker results, but also because many people are reluctant to put negative comments down in writing. At times, telephone checking is useful in that any hesitancy about the person in question can be discerned quite readily and probed diplomatically during the conversation.

On the whole, most small FBOs do not test job applicants except when a position requires special skills. Measures of typing speed and accuracy, arithmetic and spelling tests for clerical employees, flight tests for instructors, and demonstrations of ability to run specialized equipment by line personnel all come under this classification.

Some FBOs make use of a variety of paper-and-pencil tests to aid in their selection processes. These range from intelligence tests and general knowledge measures to personality batteries, tests of selling ability, and so forth. These tests are expensive to use and are generally not recommended until a business has grown to a substantial size. Their most valuable contribution is probably in screening out applicants with personality defects or below-average intelligence.

A management team may shy away from testing, however, because of anxiety over conforming to the intent of equal employment opportunity laws. Tests used must be demonstrably both valid and reliable. Medical exams can be helpful when a position requires frequent physical effort, but they can be quite expensive for the employer, especially if the number of employees is considerable.

This next step, interviewing, is very important and varies greatly among organizations. It may involve a multi-step process (a number of different interviews for each applicant), may be with one or several interviewers, and may be in-person or via the telephone. There really is no best way to structure the interview process. It depends on a number of factors, such as organizational resources, number of applicants, level of the position within the organizational structure, and geographic proximity of applicant to the organization. Although FBOs structure the interview process in different ways, one successful FBO invites the applicant to visit the FBO to not only have an interview with the Department Manager, but also to tour the FBO and meet other personnel. If pleased with the applicant, the Assistant FBO manager invites the applicant back for a second interview. During this interview, there is a focus on determining whether the individual truly desires an aviation career or simply seeks a paycheck. If the Assistant FBO manager is pleased, the FBO manager invites the applicant back for a third interview. This process is the same at this FBO whether hiring a line service specialist or a customer service representative. An alternative approach is to have one interview but invite the Department Manager, the Assistant FBO Manager, and the FBO Manager to participate in this one interview. Telephone interviews are typically only used if the applicant is located a long distance away from the organization. At least an initial telephone interview in this situation will allow the company to learn more about the applicant without either the organization or applicant having to incur travel expenses.

Once the employee is hired, the first few days on the job are crucial for the newly hired person. This period is when favorable or unfavorable work-related attitudes are formed and when the employee is either pleased or not. Of course, when an individual is given a schedule and assigned to a department, the person must receive some initial instruction, namely about the company itself, the particular department, and the nature of the work. Especially for new employees in line service, extensive on-the-job training may be necessary. In addition, it may be helpful to appoint an experienced member of the department to coach the new employee. In this same context, a well-prepared employee handbook can be extremely valuable. See the sample Table of Contents in Figure 15-1.

The final phase of the selection process should be a probationary or tryout period of a few weeks or months. This trial period is a valuable step; it will ensure that the FBO has not made an erroneous decision. During this time, the new worker should be observed and frequently rated. It is far more difficult to discharge a below-average performer after many months have elapsed, especially if the company is unionized.

Employees who have successfully survived the probation period are eligible for promotion opportunities within the organization. Many FBOs have positions available from time to time in mid- and top-level management. One option used to fill these positions is to hire individuals outside the organization. This is most appropriate for senior-level management positions that require a great deal of experience. However, for these positions, and many times for lower level management positions, many FBOs subscribe to a "promote from within" policy. This policy has advantages and disadvantages.

Advantages to "promoting from within":

- Known employee
- Ease of recruiting
- Employee knowledge of the company

EMPLOYEE HANDBOOK
SAMPLE TABLE OF CONTENTS

1. Welcome Message
2. History of the Company
3. This is your Business
4. You and Your Future
5. What You Need to Know
   - Working Hours
   - Reporting to Work
   - Time Clock
   - Rest Periods
   - Absence from Work
   - Reporting Absences
   - Employment Record
   - Pay Period
   - Shift Premiums
   - Safety and Accident Prevention
   - Use of Telephones
   - How to Air Complaints
6. These are Your Benifits
   - Vacation
   - Holidays
   - Group Insurance
   - Hospitalization and Surgical Benefits
   - Training Program
   - Christmas Bonus
   - Savings Plan
   - Profit-sharing Plan
   - Suggestion Awards
   - Jury Duty
   - Military Leave
   - U.S. Old Age Benefits
   - Unemployment Compensation
   - Equal Employment Opportunity
7. These Special Services Are for You
   - Credit Union
   - Education Plan
   - Medical Dispensary
   - Employee Purchase
   - Flight Training and Aircraft Rental
   - Annual Outing
   - Bowling League
   - Softball Team
8. Index

Figure 15-1 Sample Table of Contents for an Employee Handbook. Adopted from "Pointers on Preparing an Employee Handbook." Management Aid No. 197 (Washington D.C.: Small Business Adminisration, 1989).

Disadvantages to "promoting from within":

- No influx of new ideas
- Employee not known
- Employee lacks knowledge of the company

Whether a company decides to "promote from within" or seek new talent outside the company, promotion is one role of HR that must be handled with tact. New responsibilities may be met by the immature employee with great difficulty. However, a mature employee possessing great leadership skills can propel a company successfully into the future. In any event, FBOs must endeavor to make promotion an attractive option, as they fill open positions and allow employees to seek higher levels of growth and opportunity within the company.

Training

The training function is a vital, ongoing activity that requires the attention of the owner of a small FBO. Employees need and want training not only to perform their jobs satisfactorily but also as preparation for eventual promotion. Proper training alleviates many problems in the future.

Some of the advantages of well-trained employees are

1. better employee morale,
2. increased sales,
3. less waste,
4. lower turnover rate,
5. increased productivity,
6. reduced operational costs, and
7. speedier employee development.

Often a new employee receives adequate initial training but is thereafter expected to "go it alone." In a healthy business operation, training should be continuous. No worker attains 100 percent efficiency or output at his or her job; there is always room for improvement. Moreover, every worker should have the opportunity to move up the ladder; this implies training for a new and higher position.

In a small enterprise, most training occurs on the job; that is, the immediate supervisor is held responsible for training the worker. But as a business grows, the need for more thorough and professional training becomes evident. It's never too early to begin making plans for better training in the future, if only to fill additional niches as they open up in the organizational hierarchy.

A careful needs analysis of the organization and all the people in it should be the first step in coordinating training efforts. The following steps are recommended in establishing a training program:

1. Make a needs assessment of the company on a departmental, section, and unit basis.
2. Set the objectives to be accomplished through the training efforts.
3. Determine the curriculum (subject matter). Make certain to include not only product, company, and customer knowledge but also skills development and personal adjustment training.
4. Select the types of training that best serve the purposes of the company.

5. Select the training methods to be used.
6. Set up a timetable and schedule for the program.
7. Select the instructor(s).
8. Control costs.

A wide variety of training methods and techniques are available. Among the more frequently used approaches are lectures, small-group discussions, seminars, conferences, case analyses, programmed instruction, committee work, and role playing. Of course, the most commonly found method is on-the-job training; variations of this approach include apprenticeships and internships.

For employees pegged for eventual promotion to management levels, there are still other useful techniques: job rotation, special project assignments, management games, sensitivity training, outside training (at local colleges or by trade associations), and so on.

Salary and Benefits

Yet another role of Human Resources is to coordinate salary and benefits for all employees. Generally, department managers will notify HR of the salary of each newly hired employee (within reasonable salary ranges), so that HR can set up that employee's paychecks and deductions. Deductions take the form of taxes and items such as automatic payroll deductions for government bonds, charitable contributions, retirement account contributions, etc. In addition to these deductions, the employer is responsible for paying worker's compensation premiums, employer taxes, and matching of any retirement contributions.

Companies can pay employees weekly, biweekly, monthly, or yearly. Typically, weekly or biweekly are most popular. Although it would benefit an employer to only issue paychecks once per month, many employees (especially in lower-paying positions) cannot to afford to wait an entire month for their paycheck. Although this may be due to lack of budgeting on the employee's part, cashflow is important and only realizing income once each month makes life more difficult.

In addition to salary, many businesses (including many FBOs) include various benefits in their employment package. These benefits may include life, medical, vision, and dental insurance, contributions to an employee pension plan, matching contributions to an employee retirement plan (such as a 457 or 401k), discount admission to area attractions, employee discounts (such as 20 percent discount on flight instruction), and uniforms. In total, these benefits may account for 20 percent (or more) of an employee's annual salary. Therefore, salary plus benefits is known as compensation and can be substantially more than an employee's annual salary. This is an important fact to remember as individuals consider the employment package offered by competing FBOs, for instance. Salary is important, but benefits are important as well. Simply ask an employee with no benefits to verify this!

In sum, the HR department plays an important role for an organization by handling salary and benefits. Whether scheduling a speaker to present retirement options to employees, handling paycheck discrepancies, or matching employee retirement contributions, by performing these functions, HR allows line departments the opportunity to focus on their specific areas, rather than exerting time and energy on the ever-important salary and benefits.

The Turnover Problem

One fact of life that any small business has to live with is employee turnover. Every business has it. Some firms lose people at a faster rate than others, but whatever the turnover rate, it always hurts to lose a good employee (financially, as well as psychologically).

There are initial costs involved in locating, interviewing, hiring, and training an employee to the point where he or she reaches full potential. Then there are intermediate costs of doing without that person until a replacement is found. Still more expenses are incurred in acquiring the replacement. Clearly, it is in a company's best interest to keep good employees until retirement; however, this is typically not the case.

People leave their jobs for a variety of reasons. Some leave unexpectedly and for unavoidable reasons: ill health, death, marriage, relocation, return to school, a better paying position, and deliberate terminations for cause. Some losses are avoidable. They may be caused by poor supervisory practices on the part of owners or middle managers, by internal friction and personality clashes, by management's failure to provide proper incentives, or an opportunity to move up the ladder. In these situations, the company is inadvertently losing good employees and then expending more resources in acquiring replacements. Clearly, if a company regularly sees employees resigning, hard questions must be asked.

These hard questions can be asked in an exit interview. Wise FBO Managers make sure that each employee is interviewed, termed an "exit interview," upon departing from the company. Is the employee leaving to accept a higher-paying position elsewhere. Were there personal conflicts with management? Were other employees unkind to this employee? What about safety and security? A review of the exit interview findings will be useful to management in taking corrective action to reduce the turnover rate. This step becomes more valuable as the company grows.

In any event, as FBOs hire new employees, they must take care of their existing employees, and interview those employees resigning. Only by knowing how employees view the organization and the workplace can a company continue to improve for new and existing employees.

KEY TERMS

HR function
Cyclical industry
Multistep hiring process
Job description
Staffing process
Recruitment
Selection
Promotion
Employment interview
Training
Compensation package
Turnover Problem

REVIEW QUESTIONS

1. Describe the HR function. In what way does HR reduce the workload of other departments within the organization?
2. What types of positions do FBOs typically recruit for? Are there any shortages of skilled people to fill these various positions?
3. List the most common recruiting sources.
4. What is the purpose of interviewing? What are the typical steps in a multi-step interview process?
5. What are some advantages of having well-trained employees?
6. Identify the major sections and items under those sections in an employee handbook.
7. Describe the steps to be taken in establishing a training program.
8. Why is employee turnover such a problem?
9. What are some methods of promoting employees? What are the advantages and disadvantages of these?
10. Describe the purpose of an exit interview.

SCENARIOS

1. You are the maintenance manager of a medium-sized FBO. As you arrive into work this morning, your midnight shift maintenance crew reported that two maintenance department employees got into a fist fight during last night's swing shift. At the time, there was no supervisor on duty. Thus, the fist fight was only witnessed by coworkers. Although neither employee was apparently injured, and there were only two to three punches thrown, one of those involved in the fight later mentioned to a coworker that he knew how to "finish him off," referring to the employee he had been fighting with earlier in the evening. Both employees are scheduled to return to work at 2:00 this afternoon. What do you do?
2. As you wrapped up last fiscal year as the manager of a large FBO, an independent auditor's report found substantial loss of inventory. The auditor believes employee theft of company supplies (mainly aircraft parts) is the cause. As you think about this issue, you realize you have no idea which employees could be responsible. What do you do?
3. Your boss, the FBO Manager, has asked you to review the applications and resumes recently received for the vacant Front Desk Manager position. As Manager of Marketing and Customer Service, you feel qualified to do so. What are some things you're looking for in this position? On what dimensions will you rate applicants and short list the few you would like to interview?
4. As Manager of Human Resources for a full-service FBO, you have conducted interviews, performance evaluations, fired employees, and conducted exit interviews. However, you're caught off guard this afternoon as the front desk agent calls to report that her coworker, who just arrived for work, appears drunk. What do you do?
5. In a recent employee meeting at the full service FBO at which you're the Manager of Human Resources, several employees offered suggestions in how to improve the organization and their quality of work life. Larry, a line service employee, would like flexible work hours. He and his wife recently divorced and he needs to pick up his child from school. He would rather work 5:00AM to 1:00PM, rather than his shift of 7:00AM to 3:00PM. Jill, a customer service agent, suggests casual Fridays. She would like employees (including front desk and management) to have the option to wear jeans on Fridays. Lastly, Jacob, a maintenance employee, feels the company needs to adopt an employee suggestion program. This program, he feels, should give cash awards of $100 to employees that submit suggestions that are adopted by the company. At an executive meeting, the FBO Manager asks you, as Manager of HR, to offer your perspective on each of these suggestions.
6. In the middle of an interview for a vacant Manager of Human Resources at a large, full-service FBO, the interviewer asks you to briefly describe your philosophy regarding managing employees. In particular, he would like to hear how you plan to recruit employees, motivate employees, and discipline employees.
7. The FBO Manager has approached you, as Manager of Human Resources at a large, full-service FBO, to discuss

employee wages. The FBO recently completed a study (with your help) on wages at competing FBOs. It appears that wages at your FBO are 5 percent lower than the wages at the two competing FBOs surveyed. This is becoming a problem, as one customer service agent recently departed the company to begin work at a competitor. The FBO Manager wants your opinion on how to address this apparent wage disparity. However, he says that unless we can cut expenses in another budget area, the company is currently unable to implement across-the-board wage increase wages of 5 percent.

Notes

Chapter 16
Future Challenges

OUTLINE

OBJECTIVES

At the end of this chapter, you should be able to:

- Discuss the industry outlook for FBOs.
- Discuss the future challenges facing FBOs.
- Realize the importance of VLJs to General Aviation.
- Explain the challenges of providing exceptional customer service.
- Describe how fuel prices create challenging ties for FBOs.
- Explain the entry of LSA and their role in energizing FBOs and GA.
- Consider the security challenges facing FBOs.
- Explain how consolidation, revenue diversification, and labor issues will challenge FBOs in the future.

Introduction

As seen in the many chapters in this text, the FBO business requires success in many different areas to ensure success for the FBO into the future. Each of these areas is critical to the overall mission of the FBO; yet, they present unique challenges as well.

In this chapter, we'll first examine the outlook for the industry, paying particular attention to various trends seen among FBOs. Next, we'll tackle some serious challenges facing FBOs and consider what FBOs might do in response to these challenges.

Outlook/Trends

Trends are those items that apply to the majority of FBOs in the industry. Any factor which stimulates aircraft sales, in the long term, will help the FBO industry. An improving U.S. economy and growth in corporate net profits also contribute to an improved outlook. Analysts of the industry see the following trends among FBOs as we continue in this new millennium:

1. Long-term contracts between the aircraft operator and the aircraft maintenance facility will provide over 50 percent of that facility's maintenance income. Such contracts will allow preplanned and guaranteed labor-hours, thus allowing the provider to reduce his prices, knowing that he has exclusive access to a specific number of labor hours from a specific customer.
2. We may see the consolidation of individual and independent flight departments at a specific airport, thus allowing reductions in overhead, improved aircraft utilization, and reduced costs. These consolidated maintenance enterprises will in turn have increased negotiating power with their suppliers due to the size of their fleet.
3. FBOs at larger airports, catering to corporate clients, have created business centers to further enhance their service offering. Additional FBOs will also become business centers in the future. They will offer conference rooms, food service, video conferencing, high-speed Internet, fax services, voice mail, and other types of services which transient business aircraft passengers must now seek at an inconvenient downtown location.
4. Some FBO locations/operations may be acquired by or become partners with established hotel chains. Many top-flight American hotel chains now have locations just outside the airport fence. It is an easy migration to being on the airport and providing those services for transient business aircraft passengers. By capturing high-value pas-

sengers on the ramp, it allows vertical marketing within the hotel chains as these passengers seek other amenities and services.

5. Consolidation in the FBO industry will continue. This will not necessarily reduce the number of FBOs in the industry, it will simply reduce the number of independent FBOs and increase individual numbers for larger chain FBOs. Additionally, rather than seeing top-tier markets building opulent FBOs, there will be a continual upgrading of second-tier markets. During the 1990s, the top 40 market airports have experienced improved FBOs. In the subsequent years, the next 100 markets will have a similar improvement. With expanded travel because of spread-out demographics and the influx of fractional ownership, FBOs are facing a higher level of customer expectation.
6. Some FBOs will no longer directly dispense aircraft fuels. At airports which now offer multiple FBOs, it may simply become impractical to maintain multiple tank farms with their attendant capital costs, maintenance costs, and potential environmental liability. A single tank farm will serve FBOs, whereby the FBOs concentrate on the marketing of products and services and simply call upon the fuel provider as needed and charge commissions or fees somewhat like the into-plane charges made by providers of fuel services at commercial airline airports.
7. It is expected that some FBOs will increase sales of non-aviation products. The traditional sale of aviation sunglasses and leather jackets will be vastly expanded and will be managed in partnership with established merchandising firms. Computer terminals, catalogs, and the acceptance of video shopping networks will tend to break down existing barriers. Revenues from these concessions will constitute a large part of the FBOs' potential profits.
8. Local and regional charter services will market nationwide, being tied together through computer networks, whereby passengers can book services well in advance of their needs, while being assured of quality, safety, and dependability.
9. Cities and counties which now are "landlords" for FBO tenants will become partners with these tenants and show an increased willingness to supply capital for the FBO if they perceive that it will create jobs. They will look less towards the per square-foot rental income as a landlord and more towards the creation of jobs in a local community.

Future Challenges

The business of providing services to aircraft and their passengers is an exciting business. At the same time, however, it is a dynamic business. Indeed, just as the GA industry is dynamic, so is the industry of providing aviation services in the form of fixed base operations. Why is this business so dynamic? Mainly due to the changing industry and the challenges the industry presents to the fixed base operator.

Very Light Jets

One new challenge on the immediate horizon is the introduction and growth of very light jets (VLJs). Although small jet aircraft are not new to the world of aviation, the VLJ is considered innovative in many ways. Specifically, VLJs are turbine powered aircraft with a take-off weight of 10,000 pounds or less and certificated for single pilot operations. VLJs offer four to nine passenger seats, cruise speeds around 400 miles per hour, and an operating range between 1,100 to 2,300 miles. Along with modern turbine engine technologies, these next generation light jet aircraft incorporate highly integrated avionics, along with advanced cockpit automation, refined passenger amenities and simplified aircraft systems designed to reduce pilot workloads.

A significant marketing approach employed by VLJ manufacturers is avoiding the airfield congestion and landside inconveniencies presently experienced by major commercial airports. VLJs allow the traveler to take advantage of smaller GA airports since less congestion affords flexible arrival and departure times while allowing for shorter, direct flights to similar city pairs. As echoed by Vern Raburn, CEO of Eclipse Aviation, "VLJs will neither require nor seek regular access to major hub airports. VLJ passengers will be time sensitive and convenience minded, and they will use VLJs precisely to avoid the hassles associated with large hubs" (AOPA).

The FAA predicts that perhaps as many as 5,000 VLJs will be flying by the year 2016. Additionally, these VLJs will be able to utilize airports with runways as short as 2,300 to 3,400 feet. What does this mean for FBOs? First, even FBOs at small GA airports need to prepare for possible VLJ operations. Obviously, these VLJs will need to be serviced, maintained, and accommodated. By servicing, FBOs will need to offer Jet-A fuel services, and have the facilities and amenities expected by the owner/operator of these $1.0-$3.5M aircraft. Consider if a point-to-point air taxi operator arrives at an airport and requires service by the local FBO. The aircraft will arrive with fare-paying passengers who will need various services within the airport/FBO terminal building. Beyond the building, these passengers will likely be interested in a rental car, catering, a business center, etc. In essence, the FBO manager must not only focus on the aircraft, but on the passengers and flight crew as well. Maintaining these aircraft will require turbine-engine repair facilities, possible turbine-engine run-up areas, power-carts, and possible aircraft deicing. These aircraft will also require tie-down areas, hangars, and security. Much of this is not new to an FBO; however, servicing an increasing number of jet aircraft, in the form of VLJs, may indeed have an impact on the manner in which the FBO is operated, requiring the FBO manager and his/her staff to focus on attracting and servicing this new breed of aircraft.

Fractional Ownership

The growth in fractional ownership of aircraft, especially corporate jet aircraft, will also have a disproportionate impact on the FBO business. Why? Companies such as NetJets (which has more than 600 business jets in operation) typically fly their aircraft significantly more than an equal number of airplanes operated by a single corporation. For example, NetJets operates their aircraft on average 1,100 hours annually, whereas a corporation may only operate each aircraft for 400-700 hours annually. Thus, each NetJets aircraft is similar to two or three business jets simply because they are so heavily utilized. Although NetJets currently has a formal relationship with Signature Flight Support, there is not a Signature located at each airport that NetJets visits. Thus, NetJets searches for new FBOs to partner with, placing an emphasis on the following six criteria: safety, quality of service provided to owners and crewmembers, facilities and amenities, partnership development, maintenance capability, and price. NetJets is aware that poor FBO customer service reflects on their operation as well; thus, if an FBO is interested in attracting companies such as NetJets and riding the wave of fractional ownership, it should focus on these six criteria and endeavor to cater to NetJets clientele.

Customer Service

As discussed in chapter six, customer service is an extremely important aspect of operating a successful FBO in today's competitive GA environment. As such, customer service presents a challenge to FBOs. How can an FBO maintain, and even increase, the level of customer service offered to its patrons, while at the same time controlling expenses, retaining quality personnel, and staying ahead of the competition? Obviously, there is no simple answer. This is especially true with the diverse customers typical of an FBO. However, the focus on customer service must remain at the forefront of everything the FBO does. In fact, customer service should take the back seat only to safety. Many FBO managers would argue that if safety is made a top priority, customer service will follow. However, why leave that to chance? Yes, focus on safety, but also make sure that FBO personnel are trained in customer service.

As FBOs throughout the nation begin focusing on customer service, a smile and a handshake will no longer be enough. The successful FBO must be THE most customer-focused and safest FBO around. In fact, the number one goal of an FBO manager should be to attract customers and based tenants from competing FBOs. One way to do this is to provide superior customer service. This requires empowering employees to satisfy customers regardless of the situation. This also requires staying aware of any customer service initiatives adopted by the competition. Train, educate, and instill the importance of customer service to all employees, including those working the line (who have the first face-to-face contact with customers), as well as the front desk, and management. Whether an FBO brings in a consultant to conduct customer service training on a regular basis, or simply conducts employee meetings on a regular basis with customer service training videos, the wise FBO manager is aware of the need for continued enhancement of customer service throughout the organization. The challenge, however, will be to maintain this focus, without becoming stagnant, and bettering the competition.

Fuel prices

As the price of crude oil surpassed $100 per barrel, the aviation industry gasped. However, although this increase in the price of fuel impacted the bottom line for all airlines (except those with extensive fuel hedging contracts taking advantage of lower prices), people are still flying, and in fact, load factors during 2007-2008 averaged near 85 percent. What about GA? Obviously the impact of rising fuel prices has been greater. Although business aviation remains strong, those flying for recreation may not be flying as much, or may be looking at more fuel efficient aircraft. Indeed, as discussed in chapter two, pilot starts are down, which can be partially attributed to the rising cost of flight training (partially cased by increasing fuel costs). What does all this mean for FBOs? Obviously, FBOs have to be much more cognizant today of the prices charged for fuel. Competition among FBOs based on fuel prices alone has greatly intensified in the past few years. In fact, many GA pilots will travel outside their local area simply to gas up at an FBO offering lower fuel prices. Many pilots stay current on fuel prices by visiting Web sites such as www.airnav.com and www.100LL.com.

The margins FBOs experience between their fuel price and net profit per gallon are relatively thin. For example, if AvGas costs the FBO $3.00 per gallon and truck cost, insurance, fuel flowage fee, maintenance and rent amount to $0.92 per gallon, a retail price of $4.63 per gallon equals a net profit of $0.71 per gallon. Thus, as wholesale fuel prices increase, FBOs generally have no option but to increase their retail fuel prices. The key is to be aware of what the competition is charging per gallon and focus on cost control to the extent that fuel prices can remain competitive. An FBO manager may create elaborate spreadsheets showing their cost for fuel, their indirect costs associated with fueling, their retail price, and their net per gallon on a daily, monthly, and yearly basis. Just as fuel costs are one of the two largest costs for an airline (the other being labor), fuel is one of the largest sources of revenue for an FBO. Thus, a wise FBO manager will continually analyze fuel costs, prices, and net profit on a regular basis. As with most goods, the supply and demand equation holds true at FBOs. With fuel prices lower than the competition, demand will increase, possibly disproportionately. With disproportionate demand, an FBO may actually increase revenues by lowering fuel prices. For example, it is better to sell 10,000 gallons at $3.00 per gallon ($30,000 gross), than 7,500 gallons at $3.50 per gallon ($26,250). The key for the FBO manager is to find the balance where revenues will increase with lower fuel prices; otherwise, revenues will decrease.

Light Sport Aircraft

In an effort to increase the number of student pilot starts and those who continue flying by making flying more affordable and less complex, the FAA, in cooperation with groups such as the Experimental Aircraft Association (EAA), created the Light Sport Pilot rule in 2005. Along with this, the FAA began certifying light sport aircraft (LSA). The requirements to become a light sport pilot in an airplane are 20 hours of flight training, which will include dual instruction, cross-country flying, and solo flights. Additionally, to earn a sport pilot certificate, one must:

- Be at least 16 to become a student sport pilot (14 for glider).
- Be at least 17 to test for a sport pilot certificate (16 for gliders).
- Be able to read, write, and understand English.
- Hold a current and valid U.S. driver's license as evidence of medical eligibility (provided the FAA didn't deny, revoke, or suspend your last medical certificate application). Alternatively, you can also use a third class airman's medical to establish medical fitness.
- Pass an FAA sport pilot knowledge test.
- Pass a FAA sport pilot practical (flight) test.

Technically, there are six different light sport aircraft categories. This includes Airplane, Powered Parachute, Weight-Shift-Control (Trikes), Glider, Rotorcraft (gyroplane only), Lighter-Than-Air (airship or balloon). To be categorized as an LSA, airplanes must have a maximum gross takeoff weight of 1,320 pounds, an unpressurized cabin, a maximum stall speed of 45 knots, a fixed or ground adjustable propeller, a single reciprocating engine, fixed landing gear (retractable for seaplanes), one or two person occupancy, and a maximum speed in level flight of 120 knots.

This new type of pilot certificate and aircraft is becoming so popular, that each year the Light Sport Aircraft Expo is held in Sebring, Florida for the purpose of allowing light sport pilots and others interested in the light sport pilot certificate the opportunity to view the many models of LSA that are available. In fact, the Light Sport Aircraft Manufactures Association (LAMA) has no less than 127 industry members.

What impact will this new type of aircraft and pilot have on FBOs? Similar to the impacts of VLJs, these new light sport aircraft will need to be serviced and maintained. While they won't have any impact on Jet-A sales, most LSA will be thirsty for 100LL aviation fuel. These new LSA will introduce a new breed of pilot to aviation and should increase the activity at FBOs and GA airports. FBOs properly positioned to take advantage of this will have adequate tie-down space, maintenance, and 100LL or aviation diesel. Additionally, it will likely prove beneficial to an FBO if an LSA fly-in is held occasionally. Becoming LSA-friendly won't necessarily be difficult, but an area of focus for the wise FBO manager.

Security

As one may gain by reading this chapter, future challenges are not always new challenges. Security, while always a consideration, took place on front stage after the tragic events of September 11, 2001. While GA airports had always had some form of security in place, an active effort at enhancing security at GA airports (as well as commercial-service airports) began after September 11. As discussed in chapter 13, security is much more of a concern today, and GA airports and FBOs have taken great strides to enhance security. However, future challenges in this area remain. GA and FBOs have been viewed as a weak link in the aviation security chain for quite some time. To prevent continued concern about GA security, FBOs will have to remain vigilant about maintaining and increasing security of personnel, facilities, and equipment. This will remain a challenge because FBOs will always be confronted with the possibility of terrorists using GA to launch attacks on U.S. soil. Indeed, the absence of such attacks spells success for the GA industry and FBOs. Yet, as technology continues to advance, FBO managers must endevor toward enhanced FBO security by remaining vigilant and current on new technology that may be used to compromise FBO security.

Consolidation

Consolidation was mentioned as a trend affecting the FBO industry. This trend also presents challenges. The major challenge centers around the consideration of whether to remain independent or become part of a chain. Arguably, consolidation in the FBO industry will continue. The larger FBO chains will continually seek out successfully independent FBOs to acquire. These larger chains experience great economies of scale and may convince many independent owners to become part of a larger organization. At the same time, however, independent FBOs will have to seriously consider the pros and cons of remaining independent versus becoming part of a chain. Truly, each FBO has a unique situation and as such, becoming part of a chain FBO may or may not be appropriate.

Another challenge associated with consolidation is the "post-consolidation" phase. Just as in airline mergers (when two companies become one), the merging of an independent FBO with a nationwide chain presents challenges. The nationwide chain will promulgate certain directives that will apply to many areas of the business, including training, management information systems, uniforms and logos, and hiring practices. The culture of the FBO will likely change and employees will have to learn how to work in this new environment. Management will also likely have a difficult time during this transition as they no longer have the complete independence in decision making they once had. For these reasons, this phase is challenging, but usually eased with the corporate chain's support in these many areas.

Revenue diversification

FBOs, just like airports, wisely seek additional sources of revenue. If this additional revenue is earned from the same operation or customer base, it is not very diverse. For example, by relying only on fuel sales to pay the bills, an FBO would likely suffer financial distress if fuel sales significantly declined. Therefore to remain successful in the future, FBOs are challenged to seek additional sources of revenue. One example on how to do this would be to begin offering products such as headsets, sectional charts and approach plates, aviation books, and other items which beginning flight students and transient pilots would find useful. An FBO that does not currently offer maintenance or aircraft sales may consider offering these services to diversify revenues.

The management team of one successful FBO considers themselves "opportunists." They are always open to new possibilities and act quickly if a promising situation presents itself at the right time. As a result, this company has a connection with a personal shopper for clients, conducts pilot training in Africa, has an extensive aircraft sales and charter division, and is gearing up to offer mentor pilots to VLJ owner/operators. When asked, the management team of this FBO also sees opportunities for revenue diversification in maintaining aircraft, selling fuel, and selling aircraft. Clearly, if one aspect of this business declines dramatically, the company's revenue base is so diverse that it would not cripple the company. That will be the key to surviving the challenges that lie ahead.

At the same time, however, pursuing too many things may prove disastrous to an FBO. Although it may be best to do a lot of things at one airport, rather than one thing at many airports, each FBO is in a unique situation and, as such, will have to evaluate opportunities one by one. The management staff of the FBO mentioned previously looks at opportunities and asks this question: "If we fail at this, will it bankrupt the company?" In other words, expanding into innovative areas is fine, as long as you don't bank the entire company on it. That way, risk into these unknown areas is mitigated and success is easier to realize.

Labor issues

There is currently a pilot shortage in the aviation industry. Mechanics and other skilled aviation personnel are also in high demand. These conditions make it difficult for FBO to attract and retain experienced professionals. Additionally, FBOs hire more entry-level employees each year than any other aviation service business. As a result, properly staffing an FBO with qualified and knowledgeable employees will continue to remain a challenge. For instance, an FBO may hire a new flight instructor only to see that flight instructor leave after having acquired the minimum number of hours to be hired by a popular regional air carrier. This will force FBO managers to consider various measures necessary to attract and retain qualified employees.

What type of measures are appropriate? It depends on how dire the FBO is in attracting qualified personnel to fill required positions. Clearly, job seekers will have the upper hand as there will be more demand that they can fill. Thus, FBOs must use innovative recruiting techniques to attract these in-demand employees. Higher starting pay rates, sign-on bonuses, and attractive benefit packages will likely be necessary in the future.

KEY TERMS

Business center concept
Consolidation
Non-aviation products
Very Light Jets
Fractional Ownership
Customer Service
Fuel prices
Light Sport Aircraft
Security
Revenue Diversification
Labor issues

REVIEW QUESTIONS

1. What are some trends affecting the FBO industry? Which of these trends do you feel is of most concern?

2. Why are Very Light Jets considered a challenge to FBOs?
3. Can fractional ownership benefit FBOs?
4. How should FBOs meet the challenge of customer service?
5. Why should FBOs be concerned with fuel prices?
6. How can FBOs meet the security challenge?
7. Why is consolidation considered a challenge to FBOs?
8. How can FBOs meet the revenue diversification challenge?
9. Why should FBOs be concerned about labor issues?

REFERENCES

Aviation International News FBO Survey 2007.
Experimental Aircraft Association. http://www.sportpilot.org

SCENARIOS

1. As the manager of a small FBO at a small GA airport (as well as the airport manager), you recently had a discussion with the city manager (your boss). He asked you about these new VLJs on the market and what impact they would have on your small town. He wants you to examine the likelihood of VLJs serving your airport and what your FBO needs to cater to them. What items should you consider?
2. You are currently the FBO manager of a full-service FBO at a large commercial-service airport. This airport has a total of three FBOs on the field. A recent customer survey revealed less than satisfactory ratings for customer service at your FBO. At the same time, you hear that the two competing FBOs offer excellent customer service. How serious should you consider this? What can you do to enhance customer service at your FBO? How will you measure the results of your efforts?
3. Fuel prices continue rising and you know that many GA pilots will fly to other airports to gas up with lower-priced fuel. Here is your situation, as FBO manager of a small FBO: Your last shipment of fuel cost $3.50 per gallon and your other expenses associated with each gallon total $0.98. You desire at least an $0.80 per gallon net profit. Based on these numbers, your fuel would be priced at $5.28 per gallon. However, you must stay competitive. How would you increase your fuel revenue? Charge more? Charge less? Why?
4. As the manager of a small FBO, you are pleased to see the new LSA on the market. How can you cater to the owners/operators of these aircraft? How would you advertise to the owners/operators of these aircraft? What would make your FBO LSA-friendly?
5. Your FBO currently sells fuel and offers flight instruction. Your revenues have been relatively flat over the past two years and you need to increase these numbers. You heard another FBO manager mention revenue diversification, and you feel you need to give this a try. How do you diversify revenue at your FBO?

APPENDICES

Appendix A
Three Week On-site Training Program for a New Aircraft Salesperson

FIRST WEEK

Monday	Date Complete
1. Tour the facilities, which includes an introduction of the sales representative to key personnel. Salesperson should learn: a. Who does what. b. Where it is done. c. Where to get answers to questions. d. Where help is available when it's needed.	______
2. Review company organization, rules, and regulations: a. Who reports to whom? b. What authority do they have over the salesperson? c. What's expected from the salesperson? d. What the salesperson can expect from the company.	______
3. Study salesperson's job description and compensation plan: a. Salesperson's responsibilities and authority. b. Compensation plan. 1. How commissions are computed. 2. When and how commissions are paid.	______
4. Review opportunities for advancement and/or personal and financial growth.	______
5. Conduct an open discussion period to answer salesperson's questions.	______
Tuesday	
1. Discuss company's short- and long-term objectives.	______
2. Study company's "area of responsibility." a. Distributor's retail area. b. Dealer areas and responsibilities. c. Area and product assignments of other salespersons.	______
3. Tour the nearest dealer facility. a. Become acquainted with dealer personnel. b. Understand how distributor and dealer coordinate retail sales activities.	______

Wedneday

1. Study product brochures and underline important product benefits. __________

2. Study the Sales Data Handbook: __________
   a. Demonstrate ability to answer technical questions using the handbook as an aid.
   b. Demonstrate ability to compute operating costs using the computation guides in the handbook.

3. Make a sales call (as observer only) with an experienced aircraft salesperson. __________

4. Critique the sales call with the experienced salesperson and the sales manager: __________
   a. What was the sales call objective?
   b. Was that objective achieved?
   c. Identify problems encountered in the call.
   d. Explain attempted method of solving the problems.

Thursday

1. Study Pilots' Handbooks. __________

2. Study Performance & Specifications data. __________

3. Observe walk-around ground presentation by experienced salesperson. __________

4. Prepare personal checklist for walk-around ground presentations of aircraft. __________

5. Practice the walk-around ground presentation of aircraft. __________

6. Make a ground walk-around presentation of aircraft to the sales manager or sales trainer. __________

Friday

*1. Study flight demonstration manual. __________

*2. Receive a flight demonstration by an experienced demonstration pilot. __________

*3. Restudy flight demonstration techniques manual and prepare notes for personal flight demonstration regimen. __________

Saturday

*1. Give flight demonstration of aircraft to sales manager. __________

*2. Critique flight demonstration with sales manager. __________

*The training schedule can be interrupted at any convenient point to provide necessary flight proficiency training for the new salesperson.

SECOND WEEK

Monday

1. Study local prospect control system. Salesperson should know: __________
   a. How prospect records are maintained:
      1. By the company.

2. By the salesperson.
b. Sales call reporting procedures.
c. How sales activities are coordinated.

2. Become familiar with on-site prospect reference and qualifying materials: ____________
a. Records of aircraft owners.
b. Standard reference materials.

3. Learn how to qualify prospects for: ____________
a. Need for an airplane.
b. Ability to buy an airplane.
c. Desire for an airplane.

4. After a study period, provide the sales manager with: ____________
a. A walk-around ground presentation of the airplane.
b. A flight demonstration of the airplane.

5. Critique the above presentations with the sales manager. ____________

Tuesday

1. Practice walk-around demonstration and flight demonstration of the airplane. ____________

2. Select five good prospects from records of current aircraft owners and explain your choice to the sales manager. ____________

3. Visit the main local library and research the "five good prospects" to obtain precall information. Salesperson should know: ____________
a. The names and titles of key company officials.
b. The type of business activity.
c. The ability of the company to buy a business airplane.
d. The company's probable travel patterns as indicated by:
1. Branch offices.
2. Geographical areas covered.
3. Industry distribution methods and patterns.

Wednesday

1. Make a sales call (as observer only) with an experienced aircraft salesperson. This sales call should be a first-time call on an aircraft owner. ____________

2. Critique sales call with the experienced aircraft salesperson and the sales manager. ____________

3. Use the study period to outline presentation intended for the salesperson's first call on an aircraft owner. ____________

4. Observe experienced salesperson making telephone calls for appointments. ____________

5. Outline telephone presentation to be made when asking for appointments. ____________

6. Set up first sales call appointment by telephoning one or more of the selected "five best prospects." ____________

Thursday

1. Practice walk-around and flight demonstration procedures. ______
2. Make first "solo" sales call on one of the "five best prospects." ______
3. Critique sales call with the sales manager. ______
4. Study procedures used to write up an aircraft sales order. ______

Friday

1. Study aircraft leasing and financing procedures: ______
   a. Complete dummy lease agreement form.
   b. Complete dummy finance agreement form.
2. Accompany an experienced salesperson (as an observer only) on a "second or third-time sales call." ______
3. Critique the above sales call with the experienced salesperson and the sales manager. ______

Saturday

1. Review week's activities with the sales manager. ______
2. Research and select "five nonowner prospects" at the public library. ______

THIRD WEEK

Monday

1. Discuss the "five nonowner prospects" with the sales manager and defend their selection. ______
2. Attempt to make telephone appointments with: ______
   a. Five nonowner prospects.
   b. Or five best owner prospects.
3. Make sales calls and/or demonstrations. ______

Tuesday

1. Study used aircraft market: ______
   a. Blue books.
   b. Company appraising techniques and procedures.
   c. Company policies on trade-ins.
2. Accompany an experienced salesperson (as an observer only) on a used-aircraft sales call. ______
3. Critique the above sales call with the experienced salesperson and the sales manager. ______
4. Make sales calls and/or demonstrations. ______

Wednesday

1. Continue prospecting activities. __________

2. Make sales calls and/or demonstrations. __________

3. Study the preparation of a written proposal and prepare a sample proposal. __________

Thursday

1. Practice demonstration techniques . . . ground and flight. __________

2. Study comparative merits of own and competitive aircraft. __________

3. Make sales call with the sales manager as an observer. __________

Friday

1. Build a qualified prospect list of 20 aircraft owners and 5 nonowners. Defend selections with the sales manager. __________

Saturday

1. Review entire training schedule with sales manager and identify areas that need further study and practice. __________

Normally a sales manager will conduct in-depth interviews with the new salesperson at least once each week during the three-week training program. After several months on the job, new salespersons are generally sent to one of the manufacturers' schools for one of the many professional sales techniques courses.

Notes

Appendix B
Corporate Aircraft Sales Presentation

Appendix B is included to provide an example of a typical transportation analysis presentation. This marketing proposal is completed after extensive fact finding interviews with the prospect. The proposal includes the following essential components: introduction, aircraft selection rationale, financial analysis, and a value analysis. The business aircraft salesperson would present this proposal to the executives of the prospect corporation.

AVIATION SUPPLY, INC.

TRAVEL DATA AND FINANCIAL ANALYSIS FOR MANAGEMENT CONSULTANTS

By
William E. Pulling
and Aviation Supply Staff

To
Dr. Bruce Chadbourne
President of Management Consultants, Inc.

Reprinted with permission of William E. Pulling, 1987
Graduate of Embry-Riddle Aeronautical University
(Financial figures updated to 2002)

AVIATION SUPPLY, INC.

One Aviation Drive
Daytona Beach, Florida 32014

November 20, 200X

Dr. Bruce Chadbourne, President
Management Consultants, Inc.
2000 Prestige Drive
Tampa, Florida 32777

Dear Dr. Chadbourne:

We met on September 29, 200X to discuss your company's new transportation needs and the contracting of my firm, Aviation Supply. As you requested, my team has analyzed Management Consultants' annual transportation data; our findings and recommendations are illustrated in this report.

This report will clearly show and justify the corporate aircraft that best meets your transportation needs. Along with our recommendations, we will present a detailed analysis of the financial impact of operating a corporate aircraft. This financial analysis is composed of the Capital Recovery Guide, Fixed and Direct Operating Expenses and a Cash Flow Analysis (present value) with the effect of the depreciation and taxes. One very important section of this report will be the comparison of the scheduled air carrier to the corporate operated aircraft, in both cost and time. From this report, you will gain a stronger understanding of the positive impact a corporate aircraft presents, as well as the relevant costs associated with its operations.

If I can provide additional information, or if you still have any unanswered questions, please feel free to contact me at work (904) 123–5555, extension 999, or at my home (904) 333–7171.

Aviation Supply and I would like to thank you for the opportunity of presenting this report to you. I am looking forward to helping in the implementation of the new corporate aircraft into your company's operational system. We are also hopeful that this report will answer all your questions and meet with your approval.

Very truly yours,
AVIATION SUPPLY, INC.

William E. Pulling
President

INTRODUCTION

In this world of high technology and multi-million-dollar deals, companies must stay competitive and in tune with changing times. Just as the computer became a vital tool for business in achieving a higher level of efficiency, the corporate aircraft can also increase productivity for the company. Operating a corporate aircraft will not only increase productivity, but will also provide many other positive benefits.

These positive benefits can be subdivided into two main categories: Tangible and Intangible factors. It is essential to discuss the intangible factors at this point, although it is very difficult to assign a dollar and cents value to the direct costs and benefits. They must be evaluated and considered in any study which examines the real costs and benefits of the corporate aircraft. To illustrate these factors, Figure B-1 is used to make the company aware of the scope and nature of these intangible benefits. It is important that top management re-

1. Less executive fatigue—lower stress
2. The competitive advantage of getting there first.
3. Effortless travel versus crowded terminals, inconvenient flights and waiting at luggage lines.
4. Fewer husbandless/wifeless nights for the executives' families.
5. The availability of a superior travel service for use by customers.
7. The aircraft is a symbol of success—customers want to deal with successful companies.
8. Face-to-face communication—closing deals.

Figure B-1. Intangible Benefits

view this list and realize that there are many more benefits than just these eight.

As mentioned before, the other category is the tangible factors. These factors can be illustrated in a dollar value. The remaining portion of this report is dedicated to these cost/benefits which will be completely and clearly discussed. With both the tangible and intangible factors displayed, this feasibility study will furnish the foundation to fully realize the vital potential of a corporate aircraft in aiding a successful organization.

AIRCRAFT SELECTION

By fully reviewing the transportation data provided from Management Consultants, we had originally selected the Beechcraft Super King Air 300. This aircraft is a highly dependable twin-engine turboprop (a propeller driven by a jet engine) and can be purchased for $2,475,000. However, we have reevaluated the data given, and have chosen the Cessna Citation S/II as the best aircraft to meet the needs of Management Consultants. This small business jet is one of the most popular and reliable aircraft on the market today. The purchase price of this aircraft is $3,450,000.

Time/Aircraft Comparison

Both aircraft are excellent modes of transportation in the different categories that they represent. However, when considering the critical aspect of time, the Super King Air 300 would spend too much of it in the air. To illustrate this point, we have calculated the time to and from Pawhuska, Oklahoma (Management Consultants' longest leg at 1030 miles). In this mock situation, we have preset the departure time (7:00 a.m.) and the time allotted for the meeting (6 hours) to be the same in both cases. This will help highlight the flight time of both aircraft. As shown in Figure B-2, the result is the Cessna Cita-

	Citation S/II	Super King Air 300
Departure time (Tampa)	7:00 a.m.	7:00 a.m.
En route	2 hrs. 13 min.	3 hrs. 3 min.
Arrival Time (Pawhuska)	9:13 a.m.	10:03 a.m.
Allotted Meeting Time	6 hrs.	6 hrs.
Departure Time (Pawhuska)	3:13 p.m.	4:03 p.m.
En route	2 hrs. 13 min.	3 hrs. 3 min.
Arrival Time (Tampa)	5:26 p.m.	7:06 p.m.
Total Time Saved Per Trip	1.0 hrs. 40 min.	
Number of Trips (Annual)	30	
Total Time Saved Per Year	50.0 hrs.	

Figure B-2. Time Comparison

Destination	Statute Miles	Citation S/II Flight Time	Super King Air 300 Flight Time
Gainesville, GA	470	1:02	1:25
Montgomery, AL	410	0:54	1:14
*Bartlesville, OK	1030	2:13	3:03
Anderson, SC	430	0:56	1:18
Bessemer, AL	485	1:04	1:28

*Pawkuska's runway is too short for the Citation, so Bartlesville was chosen as the closest airport.

Figure B-3. Time/Speed Saving Comparison

tion S/II saved one hour and forty minutes of valuable flight time, over the Super King Air 300, and allows the executives to be home by 5:26 p.m. the same night.

Although one hour and forty minutes may not seem like a significant amount of time, this will become relevant if expressed over a one-year period. In this case, 50 hours are saved per year on this trip alone.

Total Picture

Based predominantly on the Cessna Citation S/II's time-saving ability, this report would not be complete unless we compared the total time savings on all destinations. The following figures (B-3 and B-4) show the flight time needed by the Citation S/II in comparison to the Super King Air 300, to reach all five of Management Consultants' destinations from Tampa, Florida. Calculations were made using the average cruise speed of 403 knots (463 mph) for the Citation and 290 knots (334 mph) for the Super King Air 300. As illustrated in Figure B-3, the destination ranging between 410–485 miles will save 20–23 minutes when using the Citation. In addition, the farther the destination, the more significant the amount of time saved, as Pawhuska (Bartlesville) shows. Total time savings annually for all five destinations is shown in Figure B-4. As a result, even the small amount of time savings will frequently add up to a significant amount. Your company will save 174 hours per year by operating the citation S/II. A special note, the Citation S/II cannot operate out of Pawhuska due to the length of the runway. The closest airport that can support the operations of the Citation S/II is Bartlesville. Executives who fly into this airport will have a 30-minute drive to Pawhuska, which will reduce the total time savings to 144 hours annually. Even this amount of time saving is meaningful and can be reallocated to an efficient maintenance program for the Citation S/II. This should reduce downtime for the aircraft that causes interference to Management Consultants' flight schedules.

Locations and Operations

It is important to know the destinations where Management Consultants needs to travel. As shown in Figure B-5, a summary of these locations and significant information for operations into these destinations is provided. Further illus-

Destination	Annual Legs	Citation Time Saving/Leg	Total Time Savings (Hours)
Gainesville, GA	80	0:23	30.67
Montgomery, AL	104	0:20	34.67
Bartlesville, OK	60	1:10	70.00
Anderson, SC	78	0:22	28.60
Bessemer, AL	24	0:24	9.60
Total Time Saved Per Year			173.56

Figure B-4. Total Annual Time Savings

Destination	VFR/ IFR	Longest Runway	Fuel Jet A	Distance from City	Arpt Hrs.	Car Hotel
Gainesville, GA	IFR	5,000 x 100'	Yes	0 mi S	daylt	both
Montgomery, AL	IFR	9,001 x 150'	Yes	6 mi SW	24 hrs	both
*Pawhuska, OK	VFR	3,200 x 100'	No	4 mi W	daylt	both
Bartlesville, OK	IFR	6,200 x 100'	Yes	1 mi NW	5a-6p	both
Anderson, SC	IFR	5,000 x 150'	Yes	3 mi SW	daylt	both
**Bessemer, AL	VFR	3,800 x 100'	Yes	4 mi SE	daylt	both
Birmingham, AL	IFR	10,000 x 150'	Yes	5 mi NE	24 hrs	both

*Citation cannot operate into Pawhuska because of the length of runway. Bartlesville is the alternative airport.
**Birmingham is Bessemer alternative if poor weather around Bessemer.

Figure B-5. Destination Summary

trated in Figure B-5, Pawhuska, Oklahoma, is not large enough to support the operation of the Citation S/II.

As expressed before, a 30-minute drive from Bartlesville is required. The meaning of VFR (visual flight rules) and IFR (instrument flight rules) are associated in the aircraft operations and in this report for the purpose of illustrating the availability of the airport. Those indicating IFR will allow aircraft to land and take off in minimum weather conditions with a higher degree of safety. In this case, all of the destinations, except Pawhuska and Bessemer, are available during minimum weather conditions. Bessemer is available only during good weather. As the weather affects the landings, the runway length is another characteristic that determines if an aircraft can land and take off safely. The Citation S/II requires 3,430 feet to take off and 3,140 feet to land. As shown in Figure B-5, all destinations, except Pawhuska, are within the minimum standards demanded for the Citation S/II operations. The other information provided in the Destination Summary is background data which is a small factor in determining operations into and out of these airports. In Figure B-6, the places where Management Consultants has the highest passenger density are indicated by an asterisk (Gainesville, Montgomery and Anderson). These locations show a passenger density of greater than 20 percent. Trip density illustrated in Figure B-7 shows the average range that is being traveled by Management Consultants personnel. In this case, the range being traveled the most is between 420–480 miles.

FINANCIAL ANALYSIS

In this portion of the report, we have enclosed all the financial information, and we have also calculated the impact associated with ownership/operations of the Citation S/II. The following list illustrates the financial information provided:

Figure B-8: Capital Recovery Guide

Destination	Number Traveler	Number Legs	Number Trips	%	Cum %
*Gainesville, GA	5	80	400	29	29
*Montgomery, AL	3	104	312	23	52
Pawhuska, OK	4	60	240	18	70
*Anderson, SC	4	78	312	23	93
Bessemer, AL	4	24	96	7	100

*Most traveled destinations.

Figure B-6. Sample Passenger Density

Range	Number Legs	%	Cum %
<410	104	30	30
410–480	158	46	76
>485	84	24	100

Figure B-7. Trip Density

Figure B-9: Fixed Costs
Figure B-10: Estimated Direct Operating Expenses

From the Capital Recovery Guide, you can see that despite the acquisition price of $3,622,500.00, the Citation S/II will only cost $10,230.00 per month. This amount was derived from 100 percent depreciation of the aircraft and 70 percent return on the purchase price to indicate disposal price in six years. In addition, the benefits of tax savings were also calculated.

As to the disposal price, we at Aviation Supply, are estimating all Cessna Citations at 70 percent of acquisition price. We feel with the combination of today's strong used aircraft market, the issue over manufacturing products liability, and the popularity of the Cessna Citation S/II, that 70 percent is a realistic calculation. At this time, we would like to address the low utilization in the first year. With present transportation data, Management Consultants' planned utilization is only 404 hours. According to the National Business Aviation Association (NBAA), the Cessna Citation should have an annual utilization of 312 hours on the low side, 955 hours on the high side and 619 hours on the average. As you can see, Management Consultants will be within the lower limit by 92 hours (404 hours–312 hours). We at Aviation Supply feel in

Citation S/II—Six Year Analysis

Aircraft Acquisition Cost			
Purchase Price			$3,450,000.00
State Sales Tax @	5%		$ 172,500.00
Total			$3,622,500.00
Depreciation Expense			$3,622,500.00
Resale Value @	70%		$2,415,000.00

Six-Year Capital Recovery

Tax Savings (39% corporate tax rate)			
Depreciation		$ 1,412,755	
Total Tax Savings			$1,412,775.00
Disposal of Aircraft			
Resale Value		$ 2,415,000	
Less Taxes on Sale		$ 941,850	
Net Proceeds From Sale			$1,473,150.00
Total Capital Recovered			$2,885,925.00
Total Acquisition Cost			$3,622,500.00
Total Capital Recovered			$2,885,925.00
Net Cost of Ownership	Six Years		$ 736,575.00
	Per Year		$ 122,763.00
	Per Month		$ 10,230.00

Figure B-8. Capital Recovery Guide

Expense Category	Estimated Cost Per Year
Crew Salaries	
Captain	$ 67,425
Co-Pilot	$ 47,352
Benefits	$ 34,433
Hangar Rental	$ 20,913
Insurance	
Hull (Physical Damage Coverage @ .28 per $100	$ 9,660
Single Limit Liability—100 M Per Occurrence	$ 14,000
Admitted Liability—$500,000/seat	$ 2,250
Recurrent Training	$ 13,400
Navigation Chart Service	$ 3,061
Computer Mx. Program	$ 1,850
Aircraft Modernization plus Uninsured Damage	$ 13,800
Refurbishing	$ 15,540
Weather Service	$ 2,300
Total Annual Fixed Costs	$ 245,984

Figure B-9. Fixed Costs

Expense Category	Estimated Cost Per Hour
Fuel (1)	$ 509.96
Fuel Additives—2% of fuel	$ 4.18
Mature Level Maintenance (2)	
Labor at $74.00 per hour	$ 168.72
Parts-Airframe, Avionics and Engine Consumables	$ 137.28
Engine Restoration (3)	$ 176.54
Miscellaneous Expenses	
Crew Expenses	$ 135.00
Landing/Parking Fees	$ 11.33
Supplies/Catering	$ 36.00
Total Direct Operating Expenses Per Hour	$ 1,179.01

NOTES:

(1) 209 gallons per hour

(2) 2.28 labor hours per flight hour

(3) 2000 Jet Support Services "Complete" for (2) Pratt & Whitney Canada JT15D-4B.

Figure B-10. Estimated Direct Operating Expenses

order to receive a proper hourly utilization from this aircraft, it should be flown around the 600 hours per year. Considering that this is Management Consultants' first year to operate a corporate aircraft, we are confident that utilization will increase. It is well-known in corporate aviation that once a company exposes its personnel to an aircraft, more personnel on the average, will want to use it. However, if the utilization does not increase, there are several options open to your company, ranging from leaseback to chartering. In preparing this report, we tried to provide vital information for the present, as well as the future. In addition, we wanted to illustrate a detailed analysis of the cost associated with the operation and ownership of a Cessna Citation S/II.

CASH FLOW/ PRESENT ANALYSIS

Review the following items to ensure an understanding of the variables in the cash flow analysis.

Cash Flow Analysis Assumption

Finance Rate	10% APR
Years Financed	9 (108 months)
Acquisition Price	$ 3,622,500
Downpayment (20%)	$ 724,500
Amount Financed	$ 2,898,000
Inflation Factor	3.1%
Federal Income Tax Rate	39%
Sales Tax Rate	5%
Monthly Payment	$ 40,800
Depreciation	Double Declining

The following cash flow analysis (shown under Figure B-11) is simply a breakdown of cost over the next six years. Starting with Total Expenditures, these represent all the costs to support the aircraft and are before the effects of taxes. The tax effect on Total Expenditures is shown under Total Tax Reduction. The change in Cash Flow represents the difference between Total Change (before taxes) and Total Tax Reduction. Finally, Total Cash Flow is the sum of all the Cash Flows over the six-year period. If you take this amount and divide it by the total six-year utilization, (2424 hrs.) you determine the Cost Per Hour. In this case, the Cessna Citation S/II will cost $1,901 per hour of use, over the next six years of operation.

VALUE ANALYSIS

In this section, we will show how the corporate aircraft can be a time machine. This is best illustrated when the corporate aircraft is compared to scheduled air carriers. The airlines operate on the basis of moving groups of people, on their timetable, and to predetermined locations. However, the principle behind a corporate aircraft is the flexibility to move individuals, or small groups, when and where they want to go.

In this comparison between the corporate aircraft and the scheduled air carriers, we have selected the trip between Tampa, Florida, and Bessemer, Alabama. Management Consultants has indicated that its personnel must travel 12 times a year into Bessemer, with an average of four persons per trip. Bessemer is located 15 miles southwest of Birmingham, the largest city that can support air carrier operations. As mentioned before, Bessemer can handle the Citation S/II during good weather only; during poor weather, Birmingham would be used. For this comparison, we are operating the corporate aircraft into Bessemer.

At the present, Delta Airlines cannot efficiently meet Management Consultants' requirements. Delta can have your four (4) executives in Burmingham by 8:23 a.m. by departing Tampa at 6:15 a.m. and having an unproductive one-hour layover in Atlanta. After arriving in Birmingham, your executives would hve to rent a car from Budget, Hertz, or National and drive to Bessemer for their 10:00 a.m. meeting. The driving time one way will be approximately 15 to 20 minutes under normal driving conditions. By our calculation, your executives would arrive one hour before the appointed time. We must also state that all our calculations are dependent upon the ability of the airline to provide an on-time schedule, which is not always the case.

According to Delta, on the return trip, the flight would depart at 7:50 p.m. This would give the executives two hours and fifty minutes waiting for the flight, boarding and flying to Atlanta for a one-hour and seven-minute wasteful layover, and finally arriving at Tampa around midnight. So, the total time of this trip would be 18 hours. We at Aviation Supply feel that this is too long a day to ask employees to work.We would recommend the executives stay overnight and fly back the next morning. However, by doing so, you would increase the cost for the trip. In this scenario, you can clearly see that the airline wastes your executives valuable time and also increases the cost of travel.

On the other side of the coin, the corporate aircraft can provide your company with a means of travel that would work to your schedule. With the same destination illustrated in the airline scenario, the Citation S/II can fly direct/non-stop to Bessemer. The airport at Bessemer is only four miles southeast of the city, a short taxi cab ride to the meeting place. After the meeting, the aircraft will leave once all four executives are onboard and will have them back in Tampa by 4:38 p.m. The total time involved in this trip is 9 hours and 38 minutes. This would be a reasonable amount of time for an executive to work. Plus you would not have the additional cost of hotel and car rental. The corporate aircraft can save your company

Input Data:			
Aircraft Cost	$ 3,450,000	Federal Income Tax Rate: 39%	Monthly Payment: $40,800
State Sales Tax @ 5%	$ 172,500	Finance Rate: 10% APR 9	Years Inflation Rate: 3.1%
Total Acquisition Cost	$ 3,622,500	Money Value Rate: 15%	Annual Hrs of Utilization: 404

Expenditures	Year 0	Year 1	Year 2	Year 3	Year 4	Year 5	Year 6
Fixed Costs		$ 245,984	$ 253,610	$ 261,471	$ 269,577	$ 277,934	$ 286,500
Down Payment (20%)	$ 724,500						
Balance of Purchase	$ 2,898,000						
Principal Payment		$ 209,217	$ 231,125	$ 255,327	$ 282,063	$ 311,598	$ 344,227
Interest Payment		$ 280,383	$ 258,476	$ 234,274	$ 207,538	$ 178,002	$ 145,374
Loan Balance Payoff							$ 1,264,443
Taxes Due on Sale							$ 941,850
Operating Expenses		$ 476,320	$ 491,086	$ 506,310	$ 522,005	$ 538,187	$ 554,871
TOTAL EXPENDITURES	$ 3,622,500	$ 1,211,904	$ 1,234,297	$ 1,257,382	$ 1,281,183	$ 1,305,721	$ 3,537,315
CASH SOURCES							
Aircraft Loan	$ 2,898,000						
Disposal of Aircraft (70%)							$ 2,415,000
TOTAL SOURCES	$ 2,898,000						$ 2,415,000
TOTAL CHANGE (before taxes)	$ (724,500)	$ (1,211,904)	$ (1,234,297)	$ (1,257,382)	$ (1,281,183)	$ (1,305,721)	$ (1,122,315)
TAX REDUCTIONS							
Fixed Cost		$ 95,934	$ 98,908	$ 101,974	$ 105,135	$ 108,394	$ 111,755
Depreciation		$ 282,555	$ 452,088	$ 271,253	$ 162,752	$ 162,752	$ 81,376
Interest		$ 109,349	$ 100,806	$ 91,367	$ 80,940	$ 69,421	$ 56,696
Operating Expenses		$ 185,765	$ 191,524	$ 197,461	$ 203,582	$ 209,893	$ 216,400
TOTAL TAX REDUCTION		$ 673,603	$ 843,326	$ 662,055	$ 552,409	$ 550,460	$ 466,277
CHANGE IN CASH FLOW	$ (724,500)	$ (538,301)	$ (609,029)	$ (595,327)	$ (728,744)	$ (755,261)	$ (656,088)

TOTAL CASH FLOW	$ (4,607,280)	Cost Per Mile	(Average Annual Cost)	$ 767,800	$4.11
Cost Per Hour	$ 1,901		(Cruise Speed x Annual Hrs)	463 x 404	
Net Present Value Cost	$ (3,120,627)	Cost/Seat Mile	(Cost Per Mile)	$ 4.11	$0.59
			(Passenger seats)	7	

Explanatory Notes for Purchase Analysis

1) Loan balance payoff is $1,264,443 because three years remain on the financing period.
2) Depreciation method is double declining balance method. Basis is equal to 100% of $3,622,500.00 (acquisition cost).
3) Deductible expenses includes fixed cost, depreciation, interest, and operating expenses. All of these items have had a 3.1% inflation factor calculated in.
4) Cash received at sale is Aviation Supply's estimate that the Citation S/II sale value after six years will be 70%. This is $2,415,000.00 minus taxes of $941,850.
5) Total Cash Flow indicates the total after-tax cost of ownership for the Cessna Citation S/II over six years.
6) Cost Per Hour is the average annual after-tax cost per hour of owning and operating the Citation S/II over the six year period.
7) Present Value Cost is derived from the discount rate of 15%. It shows the actual cash amount (in today's dollars) of the total net cash flow.

Figure B-11. Citation S/II Cash Flow Analysis

Tampa to Bessemer

	Airline (Delta)	Corporate Aircraft Citation S/II (6)
1. Office to Airport	:20	:20
2. Terminal Boarding Checkin—Atlanta	1:30	:10
3. En route Time	1:38	1:04
4. Deplaning Time	:15	:10
5. Airport to Meeting	:26	:20
	4:09	2:0

NOTES:
1. Office to Airline (Delta)/Airport is the same.
2. :30 boarding time (require by airline per regulation) plus 1:00 layover at Atlanta.
5. Deplaning, check-out rent-a-car, and the drive to Bessemer from Birmingham.
6. No notes for the corporate aircraft side.

Figure B-12. Time Comparison (one leg)

time and this is illustrated in Figure B-12, Time Comparison (one leg).

As can be seen, the time saved by using the Citation S/II is a significant amount. More important than the time savings are the intangible factors. By using the Citation S/II, your executives, can fly in comfort, are productive while en route, avoid airline layovers, and can return to their families within the same day. The latter two reasons may very well influence the length of time these executives will stay at Management Consultants, Inc.

The Bessemer illustration is just one location Management Consultants must travel to. The same time saving can be found when comparing the other five cities your company executives must visit. The location of some of the other cities may lead one to believe that the airlines are not servicing the business people.

In addition to the time saving and the intangible benefits, you will find an analysis of the cost associated with flying the corporate aircraft versus the airline. Figures B-13 and B-14 will illustrate the true benefits of the corporate aircraft.

SUMMARY

In this report, we have shown you all of the considerations involved with the acquisition of a Cessna Citation S/II. We at Aviation Supply Inc. fully recommend this aircraft because the Cessna Citation S/II will meet the needs of your transportation requirements at the present time and also in the future. As explained, the Cessna Citation's hourly utilization for the first year is low (but within the limitations), however, it will increase with exposure.

Again, my team and I would like to thank you for allowing us to bring this important information to you. I am hopeful that the information will enable you to understand the positive benefits and the total impact of the Citation S/II to Management Consultants. I have enjoyed preparing this report for you and look forward to hearing from you soon.

AIRLINE (Delta)

1. *Ticket Cost*		
$499.00 x 96 Trips		$47,904.00
Less 39% Tax Savings		-18,682.56
Total Cost of Airline Tickets		$29,221.44
2. *Value Per Man Hour*		
$\text{VMH} = \dfrac{\$120{,}000 \times 3.1}{2100} =$	$ 177.14	
3. *Cost of Executive Time*		
4.15 hrs. x 96 trips x $177.14		70,572.58
4. *Productivity Credit (15%)*		
1.63 hrs. x 96 trips x 177.14 -	$ 27,718.87	
Less 15% Productivity Factor	4,157.83	
Total Cost of Executive Time		$66,414.75
5. *Other Business Expenses*		
Hotel (4 rooms @ $95.00 x 12 times)		$ 4,560.00
Food ($45/man per day for 1.5 days x 12 times)		3,240.00
Car (2 days @ $52/day x 12 times)		1,248.00
Business Expenses		9,048.00
Less 39% Tax Savings		-3,528.72
Total Business Expenses		$ 5,519.28

Airline Cost Summary:

Total Ticket Costs	$ 29,221.44
Total Executive Time Cost	$ 66,414.75
Total Business Expenses	$ 5,519.28
Total Cost for Airline	$101,155.47

NOTES:

1. 96 Trips = 24 legs/year x 4 executives
2. $\text{VMH} = \dfrac{\text{Annual Salary} \times 3.1\ \text{(Support Factor)}}{42\ \text{hrs./week} \times 50\ \text{weeks/year}}$
3. 4.15 hours represents Total Trip Time.
4. 1.63 hours represents Actual Flight Time.
5. 12 times = 12 times/year to Bessemer.

Figure B-13. Tampa—Atlanta—Bessemer

CORPORATE AIRCRAFT (CITATION S/II)

1. *Aircraft Costs*		
$1,901.00/hr x 1.07 hrs. x 24 legs		$48,817.68
2. *Cost of Executive Time*		
2.07 hrs. x 96 trips x $177.14		$35,201.26
3. *Productivity Credit (75%)*		
1.07 hrs. x 96 trips x $177.14 =	$ 18,195.82	
Less 75% Productivity Factor =		-13,646.87
Total Cost of Executive Time		$21,554.40
Corporate Aircraft (Citation S/II):		
Total Aircraft Cost		$48,817.68
Total Executive Time Cost		21,554.40
Total Cost for Aircraft		$70,372.08
Total Comparison		
Total Airline Cost	$101,155.47	
Total Corporate Aircraft	70,372.08	
Savings/Year		$30,783.39
$1,282.64 Saved by Citation per Leg		

NOTES:

1. $1,901.00 is the operating cost per hour.
2. 1.07 is the En Route Time.
3. 2.07 hours is the Total Trip Time.

Figure B-14. Tampa—Bessemer

Appendix C
Sample FBO Lease Agreement

THIS AGREEMENT is made effective July 1, 2008, by and between the AVIATION AUTHORITY, hereinafter referred to as "AUTHORITY" and XXXXXXXXXX,
with authority to do business in the State of XXXXX, hereinafter referred to as "FBO".

WITNESSETH:

WHEREAS, AUTHORITY now owns, controls, and operates the XXXXX Airport, hereinafter referred to as "Airport", located in XXXXXXX County, State of XXXXXXX;

WHEREAS, Fixed Base Operation (FBO)services are essential to the proper accommodation of general aviation at the airport; and

WHEREAS, AUTHORITY deems it advantageous to itself and to its operation of the Airport to Lease unto FBO certain premises and to grant unto FBO certain rights, privileges and uses therein, as necessary to conduct its fixed base operation as hereinafter set forth.

NOW THEREFORE, for and in consideration of these premises and the mutual promises and covenants of the parties hereto, it is agreed as follows:

ARTICLE I

TERM

A. The term of this Agreement shall be for a period of one (1) year, commencing on XXXXXXXXXX, and ending on XXXXXXXXXX, unless earlier terminated under the provisions of this Agreement. This Lease Agreement will be automatically renewed from year to year in accordance with and acceptance of the terms and conditions herein specified. Such renewal of this Lease Agreement shall be conditional upon the satisfactory performance by it during the term of this Lease Agreement as determined by the AUTHORITY.

B. Both parties shall have the option to negotiate changes in this lease if FBO exercises its option to renew.

ARTICLE II

LEASED PREMISES

The AUTHORITY Leases to FBO and FBO leases from the AUTHORITY on a year-round basis, solely for the conduct of FBO'S business as a Fixed Base Operator at the Airport the following real property.

A. LEASEHOLD PREMISES: The leasehold premises shall consist of the Fuel and Airport Maintenance Equipment Storage Area which comprises XXX square feet, set forth, described and located on Exhibit "A" attached hereto and made a part hereof.

B. PURPOSE: The purpose of the Fuel and Airport Maintenance Equipment Storage Area shall be for the storage of FBO equipment and material related to the legal storage and dispensing of aviation fuels and lubricants. FBO may also store on leasehold premises motorized and non-motorized airport maintenance equipment and material. Further, the Airport Manager is authorized to store NON-AUTHORITY owned airport maintenance equipment only within leasehold premises.

The AUTHORITY shall also have the right to store AUTHORITY owned airport maintenance equipment only without charge by the FBO on leasehold premises for security purposes.

ARTICLE III

RIGHTS AND OBLIGATIONS OF LESSEE

A. REQUIRED SERVICES: FBO is hereby granted the non-exclusive privilege to engage in and FBO agrees to engage in the business of providing the following services:

1. FBO shall maintain vehicle mounted fuel storage and dispensing tank(s) upon the leased premises, which shall be adequate for the purposes herein described, and in accordance with the approval of AUTHORITY.

2. FBO shall maintain an adequate supply of aviation fuel and lubricants in the storage tanks located on leasehold premises to meet the reasonable demands for aviation fuels, lubricants.

B. AUTHORIZED SERVICES: In addition to the services required to be provided by FBO as described herein above, FBO is authorized, but not required, to provide the following services and to engage in the following activities:

1. Apron services including loading and unloading of passengers, baggage, mail and freight; and providing of ramp equipment and ramp service's such as repositioning of aircraft on the ramp, aircraft cleaning and other services for commercial operators and other persons or firms.

2. Special flight services, including aerial sightseeing, aerial advertising, and aerial photography.

3. The sale of new and used aircraft.

4. Flight training,

5. Aircraft rental.

6. Aircraft charter operations, conducted by FBO or a subcontractor of FBO in accordance with applicable Federal Aviation Regulations.

C. OPERATING STANDARDS: In providing any of the required and/or authorized services or activities specified in this Agreement, FBO shall operate for the use and benefit of the public and shall meet or exceed the following standards:

1. FBO shall furnish service on a fair, reasonable, and nondiscriminatory basis to all users of the Airport. FBO shall furnish good, prompt, and efficient service adequate to meet all reasonable demands for its services at the Airport. FBO shall charge fair, reasonable and nondiscriminatory prices for each unit of sale or service provided, however, FBO may be allowed to make reasonable and nondiscriminatory discounts, rebates, or other similar types of price reductions to volume purchasers.

2. FBO shall meet all expenses and payments in connection with the use of the premises and the rights and privileges herein granted, including taxes, permit fees, license fees, registrations, and assessments lawfully levied or assessed upon the premises or property at any time situated therein and thereon. FBO may, however, at its sole expense and cost, contest any tax, fee, or assessment as provided by STATE law.

3. FBO shall comply with all federal, state, and local laws, rules, and regulations which may apply for the storage and dispensing of aviation fuels and to the conduct of the businesses contemplated, including rules and regulations promulgated by AUTHORITY and FBO shall keep in effect and post in a prominent place all necessary and/or required licenses or permits.

4. FBO shall keep and maintain the leased premises in good condition and order, and shall surrender the same upon the expiration of this Agreement, in the condition in which they are required to be kept, reasonable wear and tear and damage by the elements not caused by FBO's negligence excepted.

5. FBO shall maintain and operate all facilities associated with the storage of FBO's petroleum products, chemicals, or other products located only within the Fuel and Airport Maintenance Equipment Storage Area leased premises described by Article II, paragraph A of this agreement, in compliance with all Federal and State laws. Any new fuel tank installations installed on FBO's leased Fuel and Airport Maintenance Equipment Storage Area shall require the permission of the Division and shall be above ground storage tanks and shall comply with Uniform Fire Code provisions as administered by State Fire Marshals Office and all applicable Federal rules.

6. In the event that soils or other materials are found on FBO's leased Fuel and Airport Maintenance Equipment Storage Area as described by Article II, paragraph A. that are "Hazardous or Deleterious Substances" as defined by the State Environmental Cleanup and Responsibility Act, 75-10-701 et. seq., State. Code Ann. ("CERCRA"), "Hazardous Substances" as defined by the Comprehensive Environmental Response, Compensation and Liability Act, 42 U.S.C. S9600, et.seq., ("CERCLA"), "Hazardous Waste" as defined by the State Hazardous Waste and Underground Storage Tank Act, S75-10-401, et. Seq., or the Solid Waste Disposal Act, as amended by the Resource Conservation and Recovery act,42 U.S.C. S6901 et.seq., or which require special remediation or disposal pursuant to any other applicable law, Lessee shall excavate, handle, and dispose of such soils or other materials only in compliance with such statutes and regulations. In the event that the FBO leaves any of the above described materials on the property, the AUTHORITY may, at its option, have wastes properly disposed of at the cost of storage, transport, and disposal.

All Hazardous Materials must be appropriately labeled and stored. In the event that a hazardous material spill occurs on the leased property or on AUTHORITY owned airport premises, it is the responsibility of the FBO to have the spill cleaned up according to State and Federal Laws and Regulations. FBO is aware that there are significant penalties for improperly disposing of wastes or submitting false information, including the possibility of fine and imprisonment for knowing violations.

D. SIGNS: FBO shall not erect, construct, or place any signs or advertisements pertaining to its business upon any portion of the Airport, other than upon the Fuel and Airport Maintenance Equipment Storage site. Prior to the erection, construction or placing of any signs or advertising matter upon the leasehold areas, FBO shall submit to the AUTHORITY for its approval, in writing, such drawings, sketches, designs, dimensions, type, and character of advertising matter and proposed location. Notwithstanding any other provision of this Agreement, said sign(s) shall remain the property of FBO. FBO shall remove, at its expense, all lettering, signs, and placards so erected on the Airport at the expiration of the term of this Agreement.

E. NONEXCLUSIVE RIGHT: It is not the intent of this Agreement to grant to FBO the exclusive right to provide any or all of the services described in this article at any time during the term of this Agreement. AUTHORITY reserves the right, at its sole discretion, to grant others certain rights and privileges upon the Airport which may be similar in part or in whole to those granted to FBO. However, AUTHORITY does covenant and agree that:

1. It shall enforce all minimum operating standards or requirements for all aeronautical endeavors and activities conducted at the Airport;

2. Any other operator of aeronautical endeavors or activities will not be permitted to operate on the Airport under rates, terms or conditions which are more favorable than those set forth in this Agreement;

3. It will not permit the conduct of any aeronautical endeavor or activity at the Airport except under an approved lease and operating agreement.

ARTICLE IV

APPURTENANT PRIVILEGES

A. USE OF AIRPORT FACILITIES: In connection with this Agreement, FBO shall have full access, together with its employees and invitees, its sub-lessees and their employees, without charge, to and from the leased premises, and to and from all public spaces and facilities on the airport including the use of landing areas, runways, taxiways, and aircraft parking areas designated by the AUTHORITY.

B. NONCOMPETITION: AUTHORITY shall not engage directly or indirectly in any of the activities described in Paragraphs A & B of ARTICLE III of this Agreement.

ARTICLE V

PAYMENTS

A. RENT & FEES: In consideration of the rights and privileges granted by this Agreement, FBO agrees to pay to AUTHORITY during the term of this Agreement the following:

1. RENT: The Division agrees to waive customary rental fee's charged for leasing unimproved ground for the Fuel and Airport Maintenance Equipment Storage Area in exchange for FBO to perform AIRPORT Management Duties and Responsibilities. These airport management duties are covered by separate written agreement.

2. FEES: FBO shall collect a fuel flowage fee and pay to the AUTHORITY the amount per gallon set by the AUTHORITY from time to time for all aviation fuels sold by FBO, including fuels used by FBO in its own operations except any fueling operations conducted XXXXXXXXXX. Fuel flowage fees shall be collected regardless of when such activity occurred during the calendar year and also with no regard to where the re-fueling operation occurred, for example on airport or off airport premises except at XXXXXXXXXX.

B. PAYMENTS:

1. The fees specified in ARTICLE VI, Paragraph A.2 above shall be paid to the AUTHORITY on or before the tenth (10th) day of each month following the month in which fees were paid to FBO. FBO shall keep true and accurate records, which shall show the total gallonage of aviation fuels used. With the payment of the charges specified in this paragraph, FBO shall submit a report of gallonage using Exhibit B.

C. RECORDS: In addition to records and reports required by Paragraph B.1 above, FBO shall provide and maintain accurate records of retail fuel sales and adjusted gross receipts derived under this Agreement, for a period of three (3) years form the date the record is made. The AUTHORITY or its duly authorized representative shall have the right at all reasonable times during business hours to audit the books, records, and receipts of FBO, and to verify FBO's fuel sales and adjusted gross receipts and tie down fees collected.

D. DISPUTES: In the event that any dispute may arise as to fuel sales collected, the amount claimed due by the AUTHORITY shall be paid forthwith. The dispute shall be submitted to a Certified Public Accountant, agreeable to both parties, who shall determine the rights of the parties hereunder to conformity with generally accepted accounting principles. The fees due said accountant for such service shall be paid by the unsuccessful party, or in the event the determination is partially in favor of each party, the fee shall be borne equally by the parties.

ARTICLE VI

UTILITIES

Except for utilities furnished for Airport security lighting by the AUTHORITY , FBO shall assume and pay for all costs or charges for utility services furnished to FBO during the term of this Agreement.

ARTICLE VII

INSURANCE

A. REQUIRED INSURANCE: FBO shall obtain and maintain continuously in effect at all times during the term of this Agreement, at FBO's sole expense, Public Liability and Property Damage insurance with limits of not less than XXXXXXXXXX Dollars ($XXXXXXXXXX) for injury to or death of any one person, subject to a limitation of not less than XXXXXXXXXX Dollars ($XXXXXXXXXX) for all persons injured or killed in the same accident and with limits of not less than XXXXXXXXXX Dollars ($XXXXXXXXXX) for damage to and destruction of property as the result of any injury or damage caused by FBO's negligence in its operations under this Lease.

B. NOTICE: AUTHORITY agrees to notify FBO in writing as soon as practicable of any claim, demand or action arising out of an occurrence covered hereunder of which AUTHORITY has knowledge, and to cooperate with FBO in the investigation thereof.

ARTICLE VIII

INDEMNIFICATION

FBO will indemnify and hold the AUTHORITY harmless form any loss, liability, or expense for injury to or death to any person, or loss or destruction of any property caused by FBO's negligent use or occupancy of the Leased Premises, except a loss, liability, or expense caused by the sole negligence or sole willful misconduct of the AUTHORITY, its agents or employees. FBO hereby expressly waives any and all claims against the AUTHORITY for compensation for any and all losses or damage sustained by reasons of any defect, deficiency, or impairment of any electrical service system, or electrical appliances or wires serving the Leasehold of FBO.

ARTICLE IX

LESSEE AS INDEPENDENT CONTRACTOR

In conducting its business hereunder, FBO acts as an independent contractor and not as an agent of AUTHORITY. The selection, retention, assignment, direction, and payment of FBO's employees, if any shall be the sole responsibility of FBO. FBO shall at all times during the term of this Agreement maintain Workers Compensation Insurance on its employees directly related to the operation of the FBO. Copy of Workers Compensation Certificate of Insurance shall be provided to the AUTHORITY.

ARTICLE X

ASSIGNMENT

FBO shall not, in any manner, directly or indirectly, assign, transfer, or encumber this Lease and concession agreement or any portion thereof, or interest therein, or sublet or sublease the whole or any part of the premises or facilities let to it, nor license the use of same, in whole or in part, by any other person, firm, or corporation, without the written consent of the AUTHORITY; provided that the foregoing shall not prevent the assignment of this Lease and concession agreement to any corporation with which FBO may merge or consolidate, or which may succeed to the business of FBO, and which resultant or succeeding corporation shall continue the operation of the business authorized under the concession granted herein at the Airport.

This Lease and concession agreement shall be binding upon and shall inure to the benefit of the successors, heirs and assigns of the parties hereto.

ARTICLE XI

NONDISCRIMINATION

FBO, its agents and employees shall not discriminate against any person or class of persons by reason of race, color, creed, or national origin in providing any services or in the use of any of its facilities provided for the public, in any manner prohibited by the applicable Federal Aviation Regulations.

ARTICLE XII

DEFAULT AND TERMINATION

A. TERMINATION BY LESSEE: This Agreement shall be subject to termination by FBO in the event of any one or more of the following events:

1. The abandonment of the Airport as an airport or airfield for any type, class, or category of aircraft.

2. The default by AUTHORITY in the performance of any of the terms, covenants or conditions of this Agreement, and the failure of AUTHORITY to remedy or undertake to remedy, to FBO's satisfaction, such default within a period of thirty (30) days after receipt of written notice from FBO to remedy same.

3. Damage to or destruction of all or a material part of the premises or airport facilities necessary to the operation of FBO'S business.

4. The lawful assumption by the United States, or any authorized agency thereof, of the operation, control, or use of the airport, or any substantial parts thereof, in such a manner to restrict FBO from conducting business operations for a period in excess of ninety (90) days.

B. TERMINATION BY LESSOR: This Agreement shall be subject to termination by AUTHORITY in the event any one or more of the following events:

1. The default by FBO in the performance of any of the terms, covenants, or conditions of this Agreement, and the failure of FBO to remedy, or undertake to remedy, to AUTHORITY'S satisfaction, such default within a period of thirty (30) days after receipt of written notice from AUTHORITY to remedy same.

2. FBO files a voluntary petition in bankruptcy, including a reorganization plan, makes a general or other assignment for the benefit of creditors, is adjudicated as bankrupt or if a receiver is appointed for the property or affairs of FBO and such receivership is not vacated within thirty (30) days after the appointment of such a receiver.

3. State legislative of Division action which would cause the AUTHORITY to abandon, close, return to the Airport Authority, other legal airport sponsor, or otherwise discontinue operating the airport.

C. EXERCISE: Exercise of the rights of termination set forth in Paragraphs A and B above, shall be by notice to the other party within thirty (30) days following the event giving rise to the termination.

D. REMOVAL OF PROPERTY: Upon termination of this Agreement for any reason, FBO, at its sole expense, shall remove from the premises all signs, trade fixtures, furnishings, personal property, equipment, and materials which FBO was permitted to install or maintain under the rights granted herein. If FBO shall fail to do so within thirty (30) days, then AUTHORITY may effect such removal or restoration at FBO's expense, and FBO agrees to pay AUTHORITY such expense promptly upon receipt of a proper invoice therefor.

E. CAUSES OF BREACH; WAIVER:

1. Neither party shall be held to be in breach of this Agreement because of any failure to perform any of its obligations hereunder if said failure is due to any cause for which it is not responsible and over which it has no control; provided, however, that the foregoing provision shall not apply to failures by FBO to pay fees, rents, or other charges to AUTHORITY.

2. The waiver of any breach, violation, or default in or with respect to the performance or observance of the covenants and conditions contained herein shall not be taken to constitute a waiver of any such subsequent breach, violation or default in or with respect to the same or any other covenant or condition hereof.

ARTICLE XIII

MISCELLANEOUS PROVISIONS

A. ENTIRE AGREEMENT: This Agreement constitutes the entire understanding between the parties, and as of its effective date supersedes all prior or independent agreements between the parties covering the subject matter hereof. Any change or modification hereof must be in writing signed by both parties.

B. SEVERABILITY: If a provision hereof shall be finally declared void or illegal by any court or administrative agency having jurisdiction, the entire Agreement shall not be void, but the remaining provisions shall continue in effect as nearly as possible in accordance with the original intent of the parties.

C. NOTICES: All notices shall be sent to:

XXXXXXXXXX and XXXXXX Aviation Authority, XXXXX Street, City, State Zip Code

LESSOR

XXXX AVIATION AUTHORITY

____

BY: Administrator, XXXX Aviation Authority, Date

____

LESSEE Date

____

LEGAL REVIEW Date

EXHIBIT B

XXXXX AVIATION AUTHORITY

XXXXX AIRPORT

XXXXXXXXXX

For month: , 19__

1. Fuel and Airport Maintenance Equipment Storage Area:

Tank farm, XXX sq. Ft. @ $0.0X/sq ft/

Annum, payable July 1 of each contract year $ XXXX

2. Fuel Sales:

100 Octane = gallons

Total = gallons x $.0X = $________________

PAYMENT FOR MONTH: $_________________

CHECK # __________________

By:___________________________

Title__________________________

Appendix D
FAA Advisory Circular 150/5190-7

U.S. Department of Transportation
Federal Aviation Administration
Advisory Circular

Subject: MINIMUM STANDARDS FOR COMMERCIAL AERONAUTICAL ACTIVITIES

Date: August 28, 2006

Initiated by: AAS-400
AC No: 150/5190-7

Change:

1. PURPOSE. This advisory circular (AC) provides basic information pertaining to the Federal Aviation Administration's (FAA's) recommendations on commercial minimum standards and related policies. Although minimum standards are optional, the FAA highly recommends their use and implementation as a means to minimize the potential for violations of Federal obligations at federally obligated airports.

2. CANCELLATION. AC 150/5190-5, Exclusive Rights and Minimum Standards for Commercial Aeronautical Activities (Change 1), dated June 10, 2002, is cancelled.

3. BACKGROUND. In accordance with the Airport and Airway Improvement Act of 1982, 49 United States Code (U.S.C.) § 47101, et seq., and the Airport Improvement Program Sponsor Assurances, the owner or operator of any airport (airport sponsor) that has been developed or improved with Federal grant assistance or conveyances of Federal property assistance is required to operate the airport for the use and benefit of the public and to make it available for all types, kinds, and classes of aeronautical activity.[1] The Surplus Property Act of 1944 (as amended by 49 U.S.C., §§ 47151-47153) contains a parallel obligation under its terms for the conveyance of Federal property for airport purposes. Similar obligations exist for airports that have received nonsurplus government property under 49 U.S.C. § 47125 and previous corresponding statutes.

These Federal obligations involve several distinct requirements. Most important is that the airport and its facilities must be available for public use as an airport. The terms imposed on those who use the airport and its services must be reasonable and applied without unjust discrimination, whether by the airport sponsor or by a contractor or licensee who has been granted a right by the airport sponsor to offer services or commodities normally required to serve aeronautical users of the airport.

Federal law requires that recipients of Federal grants (administered by the FAA) sign a grant agreement or covenant in a conveyance of property that sets out the obligations that an airport sponsor assumes in exchange for Federal assistance. The FAA's policy recommending minimum standards stems from the airport sponsor's grant assurances and similar property conveyance obligations to make the airport available for public use on reasonable conditions and without unjust discrimination.

4. USE OF THIS AC. This AC addresses FAA's policy on minimum standards and provides guidance on developing effective minimum standards. This AC describes the sponsor's prerogative to establish minimum standards for commercial aeronautical service providers at federally obligated airports. Additionally, this AC provides guidance for self-service operations and self-service rules and regulation of other aeronautical activities. It does not address requirements imposed on nonaeronautical entities, which are usually addressed as part of the airport's contracts, leases, rules and regulations, and/or local laws. The FAA does not approve minimum standards. However, the

FAA airports district and regional offices will review proposed minimum standards at the request of an airport sponsor. The FAA regional and district offices may advise airport sponsors on the appropriateness of proposed standards to ensure

[1] The legislative background for the provisions discussed in this AC began as early as 1938 and evolved under the Federal Aid to Airports Program (FAAP), Airport Development Aid Program (ADAP), and Airport Improvement Program (AIP).

the standards do not place the airport in a position inconsistent with its Federal obligations.

5. RELATED READING MATERIALS.

a. FAA Airport Compliance Requirements, Order 5190.6A, dated October 16, 1989.

b. Further information can be obtained at the Airports District Office (ADO) in your area. A listing of ADOs can be found at http://www.faa.gov/airports_airtraffic/airports/regional_guidance/.

David L. Bennett's signature
DAVID L. BENNETT
Director, Office of Airport
Safety and Standards

SECTION 1. MINIMUM STANDARDS

1.1. POLICY. The airport sponsor of a federally obligated airport agrees to make available the opportunity to engage in commercial aeronautical activities by persons, firms, or corporations that meet reasonable minimum standards established by the airport sponsor. The airport sponsor's purpose in imposing standards is to ensure a safe, efficient, and adequate level of operation and services is offered to the public. Such standards must be reasonable and not unjustly discriminatory. In exchange for the opportunity to engage in a commercial aeronautical activity, an aeronautical service provider engaged in an aeronautical activity agrees to comply with the minimum standards developed by the airport sponsor. Compliance with the airport's minimum standards should be made part of an aeronautical service provider's lease agreement with the airport sponsor.

The FAA suggests that airport sponsors establish reasonable minimum standards that are relevant to the proposed aeronautical activity with the goal of protecting the level and quality of services offered to the public. Once the airport sponsor has established minimum standards, it should apply them objectively and uniformly to all similarly situated on-airport aeronautical service providers. The failure to do so may result in a violation of the prohibition against exclusive rights and/or a finding of unjust economic discrimination for imposing unreasonable terms and conditions for airport use.

1.2. DEVELOPING MINIMUM STANDARDS.

a. Objective. The FAA objective in recommending the development of minimum standards serves to promote safety in all airport activities, protect airport users from unlicensed and unauthorized products and services, maintain and enhance the availability of adequate services for all airport users, promote the orderly development of airport land, and ensure efficiency of operations. Therefore, airport sponsors should strive to develop minimum standards that are fair and reasonable to all on-airport aeronautical service providers and relevant to the aeronautical activity to which it is applied. Any use of minimum standards to protect the interests of an exclusive business operation may be interpreted as the grant of an exclusive right and a potential violation of the airport sponsor's grant assurances and the FAA's policy on exclusive rights.

b. Authority Vested in Airport Sponsors. Grant Assurance 22 Economic Nondiscrimination Sections (h) and (i) (see 49 U.S.C. § 47107) provides that the sponsor may establish such reasonable, and not unjustly discriminatory, conditions to be met by all users of the airport as may be necessary for the safe and efficient operation of the airport. The sponsor may prohibit or limit any given type, kind or class of aeronautical use of the airport if such action is necessary for the safe operation of the airport or necessary to serve the civil aviation needs of the public.

Under certain circumstances, an airport sponsor could deny airport users the opportunity to conduct aeronautical activities at the airport for reasons of safety and efficiency.[2] A denial based on safety must be based on evidence demonstrating that safety will be compromised if the applicant is allowed to engage in the proposed aeronautical activity. Airport sponsors should carefully scrutinize the safety reasons for denying an aeronautical service provider the opportunity to engage in an aeronautical activity if the denial has the possible effect of limiting competition.

The FAA is the final authority in determining what, in fact, constitutes a compromise of safety. As such, an airport sponsor that is contemplating the denial of a proposed on-airport aeronautical activity is encouraged to contact the local Airports District Office (ADO) or the Regional Airports Office before taking action. Those offices will then seek assistance from FAA Flight Standards (FS) and Air Traffic (AT) to assess the reasonableness and whether unjust discrimination results from the proposed restrictions on aeronautical activities based on safety and efficiency.

[2] The word efficiency refers to the efficient use of navigable airspace, which is an Air Traffic Control function. It is not meant to be an interpretation that could be construed as protecting the "efficient" operation of an existing aeronautical service provider at the airport.

c. Developing Minimum Standards. When developing minimum standards, the most critical consideration is the particular nature of the aeronautical activity and operating environment at the airport. Minimum standards should be tailored to the specific aeronautical activity and the airport to which they are to be applied. For example, it would be unreasonable to apply the minimum standards for a fixed-base operator (FBO) at a medium or large hub airport to a general aviation airport serving primarily piston-powered aircraft. The imposition of unreasonable requirements illustrates why "fill in-the-blank" minimum standards and the blanket adoption of standards of other airports may not be effective. Instead, in Section 2 of this document, the FAA has provided guidance in the form of questions and examples to illustrate an approach to the development and implementation of minimum standards. It is important that the reader understand that what follows does not constitute a complete model for minimum standards, but rather a source of ideas to which the airport sponsor can turn when developing minimum standards.

d. Sponsor Prerogative to Establish Minimum Standards. When the airport sponsor imposes reasonable and not unjustly discriminatory minimum standards for airport operations through the use of reasonable minimum standards, the FAA generally will not find the airport sponsor in violation of the Federal obligations. Considerations for applying those standards may include, but are not limited to, the following:

(1) Apply standards to all providers of aeronautical services, from full—service FBOs to single service providers;
(2) Impose conditions that ensure safe and efficient operation of the airport in accordance with FAA rules, regulations, and guidance;
(3) Ensure standards are reasonable, not unjustly discriminatory, attainable, uniformly applied and reasonably protect the investment of providers of aeronautical services to meet minimum standards from competition not making a similar investment;
(4) Ensure standards are relevant to the activity to which they apply; and
(5) Ensure standards provide the opportunity for newcomers who meet the minimum standards to offer their aeronautical services within the market demand for such services.

Note: There is no requirement for inclusion of nonaeronautical activities (such as a restaurant, parking or car rental concession) in minimum standards since those activities are not covered under the grant assurances or covenants in conveyance of Federal property.

e. Practical Considerations. Many airport sponsors include minimum standards in their lease agreements with aeronautical service providers. While minimum standards implemented in this manner can be effective, they also render the airport sponsor vulnerable to the challenges of prospective aeronautical service providers on the grounds that the minimum standards are not objective. The FAA encourages airport sponsors to publish their minimum standards periodically. Minimum standards can be amended periodically over time; however, a constant juggling of minimum standards is not encouraged. Notifying aeronautical service providers that the changes to minimum standards are to improve the quality of the aeronautical service offered to the public can facilitate earlier acceptance of changes. An airport sponsor can provide for periodic reviews of the minimum standards to ensure that the standards continue to be reasonable. To foster a more receptive environment, the FAA encourages airport sponsors to include aeronautical users in the process leading to changes in minimum standards.

f. Factors to Consider. Numerous factors can and should be considered when developing minimum standards. Airport sponsors may avoid unreasonable standards by selecting factors that accurately reflect the nature of the aeronautical activity under consideration. It is impossible for the FAA to present every possible factor necessary for a task, mostly because of the vast differences that exist between individual airports. Obvious factors one should consider are:

(1) What type of airport is at issue? Is it a large airport or a small rural airport? Will the airport provide service to only small general aviation aircraft or will it serve high performance aircraft and air taxi operators as well?
(2) What types of aeronautical activities will be conducted on the airport?
(3) How much space will be required for each type of aeronautical activity that may prospectively operate at the airport?
(4) What type of documentation will business applicants be required to present as evidence of financial stability and good credit?
(5) To what extent will each type of aeronautical activity be required to demonstrate compliance with sanitation, health, and safety codes?
(6) What requirements will be imposed regarding minimum insurance coverage and indemnity provisions?
(7) Is each minimum standard relevant to the aeronautical activity for which it is to be applied?

g. New Versus Existing Aeronautical Service Providers. Airport sponsors are encouraged to develop minimum standards for new aeronautical business ventures it desires to attract to the airport. Minimum standards may be part of a competitive solicitation to encourage prospective service providers to be more responsive in their proposals. Minimum standards can be modified to reflect the airport's experience and to be watchful for new opportunities (i.e. such as Specialized Aviation Service Operations [SASOs]). Minimum standards should be updated to reflect current conditions that exist at the airport and not those that existed in the past. In any case, once an airport sponsor receives a proposal for a new aeronautical business, it must ascertain whether the existing minimum standards can be used for the new business or new minimum standards should be developed to better fit the new business venture. However, in all cases, the airport sponsor must ensure that in changing minimum standards for whatever reason, it is not applying unreasonable standards or creating a situation that will unjustly discriminate against other similarly situated aeronautical service providers. The FAA stands by the principle that once minimum standards have been established, airport sponsors must uniformly apply them to all similarly situated aeronautical service providers. Some points of consideration are as follows:

(1) Can new minimum standards be designed to address the needs of both existing and future aeronautical business? If not, can a tiered set of minimum standards be developed to address the same type of aeronautical activity but differ significantly in scale and investment (i.e. an FBO building large hangars and serving high performance aircraft and a second FBO building and only T-hangars and serving only smaller general aviation aircraft)?

(2) Was the minimum standard created under a lease agreement (with a specific aeronautical service provider) so the subject standard may not be reasonable if applied to other aeronautical service providers?

(3) Has conformance to the minimum standards been made a part of the contract between the aeronautical service provider and the airport sponsor?

(4) Has the financial performance of the airport improved or declined since the time the minimum standards were implemented?

1.3. MINIMUM STANDARDS APPLY BY ACTIVITY.

Difficulties can arise if the airport sponsor requires that all businesses comply with all provisions of the published minimum standards. An airport sponsor should develop reasonable, relevant, and applicable standards for each type and class of service.

a. Specialized Aviation Service Operations. When specialized aviation service operations (SASOs), sometimes known as single-service providers or special FBOs, apply to do business on an airport, "all" provisions of the published minimum standards may not apply. This is not to say that all SASOs providing the same or similar services should not equally comply with all applicable minimum standards. However, an airport should not, without adequate justification, require that a service provider desiring to provide a single service or less than full service also meet the criteria for a full-service FBO. Examples of these specialized services may include aircraft flying clubs, flight training, aircraft airframe and powerplant repair/maintenance, aircraft charter, air taxi or air ambulance, aircraft sales, avionics, instrument or propeller services, or other specialized commercial flight support businesses. Airport sponsors generally do not allow fuel sales alone as a SASO, but usually require that fuel sales be bundled with other services.

b. Independent Operators. If individual operators are to be allowed to perform a single-service aeronautical activity on the airport (aircraft washing, maintenance, etc.), the airport sponsor should have a licensing or permitting process in place that provides a level of regulation and compensation satisfactory to the airport. Frequently, a yearly fee or percentage of the gross receipts fee is a satisfactory way of monitoring this type of operation.

c. Self-Fueling and Other Self-Service Activities. Since self-service operations performed by the owner or operator of the aircraft using his or her own employees and equipment are not commercial activities, the FAA recommends that airport sponsor requirements concerning those noncommercial activities be separate from the document designed to address commercial activities. Airport rules and regulations or specific language in leases can better address requirements concerning self-service operations and other airport activities.

Self-fueling means the fueling or servicing of an aircraft (i.e. changing the oil, washing) by the owner of the aircraft with his or her own employees and using his or her own equipment. Self-fueling and other self-services cannot be contracted out to another party. Self-fueling implies using fuel obtained by the aircraft owner from the source of his/her preference. As one of many self-service activities that can be conducted by the aircraft owner or operator by his or her own employees using his or her own equipment, self-fueling, differs from using a self-service fueling pump made available by the airport, an FBO or an aeronautical service provider. The use of a self-service fueling pump is a commercial activity and is not considered self-fueling as defined herein.

In addition to self-fueling, other self-service activities that can be performed by the aircraft owner with his or her own employees includes activities such as maintaining, repairing, cleaning, and otherwise providing service to an aircraft, provided the service is performed by the aircraft owner or his/her employees with resources supplied by the aircraft owner. Title 14 Code of Federal Regulations (CFR) Part 43 permits the holder of a pilot certificate to perform specific types of preventative maintenance on any aircraft owned or operated by the pilot.

1.4. THROUGH THE FENCE OPERATOR. The owner of an airport may, at times, enter into an agreement (i.e. access agreement or lease agreement) that permits access to the public landing area by independent operators offering an aeronautical activity or to owners of aircraft based on land adjacent to, but not a part of, the airport property. However, a through-the-fence operation could undermine an airport's minimum standards unless the airport sponsor is careful to apply its minimum standards through an airport access agreement, including conditions to protect the airport's ability to meet all of its Federal obligations.

a. No Obligation to Permit Through-the-Fence. The obligation to make an airport available for the use and benefit of the public does not require the airport sponsor to permit ground access by aircraft from adjacent property. Through-the-fence arrangements can place an encumbrance upon the airport property and reduce the airport's ability to meet its Federal obligations. As a general principal the FAA does not support agreements that grant access to the public landing area by aircraft stored and serviced off-site on adjacent property.

In some cases, however, the airport sponsor may opt to grant through-the-fence access, but it should do so on a case-by-case basis and only when the airport retains its ability to meet its Federal obligations. To minimize the possibility of conflict between a through-the-fence agreement and the airports' ability to meet its Federal obligations, the airport sponsor must retain the legal right to require the off-site property owner or party granted access to the airport to conform in all respects to the requirements of any existing or proposed grant agreement or Federal property conveyance obligation. This includes requirements to ensure operating safety and equitable compensation for use of the airport. Special safety and operational requirements should be incorporated into any access agreement to ensure that the through-the-fence access does not complicate the control of vehicular and aircraft traffic or compromise the security of the airfield operations area.

Proposed new agreements granting access to a public landing area from off-site locations should be reported to the FAA Regional Airports Division with a full statement of the circumstances and a copy of the proposed through-the-fence or access agreement so the FAA can review it for consistency with the airport sponsor's Federal obligations and incorporate it into the current Airport Layout Plan (ALP).

b. Access Agreement. Any through-the-fence access should be subject to a written agreement between the airport sponsor and the party granted access. The access agreement should specify what specific rights of access are granted; payment provisions that provide, at a minimum, parity with similarly situated on-airport tenants and equitable compensation for the use of the airport; expiration date; default and termination provisions; insurance and indemnity provisions; and a clear statement that the access agreement is subordinate to the grant assurances and/or Federal property conveyance obligations and that the sponsor shall have the express right to amend or terminate the access agreement to ensure continued compliance with all grant assurances and Federal property conveyance obligations.

The access agreement should have a fixed contract period and the airport sponsor is under no obligation to accept a proposed assignment or sale of the access agreement by one party to another. It is encouraged that airport sponsors expressly prohibit the sale or assignment of its access agreement.

1.5. RESERVED.

SECTION 2. GUIDANCE ON DEVELOPING MINIMUM STANDARDS

2.1. SAMPLE QUESTIONS. As a guide for the airport sponsor, the following series of questions are provided to address some of the various types of specific services or activities frequently offered to the public:

a. Fuel Sales. The on-airport sale of fuel and oil requires numerous considerations that include, but are not limited to, the physical requirements for a safe and environmentally sound operation. Some recommended considerations are listed below:

(1) Where on the airport will the fuel tanks be installed? Who will control access to the fueling site? What parties will be granted access to the site to receive fueling services?

(2) Will fuel tanks be installed above or below ground? Will fuel trucks be utilized to fuel remotely parked aircraft?

(3) Will the fueling operator have sufficient fuel capacity and types of fuel to accommodate the mix of aircraft using the airport?

(4) How many days' supply of fuel will be available on airport? Are provisions to resupply the on-airport fuel tanks sufficient to ensure a continuous fuel supply?

(5) Will the fueling operator have suitable liability insurance and indemnify the airport sponsor for liability for its fueling operation, including fuel spills and environmental contamination?

b. Personnel Requirements. An aeronautical service provider's need for personnel will be dictated by the size of the airport and the public demand for aeronautical services. In all instances, an airport sponsor will be well advised to ensure that aeronautical service providers have sufficient personnel to run their operation safely and meet aeronautical demand for the services in question. Naturally, the personnel requirements will vary with the specific aeronautical service being offered.

(1) How many fully trained and qualified personnel will be available each day and over what hours to provide aeronautical services? Will this reasonably meet the demand by aeronautical users?

(2) Describe the training and qualifications of personnel engaged in the services provided to aeronautical users.

c. Airport and Passenger Services. This is a necessary consideration in those instances where the airport has aeronautical service providers engaged in handling services for air carrier and/or cargo carriers that do not provide their own support personnel on-site:

(1) Provide a list of the equipment and services (both above and below wing) that will be provided by the aeronautical service provider, including ground power units, over night parking areas, towing equipment, starters, remote tie-down areas, jacks, oxygen, compressed air, tire repair, sanitary lavatory service, ticketing and passenger check-in services, office and baggage handling services and storage space.

(2) What provisions have been made regarding passenger conveniences and services?

(a) Access to passenger loading bridges/steps, sanitary rest rooms, boarding hold rooms, telephones, food and beverage service, and other passenger concessions.

(b) Access to concession and ground transportation services for the benefit of passengers and/or crewmembers.

d. Flight Training Activities. On-airport flight training can be provided by the airport sponsor/owner or by a service provider. The minimum standards imposed on flight instruction operations should take the following information into consideration:

(1) What type of flight training will the service provider offer?

(2) What arrangements have been made for the office space the school is required to maintain under 14 CFR 141.25? What is the minimum amount of classroom space that the service provider must obtain?

(3) Will flight training be provided on a full-time or part--time basis?

(4) What type of aircraft and how many will be available for training at the on-airport location?

(5) What provisions have been made for the storage and maintenance of the aircraft?

(6) What provisions will be made for rest rooms, briefing rooms, and food service?

(7) What coordination and contacts exist with the local Flight Standards District Office?

e. Aircraft Engine/Accessory Repair and Maintenance. The applicant for an on-airport repair station is subject to several regulatory requirements under 14 CFR Part 145 Repair Stations. Depending on the type and size of the proposed repair station, the following questions may provide helpful guidelines:

(1) What qualifications will be required of the repair station employees? Typically, the holder of a domestic repair station certificate must provide adequate personnel who can perform, supervise, and inspect the work for which the station is rated.

(2) What repair station ratings does the applicant hold?

(3) What types of services will the repair station offer to the public? These services can vary from repair to maintenance of aircraft and include painting, upholstery, etc.

(4) Can the applicant secure sufficient airport space to provide facilities so work being done is protected from weather elements, dust, and heat? The amount of space required will be directly related to the largest item or aircraft to be serviced under the operator's rating.

(5) Will suitable shop space exist to provide a place for machine tools and equipment in sufficient proximity to where the work is performed?

(6) What amount of space will be necessary for the storage of standard parts, spare parts, raw materials, etc.?

(7) What type of lighting and ventilation will the work areas have? Will the ventilation be adequate to protect the health and efficiency of the workers?

(8) If spray painting, cleaning, or machining is performed, has sufficient distance between the operations performed and the testing operations been provided to prevent ad verse affects on testing equipment?

f. Skydiving. Skydiving is an aeronautical activity. Any restriction, limitation, or ban on skydiving on the airport must be based on the grant assurance that provides that the airport sponsor may prohibit or limit aeronautical use for the safe operation of the airport (subject to FAA approval). The following questions present reasonable factors the sponsor might contemplate when developing minimum standards that apply to skydiving:

(1) Will this activity present or create a safety hazard to the normal operations of aircraft arriving or departing from the airport? If so, has the local Airports District Office (ADO) or the Regional Airports Office been contacted and have those FAA offices sought the assistance from FAA Flight Standards (FS) and Air Traffic (AT) to assess whether safe airport operations would be jeopardized?

(2) Can skydiving operations be safely accommodated at the airport? Can a drop zone be safely established within the boundaries of the airport? Is guidance in FAA AC-90-66A Recommended Standards Traffic Patterns and Practices for Aeronautical Operations at Airports Without Operating Control Towers, 14 CFR Part 105 and United States Parachute Association's (USPA) Basic Safety Requirements being followed?

(3) What reasonable time periods can be designated for jumping in a manner consistent with Part 105? What experience requirements are needed for an on-airport drop zone?

(4) What is a reasonable fee that the jumpers and/or their organizations can pay for the privilege of using airport property?

(5) Has the relevant air traffic control facility been advised of the proposed parachute operation? Does the air traffic control facility have concerns about the efficiency and utility of the airport and its related instrument procedures?

(6) Will it be necessary to determine the impact of the proposed activity on the efficiency and utility of the airport, related instrument approaches or nearby Instrument Flight Rules (IFR)? If so, has FAA Air Traffic reviewed the matter and issued a finding?

g. Ultralight Vehicles and Light Sport Aviation. The operation of ultralights and light sport aircraft are aeronautical activities and must, therefore, be generally accommodated on airports that have been developed with Federal airport development assistance. Airport sponsors are encouraged to consider some of the following questions:

(1) Can ultralight aircraft be safely accommodated at the airport? Is guidance in FAA AC-9066A Recommended Standards Traffic Patterns and Practices for Aeronautical Operations at Airports Without Operating Control Towers and 14 CFR Part 103 being followed?

(2) Can all types of Light Sport aircraft be safely accommodated at the airport?

(3) Will this activity present or create a safety hazard to the normal operations of aircraft arriving or departing from the airport? If so, has FAA Flight Standards reviewed the matter and issued a finding?

(4) Will an FAA airspace study be necessary to determine the efficiency and utility of the airport when considering the proposed activity? If so, has FAA Air Traffic reviewed the matter and issued a finding?

h. Fractional Aircraft Ownership. Fractional ownership programs are subject to an FAA oversight program similar to that provided to air carriers, with the exception of en route inspections. The FAA has for a long time and under certain circumstances, interpreted an aircraft owner's right to self-service to include operators. For example, a significant number of aircraft operated by airlines are not owned but leased under terms that give the operator airline owner-like powers. The same is true for other aeronautical operators such as charter companies, flight schools, and flying clubs, which may not hold title to the aircraft, but through leasing arrangements, for example, retain full and exclusive control of the aircraft for long periods of time. The same is true of 14 CFR Part 91 Subpart K. Fractional ownership companies are subject to operational control responsibilities, maintenance requirements, and safety requirements not unlike 14 CFR Part 135 operators. For additional information on fractional ownership, contact your local Flight Standards District Office.

i. Other Requirements. When drafting minimum standards documents, airport sponsors may have to take into account other Federal, state, and local requirements. This includes Federal requirements and guidance by the Transportation Safety Administration (TSA) and the Environmental Protection Agency (EPA), state requirements such as aircraft registration (in some states) and local fire regulations. For guidance on matters such as these, please contact the FAA's Airports District Office (ADO) in your area and/or state aviation agency. A listing of ADOs can be found at http://www.faa.gov/airports_airtraffic/airports/regional_guidance/. Information and contacts regarding state aviation agencies is available at http://www.nasao.org/.

2.2. THROUGH 2.5. RESERVED.

APPENDIX 1. DEFINITIONS

1.1. The following are definitions for the specific purpose of this AC.

a. Aeronautical Activity. Any activity that involves, makes possible, or is required for the operation of aircraft or that contributes to or is required for the safety of such operations. Activities within this definition, commonly conducted on airports, include, but are not limited to, the following: general and corporate aviation, air taxi and charter operations, scheduled and nonscheduled air carrier operations, pilot training, aircraft rental and sightseeing, aerial photography, crop dusting, aerial advertising and surveying, aircraft sales and services, aircraft storage, sale of aviation petroleum products, repair and maintenance of aircraft, sale of aircraft parts, parachute or ultralight activities, and any other activities that, because of their direct relationship to the operation of aircraft, can appropriately be regarded as aeronautical activities. Activities, such as model aircraft and model rocket operations, are not aeronautical activities.

b. Airport. An area of land or water that is used, or intended to be used, for the aircraft takeoff and landing. It includes any appurtenant areas used, or intended to be used, for airport buildings or other airport facilities or rights-of-way, together with all airport buildings and facilities located thereon. It also includes any heliport.

c. Airport District Office (ADO). These FAA offices are outlying units or extensions of regional airport divisions. They advise and assist airport sponsors with funding requests to improve and develop public airports. They also provide advisory services to the owners and operators of both public and private airports in the operation and maintenance of airports. See the FAA Web site for a complete listing of all ADO offices at http://www.faa.gov/airports_airtraffic/airports/regional_guidance/.

d. Airport Sponsor. The airport sponsor is either a public agency or a private owner of a public-use airport that submits to the FAA an application for financial assistance (such as AIP grants) for the airport. In accepting an application for financial assistance, the FAA will ensure that the airport sponsor is legally, financially, and otherwise able to assume and carry out the certifications, representations, warranties, assurances, covenants and other obligations required of sponsors, which are contained in the AIP grant agreement and property conveyances.

e. Commercial Self-Service Fueling. A fueling concept that enables a pilot to fuel an aircraft from a commercial fuel pump installed for that purpose by an FBO or the airport sponsor. The fueling facility may or may not be attended.

f. Exclusive Right. A power, privilege, or other right excluding or debarring another from enjoying or exercising a like power, privilege, or right. An exclusive right can be conferred either by express agreement (i.e. lease agreement), by the imposition of unreasonable standards or requirements, or by any other means. Such a right conferred on one or more parties, but excluding others from enjoying or exercising a similar right or rights, would be an exclusive right.

g. Federal Airport Obligations. All references to a Federal grant program, Federal airport development assistance, or Federal aid contained in this AC are intended to address obligations arising from the conveyance of land or from grant agreements entered under one of the following acts:

(1) **Surplus Property Act of 1944 (SPA), as amended, 49 U.S.C. §§ 47151-47153.** Surplus property instruments of transfer were issued by the War Assets Administration (WAA) and are now issued by its successor, the General Services Administration (GSA). However, the law imposes upon the FAA (delegated to FAA from The Department of Transportation) the sole responsibility for determining and enforcing compliance with the terms and conditions ofall instruments of transfer by which surplus airport property is or has been conveyed to non-Federal public agencies pursuant to the SPA. 49 U.S.C. § 47151(b).

(2) **Federal Aid to Airports Program (FAAP).** This grant-in-aid program administered by the agency under the authority of the Federal Airport Act of 1946, as amended, assisted public agencies in the development of a nationwide system of public airports. The Federal Airport Act of 1946 was repealed and superseded by the Airport Development Aid Program (ADAP) of 1970.

(3) **Airport Development Aid Program (ADAP).** This grant-in-aid program administered by the FAA under the authority of the Airport and Airway Development Act of 1970, as amended, assisted public agencies in the expansion and substantial improvement of the Nation's airport system. The 1970 act was repealed and superseded by the Airport and Airway Improvement Act of 1982 (AAIA).

(4) **Airport Improvement Program (AIP).** This grant-in-aid program administered by the FAA under the authority of the Airport and Airway Improvement Act of 1982, 49 U.S.C. § 47101, et seq., assists in maintaining a safe and efficient nationwide system of public-use airports that meet the present and future needs of civil aeronautics.

h. Federal Grant Assurance. A Federal grant assurance is a provision within a Federal grant agreement to which the recipient of Federal airport development assistance has agreed to comply in consideration of the assistance provided. Grant assurances are required by statute, 49 U.S.C. § 47101.

i. Fixed-Base Operator (FBO). A commercial business granted the right by the airport sponsor to operate on an airport and provide aeronautical services such as fueling, hangaring, tie-down and parking, aircraft rental, aircraft maintenance, flight instruction, etc.

j. Fractional Ownership. Fractional ownership operations are aircraft operations that take place under the auspices of 14 CFR Part 91 Subpart K. This type of operation offers aircraft owners increased flexibility in the ownership and operation of aircraft including shared or joint aircraft ownership. It provides for the management of the aircraft by an aircraft management company. The aircraft owners participating in the program agree not only to share their own aircraft with others having a shared interest in that aircraft, but also to lease their aircraft to other owners in the program (dry lease exchange program).[3] A fractional owner or owner means an individual or entity that possesses a minimum fractional ownership interest in a program aircraft and that has entered into the applicable program agreements. For additional information, please see 14 CFR 91.1001 Applicability at http://www.access. gpo.gov/nara/cfr/waisidx_04/14cfr91_04.html and contact your local Flight Standards District Office.

k. Grant Agreement. A Federal grant agreement represents an agreement made between the FAA (on behalf of the United States) and an airport sponsor for the grant of Federal funding.

l. Public Airport. Means an airport open for public use that is publicly owned and controlled by a public agency.

m. Public-Use Airport. Means either a public airport or a privately owned airport open for public use.

[3] A dry lease aircraft exchange means an arrangement, documented by the written program agreements, under which program aircraft are available, on an as needed basis without crew, to each fractional owner.

n. Specialized Aviation Service Operations (SASO). SASOs are sometimes known as single-service providers or special FBOs performing less than full services. These types of companies differ from a full service FBO in that they typically offer only a specialized aeronautical service such as aircraft sales, flight training, aircraft maintenance, or avionics services for example.

o. Self-Fueling and Self-Service. Self-fueling means the fueling or servicing of an aircraft (i.e. changing the oil, washing) by the owner of the aircraft with his or her own employees and using his or her own equipment. Self-fueling and other self-services cannot be contracted out to another party. Self-fueling implies using fuel obtained by the aircraft owner from the source of his/her preference. As one of many self-service activities that can be conducted by the aircraft owner or operator by his or her own employees using his or her own equipment, self-fueling, differs from using a self-service fueling pump made available by the airport, an FBO, or an aeronautical service provider. The use of a self-service fueling pump is a commercial activity and is not considered self-fueling as defined herein. In addition to self-fueling, other self-service activities that can be performed by the aircraft owner with his or her own employees includes activities such as maintaining, repairing, cleaning, and otherwise providing service to an aircraft, provided the service is performed by the aircraft owner or his/her employees with resources supplied by the aircraft owner.

p. Through-the-Fence Operations. Through-the-fence operations are those activities permitted by an airport sponsor through an agreement that permits access to the public landing area by independent entities or operators offering an aeronautical activity or to owners of aircraft based on land adjacent to, but not a part of, the airport property. The obligation to make an airport available for the use and benefit of the public does not impose any requirement for the airport sponsor to permit ground access by aircraft from adjacent property.

Notes

Appendix E
Value Analysis: Costs versus Benefits

INTRODUCTION

Before getting into the specifics of value analysis, it might be valid to draw the following analogy between the purchase of a business aircraft and a computer. If a company uses a computer simply for payroll accounting or inventory control, it will be difficult to realize a payoff for its substantial investment in the equipment. The computer can handle such routine tasks more quickly, possibly more accurately and with fewer people, but the direct savings or benefits are not likely to be considerable. On the other hand, if the company uses the computer creatively, it can uncover the new world of e-business that would allow it to continuously optimize business activities through digital technology. E-business involves attracting and retaining the right customers and business partners along with digital communication, e-commerce, and online research. A computer might completely streamline supply chain management, business intelligence, customer relationship management, and the everyday tasks of order entry, purchasing, invoicing, and inventory control. This could not only allow the company to handle and retain present customers more efficiently, but also to capture new ones. Without belaboring the point, the computer, when used imaginatively, can completely revamp the company's traditional ways of conducting business and open up numerous new opportunities for economic growth.

So it might be with a business aircraft. It would be short sighted to use a plane simply to do what a company is now doing, only in a faster and cheaper manner. If a plane is to justify itself as a worthwhile investment, it must also make a major contribution to the firm's economic growth and profitability.

VALUE ANALYSIS

Value analysis is a quantitative comparison of actual business trips taken by company personnel, selected from the sample travel data developed by the sales representative. The comparison depicts the differences in travel costs, travel time, overnight stays, and value per man-hour required between present travel modes and the business aircraft under consideration. In the form presented, this comparison will substantiate the relative equivalence of the airplane's direct costs versus present travel costs. It will, in addition, provide a clear indication of the level of manpower savings that are likely to result through the utilization of a business airplane on these trips. This quantitative comparison is commonly referred to as the *tangible benefits* because they determine fairly accurate revenue producing values.

Looking at these tangible benefits first, it is not too difficult for an experienced sales representative or analyst to demonstrate the savings, if any, that can be made over airline and automobile expenses when a company uses its own aircraft. It is considerably more difficult to compute the dollars gained as a result of saving the time of key personnel.

There are several factors to consider when determining just what "saved time" is worth. One is comfort and its relationship to morale and productivity. The frustration involved in fighting heavy automobile traffic, plus standing in line at check-in counters or gates, or waiting to make connecting flights can substantially reduce a person's energy and morale. The more discomfort and inconvenience that is eliminated, the better a person is apt to perform.

Saving time for key personnel is not only important from a pure clock-time standpoint. Just one trip a week that saves five hours adds up to a saving of 22 hours a month, 264 hours a year. This is the equivalent of 33 additional working days a year. Whether the individual is a salesperson or chairman of the board, these four and one half additional weeks of productive time can be calculated to illustrate dollar savings to the company.

The value of the savings, together with the accompanying intangible benefits, should in theory, offset the annual cost in order to justify acquisition of a company aircraft. *Intangible benefits* are those that cannot be wholly quantified in terms of dollars saved or revenue produced. For example, more contacts with the firm's customers and improved morale are intangible benefits. Simply stated, business aviation helps a company obtain maximum productivity from its two most important assets—people and time. See Table E–1.

Table E–1 Time and Cost Comparison for Trip A—Montgomery, AL to Fitzgerald, GA and Return (Hypothetical)

Time Comparison

	Elapsed Time (Round Trip)	
	Automobile	**Business Aircraft**
Office to Airport	—	:30
Terminal Boarding	—	:30
En Route Time (1)	9:00	1:16
Deplaning Time	—	:30
Airport to Office		:30
Total	9:00	3:16

(1) The use of two lane highways is required between Columbus, GA and Fitzgerald, GA.

Cost Comparison—Round Trip

	Automobile	**Business Aircraft**
Travel—En Route (1)	$76.86	$1,466.85
RONs (2)	256.20	—
Rental Car (3)	—	31.72
Value per Man-Hour (VMH) (4)	2,639.25	799.54
Total Cost	$2,972.31	$2,298.11

(1) Automobile—360 miles @ $.35 per mile (Less 39% tax savings). Business aircraft—1.27 hrs. @ $1,155/hr.

(2) RONs—$140/person × 3 persons (Less 39% tax savings).

(3) Rental car—$52/day—unlimited mileage (Less 39% tax savings).

(4) (4) VMH = $\frac{2.5 \times \$92{,}000 \text{ (av. salary)}}{2{,}000 \text{ hrs.}}$ = $115.00/hr.

VMH Summary

Automobile		
Total Time: $115.00 × 9 hrs. × 3 persons		$3,105.00
En Route Time: 9 hrs.—15% productivity credit (3,105.00 × .15)		– 465.75
		$2,639.25
Business Aircraft		
Total Time: $115.00 × 3.27 hrs. × 3 persons		$1,128.15
En Route Time: $115.00 × 1.27 hrs. × 3 persons	$438.15	
Less 75% productivity credit	.75	– 328.61
		$799.54

Sample Trips

For this analysis, three round trips typical of those that might be taken by the hypothetical company, Champions Stores, Inc. have been chosen for comparison. For example, Table 10–2 in Chapter 10 shows a total of 342 trip legs including 90 in the 101 to 200 mile range in the 75% column. It is assumed that most of these trips were made by automobile. Trip A is representative of this group. Trips B and C represent distances of 401 to 500 miles, and 601 to 700 miles. Other trips could have been selected, but these are considered to be typical for this analysis. Trip B includes indirect airline service with a connecting flight in Atlanta and Trip C includes indirect airline service with a connecting flight in Dallas/Ft. Worth to Waco, TX. A rental car will be used to travel the 40 miles to Mexia, TX.

Trip A—Montgomery, AL to Fitzgerald, GA and Return
Trip B—Montgomery, AL to Greensboro, NC and Return
Trip C—Montgomery, AL to Mexia, TX and Return

Basic Assumptions

The following assumptions have been made for the sample trips:

1. All cost comparisons assume a passenger load of three key persons traveling together.

Table E–2 The Value of Executive Time*

Yearly Salary	Hourly Pay	Productivity Factor	Value/Hour	Annual Contribution
$ 10k	$ 5.00	2.50	$ 12.50	$ 18,750
20k	10.00	5.00	50.00	75,000
30k	15.00	7.50	112.50	168,750
40k	20.00	10.00	200.00	300,000
50k	25.00	12.50	312.50	468,750
75k	37.50	18.75	703.13	914,695
100k	50.00	25.00	1,250.00	1,875,000
150k	75.00	37.50	2,812.50	4,218,875
200k	100.00	50.00	5,000.00	7,500,000
250k	125.00	62.50	7,812.50	11,718,875
500k	250.00	125.00	31,125.00	46,687,500

*Source: Business & Commercial Aviation magazine

2. Airline schedules and fares are obtained from www.travelocity.com.
3. Time allowed for enplaning and deplaning airline flights is 30 minutes and for the business aircraft, 15minutes. Airline enplaning and deplaning time can vary considerably depending upon the size of the airport and whether or not baggage was checked.
4. Time required for scheduling connecting flights is 50 minutes between flights.
5. The business aircraft has a cruising speed of 283 mph and an operating cost of $1,155 per hour (from the cash flow statement, Table 10–8).
6. Hotel/motel expenses are $95 per night per person and meals and tips for those individuals remaining overnight (RONs) are $45 per person.
7. Rental car expenses are based on $52 per day with unlimited mileage.
8. Costs associated with company automobiles have been set at $.35 per mile.

Trip A—Montgomery, AL to Fitzgerald, GA and Return

A time and cost comparison for Trip A is shown in Table E–1. On a pure direct cost comparison, (automobile $333.06 vs. business airplane $1,466.85) such a trip would probably not justify a business aircraft, except for the substantial savings in time that results in less fatigue for the travelers. However, when comparing the value of each person's time, the importance of business aircraft is clearly demonstrated. The emphasis here is on value, not simply what a person earns per hour. Several formulas have been developed to evaluate the worth of executive time. The most commonly used is the *Value per Man-Hour* (*VMH*) which is determined by dividing the average salary of the travelers multiplied by a constant productivity factor by annual work hours (i.e., average salary × 2.5/2,000). The 2,000 annual work hours number is obtained by multiplying 40 hours per week times 50 weeks per year. In practice, only 1,500 hours per year are actually productive hours and might be a more realistic denominator in the formula. The standard 40-hour work week assumption is modified by some who feel that highly placed executives/managers are more apt to work 50–55 hour weeks which produce 2,500 to 2,750 annual hours.

A second method of determining the value of executive time increases the productivity factor as annual salary increases. It is generally accepted that raises in salary are justified by considerably greater increases in the individual's contribution. This method assumes that most salaried employees spend about 2,000 hours per year on the job of which about 1,500 hours per year are truly productive to the company's profitability. As Table E–2 indicates, employees in the $100,000 salary range have a value per hour of $1,250.

The National Business Aviation Association, Inc. in its Management Aids article "The Management Accountability Factor" introduced the *en route productivity* factor. This interesting concept addresses the question: "How much can executives accomplish while traveling in a commercial airliner or a business aircraft?" The productivity of a group of executives aboard a commercial airline is extremely low due to (1) lack of work facilities; (2) hesitancy to discuss sensitive corporate matters; (3) distractions resulting from the mass handling of passengers; and (4) impossibility of conducting a meeting with two or more persons. Because of these reasons, the estimated value of the time on an airline trip or automobile trip is only 15 percent. This credit of 15 percent will be used in determining the VMH in the three selected trips for Champions Stores.

Table E–3 Time Comparison for Trip B—Montgomery, AL to Greensboro, NC and Return (Hypothetical)

	Elapsed Time (Round Trip)	
	Airline	**Business Aircraft**
Office to Airport (1)	:45	:30
Terminal Boarding (2)	1:00	:30
En Route Time (3)	7:23	3:23
Deplaning Time (4)	1:00	:30
Airport to Office (5)	:45	:30
Total	10:53	5:23

(1) General aviation terminal facility is usually easier to reach, with less traffic than on the vehicular circular drive serving the airline terminal and easier parking.

(2) Airline terminal boarding includes baggage check-in, security screening, walk to gate position, waiting, and loading. This can add considerable time depending upon the time of day.

(3) Includes time required to change planes in Atlanta going and return.

(4) Includes walk to airline baggage claim area, the typical wait, and walk to ground transportation.

(5) Leaving the airport from the general aviation terminal facility is generally much quicker.

The "en route productivity" credit for time spent aboard a corporate aircraft is estimated at 75 percent. The justification for the much higher percentage is based upon the following reasons:

1. Full privacy allows open reference to and use of proprietary information and materials.
2. Cabin configurations are conducive for meetings and open discussions among members of a firm or with clients without risk of being overheard or compromising proprietary information.
3. Modern aircraft cabins can be equipped with computers, fax machines, photocopiers and phones that enable executives to work as though in their offices.
4. Improved opportunity for air to ground communications.
5. More available time to devote to working, not waiting after take off and less time to clean up before landing.

Another feature of the business aircraft compared to automobile travel on business trips such as this one is load factor. Four or five executives including assistants could make the trip and return the same day. Not only would this be uncomfortable in an automobile, the expense involved in remaining overnight would be costly. In addition, the aircraft enables junior members of management to gain valuable experience by making such business trips.

Trip B—Montgomery, AL to Greensboro, NC and Return

Time and cost comparisons for Trip B are shown in Tables E–3 and E–4. The best airline routing for this trip includes a connecting flight in Atlanta. There is very little difference in cost on this selected business trip but there is a five hour and 30 minute difference in time. The use of the business aircraft reduces the delay and fatigue associated with travel to and from the airline terminal, check-in, baggage claims, and the time to change planes in Atlanta.

The importance of load factor is clearly demonstrated in Figure E–1. After a load factor of three, additional passengers can be transported on the business aircraft at no added "out-of-pocket" costs while travel by airline increases arithmetically with the load factor.

Trip C—Montgomery, AL to Mexia, TX and Return

Time and cost comparisons for Trip C are shown in Tables E–5 and E–6. Champions Stores wanted to diversify its business model and decided to purchase a sporting goods manufacturer in Mexia, Texas. The lack of direct commercial service again demonstrates the time saved by flying on a business aircraft. The timesaving from this one trip, when annualized, will add several more productive days for the three busy executives. In addition, the elimination of overnight stays will certainly have a positive impact on employee morale and family relationships.

Again, on this trip, the importance of load factor is illustrated. Additional passengers can be taken on the business aircraft at no additional expense while the airline/charter combination would increase time and cost arithmetically. This is an important consideration for companies wishing to expose junior personnel to business situations in the field, such as having junior sales representatives accompany a senior staff member to a customer's site.

Summary

Table E–7 provides an annualized summary of the three trips. Based on only 27 trips per year or slightly less than 16

Table E–4 Cost Comparison for Trip B—Montgomery, AL to Greensboro, NC and Return (Hypothetical)

	Total Cost (Round Trip)	
	Airline	**Business Aircraft**
Travel—En Route (1)	$1,722.03	$3,903.90
Rental Car (2)	31.72	31.72
Value per Man-Hour (VMH) (3)	3,371.68	981.52
Total Cost	$5,125.43	$4,917.14

(1) Airline Ticket—$941 round trip × 3 persons (Less 39% tax savings). Business Aircraft—3.38 hrs @ $1,155/hr.

(2) Rental car—$52 per day, unlimited mileage (Less 39% tax savings).

(3) (3) VMH = 2.5 × $92,000 (av. salary) = $115.00/hr.
2,000 hrs.

VMH Summary

Airline		
Total Time: $115.00 × 10.88 hrs. × 3 persons		$3,753.60
En Route Time: $115.00 × 7.38 hrs. × 3 persons	$2,546.10	
Less 15% Productivity Credit.	.15	– 381.92
		$3,371.68
Business Aircraft		
Total Time: $115.00 × 5.38 hrs. × 3 persons		$1,856.10
En Route Time: $115.00 × 3.38 hrs. × 3 persons	$1,166.10	
Less 75% Productivity Credit	.75	– 874.58
		$981.52

percent of the annual estimate of 171 (see Table 10–2), Champions Stores could save 474 man-hours (based on three passengers) and a cost savings of $8,501.

As previously stated, the trips selected were representative of this company's travel pattern. For example, 26 percent of this company's current travel (45 trips—from Table 10–2) were made by automobile at a distance under 200 miles. The Fitzgerald, GA trip was representative of this group.

It also must be remembered that this saving was based on three passengers using each mode of transportation. Whenever load factor increases, travel costs by airline increase arithmetically where there is no additional expense, other than value per man-hour for the business aircraft.

Another value of a business aircraft lies not only in the time and cost savings involved in unproductive travel time, but in *morale costs* as well. Morale costs is another element in total savings. It includes both the off-hours travel (before 8:00 a.m. and after 5:00 p.m.) and the time spent away from home overnight. On an annualized basis this can result in a considerable savings.

INTANGIBLE BENEFITS

Business aircraft have been referred to as time machines. Speed in transportation is synonymous with time and the business aircraft of today is a time machine that compresses distances into minutes and hours. In the world of business and commerce, time means money. Wages are paid by the hour, salaries by the week, profits by the quarter and taxes by the year. Business people sitting in airline terminals, driving on highways for hours and spending nights in motels are throwing away time and money. As more and more organizations manage "rightsizing" initiatives, they are discovering the need to maximize the productivity of the same or fewer employees to accomplish equal or greater amounts of work and ensure their competitive position and long-term success. As business aircraft improve employee time management and efficiency, they can help eliminate the need for additional personnel, reducing payroll costs, and help maximize a company's competitive marketing advantage.

Table E–8 gives an insight into the perceptions of senior executives of the intangible benefits derived from the use of a business aircraft.

No matter what the particular mission of the business aircraft, the ultimate reasons for its use are the same: save time otherwise lost by inflexible schedules; compress time so that an hour-long transaction out of town does not require an overnight stay, and expand time so that productivity is greater.

It is generally agreed that a company's top decision-makers are in a position to weigh the relative importance of intan-

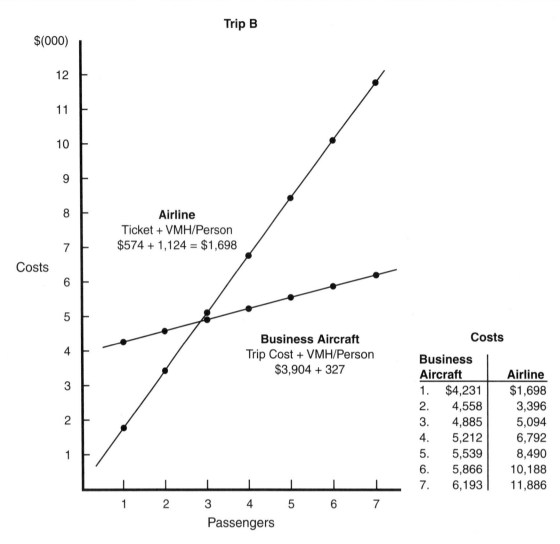

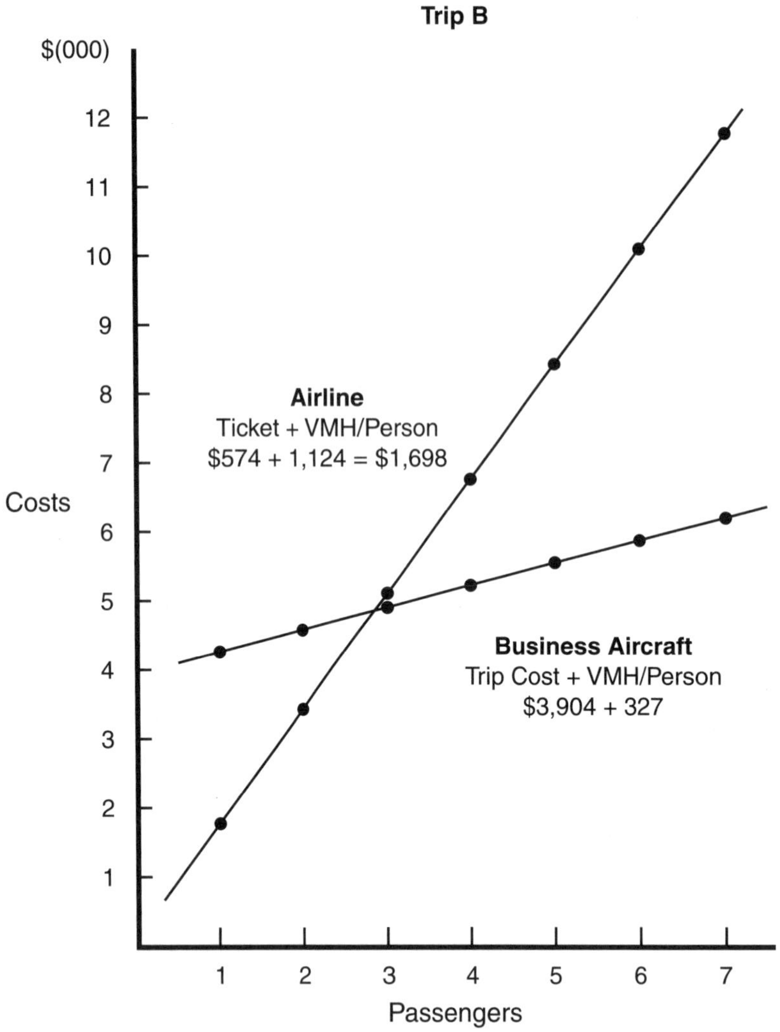

Costs

	Business Aircraft	Airline
1.	$4,231	$1,698
2.	4,558	3,396
3.	4,885	5,094
4.	5,212	6,792
5.	5,539	8,490
6.	5,866	10,188
7.	6,193	11,886

Figure E–1. Relationship of Load Factor When En Route and VMH Costs Are Compared—Trip B

Table E–5 Time Comparison for Trip C—Montgomery, AL to Mexia, TX and Return (Hypothetical)

	Elapsed Time (Round Trip)	
	Airline	**Business Aircraft**
Office to Airport	:45	:30
Terminal Boarding	1:00	:30
En Route Time (1)	7:08	4:19
Deplaning Time	1:00	:30
Airport to Plant (2)	2:00	—
Airport to Office	:45	:30
Total	12:38	6:19

(1) Connecting flight in Dallas/Ft. Worth to Waco, TX includes time required to change planes.

(2) Time required to drive from the Waco airport to the plant in Mexia

Table E–6 Cost Comparison for Trip C—Montgomery, AL to Mexia, TX and Return (Hypothetical)

	Total Cost (Round Trip)	
	Airline	Business Aircraft
Travel—En Route (1)	$1,806.21	$4,989.60
Rental Car (2)	63.44	—
RONs (3)	256.20	—
Value per Man-Hour (VMH) (4)	3,988.37	1,062.60
	$6,114.22	$6,052.20

(1) Airline Ticket—$987 round trip × 3 persons (Less 39% tax savings).Business Aircraft—4.32 hrs @ $1,155/hr.

(2) Rental Car—$52 per day, unlimited mileage (Less 39% tax savings).

(3) RONs $140/person × 3 persons (Less 39% tax savings).

(4) (4) VMH = 2.5 × $92,000 (av. salary) / 2.000 hrs. = $115.00/hr.

VMH Summary

Airline		
Total Time: $115.00 × 12.63hrs. × 3 persons		$4,357.35
En Route Time: $115.00 × 7.13 hrs. × 3 persons	$2,459.85	
Less 15% Productivity Credit	.15	– 368.98
		$3,988.37
Business Aircraft		
Total Time: $115.00 × 6.32hrs. × 3 persons		$2,180.40
En Route Time: $115.00 × 4.32 hrs. × 3 persons	$1,490.40	
Less 75% Productivity Credit	.75	– 1,117.80
		$1,062.60

Table E–7 Summary of Tangible Benefits Trips A, B, and C Based on 3 Passengers

		TIME COMPARISON (Hours)				Tangible Benefit (Savings)	
		Automobile/Airline		Business Aircraft			
Sample Trips	Trips Per Year	Each Trip	Year	Each Trip	Year	Per Trip	Year
A	9	27:00	243:00	9:48	88:12	17:12	154:48
B	9	32:39	293:51	16:09	145:21	16:30	148:30
C	9	37:54	341:06	18:57	170:33	18:57	170:33
Annual Totals: 27			877:57		404:06		473:51

		COST COMPARISON				Tangible Benefit (Savings)	
		Automobile/Airline		Business Aircraft			
Sample Trips	Trips Per Year	Each Trip	Year	Each Trip	Year	Per Trip	Year
A	9	$2,972.31	$26,750.79	$2,298.11	$20,682.99	$674.20	$6,067.80
B	9	5,125.43	46,128.87	4,917.14	44,254.26	208.29	1,874.61
C	9	6,114.22	55,027.98	6,052.20	54,469.80	62.02	558.18
Annual Totals: 27			$127,907.64		$119,407.05		$8,500.59

Table E–8 Corporate Aircraft Benefits as Reported by Senior Executives of a Major Corporation

1. Time Savings
2. Operational Reliability
3. Lessened Fatigue
4. Efficiency of Personal En Route Work
5. Avoidance of Overnight Stops
6. Ability to Visit Multiple Destinations Within Limited Time
7. Schedule Flexibility
8. Customer Contact and Support
9. Ability to Respond Promptly to Customers and Associates
10. En Route Conferences and Briefings (Group Travel)
11. En Route Rehearsals and Program Finalizations
12. Ability to Conduct Classified Meetings
13. Carriage of Parts and Displays
14. Departmental/Interdepartmental Communication and Coordination
15. Security (Cabin)
16. Security (Personnel)

gible benefits such as convenience, comfort, or even prestige. The reason for this is that the decision-makers are also usually the users of the aircraft. They recognize that the intangible, rather than the tangible factors, often provides the margin of profit in business aircraft use. Accountants and comptrollers may wish to be shown the tangible benefits of cost savings in dollars as well as increased productivity that can be measured. Their evaluations will eventually become major determinants in all major aircraft purchase decisions. There still remain the areas of subjectivity and judgment, especially in regard to the worth of an employee's time to his company and the values placed on the intangible benefits.

No universal means have been devised, as yet, to measure the benefits of these intangibles that are so readily and universally accepted as existing. These intangibles are, however, becoming major determining factors in aircraft decisions. Cost-savings analysis should not outweigh astute business judgment that considers all factors, including those that cannot be determined in the usual cost-savings analysis. David Lyall, EMJ Corporation's chief pilot states,

> Airlines are often the cheapest way to go between Boston and Chattanooga, but, often, the cheapest option can be the most costly one if you miss a meeting. Airline flights from Boston to Atlanta were delayed so often that our people would miss their airline connections to Chattanooga and would have to drive there, getting in at 2 a.m. When you have a meeting the next day at 7 a.m., that's totally unacceptable. If you can leave Boston at 7 a.m. on a business aircraft and be in Chattanooga at 9:30 a.m., that's not a bad deal.

The business aircraft's efficiency depends on the wisdom with which it is employed. The aircraft can range from a valuable cost-saving and profit-making piece of equipment, to a pure cost center incapable of revenue or profits, depending upon its utilization. With modern business methods, underutilization rarely occurs. Utilization of an aircraft is the basis for productivity.

Where cost is a trade-off against time, several factors must be considered: the intrinsic value of the person or cargo to be moved; the emergency need for travel to be accomplished; the perishable nature or deterioration rate of a situation; and, any seasonable peak demand requirement.

Convenience and comfort are other major intangible benefits closely related to timesavings. Convenience is more than just another amenity. It means flexibility—the ability to go when and where needed with little or no notice. It results in simplification of travel from point to point. The meaningfulness of comfort stems from the relationship of comfort to fatigue and the effects fatigue has on productivity. Intangible benefits fall into seven broad areas:

1. ***Recruiting and retaining key personnel.*** The right person in the right place at the right time can change everything. West coast venture capitalist Neal Dempsey said, "There's nothing more impressive to people you're trying to hire than to tell them you'll send the plane for them. Flying a candidate into our headquarters on a business aircraft lets them know we're serious." Business aircraft do provide additional comfort and convenience for busy executives who travel frequently. The use of a business aircraft can result in:
   a. Increased ability to attract and employ key personnel in competition with other companies in the industry.
   b. Improved morale factor by not being on the road constantly.
   c. Reduced travel fatigue and its effect on productivity. When employees are subjected to stress and abnormal schedules, their effectiveness begins to decline. Although the degree may vary, it is significant enough to be a factor. The following elements of mental and physical performance that contribute to overall effectiveness of employees can be adversely affected by consistent commercial air travel:
   (1). Utilization of intellect in evolving answers and

arriving at solutions to objectives of meeting.

(2). Exercise of initiative involving and expressing viewpoints that are pertinent to objectives of the meeting.

(3). Maintenance of patience.

(4). Alertness to opportunities that develop during the meeting discussions.

(5). Ability to maintain stamina so that objectives are not compromised.

d. Minimizing nonbusiness hours away from home. Family time before and after traditional business hours is critical to most key employees. Because a stable, supportive family can have a strong effect on employee morale and productivity, scheduling which minimizes time away from home can be a major benefit.

2. ***Increased management mobility.*** Competition among companies is, in the final analysis, competition among managements. Competition is not between business products or the efficiency of facilities. Over a period of time, these factors can be changed by the quality and effectiveness of the management group. Management's real value to the company, its employees, and stockholders lies in its ability to use time effectively. The quantity of executive talent needed to manage a major corporation is not limited. However, the demand for such talent is growing. The solution is to make the best use of the talents available. The near total scheduling flexibility inherent in business aircraft—even changing itineraries enroute can be a powerful asset. As aircraft can arrive and depart on the executive's schedule, typically waiting for them in the ordinary course of business, meetings can be moved up, back or extended without penalty, risk, or unnecessary scheduling pressures. Overnight trips also can be avoided. If managed proactively, this benefit can improve business results. Thus, a business aircraft can minimize additional personnel requirements by increasing an executive's area of control.

3. ***Increase sales.*** By minimizing or eliminating many of the barriers to travel, business aircraft allow business opportunities to be more readily considered and acted upon. Business aircraft users frequently form profitable new relationships in the aviation and aerospace industries, and customers in other, often-rural areas of the country—once practically unreachable and thus unconsidered—are newly accessible. The use of a business aircraft conveys the image of an efficient, well-run company committed to fast action and service.

Aviation has not lost its glamour, and there are distinctive uses of business aircraft that can and do provide the marginal edge that often can make the difference between completing a transaction and just missing one. Aaron Henschel, President, Henschel—Steinau Incorporated, Englewood, New Jersey, speaks to the potential of business aircraft assistance to increasing sales when he was interviewed by *Flying Magazine.* He says:

> General aviation is the best investment I've made. We're a medium size company in our industry, but I wouldn't have some of my top clients if it weren't for my decision to take up flying. My company designs and markets point-of-purchase advertising displays for clients such as Hershey Chocolate Company, Upjohn Company, General Foods, Philip Morris, and Burroughs-Wellcome Company. We employ twenty people including a sales staff of eight who call on accounts from Kalamazoo to Buffalo. People are impressed by the fact that our company can react quickly and airplanes give us a tremendous competitive advantage in many areas. For example, we flew one customer into Marsh Field—the small airport close to Boston—to see our supermarket displays in that region. We had him back at Teterboro Airport near New York by 10:45 a.m. and, by 11:30 a.m., he was in his mid-town Manhattan office.

A business aircraft provides shorter reaction time to new business opportunities.

4. ***Outpace competition.*** As our industrial, computerized society becomes progressively more advanced and sophisticated, the pace of doing business increases commensurately. Add to this trend the growing decentralization of business, and it is easy to see that fast transportation is one of management's major requirements in the battle for competitive supremacy. The flexibility of scheduling and the ability to get to out-of-the-way places, provide management with an increased ability to stay even with or ahead of competition. Nick A. Caporella, chairman and CEO of National Beverage Corp. of Fort Lauderdale illustrates the competitive advantage when he said,

> Today, not only do you have to have the right price, programs, brands and ingredients, but you also need a rapport with retailers. And there's no better way to build that rapport than to personally pick up a CEO in your Falcon 2000. That's the best way in the world to do business—people like to do business with people they like.

5. ***Business entertainment.*** It is quite common for businesses to entertain customers or potential customers. A business aircraft can be a viable piece of equipment in this regard. Many companies use their aircraft to fly employees and customers to hunting, fishing, sightseeing, or other recreational areas. Although considered as nonbusiness,

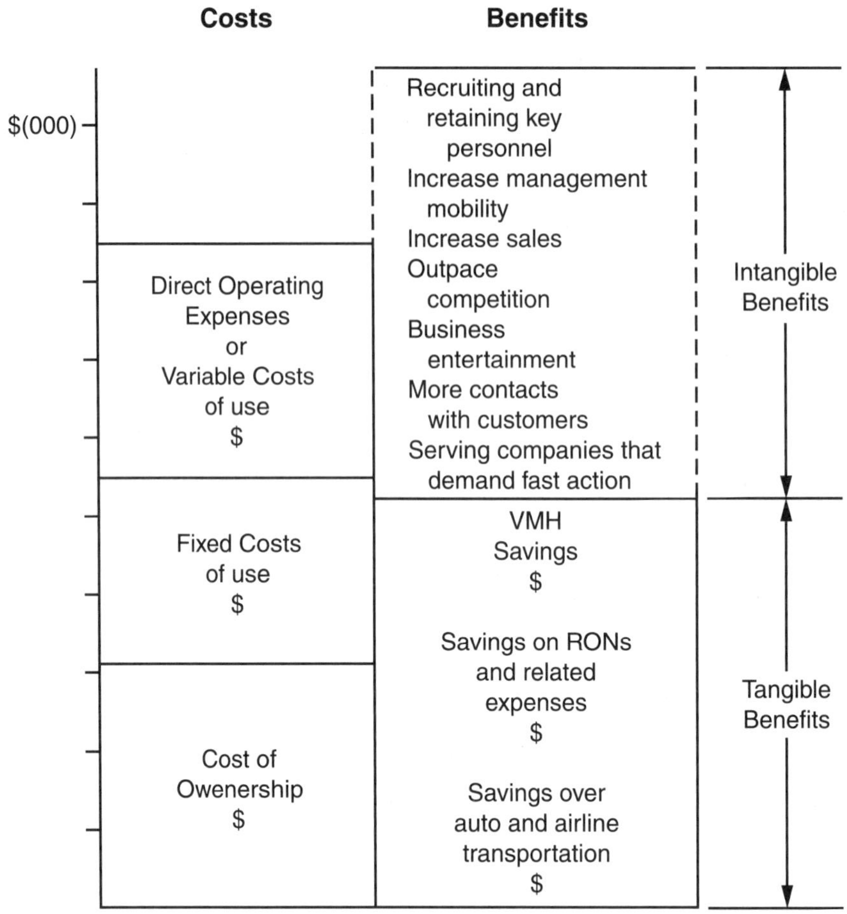

Figure E–2. Value Analysis: Costs versus Benefits

these trips often have a very direct return by serving to enhance company-customer relationships.

6. ***More contacts with present customers.*** It is a marketing adage that a company's present customers are the best prospects for additional sales. The more attention a company can give them, the better its chances to convert those customers into repeat orders. Spotting a customer problem and the ability to solve it by getting personnel to the customer's facility might save an existing account.

   Frequently, customers are so widespread that management cannot afford to contact more than one or two on a given trip. A company aircraft can give management (as well as sales, service, and technical personnel) the chance to maintain closer contact with key accounts.

   Sheldon Coleman, former Chief Executive Officer of the Coleman Company, stated in an interview with *Business and Commercial Aviation,*

   > . . . We also use our airplanes to fly our executives out into the field to talk with, and listen to, the dealers and customers. We call that "brainstorming." In our business it is essential for us to stay close to our customers, to detect any significant problems, or to spot a trend. We go where the action is. That's the firing line and that's where we have to be.

7. ***Serving companies that demand fast action.*** An increasingly greater number of companies are engaged in business that is time sensitive to high-speed transportation; for example, they may need the capability of flying in personnel or equipment to keep a customer's production line from shutting down.

CONCLUSION

This Appendix opened by drawing an analogy between the business aircraft and a computer. The evaluation or value analysis of a proposed capital investment is essentially a matter of logic. It is the process of weighing the benefits to be derived from the investment against the cost of making the investment (see Figure E–2).

Use of a business aircraft avoids airline ticketing, security clearances, missed connections, late flights, luggage lines, and highway delays in getting to and from major airports.

Many companies utilize their own aircraft as an en route conference room thus reducing unproductive travel time to a minimum.

Some of these benefits can be tangible and readily quantified in terms of dollars and cents. Others may be quite intangible and difficult to quantify. Whether the benefits are tangible or intangible, management must, in considering the wisdom of a capital investment, formulate an opinion of the beneficial effects which the proposed investment will have on the income statement, in terms of increased revenues or reduced expenses, or both. Against these, it must weigh the cost of the capital investment.

KEY TERMS

Value analysis
Value per Man-Hour (VMH)
Tangible benefits
En route productivity factor
Intangible benefits
Morale costs

REVIEW QUESTIONS

1. Why is the purchase of a business aircraft similar to the purchase of a computer? What is the difference between tangible and intangible benefits of business aircraft use? Why are business aircraft referred to as "time machines?"
2. Quarterly airline travel by employees of Modern Day Furniture Company between cites A and B (round trip) has been one person 8 times; two persons 5 times; three persons 2 times; and four persons once. Each of the eight employees named on the airline ticket stubs are in the $70,000/year salary bracket. Round trip airfare for one person between cities A and B is $450. It takes an employee 4 hours to go from City A to B by airline (also 4 hours for the return trip). Determine the (1) total quarterly fares; (2) average load factor; (3) VHM; and, (4) total quarterly airline travel expenses including VMH.

   Using a high performance single-engine aircraft and flying into a general aviation airport closer to City B takes 2.5 hours from City A. (5 hours for the round trip) Aircraft operating expense is $200 per hour. Assuming the same number of legs flown as the airline (32) and the same load factor, the total hours flown will be ________ and the total flying expense will be $________. Determine the total quarterly expenses including VMH using the business aircraft.

   Assuming the trips can be made in a total of 24 legs through better scheduling using the business aircraft, what would the load factor have to be ________? What would the total flight expense be? Using the previously determined VMH and flying 24 legs, what are the total quarterly expenses including VMH ________?

Notes

Index

Notes

Notes

Notes